SIMPLE AND COMPLEX VIBRATORY SYSTEMS

EUGEN SKUDRZYK

Professor of Physics, Ordnance Research Laboratory
and Physics Department,
The Pennsylvania State University

1968

THE PENNSYLVANIA STATE
UNIVERSITY PRESS

University Park and London

Library of Congress Catalog Card Number 66–18222

Printed in the United States of America

to Liselotte Skudrzyk

CONTENTS

Preface

The physical properties of a mechanical vibrator are reflected in its frequency response curve and in its sound radiation. An understanding of the relation between the mechanical construction, size, and form of the elements of the vibrator and its frequency response curve would be of great practical importance, since it would provide us with the knowledge of how to vary the frequency response of vibrators according to the practical requirements. Such an understanding was beyond our reach in the past for all but the simplest systems, but more recent work based on asymptotic theories and on results obtained in the theory of electrical networks seems to make it possible to approach this goal. A vibrator can be characterized by its characteristic impedance, the reflection coefficient of its discontinuities for wave trains that start out at the driving point, the frequency difference between successive resonant frequencies, the damping, and the relative symmetry of the point of excitation with respect to the boundaries of the vibrating system. This is all that is needed to sketch the approximate frequency response curve of its vibration amplitude and of its sound radiation. Vice versa, the frequency curve and its irregularities give insight into the mechanical properties of a vibratory system.

The main objective of this book is to derive the frequency curve of a vibrator of any degree of complexity in its essential features, or to deduce the properties, the shape, and the size of the mechanical vibrator from its frequency curve, and to derive general laws for the vibration and sound radiation. This knowledge should then make it possible to suppress vibrations in certain frequency ranges or to increase them in others by modifying the vibratory system. When the reader has completed this book, he will find that he is still far from this goal—but he will have made a significant step toward it.

Even scientists of high standing are frequently not acquainted with the fundamentals needed in the field of vibrations. For instance, many advanced physicists are not fully aware of the signification of complex notation and the meaning of complex symbols or of the great power of some of the methods and theorems that have been derived in the study of electric networks. The classical physicist is accustomed to using mechanical vibrators to illustrate electrical circuits since he is well acquainted with mechanical systems, but is inexperienced with electrical diagrams. However, there is no alternative. The electrical circuit diagrams are more concise and more illustrative of the behavior of the systems than the sketches used in the classical theory of vibration. A theory of vibrations that does not make full use of these modern methods of network theory would be similar to a treatise on physics that stops whenever calculus is required. An introductory chapter summarizes the various theorems and provides the required background.

Because the solution for the motion of a vibrator of any degree of complexity can always be represented as a superposition of the solutions for a series of simple point-mass spring vibrators, it is natural to start a study of complex vibratory systems with the point-mass spring vibrator, the prototype of all vibrators. It is necessary that the reader become completely familiar with the methods described in Chapter II and with the fundamental formulas and results.

Chapter III introduces the concepts of external and internal friction and of solid damping. It deals with the dissipation of mechanical energy into heat and should enable an understanding of the significance of complex elastic constants. It proves that, for periodic or periodically decaying vibrations, energy dissipation can be neglected in all but the final formulas —the computations are performed as if there were no losses. Any kind of internal or external friction, such as elastic lags, and hysteresis can then be rigorously taken into account by introducing complex masses and complex elastic constants in the final result.

Chapter IV is devoted to lumped parameter systems. The theory of the point-mass compliant element system is applied to some interesting examples that illustrate the great power of the methods originating in circuit theory. Solutions are derived for systems with many mass points and compliant elements. This chapter also deals with the influence coefficients and with close and far complied systems. The reader will find that lumped parameter systems are considerably more complex than systems with continuously distributed mass and compliance.

Chapter V is an introduction to vibrators with continuously distributed mass and compliance; the transverse vibrations of a string and the longitudinal vibrations of a rod are studied. This chapter shows that the natural mode solution represents the partial fraction development of the classical solution, and it introduces the concept of the characteristic impedance of a vibrator. It also presents the methods that are needed for dealing with more complex vibrators.

Chapter VI deals with the next higher case, the transverse vibrations of beams. It proves that bending moments are particularly effective in exciting high-frequency vibrations and, consequently, should be minimized in vibration isolation. This chapter also acquaints the reader with the so-called end distortions that are generated because of the complex boundary conditions. These end distortions lead to strange phenomena. For instance, at the higher frequencies the ends of a rod behave like cavity resonators and absorb a considerable amount of the vibrational energy.

Chapter VII summarizes the methods of the two preceding chapters and generalizes them for homogeneous vibrators of any complexity. This chapter presents the important proof of the fundamental theorem that a homogeneous vibrator of any complexity can be represented by a canonical circuit and proves that Foster's theorem and all the others derived in electrical communications and network theory are applicable to mechanical vibrators. For the higher frequencies, the solution that has been derived in terms of the natural modes can be transformed into an integral. This integral can be evaluated, and the characteristic impedance, the driving-point impedance, and the transfer impedance become simple functions of the average frequency difference between successive modes, the mode masses, the quality factor of the system, and the co-ordinates of the point of excitation. A similar computation can be performed for the vibrational energy of the system.

Chapter VIII deals with the theory of vibrating plates, and in it the solution is derived for the vibration of circular and rectangular plates. The resonance peaks in the frequency curve of a system whose resonant frequencies do not occur at constant frequency intervals are still proportional to the quality factor of the system. But, the antiresonance depressions depend greatly on the relative spacing of the resonant frequencies and, to a lesser extent, on the quality factor of the system. This chapter deals with two-dimensional point sources and introduces two-dimensional waves that propagate in plates. A very simple asymptotic solution is derived that makes it possible to predict the velocity amplitude as a function of the applied point force with an accuracy that appears to be sufficient for practical purposes. This chapter contains a considerable amount of information that will be needed in deriving a general theory of the vibrations of homogeneous and inhomogeneous systems.

In Chapter IX, the mode parameters for the various simple vibrators are computed so that they are available for practical computations.

Chapter X is the reason for this book. This chapter should convince the most skeptical reader that the methods that stem from communications are considerably more powerful in dealing with complex vibratory systems than any other method known today. This chapter deals with homogeneous and inhomogeneous vibrators of any complexity, shells with stiffening rings, joints, and coupled vibrators. The theory is simple, and this chapter can be read outside the context of the book.

Chapter XI deals with the Greene's function, the impulse response, and the correlation function of the vibration of a homogeneous system. It shows that the assumption of a constant loss factor is similar to that of no phase distortion in network theory. The system is deflected before the impulse has acted (whereas in the theory of filters, the signal arrives before it has been emitted). But the error that is introduced in the computations because of this assumption is negligible in all practical cases.

In dealing with statistical force distributions, like wind forces or forces produced by the turbulent velocity fluctuations in the boundary layer of a moving body, correlation methods have certain advantages. Chapter XI contains the basic theory and may be of use to those working in this field.

Chapter XII deals with the radiation of sound. The fundamental equations and results are transformed into a form that makes them useful for dealing with the sound radiation of small sound sources that generate a volume flow or move like rigid bodies and with the sound radiation of large sound sources whose radiation resistance per unit area is ρc. The sound radiation of the equivalent sphere is shown to be a very good approximation to the sound radiation of any vibrator of any size that does not exhibit nodal lines. Finite plates and shells are studied in great detail as examples for vibrators with nodal lines.

Chapter XIII is concerned with the theory of noise and vibration isolation.

Chapters II to XIII are based on the classical theory of elasticity, which is valid only at the lower frequencies. At the higher frequencies, different phenomena are observed. For instance, as the frequency is increased, the loss factor for bending vibrations of a rod increases from that of Young's modulus to that of the shear modulus. The ends of a rod act like cavity resonators and pass through a kind of resonance phenomenon; the amplitude of the ends may be as much as eighty times larger than the amplitude that is transmitted through the rod. At still higher frequencies, this cavity effect is replaced by mode transformations, and a dilatational pulse may then be partially reflected as a shear pulse. For a plate, the loss factor is found to fluctuate between its value for shear and for longitudinal vibrations. The theoretical study of these phenomena is difficult. Since it is doubtful that a reasonably good understanding of our subject can be attained without at least some acquaintance with some of the phenomena outside the range of validity of the classical theory, a survey of some of the recent work on the improved theories of elasticity is included in the last chapter. The reader is strongly advised to supplement this study by further reading in the original literature.

The references that follow each chapter should be helpful. The author urges the reader to look through the shelves of the libraries and to select the books that he likes best. An index of the literature on vibration is not given, since such indexes are available as supplements to the *Journal of the Acoustical Society of America*; and since very complete lists of references are given in other books, such as those in C. H. Crede, *Vibration and Shock Isolation* (John Wiley & Sons, Inc.; New York, 1961), and in L. S. Jacobson and R. S. Ayre, *Engineering Vibrations* (McGraw-Hill, Inc.; New York, 1958).

Acknowledgments

Much of the work described in the later part of this book was sponsored by the Air Force Office of Scientific Research (Grants AFOSR No. 43-63, No. 43-65), the Atomic Energy Commission, the Bureau of Weapons, and by the office of Naval Research (Contract NRO64-475). The author wishes to thank Dr. Nicholas Perrone (ONR) for the great help he received from him, and from the skillfully directed working group he directed, in preparing Chapters VII, X, XI, and XII. Through Dr. Perrone, the author was made to realize the basic importance of the theory of curved vibrators and the significant difference between this class of vibrators and those studied in the classical treatises. The author is also greatly indebted to Dr. Vernon M. Albers, of the Ordnance Research Laboratory, The Pennsylvania State University, for his corrections of the manuscript, to Professor Carroll L. Key, Jr., for his stimulating influence, to Dr. Robert N. Hamme for his advice and valuable suggestions; to his students, in particular Mr. James N. Lange, for help in writing the manuscript and to Mrs. Lucille J. Strauss and her staff of the Physics-Chemistry Library at the Pennsylvania State University. Special thanks go to Mrs. Carolee Rowley for her ability to type the manuscript from crude and frequently almost illegible notes.

The author also wishes to thank his esteemed teachers, Professor W. G. Bickley, of the London Imperial College of Science and Technology, who introduced him to the subject of vibrations, and Professor E. Meyer and his group at Göttingen, who, over a period of fourteen years, trained the author in acoustics.

Thanks are expressed to the various authors for permission to include their results, and to the McGraw-Hill Book Company, Harvard University Press, and John Wiley and Sons, Inc., for permission to use the copyrighted material acknowledged in the text.

List of Figures

List of Tables

The Symbols

In the study of vibrations it soon becomes apparent that the methods of classical analysis are inadequate and that more comprehensive and less cumbersome methods are needed. These new methods are borrowed from circuit theory. In fact, electrical circuit theory has proved to be the most important tool in the study of systems of differential equations as they arise in the theory of mechanical lumped element systems and in the study of systems with continuously distributed mass and compliance. It is natural that the notation and the methods derived in the theory of electrical circuits are used in this book.

There is no reason to replace the well-established names "impedance" and "admittance" by the terms "receptance" and "mobility" or to use the awkward symbols that have been used in the past for the mechanical elements, i.e., to draw a mechanical resistance as a dashpot because in one out of a thousand cases the mechanical resistance is a dashpot, or to draw a compliance like a spiral because in one out of ten thousand cases the compliance is a spiral spring. The well-established symbols for the electrical circuit elements and the concepts of impedance and admittance will, therefore, be used exclusively. The letters K, M, and R_m that are attached to the mechanical elements will clearly distinguish them from the corresponding electrical elements. It is of no consequence that the mechanical impedance or the mechanical circuit elements K, M, and R_m have different dimensions from those of the electrical impedance or the electrical circuit elements L, C, and R.

It is expedient to distinguish between complex quantities and rotating vectors; complex quantities will be characterized by a bar above the symbol, rotating vectors by a wavy line above the symbol; e.g.,

$$\tilde{u} = \bar{Z}\tilde{\imath}$$

The absolute value of a complex quantity $\bar{Z}$ will be designated by the letter Z or by the symbol $\bar{Z}$ between two vertical lines:

$$Z = |\bar{Z}|$$

Amplitudes will be denoted by capital letters or by Greek letters with a caret above them:

$$v = V \cos \omega t$$
$$\xi = \hat{\xi} \cos \omega t$$

and complex amplitudes by an additional line above the letter:

$$\tilde{v} = \bar{V} e^{j\omega t} = V e^{j(\omega t + \Psi_v)}$$
$$\tilde{\xi} = \bar{\hat{\xi}} e^{j\omega t} = \hat{\xi} e^{j(\omega t + \Psi_\xi)}$$

where

$$\bar{V} = V e^{j\Psi_v} \qquad \text{and} \qquad \bar{\hat{\xi}} = \hat{\xi} e^{j\Psi_\xi}$$

The number of letters of the alphabet is far too small to name the quantities that are involved in acoustics. The letter *R*, for instance, may denote radius, resistance, or reflection factor. Sometimes within one equation, the same letter may occur several times with different meanings. It would seem to be necessary to change the letter temporarily until, in another derivation, the changed letter collides with another established symbol; however, there is a way to avoid this difficulty. We may underline the symbol to indicate that it is now used with some meaning other than the standard. For instance, in the equation

$$\tilde{v} = \frac{\tilde{f}}{R(1+jQ\underline{\nu})}$$

v denotes the particle velocity, while

$$\underline{\nu} = \frac{\omega}{\omega_0} - \frac{\omega_0}{\omega}$$

denotes the frequency variable.

Small letters will be used to represent specific magnitudes, such as r for the resistance per unit area and m for the mass per unit area. If a capital letter has to be used, such as for the power N, a specific quantity will be denoted by the subscript zero. For instance, the power per unit area will be denoted by N_0.

Some readers may object to the use of the K for compliance instead of the usual designation C; however, C is an internationally used symbol for capacity and should be retained as such. The letter λ is very convenient for stiffness, spring constant, or elastic modulus, since the subscripts that are usually used with it provide adequate differentiation from its normal use for wave length; e.g., λ_E will denote Young's modulus, λ_K, bulk modulus, and λ_S, sound modulus. In the context λ is used, there can be no possible confusion with the wave length.

The following symbols are used:

A	constant, constant of integration, amplitude, amplitude of a progressive wave, symbol for the co-ordinates x_A, y_A, z_A of a point (reference point) on a vibrator whose motion is being studied
A_ν, a_ν	Fourier amplitude cosine component, coefficients of polynomial
$\vec{A}$	vector potential
a_x, a_y, a_z, etc.	amplitudes of the periodic components of a vector potential (Eq. 14.172)
a	radius of a cylinder or disc, longer axis of ellipse
a_{ij}	matrix element

B	flux density, constant, amplitude, reactive component of admittance
B_ν, b_ν	Fourier-amplitude sine component, coefficients of polynomial
b	shorter axis of ellipse
C	constant, amplitude, capacity
C_ν, c_ν	Fourier amplitude, resultant of A_ν and B_ν term.
c	Sound velocity; c_g group velocity, c_{ph} phase velocity, c_0 sound velocity in medium adjacent to vibrator, c_{pl} sound velocity in thin plate $(c_{pl}=c/\sqrt{1-\nu^2})$, c_B bending wave velocity
c_d, c_s, c_R	propagation velocity of distortional waves, shear waves, and Rayleigh waves respectively
c_{ij}	constants
D	constant, plate stiffness $(\lambda_E h^3/12(1-\nu^2)$ distortion maximum, linear differential operator, determinant
D_{ij}	subdeterminant to element a_{ij}
d	linear dimension, diameter, symbol used in total derivative
E	constant
E, E_k, E_p	energy, kinetic, potential energy
$e=2.718$	basis of natural logarithmic
e_{ik}	direction cosine $(\cos(x_i, x_k))$
$\vec{e}_i$	unit vector
F	force, symbol for coordinates x_F, y_F, x_F of force point, shear force on beam
F_0	total driving force
f	frequency
f_0	coincidence frequency, resonant frequency of single degree of freedom system
$f(x)$	function of x
$G(z)$	function of z
G	conductance $(1/R)$, plate bending moment (Eqs. 14.223, 8.5), shear modulus

$G(\omega)$, $G(k)$	power spectrum per unit frequency (cycles/sec) interval or per unit $dk/2\pi$ interval relative to the frequency or wave number range $-\infty$ to $+\infty$
g	acceleration due to gravity
$g(t)$	time dependent part of mode solution
g_{ik}	elements of metric tensor (Eq. 14.129)
H	(M_{yx}) plate twisting moment (Eq. 14.222), two dimensional vector potential (Eq. 14.270)
$H_\nu^{(1)}(x)$, $H_\nu^{(2)}(x)$	Hankel's function of first and second kind
h	height, thickness
h_1, h_2, h_3	measures of element of length $ds_\nu = h_\nu dq_\nu$ (Eq. 14.132)
h'	radial wave number of vibrating cylinder (Eq. 14.176)
I	current amplitude, moment of inertia
I_t, I_ν	abbreviation for time and space integrals respectively
I_ν	Bessel function (Eq. 8.52, 8.79)
i	instantaneous current
i_l	current at length l of line
i_s	sending end current
J	second moment of area of cross section
$J_\nu(x)$	Bessel function of first kind (Eqs. 8.52, 8.79)
j	imaginary unit $\sqrt{-1}$
K	compliance, plate bending moment (Eq. 14.224), mode compliance
$K_\nu(x)$	Bessel function of third kind, as defined in Watson, *Theory of Bessel Functions,* Cambridge University Press, pp. 78 and 202 (see also Eq. 8.52, Eq. 8.80)
k	wave number, radial shear wave number for vibrating cylinder (Eq. 14.176)
k_1	constant of electromagnetic force law ($f = k_1 i$)
k_2	constant of piezoelectric force law ($f = k_2 u$)
L	Self inductance, real part of Lamé's constant. Driving bending moment, $2L$ correlation length (Eq. 11.181)
L_{ik}	mutual inductance
l	loss factor of Lamé's dilatation constant
l_1, l_x, l_y	length, length in x direction etc.

M	total mass, or point mass, bending moment, M_0 real part of complex mass (Eq. 3.4)
M_ν	mode mass (Eqs. 7.23, 7.24)
M_{yx}	plate bending moment (Eq. 14.222)
M, M_{ij}	mutual inductance, or coupling mass
M_x	plate bending moment (Eq. 14.223)
m	mass per unit length or unit area
$m=1, 2, 3,..$	number of nodal areas in the x direction
m_{rad}	apparent mass per unit area of the vibrator, accession to inertia divided by ω
N	power, plate shear stress (Eq. 14.221)
N_0	power per unit area, N_1 power per unit width
$N_\nu(x)$	Neumann's function (Bessel function of second kind)
$\vec{n}(n_x, n_y, n_z)$	unit vector in the direction of the sound and its components
$n=0, 1, 2, 3..$	number of nodal areas along the y direction
P	symbol for point or for its coordinate x_p, y_p, z_p, pressure amplitude, integrated rod stress, (Eq. 14.202 to 204)
p	instantaneous pressure, force per unit area, p_{xx} pressure tensor symbol for d/dt
Q	integrated rod bending moment (Eq. 14.205); $Q_x=Z_x$, $Q_y=Y_x$ plate shear stress (Eq. 14.221, Eq. 14.220), Q' quality factor ($Q'=Q\,\omega_0/\omega$) for solid friction (Eq. 2.126)
Q	quality factor, shear stress due to load
Q, q	source strength, volume flow, Q_H volume flow into half space
q	depth decay constant for Rayleigh waves (Eq. 14.100), generalized coordinate
$q=\langle\zeta_\nu^2\rangle/\zeta_\nu^2$ (A)	factor included in mode masses (Eq. 7.15)
R	reflection factor
R, R_ν	resistance, radius of sphere, radial stress (Eq. 14.201)
R_e	resistance due to external friction
R_ν, R_ν^*	mode resistance (Eqs. 7.23 to 7.25)
r	radial coordinate, resistance per unit area
r_{rad}	radiation resistance per unit area

$rr, r\varphi, rz, \varphi z$	abbreviations for shear stress components in curvilinear coordinates
S	plate shear stress (Eq. 12.220)
$S_p(\kappa)$, $S_p(\omega)$	Fourier amplitude of the variable p of the wave number κ, or frequency ω respectively, referred to the interval $-\infty$ to $+\infty$ and to $d\omega/2\pi$ or $d\kappa/2\pi=1$ respectively
s	length of arc, coordinate in tangential direction
$\vec{s}(s_x, s_y, s_z)$	displacement vector and its components
$S(t)$	function of the time
s	depth decay constant of Rayleigh waves (shear part (Eq. 14.103))
T, T_1, T_2	normal plate stress (Eq. 14.219), period of fundamental, of first overtone etc., tension, amplitude of transmitted wave.
t	time, t_e: time for decay to e^{-1}
U	voltage amplitude, impulse (force-time integral), U_0 unit impulse
u	instantaneous voltage, u_s sending end voltage, u_δ component of displacement or velocity, u_l voltage at end $x=l$ of line
V	velocity amplitude
$v(v_x, v_y, v_z)$	instantaneous velocity or y component of displacement or velocity
$\underline{\nu}=\omega/\omega_\nu-\omega_\nu/\omega_1$	normalized frequency variable
$\underline{\nu}'=(\omega^2/\omega_\nu^2)-1$	normalized frequency variable for solid friction
W	energy
$W_p(\kappa)=\langle p^2\rangle w_p(\kappa)$	power spectrum of variable p, referred to interval $d\kappa/2\pi=1$, $W_p(\omega, \xi, \xi')=\langle p^2\rangle w_p(\omega, \xi, \xi')$ cross spectral density of pressure for points ξ and ξ'
$W_p(\kappa)=\langle p^2\rangle w(\rho)$	correlation function, $W_p(\tau, \xi, \xi')$ cross correlation function for points ξ and ξ'
w	z component of displacement or velocity
X	reactance, X_ν mode reactance
$x(=x_1)$	coordinate

Y	admittance, Y_ν mode admittance
$Y_\nu(x)$	the Bessel function as defined by the bold face symbol $Y_\nu(x)$ in Watson's *Theory of Bessel Functions*, Cambridge University Press, 1958, p. 60, Eq. (2), (Eq. 8.52, 8.78).
$y(=x_2)$	coordinate
Z	impedance, shear stress perpendicular to rod axis (Eq. 17.201)
Z_ν	mode impedance, Z_c characteristic impedance, Z_0 factor of the dimension of an impedance
$z(=x_3)$	coordinate, integration variable
z	acoustic impedance per unit area
z_ν	acoustic impedance for mode ν per unit area

Lower Case Greek Letters

α, β, γ	angles, constants, or abbreviations for a group of parameters defined where used, curvilinear coordinates: $\alpha=$const, $\beta=$const, $\gamma=$const, α^4 constant in plate equation (Eq. 8.1)
α, β	real part, imaginary part of a variable, α running index for new transformed coordinates
γ	ratio of specific heat, constant in Timoshenko beam equation (Eq. 6.15)
δ	decay constant, small increment, $\delta(x)$ delta functions
ϵ, ϵ_{ik}	strain, strain tensor
ϵ_ν	radial frequency difference between successive resonant frequencies
θ	angle, θ_1, θ_2 angle due to bending and to shear respectively. correlation time
φ	displacement, z component of displacement normalized acoustic impedance per unit area ($\zeta=z/\rho c$)
$\eta, \eta_\lambda, \eta_E$	loss factor, subscript referring to elastic modulus
κ	space wave number (bending wave number), electromechanical coupling coefficient, κ_0 bending wave number of plate at frequency of driving force, coincidence wave number
κ_ν	excitation constant (Fourier component of force that excites νth mode, divided by total driving force)

$\kappa, \kappa_1, \kappa_2$	shear correction in Mindlin's rod and plate theory
λ	stiffness constant, Lamé's dilatation modulus (first Lamé constant), wavelength
$\lambda_E, \lambda_B, \lambda_S$	Young's bulk, shear elastic modulus, subscript denoting the type λ_0 real part of stiffness constant. λ_{ik} elastic tensor
μ	shear modulus (second Lamé constant), μ' effective shear modulus (if strain varies over cross section)
$\mu=0, 1, 2, 3..$	running index
ν	Poisson's constant
$\nu=0, 1, 2, 3..$	running index, number of modes
ξ	displacement, x component of displacement, ξ_1, ξ_2 deflection due to bending and shear respectively
$\xi_\nu(x, y, z)$	natural function
π	Ludolf's number 3.1416
ρ	density
σ	area
σ, σ_{ik}	stress, stress tensor
τ	volume, time constant, shear stress in beam, τ_ξ, τ_σ relaxation time of displacement and of stress respectively
φ	angle
φ_ν	natural function
Ψ	angle
Ψ_ν	natural function
ω	circular frequency
ω_0, ω_ν	resonant frequency of point mass compliant element system, resonant frequencies of systems with many resonances
ω_ν^*	frequency of decaying vibration
$\bar{\omega}_\nu^2=\omega_\nu^2(1+j\eta)$	square of complex natural frequency
$\bar{\omega}^2=\omega^2(1-j\, r/\omega_\nu M)$	complex frequency if external friction is present
$\bar{\omega}_\nu^2=\omega_\nu^2/(1+j\eta)$	abbreviation, when performing certain integrations

Capital Greek Letters

$\Gamma(n)=(n-1)!$	gamma function
Γ_x etc.	plate strain components (Eq. 14.232)
∇^2	Laplace operator
Δ	dilatation
Λ	logarithmic decrement
Π	product
Σ	sum
Φ	velocity potential
Ψ	streaming potential
Ω	normalized frequency
Ω_r	defined by Eq. 14.217

List of Formulas for the Computations with Harmonic and Hyperbolic Functions of Real and Complex Argument

Euler's formula

$$e^{jx}=\cos x+j\sin x \tag{1}$$

$$\cos x=\frac{e^{jx}+e^{-jx}}{2} \qquad \sin x=\frac{e^{jx}-e^{-jx}}{2j} \tag{2}$$

$$\tan x=\frac{1}{j}\frac{e^{jx}-e^{-jx}}{e^{jx}+e^{-jx}}=\frac{1}{j}\frac{e^{2jx}-1}{e^{2jx}+1} \qquad \operatorname{cotg} x=\frac{1}{\tan x} \tag{3}$$

Series developments

$$e^{jx}=1+\frac{jx}{1!}-\frac{x^2}{2!}-\frac{jx^3}{3!}+\dots \tag{4}$$

$$\cos x=1-\frac{x^2}{2!}+\frac{x^4}{4!}-\frac{x^6}{6!}+\dots \tag{5}$$

$$\sin x=x-\frac{x^3}{3!}+\frac{x^5}{5!}-\frac{x^7}{7!} \tag{6}$$

$$\tan x=x+\frac{x^3}{3}+\frac{2x^5}{15}+\dots \tag{7}$$

$$\sin^{-1}x=x+\frac{x^3}{6}+\frac{3x^5}{40}+\dots \tag{8}$$

$$\cos^{-1}x=\frac{\pi}{2}-\sin^{-1}x \tag{9}$$

$$\tan^{-1}x=x-\frac{x^3}{3}+\frac{x^5}{5}-\dots \tag{10}$$

Addition laws

$$\cos\theta=\pm\sin\left(\theta\pm\frac{\pi}{2}\right) \tag{11}$$

$$\sin\theta=\pm\cos\left(\theta\mp\frac{\pi}{2}\right) \tag{12}$$

$$\sin^2\alpha+\cos^2\alpha=1 \tag{13}$$

$$\sin(\alpha\pm\beta)=\sin\alpha\cos\beta\pm\cos\alpha\sin\beta \tag{14}$$

$$\cos(\alpha \pm \beta) = \cos\alpha\cos\beta \mp \sin\alpha\sin\beta \tag{15}$$

$$\sin 2\theta = 2\sin\theta\cos\theta \tag{16}$$

$$\sin 3\theta = 3\sin\theta - 4\sin^3\theta \tag{17}$$

$$\sin n\theta = 2\sin(n-1)\theta\cos\theta - \sin(n-2)\theta \tag{18}$$

$$\cos 2\theta = \cos^2\theta - \sin^2\theta = 1 - 2\sin^2\theta = 2\cos^2\theta - 1$$

hence: $$\cos^2\theta = \frac{(1+\cos 2\theta)}{2}$$

$$\sin^2\theta = \frac{(1-\cos 2\theta)}{2} \tag{19}$$

$$\cos 3\theta = 4\cos^3\theta - 3\cos\theta \tag{20}$$

$$\cos n\theta = 2\cos(n-1)\theta\cos\theta - \cos(n-2)\theta \tag{21}$$

$$\tan 2\theta = \frac{2\tan\theta}{1-\tan^2\theta} \tag{22}$$

$$\sin\alpha \pm \sin\beta = 2\sin\frac{\alpha\pm\beta}{2}\cos\frac{\alpha\mp\beta}{2} \tag{23}$$

$$\cos\alpha + \cos\beta = 2\cos\frac{\alpha+\beta}{2}\cos\frac{\alpha-\beta}{2} \tag{24}$$

$$\cos\alpha - \cos\beta = -2\sin\frac{\alpha+\beta}{2}\sin\frac{\alpha-\beta}{2} \tag{25}$$

$$\sin\alpha\sin\beta = -\frac{1}{2}[\cos(\alpha+\beta) - \cos(\alpha-\beta)] \tag{26}$$

$$\sin\alpha\cos\beta = \frac{1}{2}[\sin(\alpha+\beta) + \sin(\alpha-\beta)] \tag{27}$$

$$\cos\alpha\cos\beta = \frac{1}{2}[\cos(\alpha-\beta) + \cos(\alpha+\beta)] \tag{28}$$

$$a\sin\theta + b\cos\theta = \sqrt{a^2+b^2}\sin\left(\theta + \tan^{-1}\frac{b}{a}\right)$$

$$= \sqrt{a^2+b^2}\cos\left(\theta - \tan^{-1}\frac{a}{b}\right) \tag{29}$$

$$\tan(\alpha\pm\beta) = \frac{\tan\alpha \pm \tan\beta}{1 \mp \tan\alpha\tan\beta} \tag{30}$$

Hyperbolic functions

$$\cosh x = \frac{e^x + e^{-x}}{2} \qquad \sinh x = \frac{e^x - e^{-x}}{2} \tag{31}$$

$$\tanh x = \frac{e^x - e^{-x}}{e^x + e^{-x}} = \frac{e^{2x}-1}{e^{2x}+1} \qquad \coth x = \frac{1}{\tanh x} \tag{32}$$

Series developments

$$e^x = 1 + \frac{x}{1!} + \frac{x^2}{2!} + \frac{x^3}{3!} + \ldots \tag{33}$$

$$\cosh x = 1 + \frac{x^2}{2!} + \frac{x^4}{4!} + \frac{x^6}{6!} + \ldots \tag{34}$$

$$\sinh x = x + \frac{x^3}{3!} + \frac{x^5}{5!} + \frac{x^7}{7!} + \ldots \tag{35}$$

$$\tanh x = x - \frac{x^3}{3} + \frac{2x^5}{15} - \frac{17x^7}{315} + \ldots \left(x^2 < \frac{1}{4}\pi^2\right) \tag{36}$$

$$\sinh^{-1} x = x - \frac{1}{2} \cdot \frac{x^3}{3} + \frac{1\cdot 3}{2\cdot 4} \cdot \frac{x^5}{5} - \frac{1\cdot 3\cdot 5}{2\cdot 4\cdot 6} : \frac{x^7}{7} + \ldots (x^2 < 1) \tag{37}$$

$$\cosh^{-1} = \log 2x - \frac{1}{2} \cdot \frac{1}{2x^2} - \frac{1\cdot 3}{2\cdot 4} \cdot \frac{1}{4x^4} - \frac{1\cdot 3\cdot 5}{2\cdot 4\cdot 6} \cdot \frac{1}{6x^6} - \ldots (x^2 > 1) \tag{38}$$

$$\tanh^{-1} x = x + \frac{x^3}{3} + \frac{x^5}{5} + \frac{x^7}{7} + \ldots (x^2 < 1) \tag{39}$$

Addition laws

$$\cosh^2 \alpha - \sinh^2 \alpha = 1 \tag{40}$$

$$\sinh(\alpha \pm \beta) = \sinh\alpha \cosh\beta \pm \cosh\alpha \sinh\beta \tag{41}$$

$$\cosh(\alpha \pm \beta) = \cosh\alpha \cosh\beta \pm \sinh\alpha \sinh\beta \tag{42}$$

$$\sinh 2\theta = 2 \sinh\theta \cosh\theta \tag{43}$$

$$\cosh 2\theta = \cosh^2\theta + \sinh^2\theta = 1 + 2\sinh^2\theta = 2\cosh^2\theta - 1 \tag{44}$$

$$\sinh\alpha \pm \sinh\beta = 2\sinh\frac{\alpha \pm \beta}{2} \cosh\frac{\alpha \mp \beta}{2} \tag{45}$$

$$\cosh\alpha + \cosh\beta = 2\cosh\frac{\alpha + \beta}{2} \cosh\frac{\alpha - \beta}{2} \tag{46}$$

$$\cosh\alpha - \cosh\beta = 2\sinh\frac{\alpha + \beta}{2} \sinh\frac{\alpha - \beta}{2} \tag{47}$$

$$\sinh\alpha \cosh\beta = \frac{1}{2}[\sinh(\alpha + \beta) + \sinh(\alpha - \beta)] \tag{48}$$

$$\cosh\alpha \cosh\beta = \frac{1}{2}[\cosh(\alpha + \beta) + \cosh(\alpha - \beta)] \tag{49}$$

$$\sinh\alpha \sinh\beta = \frac{1}{2}[\cosh(\alpha + \beta) - \cosh(\alpha - \beta)] \tag{50}$$

$$a \sinh \theta \pm b \cosh \theta = \sqrt{a^2 - b^2} \sinh\left(\theta \pm \tanh^{-1} \frac{b}{a}\right)$$

$$= \sqrt{b^2 - a^2} \cosh\left(\theta \pm \tanh^{-1} \frac{a}{b}\right) \qquad (51)$$

Complex argument

$$\cos jx = \cosh x \qquad \cosh jx = \cos x \qquad (52)$$

$$\sin jx = j \sinh x \qquad \sinh jx = j \sin x \qquad (53)$$

$$\tan jx = j \tanh x \qquad \tanh jx = j \tan x \qquad (54)$$

$$\cos x = \cosh jx \qquad \cosh x = \cos jx \qquad (55)$$

$$\sin x = -j \sinh jx \qquad \sinh x = -j \sin jx \qquad (56)$$

$$\tan x = -j \tanh jx \qquad \tanh x = -j \tan jx \qquad (57)$$

$$\sinh\left(x \pm j\frac{\pi}{2}\right) = \pm j \cosh x \qquad (58)$$

$$\cosh\left(x - j\frac{\pi}{2}\right) = \pm j \sinh x \qquad (59)$$

$$\tanh(x \pm jn\pi) = \tanh x \qquad n = 0, 1, 2, \ldots \qquad (60)$$

$$\tanh\left(x \pm j\frac{n\pi}{2}\right) = \frac{1}{\tanh x} \qquad n = 1, 3, 5, \ldots \qquad (6$$

$$\sin(a \pm jb) = \sin a \cosh b \pm j \cos a \sinh b$$

$$\cos(a \pm jb) = \cos a \cosh b \mp j \sin a \sinh b$$

$$\tan(a \pm jb) = \frac{\tan a \pm j \tanh b}{1 \mp j \tan a \tanh b} = \frac{\sin 2a \pm j \sinh 2b}{\cos 2a + \cosh 2b}$$

$$\sinh(a \pm jb) = \sinh a \cos b \pm j \cosh a \sin b \qquad ($$

$$\cosh(a \pm jb) = \cosh a \cos b \pm j \sinh a \sin b \qquad (6$$

$$\tanh(a \pm jb) = \frac{\tanh a \pm j \tan b}{1 \pm j \tanh a \tan b} = \frac{\sinh 2a \pm j \sin 2b}{\cosh 2a + \cos 2b} \qquad (67)$$

Complex argument a + jb, *small imaginary part*

$$\cos b = \cosh b = 1 \qquad \sin b = \sinh b = b \qquad (68)$$

$$\sin(a \pm jb) = \sin a \pm jb \cos a \qquad (69)$$

$$\cos(a \pm jb) = \cos a \mp jb \sin a \qquad (70)$$

$$\tan(a \pm jb) = \frac{\sin 2a \pm j2b}{\cos 2a + 1} \tag{71}$$

$$\sinh(a \pm jb) = \sinh a \pm jb \cosh a \tag{72}$$

$$\cosh(a \pm jb) = \cosh a \pm jb \sinh a \tag{73}$$

$$\tanh(a \pm jb) = \frac{\sinh 2a \mp j2b}{\cosh 2a + 1} \tag{74}$$

An important formula in network theory

If $\tanh(a + jb) = M \angle \theta$

then $a + jb = \text{area tanh}\,(M \angle \theta)$

$$= \frac{1}{2}\left[\text{area tanh}\left(\frac{2M\cos\theta}{1+M^2}\right) + j\tan^{-1}\left(\frac{2M\sin\theta}{1-M^2}\right)\right] \tag{75}$$

SIMPLE AND COMPLEX VIBRATORY SYSTEMS

I / INTRODUCTION

This chapter provides some of the essential tools for solving more complicated vibration problems. It is assumed that the reader is well acquainted with the standard mathematical methods, but is less familiar with some of the fundamentals and the more recent results that have been derived in the study of electrical systems and mechanical circuit diagrams.

Complex Notation and Symbolic Methods

Complex Notation and Rotating Vectors

The mathematical description of the vibration of a complex structure is very complicated because of the many modes of motion in which the structure can respond. However, we are primarily interested in periodic vibrations as they are excited by harmonically varying forces and in the building up and decay of such vibrations, since the response of a vibrator to unsteady forces can be deduced from its response to harmonic forces with the aid of Fourier analysis or the Laplace transform. The harmonic sine and cosine functions are inconvenient because of their complicated addition and multiplication theorems. A condensed notation can be introduced that is based on the fact that the projection of a rotating vector of unit length on the x axis represents the cosine and that on the y axis, the sine of the angle between the rotating vector and the x axis. Thus, it is permissible to replace the sinusoidal functions by rotating vectors and to consider these rotating vectors as the primary variables. The harmonic functions can then easily be reconstructed from the rotating vectors.

The representation of rotating vectors is greatly aided by the use of complex notation, which is based on the use of complex magnitudes called complex vectors or phasors. The x component of such a complex vector is called its real part, and the x axis is called the real axis. The y component of the complex vector is called its imaginary part, and the y axis is called the imaginary axis. The unit vector in the x direction is represented by the number 1, and the unit vector in the y direction is represented by the symbol j. The plane that contains the real and imaginary axis is called the complex plane. The vector character of a complex quantity $\bar{A}$ is denoted by a bar over the letter that represents it. The length of a complex vector is called its magnitude or its absolute value; it is denoted by the simple letter A or by the letter $|\bar{A}|$ between two vertical lines.

Thus far a complex vector in the complex plane has been defined simply by its two components; rotation is built into the new calculus by defining the symbol j as having the same properties as $\sqrt{-1}$:

$$j=\sqrt{-1}, \qquad j^2=-1, \qquad j^3=-j, \qquad j^4=1, \quad \text{etc.} \tag{1.1}$$

Multiplying the unit vector by j turns it 90°, while multiplication by j^2 turns the unit vector 180°, reversing its direction. Multiplication by the factor $\cos\varphi+j\sin\varphi$ rotates the real unit vector or any other complex vector $\bar{A}=A(\cos\alpha+j\sin\alpha)$ by an angle φ, as is proved as follows:

$$\begin{aligned}\bar{A}(\cos\varphi+j\sin\varphi)&=[A(\cos\alpha+j\sin\alpha)](\cos\varphi+j\sin\varphi)\\&=A[(\cos\alpha\cos\varphi-\sin\alpha\sin\varphi)+j(\sin\alpha\cos\varphi+\cos\alpha\sin\varphi)]\\&=A[\cos(\alpha+\varphi)+j\sin(\alpha+\varphi)]\end{aligned} \tag{1.2}$$

Thus, the resultant vector is a vector of the same length, but its angle with the real axis is $\alpha+\varphi$. Euler's identity

$$\cos\varphi+j\sin\varphi=e^{j\varphi} \tag{1.3}$$

makes it possible to represent a complex vector by a simple complex exponential in the so-called polar form:

$$\bar{A}=Ae^{j\alpha} \tag{1.4}$$

A rotating vector is obtained by setting $\alpha=\omega t+\varphi$. A vector that rotates with constant angular velocity ω is denoted in this text by a wavy line above the letter, to distinguish it from a constant vector, which is described by a horizontal bar above the letter. Thus,

$$\tilde{A}=Ae^{j(\omega t+\varphi)}=A\cos(\omega t+\varphi)+jA\sin(\omega t+\varphi) \tag{1.5}$$

The angle α represents the angle the rotating vector subtends with the real axis at any time, t; the constant ω denotes the angular frequency, and the constant φ, the initial phase angle of the rotating vector.

A complex quantity can be represented by its components

$$\bar{A}=a+jb=A\cos\varphi+jA\sin\varphi \tag{1.6}$$

or by its magnitude A and its phase angle φ in the polar form:

$$\bar{A}=Ae^{j\varphi}=A\angle\varphi \tag{1.7}$$

The last form of the right-hand side of Equation 1.7 is frequently used as an abbreviation; it is read, "A at the angle φ." The quantity A, which represents the length of the complex vector, is called its magnitude or its absolute value. It is given by the theorem of Pythagoras:

$$A=|\bar{A}|=\sqrt{A^2\cos^2\varphi+A^2\sin^2\varphi}=\sqrt{a^2+b^2} \tag{1.8}$$

Note that the squares always occur with positive signs. The tangent of the phase angle is obtained from Equation 1.6 by dividing the imaginary part by the real part.[1]

[1] The calculus with complex numbers obeys the rules of algebra. If the reader is not familiar with these rules, he can easily consult books on complex variables.

Symbolic Method for Solving Linear Differential Equations

Since the systems of interest in the theory of vibration are usually linear, and the loss resistance is constant or inversely proportional to the frequency, the vibrations build up and decay exponentially. For a rotating vector $\bar{\xi}$ whose length is constant or decreases exponentially with time, differentiation is equivalent to multiplication, and integration to division by a complex constant:

$$\frac{d}{dt}\bar{\xi}=\frac{d}{dt}\hat{\xi}_0 e^{(-\delta+j\omega)t}=\frac{d}{dt}(\hat{\xi}_0 e^{j\bar{\omega}t})=j\bar{\omega}e^{j\bar{\omega}t}\hat{\xi}_0=j\bar{\omega}\bar{\xi} \tag{1.9}$$

$$\int\bar{\xi}dt=\int\hat{\xi}_0{}^{(-\delta+j\omega)t}dt=\int\xi_0 e^{j\bar{\omega}t}dt=\frac{1}{j\bar{\omega}}\bar{\xi} \tag{1.10}$$

where a complex angular frequency has been introduced by the relation

$$j\bar{\omega}=-\delta+j\omega$$

or

$$\bar{\omega}=j\delta+\omega \tag{1.11}$$

If the variables are of constant amplitude or are exponentially decreasing rotating vectors, the differential equations become equivalent to simple algebraic relations.

The equations that can be dealt with in a simple manner are linear and have real coefficients, as, for instance, the equation for the point-mass spring vibrator:

$$\frac{d^2\xi}{dt^2}+\frac{Rd\xi}{Mdt}+\frac{\xi}{KM}=\frac{F}{M}\cos(\omega t+\varphi) \tag{1.12}$$

They are all of the form

$$D\cdot\xi=f \tag{1.13}$$

where D is a differential operator that may contain derivatives of any order with respect to the time and the space co-ordinates. The coefficients of these derivatives have to be real, and the variables themselves must not appear in them. In the above example, the operator D is $d^2/dt^2+Rd/Mdt+1/KM$, and it acts on the variable ξ.

A linear differential operator and a linear differential equation both exhibit two fundamental properties. If the force f_1 produces a deflection ξ_1, that is if

$$D\cdot\xi_1=f_1 \tag{1.14}$$

and if the force f_2 produces a deflection ξ_2, that is if

$$D\cdot\xi_2=f_2 \tag{1.15}$$

then the force f_1+f_2 will produce a deflection $\xi_1+\xi_2$ because of the supposed linearity of the operator D. This is proved by adding the last two equations:

$$D\cdot\xi_1+D\cdot\xi_2=D\cdot(\xi_1+\xi_2)=f_1+f_2 \tag{1.16}$$

The deflection that is produced in the system by a given force is thus independent of other forces that may already be acting, and the displacements produced by the various forces can be added. The second fundamental property of a linear equation is demonstrated by multiplying the left and right sides of the equation by a constant a. Since the differential equation contains only the first power of ξ, the relation $aD\cdot\xi=D\cdot a\xi$ holds, and

$$a\cdot D\cdot\xi=D\cdot(a\xi)=af \tag{1.17}$$

Thus, an increase of the force by a factor a leads to an increase of the deflection by the same factor. Such a procedure would not hold if the differential equation contained a term involving ξ^2 or any other power of ξ, because

$$a\xi^n\neq(a\xi)^n \tag{1.18}$$

unless $n=1$.

Let the external force be periodic and of the form

$$f_1=F\cos(\omega t+\varphi) \tag{1.19}$$

This force will generate the vibration ξ_1, where ξ_1 satisfies the differential equation

$$D\cdot\xi_1=F\cos(\omega t+\varphi) \tag{1.20}$$

A similar periodic force that lags 90° behind f_1

$$f_2=F\cos\left(\omega t+\varphi-\frac{\pi}{2}\right)=F\sin(\omega t+\varphi) \tag{1.21}$$

generates a vibration that is given by the solution of the differential equation

$$D\cdot\xi_2=f_2=F\sin(\omega t+\varphi) \tag{1.22}$$

The force f_1 may then be considered to represent the real part, and the force f_2, the imaginary part of a complex force

$$\tilde{f}=f_1+jf_2=F[\cos(\omega t+\varphi)+j\sin(\omega t+\varphi)]=Fe^{j(\omega t+\varphi)}=\bar{F}e^{j\omega t} \tag{1.23}$$

where $Fe^{j\varphi}=\bar{F}$.

In a similar manner a complex variable $\tilde{\xi}$ may be defined by the relation

$$\tilde{\xi}=\xi_1+j\xi_2=\hat{\xi}e^{j(\omega t+\Psi)} \tag{1.24}$$

where $\xi_1=Re(\tilde{\xi})$ is the real part of $\tilde{\xi}$, and $\xi_2=Im(\tilde{\xi})$ is the imaginary part of $\tilde{\xi}$. In the steady state, force and displacement are necessarily of the same frequency, and the variable $\tilde{\xi}$ is of the form shown at the right-hand side of the last equation. Equations 1.20 and 1.22 may then be incorporated into one equation by multiplying Equation 1.22 by the factor j and adding it to Equation 1.20:

$$D\cdot(\xi_1+j\xi_2)=D\cdot\tilde{\xi}=\bar{F}e^{j\omega t} \tag{1.25}$$

The coefficients of the differential equation have been assumed to be real. The operator D, therefore, does not change the real character when it acts on ξ_1, nor does it change the imaginary character when it acts on $j\xi_2$, and the real and imaginary parts can be separated again in the result. The same rules apply for exponentially varying forces or decaying vibrations.

The preceding results make it possible to reduce differential equations for harmonic or decaying vibrations to algebraic equations and to solve them in a very efficient manner. For exponential functions, time differentiation reduces to multiplication with $j\omega$; time integration, to division by $j\omega$. The complex solution can, therefore, be worked out easily. The real part of this solution, then, corresponds to a driving force

$$f_1 = F\cos(\omega t + \varphi) \tag{1.26}$$

and the imaginary part corresponds to a driving force

$$f_2 = F\sin(\omega t + \varphi) = F\cos\left(\omega t + \varphi - \frac{\pi}{2}\right) \tag{1.27}$$

The two real solutions differ only by a phase angle $\pi/2$. Since the phase of the force can be selected in any arbitrary manner, the two solutions are equivalent. The transition from the complex solution to the real solution is trivial, since it represents only a splitting up of the complex solution into its real and imaginary parts. The problem can therefore be considered to be solved whenever the complex solution has been found.

Complex Solution and Boundary Conditions

The mathematicians usually write the solutions for periodic motion in the form

$$\bar{A}e^{j\omega t} + \bar{B}e^{-j\omega t} \tag{1.28}$$

This solution is equivalent to two real solutions, one being the real part of this expression, the other its imaginary part. Equating this solution (Eq. 1.28) to real initial conditions leads to a real solution (the real part of the above expression, which satisfies the given initial condition, while the imaginary part satisfies the initial condition that it is zero). For example, the initial conditions may be

$$t=0 \qquad \xi=\xi_0 \qquad v=v_0 \tag{1.29}$$

If the complex solution is formally adapted to these conditions:

$$t=0 \qquad \tilde{\xi}=\xi_1+j\xi_2=\xi_0+(j)\cdot(0)$$
$$\tilde{v}=v_1+jv_2=v_0+(j)\cdot(0) \tag{1.30}$$

the real part will satisfy the given boundary conditions, and the imaginary part will satisfy the conditions

$$\xi_2=0 \qquad v_2=0 \tag{1.31}$$

Thus, instead of one boundary condition at a time, the complex solution must comply with two boundary conditions; since Equation 1.28 is equivalent to two solutions, the number of free constants in the complex solution is sufficient for this.

In the theory of vibrations and in acoustics it is preferable to reject the term $\bar{B}e^{-j\omega t}$ in the solution (Eq. 1.28). The solution is still complete, because the complex constant $\bar{A}$ is equivalent to two real constants (amplitude and phase), but it is only its real part that must satisfy the boundary conditions. Boundary conditions can no longer be specified for the imaginary part, nor may the imaginary part be equated to zero.

Computation of Power

The complex solution can be used only with linear equations. In the computation of squares and products of complex quantities, the relation $j^2 = -1$ transforms the squares or products of imaginary parts into real quantities; real and imaginary parts become mixed and can no longer be reobtained by simple computations. For a square, for instance,

$$\xi^2 = (\xi_1 + j\xi_2)^2 = (\xi_1^2 - \xi_2^2) + 2j\xi_1\xi_2 \tag{1.32}$$

The real part becomes equal to the difference of the squares of the real and the imaginary parts, and the imaginary part becomes equal to twice the product of its real and imaginary parts.

Squares, products, and higher powers of the real solution can be computed with the aid of the conjugate complex vector. The power, for instance, is given by the product of the force and the velocity

$$fv = Re(\tilde{f})\, Re(\tilde{v}) \neq Re(\tilde{f}\tilde{v}) \tag{1.33}$$

where *Re* designates the real part. But if $\tilde{f} = \alpha + j\beta$, $\tilde{f}^* = \alpha - j\beta$, and

$$f = Re(\tilde{f}) = \alpha = \frac{1}{2}(\tilde{f} + \tilde{f}^*) \tag{1.34}$$

Similarly,

$$v = Re(\tilde{v}) = \frac{1}{2}(\tilde{v} + \tilde{v}^*) \tag{1.35}$$

Hence, the power is

$$\begin{aligned} fv &= \frac{1}{4}(\tilde{f} + \tilde{f}^*)\,(\tilde{v} + \tilde{v}^*) = \frac{1}{4}[\,(\tilde{f}\tilde{v} + \tilde{f}^*\tilde{v}^*) + (\tilde{f}\tilde{v}^* + \tilde{v}\tilde{f}^*)\,] \\ &= \frac{1}{2}[Re(\tilde{f}\tilde{v}) + Re(\tilde{f}\tilde{v}^*)\,] \\ &= \frac{1}{2}Re\,[FVe^{j(2\omega t + \varphi_f + \varphi_v)} + FVe^{j(\varphi_f - \varphi_v)}] \\ &= \frac{1}{2}FV\,[\cos(2\omega t + \varphi_f + \varphi_v) + \cos(\varphi_f - \varphi_v)\,] \end{aligned} \tag{1.36}$$

The time average of the first term on the right-hand side of the last equation is zero; the time average value of the power is, therefore, given by the constant term

$$\langle fv\rangle_t=\frac{1}{2}FV\cos(\varphi_f-\varphi_v)=\frac{1}{2}Re(\tilde{f}\tilde{v}^*)=\frac{1}{4}(\tilde{f}\tilde{v}^*+\tilde{f}^*\tilde{v})=\frac{1}{2}Re(\tilde{f}^*\tilde{v}) \tag{1.37}$$

where the angular brackets with the subscript t denote time average. Thus, for a real product either the real parts of both $\tilde{f}$ and $\tilde{v}$ must be computed first, or else, the complex conjugate of one of them must be taken before the product is formed.

Elementary Circuit Theory

The rapid development of the methods of communication in recent years has been accompanied by a corresponding progress in the theories of electrical networks. Much effort was expended in these fields, and powerful methods have been developed to cope with the problems that have arisen. These methods are now available for use in other branches of science.

Network theory can be described as the theory of systems of linear differential equations. The circuit elements represent differential or integral operators, which, acting on the currents, yield the voltage across them or, acting on the voltage drops, yield the currents through them; and the electrical circuits themselves are a shorthand method of representing these differential equations and the boundary conditions. The inductance operator, for instance, operates on the current and differentiates it: $u_L=L(di/dt)$; the capacitance operator integrates the current: $u_C=(1/C)\int idt;$ and the resistance operator is a mere multiplier: $u_R=Ri.$

Mechanical systems of point masses, compliant elements, and resistances obey the same differential equations as electrical systems composed of inductors, capacitors, and resistors. The mechanical elements mass $M,$ compliance $K,$ and mechanical resistance R can be interpreted as operators that furnish the force $f;$ they differentiate the velocity, $f_M=M(dv/dt)$; integrate it, $f_K=(1/K)\int vdt=(1/K)\xi$; or multiply it by a constant, $R_m:f_R=R_m v$. Therefore, they are identical to the electrical operators, except for the different letters ($M,\ K,\ R_m$) that are attached to them.

Because of these so-called electromechanical analogies, mechanical systems can be represented by circuit diagrams, electrical methods become applicable to mechanical systems, and solutions that are out of the reach of the classical theories can be derived with relative ease. Examples of the great power of these new methods will be given in Chapter IV and in most of the chapters that follow it. The following sections outline the basic electrical methods and theorems.

Kirchhoff's Laws

An electric network consists of branches, nodes, meshes, and circuits or loops. The branches are two-terminal elements that contain resistances, capacitances, inductances, circuital wiring, or cables. The nodes are points where two or more branches meet (Fig. 1.1*a*), the meshes are the smallest closed circuits that can be traced in a network by following its branches (Fig.1.1*b*).

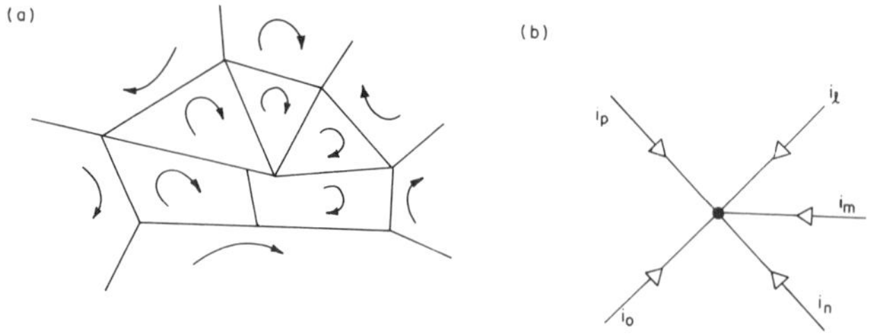

Fig. 1.1 Meshes and nodes. The nodes are points where two or more branches meet (*a*); the currents are usually considered positive, if they flow into the node as shown here (*b*).

Most networks of interest in the theory of vibrations are planar networks. They can be drawn on the surface of a sphere in such a manner that no two branches cross one another. If a planar network is laid out on a sphere, the outer boundary of the network becomes a mesh like any other mesh of the network. The boundary of the network is, therefore, also considered to be a mesh. Nonplanar networks have to be drawn on higher-order topological surfaces—for instance, on doughnut-shaped bodies—if crossing branches are to be eliminated.

The fundamental laws of network theory are expressions of Kirchhoff's two laws. The first law states that the sum of the voltages around any closed circuit is zero:

$$\Sigma u_\nu = 0 \tag{1.38}$$

This law is a consequence of the uniqueness of the potential. The second law is a consequence of the conservation of charge, i.e., that electrons are neither generated nor destroyed. The currents that enter a node through one set of branches must leave the node through some other set of branches. The currents are usually considered positive, if they flow into the node (Fig. 1.1*b*). The node law may be stated as:

$$\Sigma i_\nu = 0 \tag{1.39}$$

Kirchhoff's equations apply to the instantaneous values of currents and voltages. Frequently, the currents and voltages are expressed symbolically by complex rotating current and voltage vectors. Since real and imaginary components of these vectors are possible solutions that differ only in the zero of the time scale, Kirchhoff's laws apply equally well to their real and imaginary components. Consequently, Kirchhoff's laws apply to the complex rotating vectors too.

Resistance, Inductance, and Capacitance

The branches of a network are made up of circuit elements, such as resistances, inductances, and capacitances. Resistance is defined by the algebraic equation

$$u_R = R \cdot i \tag{1.40}$$

The voltage u_R across the resistance R is proportional to the current i through R at all times. The inductance L is defined by the differential equation

$$u_L = \frac{Ldi}{dt} \tag{1.41}$$

The capacitance C is defined by the equation

$$q = Cu_C \qquad \text{or} \qquad i = \frac{Cdu_C}{dt} \qquad \text{or} \qquad \frac{du_C}{dt} = \frac{1}{C}i \tag{1.42}$$

where q is the charge. The time differentials are zero if current and voltage are constant; so the inductance acts like a short circuit (like a connection of zero resistance), and the capacitance, like an open circuit (as if it were an opened switch).

If the current varies sinusoidally and

$$i = I\cos(\omega t + \varphi_i) \tag{1.43}$$

where φ_i is an arbitrary phase angle, the above relations are equivalent to the equations

$$u_R = RI \cdot \cos(\omega t + \varphi_i) \tag{1.44}$$

$$u_L = -\omega LI \sin(\omega t + \varphi_i) = \omega LI \cos\left(\omega t + \varphi_i + \frac{\pi}{2}\right) \tag{1.45}$$

$$\frac{du_C}{dt} = \frac{1}{C}i = \frac{I}{C}\cos(\omega t + \varphi_i) \qquad \text{and} \qquad u_C = \frac{I}{\omega C}\sin(\omega t + \varphi_i)$$
$$= \frac{I}{\omega C}\cos\left(\omega t + \varphi_1 - \frac{\pi}{2}\right) \tag{1.46}$$

or to the symbolic equations

$$\tilde{u}_R = R \cdot \tilde{\imath} \tag{1.47}$$

$$\tilde{u}_L = j\omega L\tilde{\imath} \tag{1.48}$$

$$j\omega\tilde{u}_C = \frac{1}{C}\tilde{\imath} \qquad \text{or} \qquad \tilde{u}_C = \frac{1}{j\omega C}\tilde{\imath} \tag{1.49}$$

If the symbolic notation is used, an inductance L formally obeys the same equation as a resistance of value:

$$jX_L = j\omega L \tag{1.50}$$

and the capacitance C obeys the same equations as a resistance of value:

$$jX_C = \frac{1}{j\omega C} = j\left(-\frac{1}{\omega C}\right) \tag{1.51}$$

To distinguish the quantities X from true resistances, they are called reactances. Thus, the reactance of an inductance is positive and

$$X_L = \omega L \tag{1.52}$$

That of a capacity is negative and equal to

$$X_C = -\frac{1}{\omega C} \tag{1.53}$$

The reciprocal of a resistance is called conductance and is denoted by the letter G; the conductance is defined by the equation

$$\tilde{\imath} = G\tilde{u} \tag{1.54}$$

where $G = 1/R$. The reciprocal of a reactance is called susceptance. The susceptance is denoted by the letter B. The susceptance of an inductance is defined by the equation

$$\tilde{\imath} = jB_L\tilde{u}_L = \frac{\tilde{u}_L}{j\omega L} = -\frac{j}{\omega L}\tilde{u}_L \tag{1.55}$$

where $B_L = -1/\omega L$. The susceptance of a capacitance is defined by the corresponding equation

$$\tilde{\imath} = jB_C\tilde{u}_C = j\omega C\tilde{u}_C \tag{1.56}$$

where $B_C = \omega C$.

Two-terminal networks that contain resistances and reactances are called impedances, and the ratio of the terminal voltage to the current is defined as the (complex) impedance:

$$\bar{Z} = \frac{\tilde{u}}{\tilde{\imath}} \tag{1.57}$$

The reciprocal of the impedance is called the admittance:

$$\bar{Y} = \frac{1}{\bar{Z}} = \frac{\tilde{\imath}}{\tilde{u}} \tag{1.58}$$

The impedance is always denoted by the letter $\bar{Z}$, and the admittance, by the letter $\bar{Y}$. The concept of an electrical impedance makes it possible to extend Ohm's law ($\tilde{u} = \bar{Z}\tilde{\imath}$) to inductances, to capacitances, and to two-terminal networks built of such elements.

Elementary Theorems

Work with electrical and mechanical circuit diagrams is greatly aided by elementary and advanced theorems that have been discovered in the study of electric networks. The fundamental theorems are:

(1) Impedance of series connection:

$$\bar{Z}=\bar{Z}_1+\bar{Z}_2 \tag{1.59}$$

(2) Series connection, expressed in terms of admittances:

$$\bar{Y}_1=\frac{1}{\bar{Z}_1} \qquad \bar{Y}_2=\frac{1}{\bar{Z}_2}$$

$$\frac{1}{\bar{Y}}=\frac{1}{\bar{Y}_1}+\frac{1}{\bar{Y}_2} \quad \text{or} \quad \bar{Y}=\frac{\bar{Y}_1\bar{Y}_2}{\bar{Y}_1+\bar{Y}_2} \tag{1.60}$$

(3) Parallel connection of impedances:

$$\frac{1}{\bar{Z}}=\frac{1}{\bar{Z}_1}+\frac{1}{\bar{Z}_2} \quad \text{or} \quad \bar{Z}=\frac{\bar{Z}_1\bar{Z}_2}{\bar{Z}_1+\bar{Z}_2} \tag{1.61}$$

(4) Parallel connection, expressed in terms of admittances:

$$\bar{Y}=\bar{Y}_1+\bar{Y}_2 \tag{1.62}$$

(5) Distribution of current between two branches (Fig. 1.2):

$$\tilde{\imath}_1=\tilde{\imath}_0\frac{\bar{Z}_2}{\bar{Z}_1+\bar{Z}_2} \tag{1.63}$$

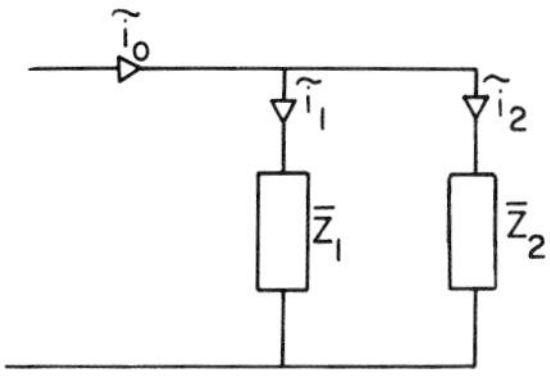

Fig. 1.2 Parallel connection of two impedances

The current through branch 1 is given by the product of the total current and the ratio of the impedance of branch 2 to the sum of the two impedances. If branch $\bar{Z}_2$ is a short circuit (an ideal connection of no resistance), all the current will flow through it, and the current in $\bar{Z}_1$ will be zero. Equation 1.63 should be remembered. Proof: The total current (Fig. 1.2) is:

$$\tilde{\imath}_0=\tilde{\imath}_1+\tilde{\imath}_2 \tag{1.64}$$

The voltage across the impedances $\bar{Z}_1$ and $\bar{Z}_2$ is:

$$\tilde{\imath}_1\bar{Z}_1=\tilde{\imath}_2\bar{Z}_2 \tag{1.65}$$

The unknown $\bar{\imath}_2=\bar{\imath}_1\bar{Z}_1/\bar{Z}_2$ can be eliminated in the first equation:

$$\bar{\imath}_0=\bar{\imath}_1+\bar{\imath}_2=\bar{\imath}_1\left(1+\frac{\bar{Z}_1}{\bar{Z}_2}\right) \tag{1.66}$$

and

$$\bar{\imath}_1=\bar{\imath}_0\frac{\bar{Z}_2}{\bar{Z}_1+\bar{Z}_2} \tag{1.67}$$

Representation of a Loss Resistance

The energy dissipation of a reactive element can be represented by a resistance either in series with it or in parallel with it (Fig. 1.3). Such a resistance is usually called a loss or dissipation resistance. The frequency variation of the losses and of the total impedance is slightly different in the two cases, as is illustrated by the following two formulas. The first represents the impedance of an inductance whose losses are expressed by a resistance in series with it. The resultant impedance and its phase are given by:

$$\bar{Z}_s=R_s+j\omega L_s=\sqrt{R_s^2+\omega^2L_s^2}\;e^{j\tan^{-1}(\omega L_s/R_s)} \tag{1.68}$$

The second formula applies to an inductance whose losses are expressed by a resistance in parallel with it. The resultant impedance then is:

$$\bar{Z}_p=\frac{1}{\dfrac{1}{R_p}+\dfrac{1}{j\omega L_p}}=\frac{R_p\omega L_p}{\sqrt{R_p^2+\omega^2L_p^2}}\;e^{j\tan^{-1}(R_p/\omega L_p)} \tag{1.69}$$

The two frequency curves are represented in Figure 1.3.

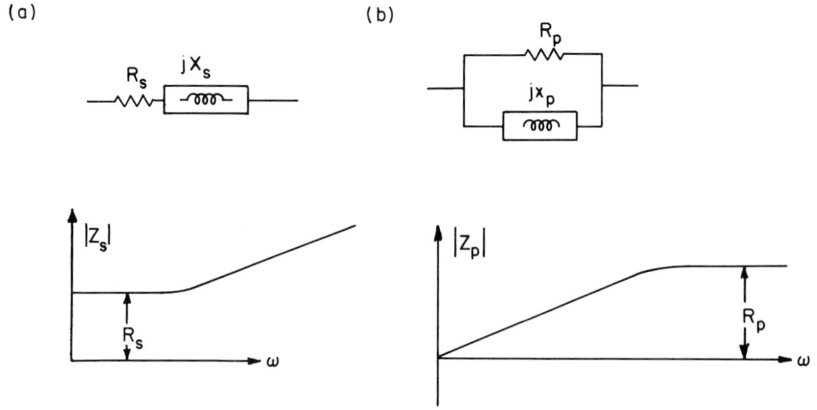

Fig. 1.3 Representation of the losses by a series (*a*) and a parallel (*b*) resistance.

One of the most useful formulas in dealing with complicated mechanical vibrators is that for the transformation of a resistance R_s in series with a reactance X_s into a resistance R_p in parallel with a reactance X_p. The impedances of the series and of the parallel combination can be made the same for only one particular frequency, ω. This is no serious disadvantage since the losses, unless they are very great, affect the system or circuit only near its resonant frequency.[2] In the theory of vibrations the tuned circuit is of primary interest. A small variation of the loss resistance with frequency has practically no effect on the response of the circuit, and we are free to represent the losses either by a series combination R_s and jX_s or by a parallel combination R_p and jX_p. The task then simply involves the selection of the circuit elements in such a manner that the combination represents the same impedance at the frequency of interest. We thus demand that at the frequency ω_0

$$\bar{Z}_s = \bar{Z}_p \tag{1.70}$$

But

$$\frac{1}{\bar{Z}_s} = \frac{1}{R_s + jX_s} \cdot \frac{R_s - jX_s}{R_s - jX_s} = \frac{R_s}{R_s^2 + X_s^2} - \frac{jX_s}{R_s^2 + X_s^2} = \frac{R_s}{Z_s^2} - j\frac{X_s}{Z_s^2} \tag{1.71}$$

where

$$Z_s^2 = R_s^2 + X_s^2 = Z_p^2 \tag{1.72}$$

is the square of the impedance of the combination, and

$$\frac{1}{\bar{Z}_p} = \bar{Y}_p = \frac{1}{R_p} + \frac{1}{jX_p} = \frac{1}{R_p} - \frac{j}{X_p} \tag{1.73}$$

Equating Equation 1.71 to Equation 1.73, we get

$$\frac{R_s}{Z_s^2} - j\frac{X_s}{Z_s^2} = \frac{1}{R_p} - \frac{j}{X_p} \tag{1.74}$$

Equating the real and imaginary parts leads to the two relations,

$$\frac{R_s}{Z_s^2} = \frac{1}{R_p} \quad \text{and} \quad \frac{X_s}{Z_s^2} = \frac{1}{X_p} \tag{1.75}$$

Equations 1.75 can be written in a more convenient form:

$$R_s R_p = Z_s^2 = X_s X_p \tag{1.76}$$

or

$$R_s R_p = X_s^2\left(1 + \frac{R_s^2}{X_s^2}\right) = X_s^2(1 + \eta^2) \tag{1.77}$$

and

$$X_s X_p = X_s^2\left(1 + \frac{R_s^2}{X_s^2}\right) = X_s^2(1 + \eta^2) \tag{1.78}$$

[2] E.g., see Fig. 2.8, p. 73.

or

$$X_p = X_s(1+\eta^2) \tag{1.79}$$

where the magnitude

$$\eta = \frac{R_s}{X_s} \tag{1.80}$$

is defined as the loss factor; its reciprocal

$$Q = \frac{X_s}{R_s} = \frac{1}{\eta} \tag{1.81}$$

is called the quality factor.

If the circuit is not heavily damped, η is small, $R_s^2/X_s^2 = \eta^2 \ll 1$, and the above equations reduce to

$$X_s = X_p = X \quad \text{and} \quad R_p = \frac{X^2}{R_s} = \frac{X^2}{R_s^2} R_s = Q^2 R_s \tag{1.82}$$

Thus, the reactance is very nearly the same, whether the resistance is in parallel or in series with it. But parallel and series resistances are inversely proportional to one another, the factor of proportionality being the square of the absolute values of the impedance X. The last formula can easily be remembered: It is obvious that a small resistor has little effect on the resulting impedance if it is connected in series with the reactance and that it has a great effect on it if it is connected in parallel with the reactance. Therefore, large damping requires a large series resistor or a small parallel resistor.

Voltage and Current Generators

The source that feeds a network may be represented either as a voltage generator or as a current generator. A voltage generator can be represented by a generator that produces an internal electromotive force $\tilde{u}_0$ and has a winding of an impedance $\bar{Z}_i$ (or R_i). Figure 1.4*a* shows the circuit of a voltage generator. Its output voltage (which is smaller than its $\tilde{u}_0$ because of the voltage drop across its internal impedance) is given by:

$$\tilde{u} = \tilde{u}_0 - \tilde{\imath}\bar{Z}_i \tag{1.83}$$

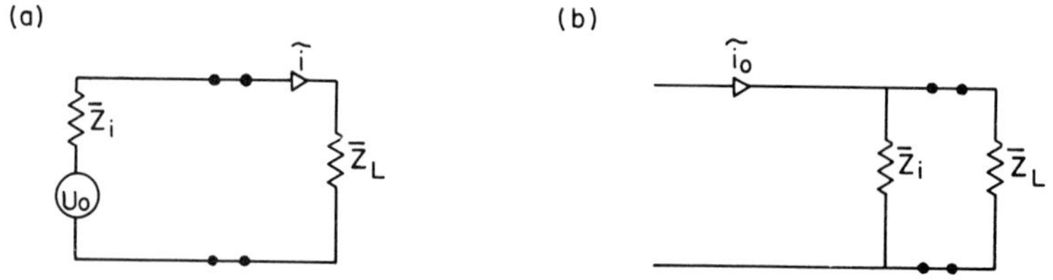

Fig. 1.4 Fundamental forms of a voltage (*a*) and a current (*b*) generator.

If $\tilde{\imath}=0$ ($\bar{Z}_L=\infty$), $\tilde{u}=\tilde{u}_0$, the terminal voltage is equal to the electromotive force of the generator. If the load $\bar{Z}_L$ is finite, the current that flows into $\bar{Z}_L$ is

$$\tilde{\imath}=\frac{\tilde{u}_0}{\bar{Z}_i+\bar{Z}_L} \tag{1.84}$$

It the load is zero, the short-circuit current is:

$$\tilde{\imath}_0=\frac{\tilde{u}_0}{\bar{Z}_i} \tag{1.85}$$

The voltage generator has been conceived as a generator whose winding has a resistance. The current generator has no such simple interpretation and must be considered a mathematical artifice.[3] The ideal current generator has infinite internal impedance, since the current it generates is independent of the circuit it drives. The ideal current generator is, therefore, represented by an open circuit ($\bar{Z}_i\to\infty$, $\tilde{u}_0\to\infty$, but $\tilde{u}_0/\bar{Z}_i=\tilde{\imath}_0$ is finite) and a triangular arrow with the symbol $\tilde{\imath}_0$ attached to it (Fig. 1.4*b*). If the current generator is not an ideal current generator, its internal impedance appears as a shunt branch in the equivalent circuit, as shown in the figure. If the generator is short-circuited, $\tilde{u}=0$, and the current becomes

$$\tilde{\imath}=\tilde{\imath}_0 \tag{1.86}$$

Thus, the magnitude $\tilde{\imath}_0$ represents the short-circuit current of the generator. The open-circuit voltage is

$$\tilde{u}_0=\tilde{\imath}_0\bar{Z}_i \tag{1.87}$$

The current that flows through the load is given by the total current $\tilde{\imath}_0$ generated by the current source less the current that flows through the shunt branch $\bar{Z}_i$, or

$$\tilde{\imath}=\tilde{\imath}_0-\frac{\tilde{u}}{\bar{Z}_i}=\frac{\tilde{u}_0}{\bar{Z}_i}-\frac{\tilde{u}}{\bar{Z}_i} \tag{1.88}$$

where $\tilde{u}$ is the terminal voltage and $\tilde{u}_0$, as before, is the open-circuit voltage. This equation is identical to Equation 1.83; two generators that have the same open-circuit voltage and the same short-circuit current are electrically equivalent: they furnish the same power to the same load under all conditions.[4] The source that drives the network can, therefore, be represented in either of the above ways. Sometimes the voltage generator turns out to be more convenient, and at other times the current generator will be more convenient as an analytical tool.

[3] A pentode approaches the behavior of an ideal current generator. Its plate current is practically independent of the impedance of the plate circuit; it is given by the product of the grid voltage and the mutual conductance of the tube. Transistors are also very similar in behavior to current generators.

[4] Note that the power dissipated in the internal impedance Z_i is different in the two cases. For the current generator, the voltage across Z_i is equal to the output voltage of the generator; this voltage is a maximum for open-circuit conditions. For the voltage generator, the voltage across Z_i is zero for open-circuit conditions and equal to the open-circuit voltage if the generator is short-circuited.

Thévénin's and Norton's Theorems

A two-terminal network that contains internal sources may be represented as a voltage generator whose open-circuit voltage is equal to the voltage at the two terminals and whose internal impedance is equal to the impedance of the network measured between its two terminals when all internal voltage generators are short-circuited and all internal current sources are open-circuited. The validity of this theorem (Thévénin's) is a consequence of the linearity of the electric circuits. If the output currents and the output voltages of the two networks are the same for two different loads (for instance, open circuit $\bar{Z}_L = \infty$ and short circuit $\bar{Z}_L = 0$), they must be the same for all other values of the load $\bar{Z}_L$, and the two circuits necessarily behave the same under all conditions. No other proof is needed.

That the network can also be represented by an equivalent current generator in parallel with the impedance $\bar{Z}_i$ is the contents of Norton's theorem. The current the source furnishes is the current $\bar{i}_0$ at the terminals when they are short-circuited, and the impedance $\bar{Z}_i$ is the impedance seen looking in at the terminals when the voltage sources are replaced by zero impedances and the current sources are open-circuited.

Matching

The power that can be absorbed by a given load depends on its impedance and on the internal impedance of the generator. For maximum output power, the load impedance must be adjusted by the use of transformers or other means until the maximum power is absorbed by it. This process is called matching. If the internal impedance of the generator is a resistance R_i and the load is purely resistive, the power N consumed by the load is given by:

$$N = i^2 R_L = \frac{U_0^2}{(R_i + R_L)^2} R_L = \frac{U_0^2 \dfrac{R_L}{R_i}}{R_i\left(1 + \dfrac{R_L}{R_i}\right)^2} = \frac{U_0^2}{4R_i} \frac{4r}{(1+r)^2} \tag{1.89}$$

where $r = R_L/R_i$. (See Fig. 1.5*a*.) The maximum power is computed by equating its derivative to zero. Since the logarithm is a monotonic function of its argument, we can compute the logarithm of the power and equate the derivative of the logarithm to zero. In this way, all the constants drop out and the computation becomes much simpler. Thus,

$$\log N = \log(\text{const}) + \log r - 2 \log(1+r) \tag{1.90}$$

$$\frac{\partial \log N}{\partial r} = \frac{1}{r} - \frac{2}{1+r} = 0 \tag{1.91}$$

or

$$r = 1 \quad \text{and} \quad R_L = R_i \tag{1.92}$$

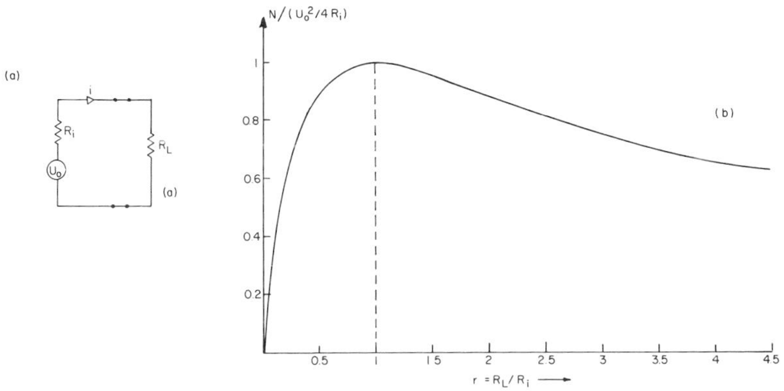

Fig. 1.5 Matching (*a*) and power output as a function of the resistance (*b*).

and

$$N_{\max} = \frac{U_0^2}{4R_i} \tag{1.93}$$

For maximum power transfer, the load resistance must be equal to the internal resistance of the generator. Figure 1.5*b* shows the power fed into the load as a function of the ratio R_L/R_i. The power decreases rapidly with the load resistance if $R_L < R_i$. On the other hand, increasing the load resistance above the optimum value R_i has a relatively small effect on the power output. In cases of doubt, it is always better to risk using a load resistance that is too large rather than too small.

If the generator has a reactive component, this component may be compensated by connecting a reactive impedance of the same magnitude but of opposite sign in series with the load, that is, by tuning the circuit. The matching condition then is the same as for a purely resistive generator and load.

If the generator has a reactive component jX_i that cannot be tuned out and if the load impedance is reactive, too, and has the resistive component R_L, the following relations hold:

$$\tilde{\imath} = \frac{\tilde{u}_0}{(R_i + R_L) + jX} \qquad |I^2| = \frac{U_0^2}{(R_i + R_L)^2 + X^2}$$

$$N = |I^2| R_L = \frac{U_0^2}{(R_i + R_L)^2 + X^2} R_L \tag{1.94}$$

where X is the total reactance (source and load) of the circuit. The optimum value of the load resistance, then, is given by:

$$\log N = \text{const} + \log R_L - \log[(R_i + R_L)^2 + X^2]$$

$$\frac{\partial \log N}{\partial R_L} = \frac{1}{R_L} - \frac{2(R_i + R_L)}{(R_i + R_L)^2 + X^2} = 0 \tag{1.95}$$

or

$$2(R_i+R_L)R_L=(R_i+R_L)^2+X^2$$
$$2R_iR_L+2R_L^2=R_i^2+2R_iR_L+R_L^2+X^2$$
$$R_L^2=R_i^2+X^2 \qquad (1.96)$$

For maximum power transfer, the load resistance must be equal to the absolute value of the impedance of the generator. If both load and generator are reactive, then the sum of the reactances enters the result, as shown in the last formula.

Star-Mesh Transformation

Another valuable artifice that serves to simplify the analysis of circuits is the star-mesh transformation (Fig. 1.6). With the aid of this transformation, the node at the center of a star can be removed by transforming the star into a mesh. Some or all branches of the mesh can then usually be combined with the branches of the remaining circuit.

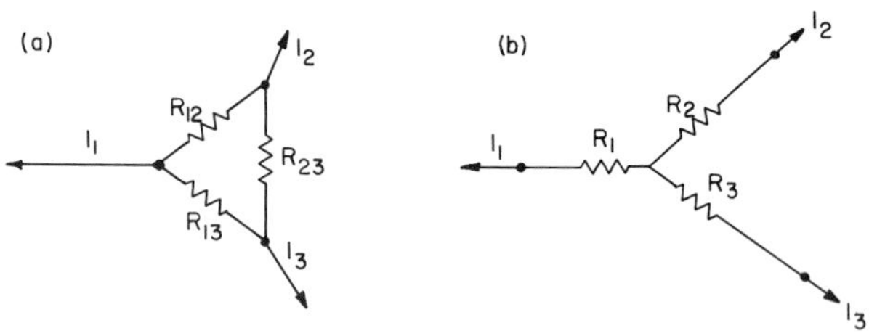

Fig. 1.6 Star-mesh transformation; *a*, the mesh; *b*, the star.

The mesh and the star shown in Figure 1.6 are equivalent if the same currents generate the same terminal voltages. Since the currents are arbitrary, let $I_3=0$. For the mesh, R_{12} and $R_{13}+R_{23}$ then are in parallel, and the voltage between the two terminals is:

$$u_{12}=I_1\frac{R_{12}(R_{13}+R_{23})}{R_{12}+R_{13}+R_{23}} \qquad (1.97)$$

For the star, R_1 and R_2 are in series, and

$$u_{12}=I_1(R_1+R_2) \qquad (1.98)$$

These two voltages must be the same. Hence,

$$R_1+R_2=\frac{R_{12}(R_{13}+R_{23})}{R_{12}+R_{23}+R_{13}} \qquad (1.99)$$

Similarly, by assuming successively that I_1 and I_2 are zero or simply by cyclic rotation of the subscripts ($1\rightarrow2$, $2\rightarrow3$, $3\rightarrow1$), two more relations are obtained:

$$R_2+R_3=\frac{R_{23}(R_{13}+R_{12})}{R_{12}+R_{23}+R_{13}}$$
$$R_3+R_1=\frac{R_{13}(R_{23}+R_{12})}{R_{12}+R_{23}+R_{13}} \tag{1.100}$$

These equations are satisfied if the resistances in the star are:

$$R_1=\frac{R_{12}R_{13}}{R_{12}+R_{23}+R_{13}} \qquad R_2=\frac{R_{12}R_{23}}{R_{12}+R_{23}+R_{13}} \qquad R_3=\frac{R_{23}R_{13}}{R_{12}+R_{23}+R_{13}} \tag{1.101}$$

If a conversion parameter R is defined, then

$$R_1=\frac{R}{R_{23}} \qquad R_2=\frac{R}{R_{13}} \qquad R_3=\frac{R}{R_{12}}$$

where

$$R=\frac{R_{12}R_{23}R_{13}}{R_{12}+R_{23}+R_{13}} \tag{1.102}$$

which is easy to write and to remember.

A similar set of equations may be derived in terms of the conductances. The conductances of the branches of the mesh must satisfy the relations:

$$G_{12}=\frac{G_1G_2}{G_1+G_2+G_3} \qquad G_{23}=\frac{G_2G_3}{G_1+G_2+G_3} \qquad G_{31}=\frac{G_1G_3}{G_1+G_2+G_3} \tag{1.103}$$

The same relations hold if the resistances and conductances are replaced by complex impedances or admittances. However, because of the frequency dependence of complex circuit elements, the above relations can be satisfied at only one frequency.

Advanced Circuit Theory

A number of valuable conclusions can be derived from the basic properties of electric circuits. The network equations are linear and can be solved by Cramer's rule. The information obtained with the formal solution is sufficient to derive a number of theorems that make it possible to predict many of the properties of complicated networks. The principle of duality will frequently prove useful; seemingly different networks are found to have similar properties. Foster's theorem and the related theorems about the driving-point impedance and the transfer impedance will prove basic for advanced work in circuitry and vibrations.

Concept of Duality

The concept of duality leads to considerable simplifications in the theory of networks. Dual networks obey similar equations, and the theory of one network can then be deduced from that of another without computation.

Probably the most interesting examples for dual networks are the equivalent circuits of the electrostatic and electrodynamic transducers; these two entirely different kinds of transducers can be described by the same circuit diagram.[5] The laws derived for the frequency variation of the voltage of one type of transducer on the basis of its equivalent circuit apply for the frequency variation of the currents of the other, and vice versa.

The concept of duality is also very useful for finding similar properties of different networks. The impedance of a series-resonant circuit (a resistance *R*, an inductance *L*, and a capacitance *C* in series), for instance, is:

$$\bar{Z}_s = R + j\omega L + \frac{1}{j\omega C} = R(1 + jQ\underline{\nu}) \qquad (1.104)$$

where $Q = \omega_0 L/R = X_s/R$, $X_s = \omega_0 L$, $\underline{\nu} = \omega/\omega_0 - \omega_0/\omega$, and $\omega_0 = 1/\sqrt{LC}$. This impedance is of the same mathematical form as the admittance $\bar{Y}_p$ of a parallel-resonant circuit (a conductance *G*, a capacitance *C*, and an inductance *L* in parallel):

$$\bar{Y}_p = G + j\omega C + \frac{1}{j\omega L} = G(1 + jQ\underline{\nu}) \qquad (1.105)$$

where $Q = \omega_0 C/G$. Since

$$\tilde{\imath} = \frac{\tilde{u}_0}{\bar{Z}} \quad \text{and} \quad \tilde{u} = \frac{\tilde{\imath}_0}{\bar{Y}} \qquad (1.106)$$

and since the $\bar{Y}$ and $\bar{Z}$ for the two circuits describe the same frequency variation, the frequency response of the current in the one case is similar to the frequency response of the voltage in the other, and vice versa. Circuits of this nature are said to be impedance-inverse. The property of being impedance-inverse is a special case of duality.

Impedance-Inverse Networks

The most common type of dual circuit is the impedance-inverse circuit: The input (or driving-point) impedance of the impedance-inverse network is inversely proportional to the input (or driving-point) impedance of the other; hence, it is directly proportional to the input or driving-point admittance of the other at all frequencies. If $\bar{Z}'$ is the input impedance of the original network, and $\bar{Y}''$, the input admittance of the derived network, the following relation must hold:

$$\bar{Z}' = \text{const}\ \bar{Y}'' = Z_0^2 \bar{Y}'' = \frac{Z_0^2}{\bar{Z}''} \qquad (1.107)$$

where $\bar{Z}'' = 1/\bar{Y}''$. The constant Z_0 may have any magnitude we desire; it has the dimensions of a resistance, and the factor of proportionality Z_0^2 takes care of the dimensions. Since an ideal transformer transforms voltages by

[5] See E. J. Skudrzyk, *Die Grundlagen der Akustik* (Springer Verlag; Vienna, 1954), p. 400.

a factor n and resistances by a factor n^2, the term Z_0 can be interpreted as a step-up transformation with an ideal transformer. The turns ratio of this transformer is equal to the numerical value of Z_0, and the term $\bar{Z}'$ can be thought of as the input impedance of this transformer when its secondary is loaded by an impedance equal to the numerical value of $\bar{Y}''$. But note that the physical dimensions have been changed.

If the original network consists of a number of series and parallel connections, the impedance-inverse circuit will also consist of series and parallel connections. Equation 1.107 will then take the form:

$$\bar{Z}' = \bar{Z}_1' + \bar{Z}_2' + \ldots + \frac{\bar{Z}_i'\bar{Z}_k'}{\bar{Z}_i' + \bar{Z}_k'} = Z_0^2\,\bar{Y}''$$
$$= Z_0^2\left(\bar{Y}_1'' + \bar{Y}_2'' + \ldots + \frac{\bar{Y}_i''\bar{Y}_k''}{\bar{Y}_i'' + \bar{Y}_k''} + \ldots\right) \qquad (1.108)$$

This equation will be satisfied with certainty, if the terms with the same subscripts on the left and the right are identical; that is, if they are equal in magnitude and have the same frequency variation. It is necessary, then, that every term on the left of Equation 1.108 have a corresponding term on the right, so that

$$\bar{Z}_1' = Z_0^2\,\bar{Y}_1'' \qquad \bar{Z}_2' = Z_0^2\,\bar{Y}_2'' \qquad \text{etc.} \qquad (1.109)$$

The impedances $\bar{Z}_\nu'$ consist of resistances, inductances, and capacitances. To satisfy the equations (1.109), the admittances $\bar{Y}_\nu''$ must be of the same form as impedances $\bar{Z}_\nu'$. The only element with an admittance proportional to ω is a capacitance; therefore, if $\bar{Z}_\nu'$ is the impedance of an inductance, Y_ν'' must be the admittance of a capacitance:

$$j\omega L_\nu' = Z_0^2 j\omega C_\nu'' \qquad (1.110)$$

Capacitances in the dual circuit correspond to inductances in the original circuit, and their values are given by:

$$C_\nu'' = \frac{L_\nu'}{Z_0^2} \qquad (1.111)$$

Similarly, if Z_ν' is the impedance of a capacitance, Y_ν'' must be the admittance of an inductance:

$$\bar{Z}_\nu' = \frac{1}{j\omega C_\nu'} = \frac{Z_0^2}{j\omega L_\nu''} \qquad (1.112)$$

or

$$L_\nu'' = Z_0^2 C_\nu' \qquad (1.113)$$

Finally, the only admittance that has the same frequency variation as a resistance (i.e., is frequency-independent) is that of a conductance. Hence,

$$R_\nu' = Z_0^2 G_\nu'' \qquad (1.114)$$

or

$$G_\nu'' = \frac{R_\nu'}{Z_0^2} \quad \text{and} \quad R_\nu'' = \frac{1}{G_\nu''} = \frac{Z_0^2}{R_\nu'} \qquad (1.115)$$

Corresponding relations must exist for more complex circuit elements, such as elements in series or parallel. The following correspondence must also hold (from Eq. 1.108):

$$\frac{\bar{Z}_i'\bar{Z}_k'}{\bar{Z}_i'+\bar{Z}_k'}=Z_0^2\frac{\bar{Y}_i''\bar{Y}_k''}{\bar{Y}_i''+\bar{Y}_k''} \tag{1.116}$$

The left-hand side represents a parallel connection of the impedances $\bar{Z}_i'$ and $\bar{Z}_k'$; the right-hand side, a series connection of the admittances $\bar{Y}_i''$ and $\bar{Y}_k''$.

The dual circuit, then, is obtained by replacing the resistances by resistances proportional to their reciprocal value, the inductances by capacitances of magnitudes proportional to the inductances they replace, the capacitances by inductances proportional to the capacitances they replace, all series connections by parallel connections, and all parallel connections by series connections. The step from a series- to a parallel-resonant circuit (Eqs. 1.104 and 1.105) is exactly of this nature, and a comparison between the impedance of the series circuit and the admittance of the parallel circuit shows that the capacity does take the place of the inductance and the inductance, that of the capacitance. Also, if the first network is driven by a voltage generator $\underline{u}_0'$, the second by a current generator

$$\tilde{\imath}_0''=\frac{\tilde{u}_0'}{Z_0} \tag{1.117}$$

then the voltage across the terminals of the second network

$$\tilde{u}''=\frac{\tilde{\imath}_0''}{\bar{Y}''}=\frac{\tilde{u}_0'}{Z_0}\cdot\frac{Z_0^2}{\bar{Z}'}=Z_0\tilde{\imath}' \tag{1.118}$$

is proportional to the current that flows into the first network, the factor of proportionality being Z_0.

The construction of the dual circuit is greatly facilitated by the following procedure. Each mesh of the original network is made to correspond to a node of the derived network by assuming the nodes of the dual network inside the meshes of the original network. The boundary of the network (the outside mesh when the network is drawn on a sphere) is made to correspond to a node outside the network. The nodes are denoted by Roman numerals; the number of the node is the same as that of the corresponding mesh. The new nodes are connected by lines that cross only one branch of the original network. These connecting lines, then, represent the branches of the dual network, and the dual network is obtained by making the admittance of each of its branches equal to the impedance of the crossed branch of the original network divided by Z_0^2. If the original network contained a voltage source of zero internal impedance, the dual network contains a current source of infinite internal impedance, and vice versa. This procedure for deriving the impedance-inverse network is represented in Figure 1.7. Interesting examples of impedance-inverse circuits are the T and the π sections of a filter (Fig. 1.8).

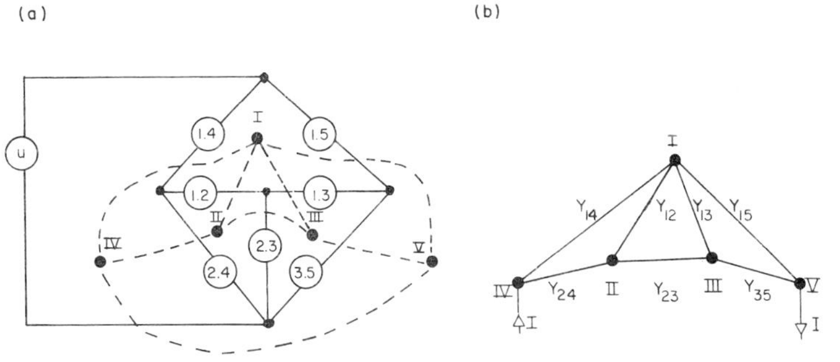

Fig. 1.7 Bridge circuit and its impedance-inverse network; *a*, the original network; *b*, the dual network.

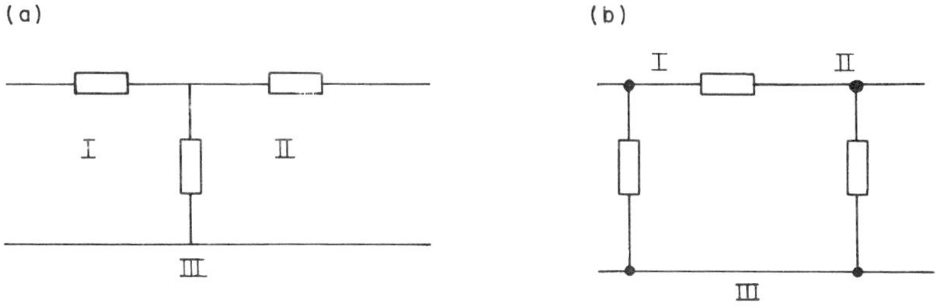

Fig. 1.8 T- and π-sections of a filter, an example of impedance-inverse circuits; *a*, T section; *b*, π-section.

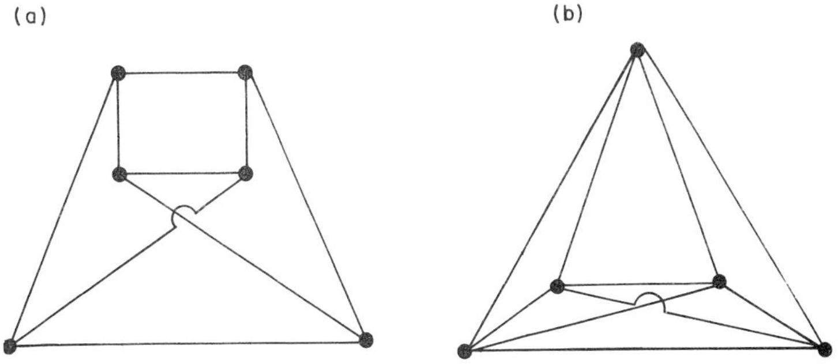

Fig. 1.9 The two simplest types of nonplanar networks.

The above procedure breaks down if a branch belongs to more than two meshes.[6] It then becomes impossible to specify the admittances of the branches of the dual circuit in the unique manner outlined above, and the impedance-inverse circuit does not exist. A more detailed study reveals that networks that cannot be drawn on a sphere (networks that are nonplanar) have no dual. Such cases may arise if the network has more than eight branches or more than four nodes. Figure 1.9 shows the two fundamental types of nonplanar networks. It can be shown that more complicated nonplanar networks can always be reduced to this form by short-circuiting or open-circuiting some of their branches.

Frequency-Inverse Networks

If the inductive impedances in a network are replaced by capacitive impedances of the same magnitudes, and the capacitive impedances by inductive impedances of the same magnitudes, the magnitudes of the voltages and currents remain unaltered, but the phases change signs. In this transformation, the actual frequencies at which the two networks are driven are immaterial and need not be the same. Let the original network be driven with a frequency ω', and let its elements be denoted by primed symbols; let the derived network be driven with a frequency ω'', and let its elements be denoted by double-primed symbols. Then, the following relations must exist for all elements:

$$\omega' L_\nu' = \frac{1}{\omega'' C_\nu''} \qquad \frac{1}{\omega' C_\nu'} = \omega'' L_\nu'' \qquad R_\nu' = R_\nu'' \tag{1.119}$$

Hence,

$$C_\nu'' = \frac{1}{\omega'' \omega' L_\nu'} \tag{1.120}$$

and

$$L_\nu'' = \frac{1}{\omega' \omega'' C_\nu'} \tag{1.121}$$

One of the many possibilities is to assume that the frequency ω'', at which the derived network is operated, is inversely proportional to the frequency of the voltages and currents of the original network:

$$\omega'' = \frac{\omega_0^2}{\omega'} \tag{1.122}$$

The magnitude ω_0 is called the inversion frequency; it is an arbitrary constant that has the dimensions of a frequency. Equations 1.119 to 1.122, then, lead to the following relations:

$$C'' = \frac{1}{\omega_0^2 L'} \qquad L'' = \frac{1}{\omega_0^2 C'} \qquad \frac{L'}{L''} = \frac{C'}{C''} \qquad \text{and} \qquad R' = R'' \tag{1.123}$$

[6] For instance, if a branch common to two meshes is coupled with a branch of another mesh by a mutual inductance.

or

$$L'=\frac{1}{\omega_0^2 C''} \quad \text{and} \quad C'=\frac{1}{\omega_0^2 L''} \tag{1.124}$$

The inversion frequency ω_0 can be deduced by multiplying the first two of the above relations:

$$\omega_0^4=\frac{1}{L'C'L''C''}=\omega'^2\omega''^2 \tag{1.125}$$

In the simplest case, $\omega_0=1$ radian per second, the capacitances become numerically equal to the reciprocal values of the inductances, and the inductances become numerically equal to the reciprocal values of the capacitances.

The impedance of one network at the frequency ω' is equal in magnitude and phase to that of the derived network at the frequency $-\omega_0^2/\omega'$. The minus sign is unimportant, but it corrects formally for the opposite phases of the impedances $\bar{Z}'(\omega')$ and $\bar{Z}''(-\omega_0^2/\omega')$; thus,

$$\bar{Z}'(\omega')=\bar{Z}''\left(-\frac{\omega_0^2}{\omega'}\right) \tag{1.126}$$

If the impedance of one network increases as the frequency increases, the impedance of the other network will decrease as the frequency increases. At the two corresponding frequencies ω' and $-\omega_0^2/\omega'$, the two impedances are always equal in magnitude and phase.

If one network has a pass range at low frequencies, the other will have a similar pass range at high frequencies. The method makes it possible to derive, without computation, networks that have a frequency response that is the inverse of that of the given network. High-pass and low-pass filters are examples of inverse-frequency networks.

More general frequency transformations are in current use in network theory. For instance, it is possible to transform the equations for a band-pass filter into those for a low-pass filter. However, such transformations have not yet been used in acoustics or in vibrations.

Two-Terminal Reactance Networks

A very significant result derived in the study of electric networks is Foster's reactance theorem. This theorem makes it possible to predict the number of resonances and the essential features of the frequency curve of a mechanical system or of a two-terminal network of any complexity and eliminates the need for detailed computation. The reactance theorem alone would justify the labor expended in the study of electrical networks.

Partial-fraction expansion of the network solution. A passive reactance network contains only inductances and capacitances and does not contain internal sources or sinks of energy. The mesh equations for such a network are of the following form:

$$-\bar{Z}_{\nu 1}\bar{\imath}_1-\bar{Z}_{\nu 2}\bar{\imath}_2 \ldots +\bar{Z}_{\nu\nu}\bar{\imath}_\nu \ldots -\bar{Z}_{\nu n}\bar{\imath}_n=\tilde{u}_\nu \tag{1.127}$$

where $\nu=1, 2, 3, \ldots n$ is the number of the mesh. The impedances $\bar{Z}_{\nu j}$ are coupling impedances. They are defined by the equation:

$$\tilde{u}_\nu'=\sum_{j=1}^{n}\bar{Z}_{\nu j}\bar{\imath}_j \tag{1.128}$$

where $\tilde{u}_\nu'$ is the voltage induced in the νth mesh in the direction of its orientation by the currents $\bar{\imath}_j$ that circulate in all the other meshes.

Coupling may result either through mutual inductances or from impedance elements common to the two meshes. It is to be noted that reversing the order of the subscripts of $\bar{Z}$ in circuits that contain no amplifiers or relays does not alter the value of the mutual impedances, and

$$\bar{Z}_{ik}=\bar{Z}_{ki} \tag{1.129}$$

This fact can easily be proved by writing out the equations for two meshes that are coupled by either a mutual inductance or a common impedance element. The signs of the coupling impedances depend on the orientation of the meshes and if $\bar{Z}_{\nu j}$ is a mutual inductance, also on the sense of the circulating currents through the coupling branch, if the meshes are oriented all in the same sense (either clockwise or counterclockwise), then the directions of the two mesh currents $\bar{\imath}_\nu$ and $\bar{\imath}_j$ that flow through the same branch

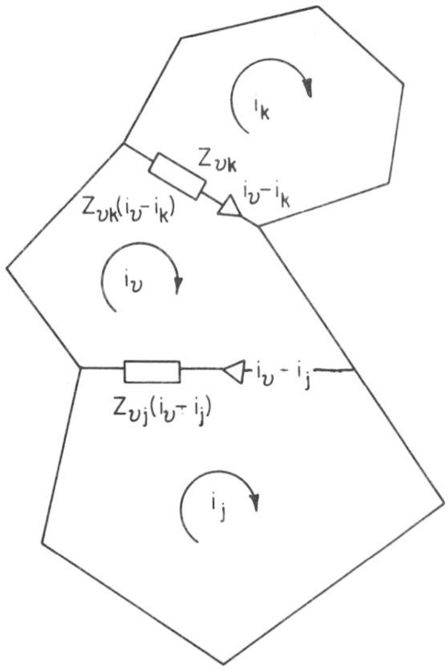

Fig. 1.10 Coupling impedances. If circulating currents flow with opposite sense through a branch (usual situation), the coupling impedances are associated with negative signs in the mesh; if the currents flow with the same sense through the coupling branch, the negative signs of the corresponding terms in the mesh equation have to be replaced by plus signs.

are always opposite, and the coupling impedances have a negative sign in the above equation (Fig. 1.10). If the direction of the currents in the branch νj is the same, the coupling impedance appears with a positive sign. This fact can easily be verified by considering simple special cases and applying Kirchhoff's law around a mesh.

Equation 1.129 is a special case of the principle of reciprocity. If a force at point F produces a deflection ξ at point P, and if the point of attack of the force and the point of observation are interchanged, the same deflection ξ will be registered at the new point of observation. This fact is well known in the theory of elasticity, and it can be proved in a very general manner. Similarly, if a voltage source acts in one mesh, and the current is measured in another mesh, the same current will be measured if voltage source and ammeter are interchanged.

A reactance network does not contain resistances, and its impedances are of the following form:

$$Z_{\nu j}=M_{\nu j}p+\frac{1}{pC_{\nu j}} \tag{1.130}$$

where p is an abbreviation for $j\omega$. The magnitudes $M_{\nu j}$ are inductances or mutual inductances, and $C_{\nu j}$ are capacitances if the coupling is due to a common branch; otherwise, $C_{\nu j}=0$. The impedance $\bar{Z}_{\nu\nu}$ is the sum of all the impedances in the νth mesh; $\bar{Z}_{\nu\nu}$ is the impedance that would be measured if all other meshes were opened, and it is of the form:

$$\bar{Z}_{\nu\nu}=pL_{\nu\nu}+\frac{1}{pC_{\nu\nu}} \quad \text{or} \quad p\bar{Z}_{\nu\nu}=p^2L_{\nu\nu}+\frac{1}{C_{\nu\nu}} \tag{1.131}$$

If the network is excited by a single voltage source $\tilde{u}_1$ and has no internal voltage sources, the network equations then become:

$$\begin{aligned}
&\left(p^2L_{11}+\frac{1}{C_{11}}\right)\tilde{\imath}_1-\left(p^2M_{12}+\frac{1}{C_{12}}\right)\tilde{\imath}_2-\ \dots\ -\left(p^2M_{1n}+\frac{1}{C_{1n}}\right)\tilde{\imath}_n=p\tilde{u}_1\\
&-\left(p^2M_{21}+\frac{1}{C_{21}}\right)\tilde{\imath}_1+\left(p^2L_{22}+\frac{1}{C_{22}}\right)\tilde{\imath}_2-\ \dots\ -\left(p^2M_{2n}+\frac{1}{C_{2n}}\right)\tilde{\imath}_n=0\\
&-\left(p^2M_{n1}+\frac{1}{C_{n1}}\right)\tilde{\imath}_1-\left(p^2M_{n2}+\frac{1}{C_{n2}}\right)\tilde{\imath}_2-\ \dots\ +\left(p^2L_{nn}+\frac{1}{C_{nn}}\right)\tilde{\imath}_n=0
\end{aligned} \tag{1.132}$$

where $M_{ij}=M_{ji}$ and $C_{ij}=C_{ji}$. These equations can be solved for $\tilde{\imath}_1$ by Cramer's rule:

$$\bar{Y}_1=\frac{\tilde{\imath}_1}{\tilde{u}_1}=p\frac{D_{11}}{D} \tag{1.133}$$

The magnitude $\bar{Y}_1$ represents the input admittance at the terminals of the voltage source $\tilde{u}_1$; D_{11} is the determinant of the above equations after the first row and the first column have been crossed out, and D is the determinant of the above system of equations.

A determinant of nth degree represents a sum of n terms, each of which is made up of the products of n terms, one from each line. We shall assume that all the impedances are of the form of Equation 1.130 and that none is degenerate. Therefore, each term of D_{11} contains a factor $(p^2L_{\mu\nu}+1/C_{\mu\nu})$ less than D, and D_{11} is a polynomial by two degrees smaller in p than D. The roots of D determine the frequencies for which the terminal current is finite (the system being assumed as dissipationless), even if the voltage source is short-circuited. These frequencies are specified, by definition, as the series-resonant frequencies, and the corresponding solutions are specified as the resonant modes of the network. In contrast, the roots of D_{11} determine the frequencies for which the current is zero, irrespective of the voltage applied to the circuit; they specify the "antiresonant" frequencies of the network. It can easily be shown that a root $p=j\omega-\delta$ represents a decaying vibration of the type:

$$\tilde{i}=Ae^{j\omega t-\delta t} \tag{1.134}$$

Similarly, a root $p=j\omega+\delta$ gives rise to a growing vibration. But a vibration can decay only if energy is dissipated in resistance, and it can grow only if energy sources are contained in the network. But both these cases have been excluded in specifying the network as purely reactive and passive. The roots of both D and D_{11} must, therefore, be purely imaginary.

If $p_\nu^2=-\omega_\nu^2$ ($\nu=1, 2 \ldots n$) are the roots of the determinant D, the solution can be written in the form:

$$\frac{\tilde{i}_\nu}{\tilde{u}_1}=p\frac{P_{n-1}(p^2)}{a_0(p^2-p_1^2)\,(p^2-p_2^2)\ldots(p^2-p_n^2)} \tag{1.135}$$

It is expedient to assume that each $p\bar{Z}_{\nu\mu}$ is of the form p^2M+1/C and to treat separately deviations from this assumption; $P_{n-1}\,(p^2)$, then, is a polynomial of degree n—1 in p^2. Partial-fraction development[7] leads to the following series:

$$\bar{Y}_1=\sum_{\nu=1}^{n}\frac{pA_\nu}{p^2-p_\nu^2}=\sum_{\nu=1}^{n}\frac{-\dfrac{j\omega}{L_\nu}}{\omega^2-\omega_\nu^2} \tag{1.136}$$

[7] An expression of the form

$$f(p^2)=\frac{b'p^{2n-2}+c'p^{2n-4}+\ldots s'}{p^{2n}+c^{2n-2}+\ldots s}$$

can always be developed into partial fractions. The denominator is written as a product:

$$p^{2n}+cp^{2n-2}+\ldots+s=(p^2-p_1^2)(p^2-p_2^2)\ldots(p^2-p_n^2)$$

where the p_ν^2 are its roots (the roots of the determinant D). The partial-fraction development may now be set up with unknown coefficients A_1, A_2, . . .:

$$f(p^2)=\frac{b'p^{2n-2}+\ldots s'}{(p^2-p_1^2)\ldots(p^2-p_n^2)}=\frac{A_1}{p^2-p_1^2}+\frac{A_2}{p^2-p_2^2}+\ldots+\frac{A_n}{p^2-p_n^2}$$

If we multiply both sides by the factor $p^2-p_\nu^2$ and, after multiplication, set $p^2=p_\nu^2$, we obtain:

$$\left[(p^2-p_\nu^2)f(p^2)\right]_{p^2=p_\nu^2}=A_\nu$$

because all other terms on the right contain the factor $p^2-p_\nu^2$ and are zero for $p^2=p_\nu^2$. On the left, the factor $p^2-p_\nu^2$ cancels with the corresponding factor in the denominator, and the result is finite. Thus, the A_ν term is determined.

where the constant A_ν in the partial-fraction development has been replaced by the new constant $L_\nu = 1/A_\nu$, and p has been replaced by $j\omega$, and p_ν^2 has been replaced by $-\omega_\nu^2 = 1/L_\nu C_\nu$.

It can be shown that for a reactance network the constants L_ν and C_ν are positive. Every term on the right-hand side, then, represents the admittance of a series-resonant circuit, and the sum can be interpreted as the parallel connection of n series-resonant circuits:

$$\bar{Y}_\nu = \sum \frac{1}{j\omega L_\nu + \dfrac{1}{j\omega C_\nu}} = \sum \frac{1}{j\omega L_\nu\left(1 - \dfrac{1}{\omega^2 L_\nu C_\nu}\right)}$$

$$= \sum \frac{1}{j\omega L_\nu\left(1 - \dfrac{\omega_\nu^2}{\omega^2}\right)} = \sum \frac{-\dfrac{j\omega}{L_\nu}}{\omega^2 - \omega_\nu^2} \tag{1.137}$$

The frequencies $\omega_\nu = 1/\sqrt{L_\nu C_\nu}$ represent the series resonances of the circuit. A circuit of this type is called a canonical circuit. The partial fractions have been derived for a network without dissipation. If damping is small, the losses can be taken into account by series resistances as shown (Fig. 1.11).

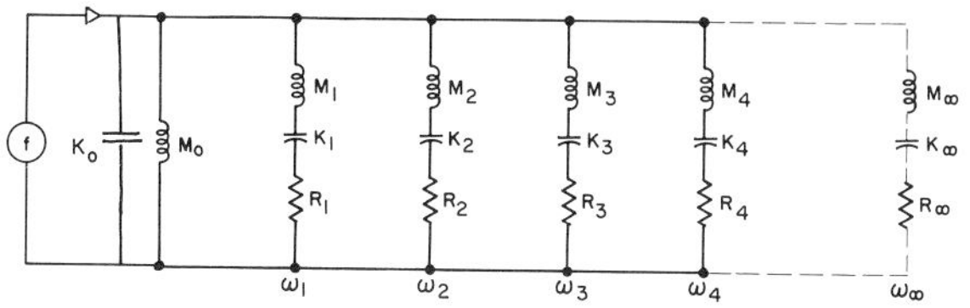

Fig. 1.11 Canonical series-resonant circuit.

Some of the series-resonant circuits may be degenerate; they may reduce to an inductance or to a capacitance. Therefore, in the most general case, the canonical circuit consists of the parallel connection of an inductance, a capacitance, and a number of series-resonant circuits.

A network can also be described by the node equations:

$$\begin{aligned} \bar{Y}_{11}\tilde{u}_1 - \bar{Y}_{12}\tilde{u}_2 - \dots - \bar{Y}_{1n}\tilde{u}_n &= \bar{I}_1 \\ -\bar{Y}_{21}\tilde{u}_1 + \bar{Y}_{22}\tilde{u}_2 - \dots - \bar{Y}_{2n}\tilde{u}_n &= 0 \\ -\bar{Y}_{n1}\tilde{u}_1 - \bar{Y}_{n2}\tilde{u}_2 - \dots + \bar{Y}_{nn}\tilde{u}_n &= 0 \end{aligned} \tag{1.138}$$

If N is the number of nodes, there are $N-1=n$ equations of this type, one for each independent node pair. The solution

$$\bar{Z}_1 = \frac{\tilde{u}_1}{\tilde{\imath}_1} = \sum_{\nu=1}^{n} \frac{-\dfrac{j\omega}{C_\nu}}{\omega^2 - \omega_\nu^2} \tag{1.139}$$

is formally similar to the preceding one, except that each term in the partial-fraction development represents the impedance of an inductance in parallel with a capacitance, and the sum represents the impedance of a series connection of parallel-resonant circuits (Fig. 1.12), where $p_\nu^2 = -\omega_\nu^2$ are the roots of the determinant of the system. The frequencies ω_ν now represent the antiresonant frequencies: At an antiresonant frequency, the voltages can be finite (the system being assumed as dissipationless), even if only an infinitesimally small current flows into the system. The resulting circuit is a canonical network that consists of the series connection of parallel-resonant circuits. Some of the circuits may be degenerate. The most general form of this canonical circuit, then, contains an inductance and a capacitance in series with a number of antiresonant circuits. If damping is small, it can be taken into account by large parallel resistances, as shown in Figure 1.12.

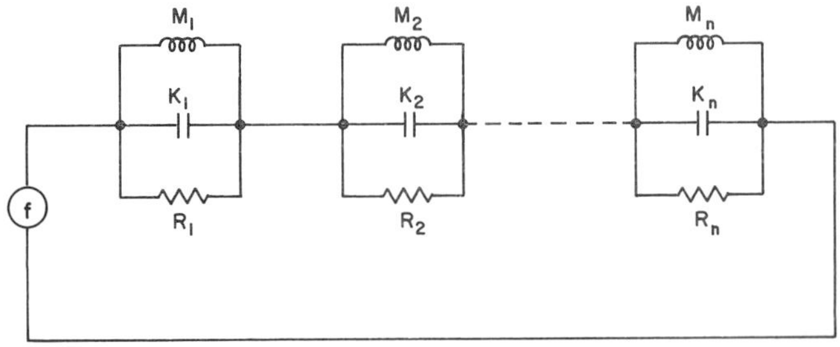

Fig. 1.12 Canonical antiresonant circuit.

A network can thus be represented either by a series connection of parallel-resonant circuits or a parallel connection of series-resonant circuits. One circuit describes the electrical properties of the original network on the basis of its series resonances, and the other, on the basis of its parallel resonances or antiresonances.

Foster's theorem for the driving-point impedance. Every one of the terms in the partial-fraction development of the driving-point admittance (Eq. 1.137) or the driving-point impedance (Eq. 1.139) of the network increases with increasing frequency, and the frequency curve of each has a positive tangent. The frequency curve of the network—represented by the sum of a finite number of such terms—must, therefore, have a positive slope. Each resonance or pole point is a point of discontinuity, and the value of the corresponding term jumps from $+j\ \infty$ to $-j\ \infty$, increasing again if the frequency is increased. The sum of a finite number of such terms also increases with increasing frequency. At a resonance, one of the terms becomes infinite, and the sum jumps from $+j\ \infty$ to $-j\ \infty$. But at other frequencies the slope of the frequency curve is finite and positive (Foster's theorem). Because of the positive value of the slope, resonances and antiresonances must alternate, and between any two resonances (zeros of impedance) there is an antiresonance (impedance pole), and between any two antiresonances, a resonance (Fig. 1.13). At zero frequency, a reactive circuit behaves either like a capacitance or like an inductance. The inductances

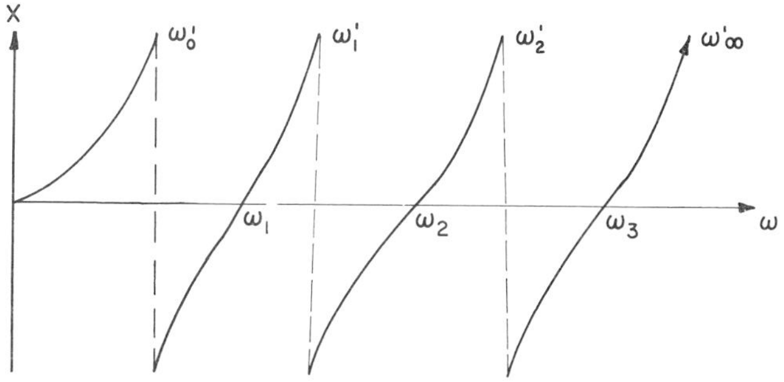

Fig. 1.13 Basic shape of the frequency curve of reactance or susceptance of a reactive circuit.

can then be replaced by solid connectors; the capacitances can be taken into account by opening branches that contain them. If the terminal impedance is infinite, as if the network were open-circuited, the circuit is said to behave like a capacitance, and

$$(\bar{Z})_0 = -\frac{j}{\omega C} \to -j\infty \tag{1.140}$$

If the terminal impedance is zero when the frequency approaches zero, as if the network were short-circuited, the network is said to behave like an inductance, and

$$(\bar{Z})_0 = j\omega L \tag{1.141}$$

Thus, the zero frequency can be a resonant frequency ($\bar{Z}=0$, the case of the inductance) or an antiresonant frequency ($\bar{Z}=-j\infty$, the case of the capacitance). Similarly, the infinite frequency can correspond either to a resonance ($\bar{Z}=0$) or to an antiresonance ($\bar{Z}=j\infty$).

A single reactive element, such as an inductance, has a resonance at zero frequency and an antiresonance at infinite frequency. A capacitance has an antiresonance at zero frequency and a resonance at infinite frequency (Fig. 1.14). An additional element introduces a resonance or an antiresonance at a finite fiequency. Three elements lead to a resonance or antiresonance at zero and at infinite frequency and to a resonance and an antiresonance at finite frequencies; thus, the frequency curve of a combination of three reactive elements has four resonances. Similarly, n independent elements lead to $n+1$ resonances and antiresonances if the frequencies 0 and infinity are included or to $n-1$ resonances and antiresonances st finite frequencies (Fig. 1.14).

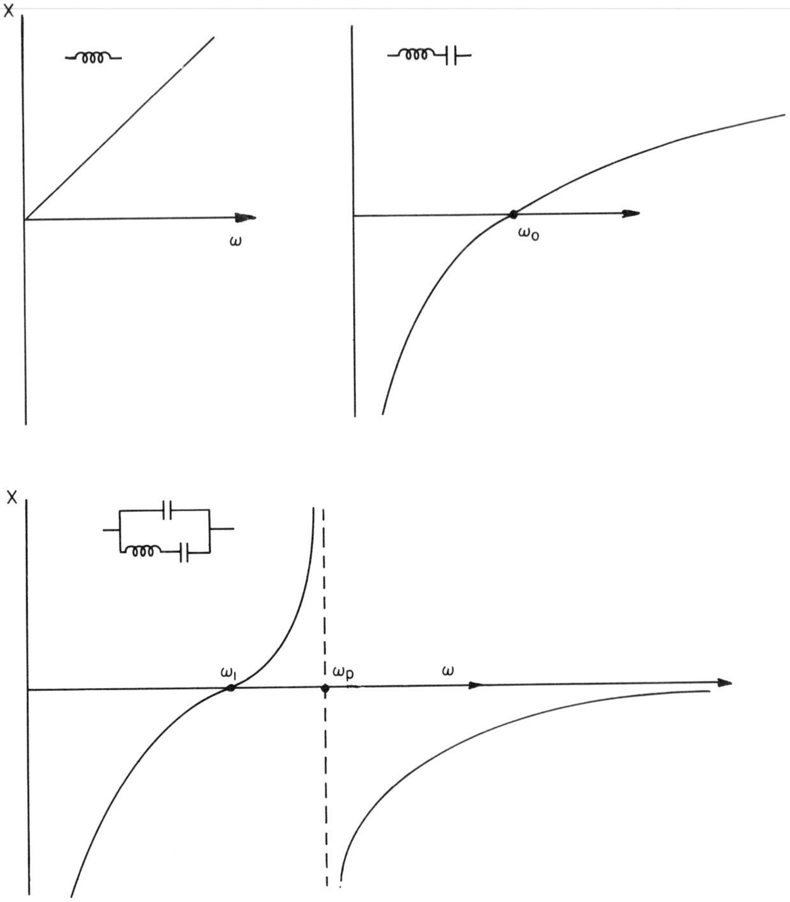

Fig. 1.14 Simple examples illustrating Foster's theorem.

Networks frequently contain redundant elements—parallel or series-connected elements of the same kind or meshes with more elements than are needed for the generation of the desired impedance. The safest way to find the number of independent elements is to determine the degree of the determinant of the network equations. One very simple procedure that usually works is as follows: The meshes are considered individually; a capacitance and an inductance are deleted in each mesh, provided that such elements are present and have not been deleted previously during consideration of the neighboring meshes. (If a mesh has only one capacitance or inductance, it has only one independent element.) In this procedure, the input and output circuits must be counted as separate meshes if they contain reactive elements in series that are not contained in other meshes. In

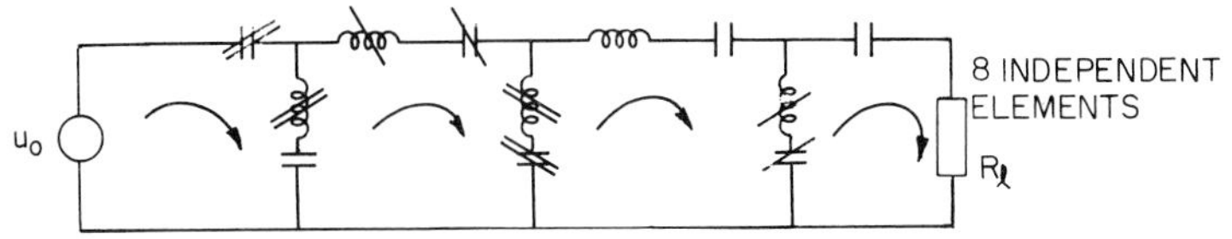

Fig. 1.15 Simple method (usually, but not always, successful) for determining the number of independent reactive elements (eight here).

Figure 1.15, the input circuit is an independent mesh; in contrast, the output circuit is not, since R_l is a resistance. The number of deleted elements is equal to the number of independent reactive elements of the network. The circuit in Figure 1.15 has four meshes and eleven reactive elements, eight of which are independent. For instance, the two series-resonant circuits at the extreme right represent a trivial series connection.

Fundamental Property of the Transfer Impedance

The driving-point impedance has been defined as the ratio of the input voltage to the input current. The properties of the driving-point impedance are described by Foster's theorem and the group of theorems derived from Foster's theorem. Another very important parameter is the transfer impedance, which is defined as the ratio of the input voltage to the output current,

$$\bar{Z}_t = \frac{\tilde{u}_1}{\tilde{i}_\nu} \tag{1.142}$$

where the output current is the current through some other branch of the network. The transfer impedance can be computed in a manner similar to that used to calculate the driving-point impedance, with the aid of the determinants D and $D_{\nu\nu}$, and the result can again be represented by a partial-fraction development. However, it can no longer be proved that the significant constants are all positive; therefore, the resultant curve need no longer have a positive slope.

Generation of an Antiresonance or a Shallow Trough between Two Resonances

Purely reactive circuits. In the expression for the driving-point impedance or the driving-point admittance, all the constants that resulted from the partial-fraction development have a positive sign, and the resultant fraction represents the admittance of a real tuned circuit. The sum of two successive terms corresponding to any two successive resonant frequencies ω_1 and ω_2 is given by:

$$\bar{Y}_1+\bar{Y}_2=\frac{1}{j\omega L_1+\dfrac{1}{j\omega C_1}}+\frac{1}{j\omega L_2+\dfrac{1}{j\omega C_2}}$$
$$=-j\frac{1}{\omega L_1\left(1-\dfrac{\omega_1{}^2}{\omega^2}\right)}-j\frac{1}{\omega L_2\left(1-\dfrac{\omega_2{}^2}{\omega^2}\right)} \tag{1.143}$$

where

$$\omega_1{}^2=\frac{1}{L_1C_1} \quad \text{and} \quad \omega_2{}^2=\frac{1}{L_2C_2} \tag{1.144}$$

This sum is infinite at either of the two resonant frequencies. In the frequency range between ω_1 and ω_2, the first term is negative-imaginary because $\omega>\omega_1$, and the second is positive-imaginary because $\omega<\omega_2$. There is a frequency, then, for which the two terms cancel: the admittance becomes zero, and the impedance becomes infinite. Thus, an antiresonance is generated between two resonances.

In the partial-fraction development of the transfer admittance, some of the constants A_ν may be negative. If the constants A_ν of two successive

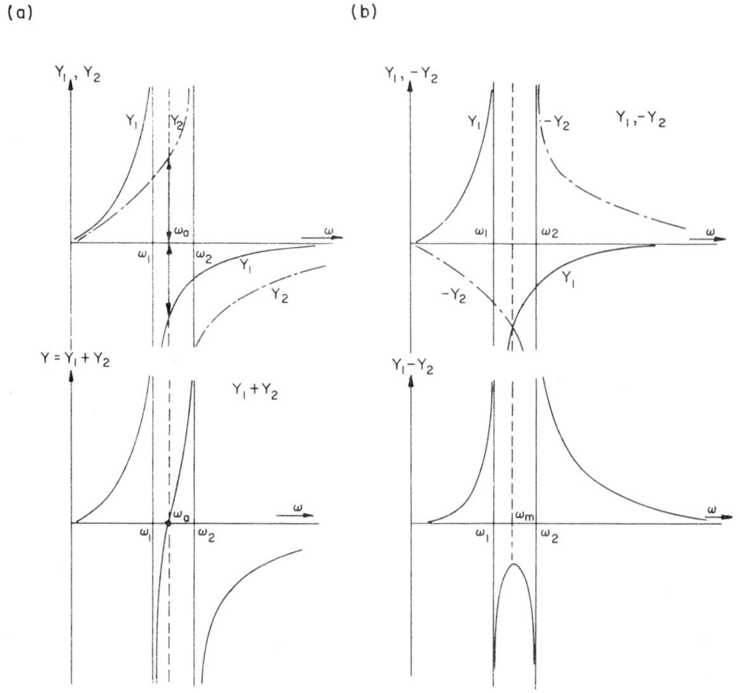

Fig. 5 The generation of (a, b) an antiresonance, (c, d) a shallow trough in the transfer impedance of a canonic circuit.

Fig. 1.16 The generation of an antiresonance (*a*) and a shallow trough (*b*) in the transfer admittance of a canonical circuit.

terms have opposite signs, their contributions have the same sign in the frequency range between their resonant frequencies. They no longer compensate one another, and, instead of an antiresonance (Fig. 1.16*a*), a shallow trough (*b*) is generated. The remaining terms in the partial-fraction development are finite at and between the frequencies ω_1 and ω_2 and have no basic effect on the result.

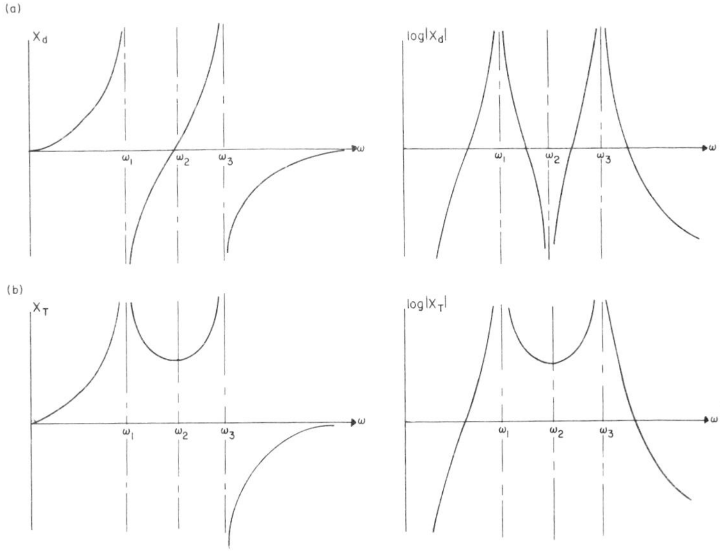

Fig. 1.17 Typical frequency curves for a driving-point (*a*) and a transfer (*b*) impedance to a linear and to a logarithmic scale.

Figure 1.17 shows a comparison of typical frequency curves for a driving-point impedance (*a*) and a transfer impedance (*b*) to a linear and to a logarithmic scale. Since most recorders record the logarithm of the input voltage, the recordings will be similar to the curves plotted to a logarithmic scale. The reader will recognize the shape of these curves as typical for frequency response curves of more complex vibratory systems.

Effect of damping. The derivations in the preceding sections were based on the assumption that the network does not contain dissipative elements. It will be shown in a later chapter that losses can be taken into account by replacing the natural frequencies ω_ν by complex frequencies $\bar{\omega}_\nu$, where

$$\bar{\omega}_\nu = \omega_\nu + j\delta \tag{1.145}$$

The imaginary part of $\bar{\omega}_\nu$, then, represents the decay constant of the νth natural vibration (or the effect of the losses on the steady-state vibrations). If damping is small and the frequency approaches a series-resonant frequency, the impedance of the dissipative system can be developed into a

Taylor series, as follows:

$$\bar{Z}(\omega_\nu + j\delta_\nu) = \bar{Z}(\omega_\nu) + j\delta_\nu \frac{\partial \bar{Z}(\omega_\nu)}{\partial \omega_\nu} + \ldots \tag{1.146}$$

where $\bar{Z}(\omega)$ is the impedance of the nondissipative system. Since $\partial \bar{Z}(\omega_\nu)/\partial \omega_\nu$ is imaginary, and since $\partial \bar{Z}(\omega_\nu)/\partial \omega_\nu = -j(\partial Z/\partial \omega)_{\omega=\omega_\nu}$, as can be read directly from the curves of $Z(\omega)$, the magnitude

$$j\delta_\nu \frac{\partial \bar{Z}(\omega_\nu)}{\partial \omega_\nu} = R(\omega_\nu) \tag{1.147}$$

represents a loss resistance in series with the remaining inductance or capacity of the circuit ω_ν. At the antiresonant frequencies, the Taylor series of the impedance will not converge. However, a similar computation can be performed by developing the admittance into a Taylor series. We then obtain a conductance $1/R_\nu$ in parallel with the antiresonant circuit. Since the loss resistances (damping being assumed to be small) affect the impedance of the circuit only in the vicinity of its resonant peaks, the frequency dependence of $R(\omega_\nu)$ can be neglected.

Because of the loss resistances, the terms in the series development of the impedances and admittances are no longer simple reactances, but represent dissipative elements. Provided that damping is small, resistive components have very little effect outside the resonance ranges of the system; but, because of the resistive components, the admittances no longer cancel completely at the antiresonant minima; nor do the impedances cancel completely at the resonance maxima. As a consequence, the antiresonance between two series resonances are sometimes reduced to a simple dip in the frequency curve, or can even completely disappear, if the spacing of the resonance peaks is very close as compared with the band width of the contributions of the series terms.

The resonant peaks then become finite, and the antiresonance depressions, limited in depth; and double peaks may occur in the frequency curve of the system, or some peaks or troughs may disappear completely. These phenomena will be discussed in more detail in later chapters. However, in the frequency range where the resonance peaks are separate, Foster's theorem and the corresponding theorems for the transfer impedance lead to a very good description of the vibrational behavior of the system.

Poles and Zeros of a Driving-Point and a Transfer Impedance or Admittance

Because of the loss resistance, the free vibrations of a network must decay with time, and the zeros and poles of a driving-point impedance or admittance must have a negative real part. But a similar condition no longer applies for the transfer admittance because of the possibilities of negative signs in the partial-fraction development. A negative transfer impedance or admittance simply means that the phase of the vibration at the receiver is opposite to the phase of the force at the driven point; since the phase of the vibrations jumps 180° wherever a nodal line is crossed, the transfer quantities also change signs. It is shown in network theory that roots of the transfer impedance in the positive half plane express a time delay in the propagation of the energy from input to output.[8]

Electromechanical Analogies and Circuit Diagrams

Many physicists are reluctant to become acquainted with mechanical circuit diagrams, even though the use of such diagrams enables the essential characteristics of a mechanical system to be understood immediately. This chapter shows how mechanical circuits are derived. Particular attention is paid to the fundamental circuits, such as two masses moving together, a force acting between two masses or between the two ends of a spring, or the dumbbell vibrator. These instances are of fundamental importance and are treated in great detail and from several points of view; once they are understood, the reader should have no difficulty with the more complex cases, such as those discussed in Chapter IV. For completeness, the circuits that are derived on the basis of the force-current analogy are also included.

Force-Voltage Analogy

The equation defining inductance can be written in a form that is identical with Newton's law:

$$f_M = M\frac{dv}{dt} \qquad u_L = L\frac{di}{dt} \tag{1.148}$$

The equation for capacitance can be written in a form that is identical with Hooke's law for a spring, one end of which is rigidly clamped:

$$\xi = K f_K \qquad q = C u_C \tag{1.149}$$

or

$$v = K\frac{df_K}{dt} \qquad \dot{q} = i = C = \frac{du_C}{dt} \tag{1.150}$$

Mechanical resistance and electrical resistance are defined by the equations:

$$f_R = R_m v \qquad u_R = Ri \tag{1.151}$$

Because of the similarity of the differential equations, mechanical elements can be represented by the same pictorial symbols as electrical elements (Fig. 1.18); they can be distinguished from the electrical elements by the constants M, K, and R_m that will be associated with them. Since the elec-

[8] For further study, H. W. Bode, *Network Analysis and Feedback Amplifier Design* (New York, 1945), may be particularly recommended.

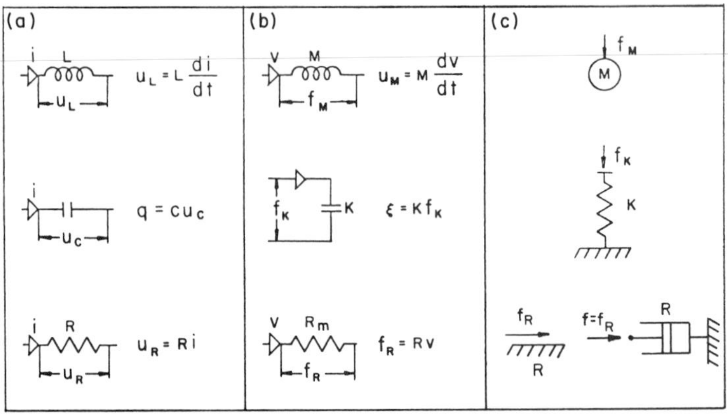

Fig. 1.18 Electromechanical analogies; *a*, electrical circuit; *b*, mechanical circuit; *c*, pictorial representation.

trical symbols are well established, there is no reason to use different symbols for the mechanical differential operators. The last column in Figure 1.18 shows the classical pictorial way of representing the mechanical elements.

The similarity between electrical and mechanical systems is described by the so-called electromechanical analogies. In the force-voltage analogies that are represented by Equations 1.148 to 1.151, the voltage corresponds to the mechanical force, the current to the velocity, the inductance to the mass, the capacitance to the compliance, and the electrical resistance to the mechanical resistance. Because of these relations, the mechanical circuits can be drawn and handled with the same facility as electrical circuits. The electrical mesh equations

$$\sum_0^n u_\nu = 0 \tag{1.152}$$

are of the same mathematical form as d'Alembert's principle, which states that the resultant force (including inertia and friction) that acts on a mechanical element is zero:

$$\sum_0^n f_\nu = 0 \tag{1.153}$$

Figure 1.19 illustrates this principle for a point-mass compliance system. The external force f has to overcome the inertia of the point mass, the friction force, and the restoring force that is generated by the compliance. The sum of all these forces is zero.

The electrical node conditions

$$\sum_0^m i_\nu = 0 \tag{1.154}$$

$$\Sigma f = f - f_M - f_R - f_K = 0$$

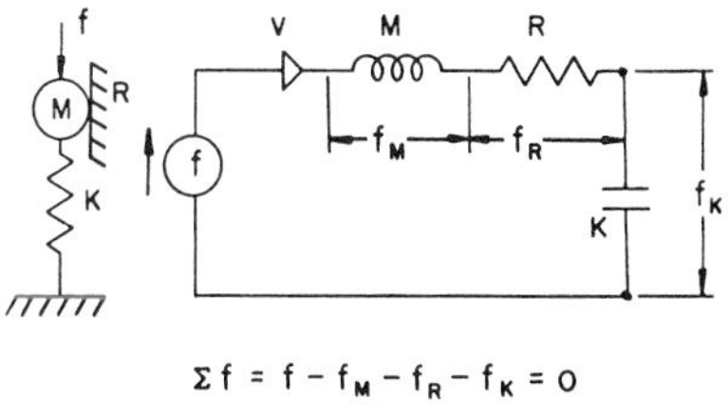

Fig. 1.19   Equivalence of the mesh equations with d'Alembert's principle.

express the fact that current does not accumulate at a node or the fact that the current that enters a node through a set of branches must leave the node through some other set of branches. The Kirchhoff node equations have no direct force-voltage analogue in mechanical systems. But such an analogue is essential if network theory is to be applied to mechanical systems. To enter the node conditions into the mechanical equations, a decrease in velocity must be represented by the current through a shunt branch of the mechanical diagram: the current that leaves a node through a shunt branch then represents the loss in velocity brought about by the compression of a spring or the yielding of some other part of the system. The node conditions are automatically satisfied by representing the general compliant element by a four-terminal network,[9] as shown in Figure 1.20. The ideal compliant element has no mass and, consequently, no inertia. The force applied to it is fully transmitted (principle of action equals reaction):

$$f_1 = f_2 = f \tag{1.155}$$

and the upper two terminals in the diagram (Fig. 1.20) are connected by a

$$f_2 = f_1 = f$$

$$\xi_2 - \xi_1 = Kf$$

$$v_2 - v_1 = K\frac{df}{dt} = j\omega K f = f/(1/j\omega K)$$

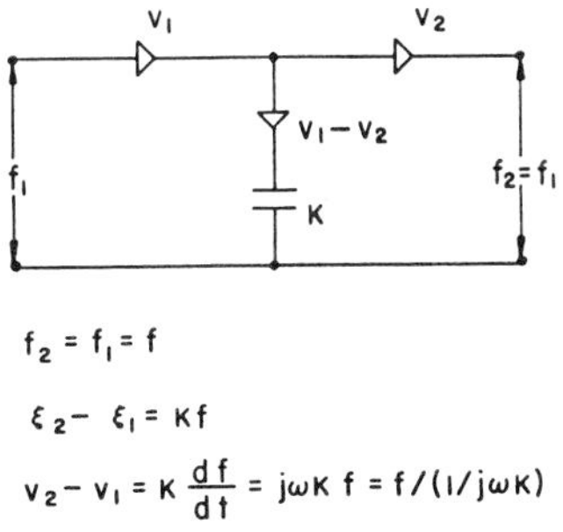

Fig. 1.20   Four-terminal network for a compliant element whose ends move.

[9] That the spring is best represented by a four-terminal network, and not just by a shunt branch, is the most important step in the derivation of the force-voltage analogies. Once this fact is recognized, the force-voltage analogies represent a practically foolproof method for dealing with vibrators.

short circuit. But the transmitted amplitude is smaller because of the yielding of the spring. Since both ends of the spring usually move, Hooke's law takes the form:

$$\xi_2 - \xi_1 = Kf \tag{1.156}$$

Since the force that compresses the compliance is represented as the voltage across the condenser K, the principle that action (voltage across the left terminal pair) equals reaction (voltage across the right terminal pair) is always satisfied. The velocity of the left-hand end of the spring is represented by the current that enters the upper left-hand terminal; the velocity of the right-hand end of the spring, by the current that leaves the upper right-hand terminal; and the loss in velocity because of the compression of the spring is represented by the current that flows through the shunt branch and back to the lower terminal of the source. That the mechanical equations of a spring in the force-voltage analogy is represented by a four-terminal electric network rather than by a two-terminal network is not objectionable, since there is no reason that the equivalent electrical network should look similar to mechanical element that it represents. If periodic vibrations are considered, we obtain (by differentiating Eq. 1.156):

$$\tilde{v}_2 - \tilde{v}_1 = K\frac{d\tilde{f}}{dt} = j\omega K\tilde{f} = \frac{\tilde{f}}{\dfrac{1}{j\omega K}}$$

$$\left(\tilde{\imath}_2 - \tilde{\imath}_1 = C\frac{d\tilde{u}}{dt} = Cj\omega\tilde{u} = \frac{\tilde{u}}{\dfrac{1}{j\omega C}}\right) \tag{1.157}$$

which is exactly the relation represented by the shunt branch in the diagram (Fig. 1.20). The statement that the current through the shunted branch is equal to the ratio of the voltage to the electrical impedance $1/j\omega C$ of the capacitance C now is equivalent to the statement that the decrease in the transmitted velocity—the compressional velocity of the spring—is equal to the ratio of the force to the mechanical impedance $1/j\omega K$ of the compliant element K. If one end of the spring is attached to a rigid point, as shown in Figure 1.21, its velocity is zero and Equation 1.150 is reobtained.

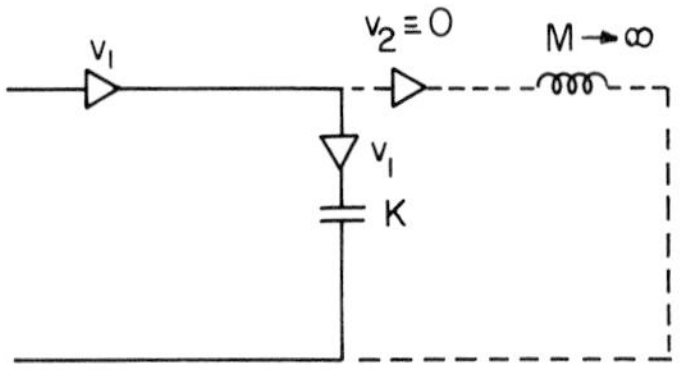

Fig. 1.21 Compliance whose second end is rigidly clamped.

Force-Current Analogy

The analogies just discussed are not unique. If the left- and right-hand sides of the mechanical equations are interchanged and their sequence is altered, correspondence between force and current, velocity and voltage, can be constructed. Hooke's law for the compliance can then be formulated in a manner similar to the equation for the inductance:

$$\triangle v = v_2 - v_1 = K\frac{df_K}{dt} \quad \text{or} \quad \xi = Kf_K$$

$$\left(u_L = L\frac{di}{dt}\right) \tag{1.158}$$

Newton's law can be written in the same form as the equation that defines capacitance:

$$f_1 - f_2 = f_M = M\frac{dv}{dt}$$

$$\left(i = C\frac{du_C}{dt}\right) \tag{1.159}$$

where f_1 is the force that acts on the mass, and f_2, the reaction of the rest of the system to the motion of the mass, and $f_1 - f_2$ is the force neutralized by the mass because of its inertia. In this system of analogies, the mass has to be represented by a four-terminal network. The current that enters this network at its upper left-hand terminal represents the force that acts on the mass; the current that leaves this network at the upper right-hand terminal represents the force that the mass exerts (transmits) on the remaining parts of the system. The loss in force because of the inertia of the mass is represented by the current that flows through the shunted element back to the source.

The resistance equation becomes:

$$v = \frac{1}{R_m} f_R = G f_R$$

$$(u_R = Ri) \tag{1.160}$$

where $1/R_m = G_m$. In this notation, the electrical current corresponds to the mechanical force, and a force generator is equivalent to an electrical current source. The velocity decrease along an element is equivalent to the voltage drop across it (Eq. 1.158). The compliance causes a loss of velocity, but it transmits the applied force without reduction. The compliance is represented by a series impedance $1/j\omega K$. The mass, on the other hand, reduces the transmitted force across it; therefore, the mass generates a parallel admittance. In this dual system of network equations, the resistance corresponds to a shunt conductance; the resistance reduces the transmitted force, but does not reduce the transmitted velocity. Figure 1.22 shows the fundamental circuits. The topology of the force-current analogies corresponds to that of the mechanical system. For instance, d'Alembert's

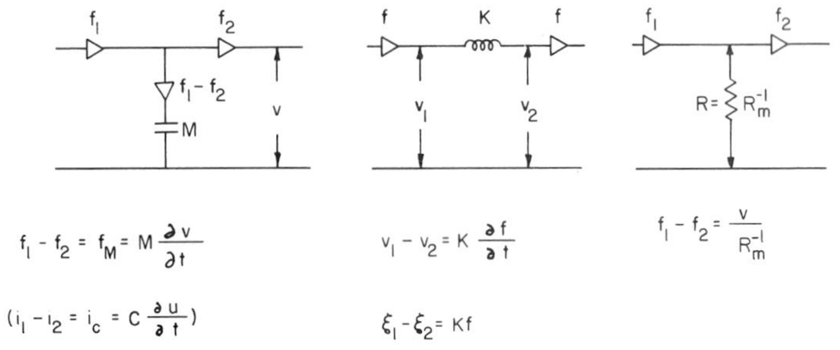

f_1
f_2
$f_1 - f_2$
M
v
f
K
f
v_1
v_2
f_1
f_2
$R = R_m^{-1}$
$f_1 - f_2 = f_M = M \frac{\partial v}{\partial t}$
$(i_1 - i_2 = i_c = C \frac{\partial u}{\partial t})$
$v_1 - v_2 = K \frac{\partial f}{\partial t}$
$\xi_1 - \xi_2 = Kf$
$f_1 - f_2 = \frac{v}{R_m^{-1}}$

Fig. 1.22 Force-current system of electromechanical analogies.

principle $\sum f_\nu = 0$, which is a point law, now corresponds to the node equation $\sum i_\nu = 0$, which also is a point (node) law. Because the topology is the same, the diagrams derived on the basis of the force-current analogy frequently resemble the schematic mechanical diagrams (see below). The result is that all the equations and all the circuits so obtained are the exact duals of those derived on the basis of the force-voltage analogy. One set of circuits can be derived from the other by the simple method outlined above[10] without the need for any computations.

Topology of a Mechanical System and of Its Electromechanical Analogue

Hardly ever has so much discussion been raised and disputes carried out as on the subject of the electromechanical analogies. With the appearance of Horace Trent's basic paper on "Isomorphisms between oriented linear graphs and lumped physical systems" (see references at end of chapter), the topological background of the analogies has been clarified, and all the answers to the questions raised in the past are given in a unique mathematical form. The following is a summary, partly in H. Trent's own words.

It must be made clear at the outset that we are interested only in the dynamical aspects of the system and not in the gross appearance of the components which comprise the system. It is possible to establish an isomorphism (that is, a one-to-one correspondence between the dynamical properties (elements) of a lumped mechanical system and an oriented linear graph (circuits). With the aid of this isomorphism it becomes possible to construct schematic diagrams of the mechanical system.

The process of analyzing a mechanical lumped element system is always connected with a mental decomposition of the system into simple parts, whose dynamical properties are known to the investigator. Each part has a number of points (connection points) at which it is connected to the re-

[10] See pp. 22–26.

mainder of the system. The parts may be decomposed further into subparts, called the components. The components may be dissipative or nondissipative. They may be simple elements, generators or couplers. The dynamical properties of a component can be expressed mathematically by a finite set of relations involving a finite number of scalar variables. These variables can be divided into two types, into across-variables and into through-variables. At least conceptually, the across-variables are measured by attaching an indicating instrument to two points on the component without cutting the system at the connection points. If the indication of the instrument is zero, the two points are identical; if it is not zero, the two points are different points. For instance, the voltage is an across-variable. Through-variables are measured by cutting the system at the connection point, so that a measuring instrument can be inserted. Topologically, through-variables follow the incidence law; they either flow into a connecting point or leave it. The current, for instance, is a through-variable. Through-variables are characterized by the conceptual propagation of a scalar magnitude into or out of a simple connection point.

The first step in constructing the schematic diagram is to focus attention on the measuring instruments. First, we select a group of instruments which measure an across-variable, such as the voltage drop. We connect the instruments together just as the components were joined to form objects, and the objects in turn are joined to form the system, subject to the condition that instrument terminals attached to points in the system, between which the corresponding cross-quantity is always null, are joined at a common node.

The process just described produces a network of instruments. We now replace each instrument by a line segment connected between its terminals and assign a direction to the segment in accordance with the polarity of the instrument. The result is an oriented linear network in which each node stands in a one-to-one correspondence with a junction point of components, and each segment stands in a one-to-one correspondence with indicating instruments, corresponding to all the connections and all the across-variables of the system.

Across-variables contain one feature not associated with the boundaries; namely, they possess a definite magnitude. Let it be recalled that in topology the transformation law for graphical boundaries is such that the sum of the boundaries around a mesh is always zero. If then the algebraic sum of the meter indications around a closed loop or mesh is always zero, it follows that the numbers associated with boundary variables combine algebraically just like boundaries of a graph. Across-variables which have these properties are said to follow the mesh law. An isomorphism exists, therefore, between the across-variables of a lumped system and the boundaries of a graph, provided the letter follows the mesh law. Thus, the existence of an isomorphism depends on one's ability to find across-variables that follow the mesh law. Such variables are found with the greatest ease. In mechanical systems relative position, or any time derivative of it, and in electrical networks voltage difference, or any time derivative of it, have the mesh property.

A similar isomorphism can be derived foı the through-variables by cutting the system at junction points and inserting instruments that measure the through-variables.

Thus, the dynamical properties of a system can be formulated either on a nodal or on a mesh basis. If the system is linear, the bulk of the labor of evaluating the system equations will usually revolve around the determination of the roots of the determinant equation. But the determinant equation is the same, regardless of whether we made a node or a mesh analysis. It seems, therefore, reasonable to believe that the most important factor involved is the nature of the information desired by the investigator. If he wishes information about across-variables, he uses a nodal formulation, if he desires through-variables, then he should use a mesh formulation.

The analogy between two systems is complete, if it satisfies three conditions; namely,

(1) The two systems are isomorphic to the same linear graph.

(2) The dynamical equations for the two systems are of the same form on any one basis, nodal or mesh.

(3) The scalar invariants of the two systems have the same physical dimensions and are both null.

The force-current analogy satisfies all three of these conditions; the force-voltage analogy does not. In the force-voltage analogy, (a) a one-to-one correspondence of components cannot be maintained if the graph that is isomorphic to the mechanical system is nonplanar. There are, therefore, a number of cases where the voltage-force analogy will break down; (b) external references are lost in the force-voltage analogue (see Fig. 1.28).

In practical work, the cases where the analogies break down are extremely rare, and also the loss of external references is of no bearing. From a mathematical, topological point of view, there is therefore no real basic reason to favor one or the other system of electromechanical analogies.

Advantages of the Two Systems of Analogies

The force-current system of analogies has been preferred by many authors. But there is no reason to ban one system or the other, since both are equivalent and since the transformation from one to the other usually can be performed without difficulty. It is insignificant that from the standpoint of topology the force-current system is the superior one or that in certain cases the force-voltage system of analogies may lead to nonplanar networks, whereas the force-current system may lead to planar networks. There are cases in which the force-current analogy leads to diagrams that contain a smaller number of meshes or to diagrams that are particularly suited for node analysis. But under all circumstances, because it is so easy to derive it, the dual circuit should be examined simultaneously. If we are not equally interested in both velocities and forces, for instance—if we are interested only in the velocities—the force-voltage system will be the natural one to use and will usually lead more easily to results. If we are interested only in the forces, the force-current system will almost always be preferable.

In the force-current system, the mechanical impedances correspond to electrical admittances, and series connections are replaced by parallel connections. In the force-current system of network equations, the stiffer mechanical system corresponds to the electrical system that has the smaller impedance. Two masses mounted together are then represented by two condensers in parallel. The condensers take twice the current, and consequently twice the force is needed to drive them. The author personally prefers the force-voltage analogy, because the electrical force corresponds to the mechanical force, the velocity to the current, the electrical impedance to the mechanical impedance. In this analogy, the heavier system has the greater impedance.

Mechanical Impedance

The fundamental electrical and mechanical equations are linear. This linearity manifests itself in Ohm's law or in its mechanical equivalent:

$$u = Ri \qquad \frac{u}{i} = R \qquad \text{and} \qquad f = Rv \qquad \frac{f}{v} = R \tag{1.161}$$

The current is proportional to the voltage, and the factor of proportionality is called the resistance. This resistance can be measured by determining the ratio of the current through the resistive element to the voltage across it, or it can be computed.

The mass impedance is determined by Newton's law, which for periodic forces takes the form:

$$\bar{Z}_M = jX_M = \frac{\tilde{f}_M}{\tilde{v}} = j\omega M \qquad \text{or} \qquad \tilde{f}_M = j\omega M\tilde{v} \tag{1.162}$$

The magnitude X_m is similar in form to the reactance of an inductance ($X = j\omega L$). It represents the mechanical impedance of a mass that moves without friction. The impedance of a compliance is defined by:

$$\bar{Z}_K = \frac{\tilde{f}_K}{\tilde{v}} = \frac{1}{j\omega K} \qquad \tilde{v} = j\omega K\tilde{f}_K \tag{1.163}$$

Its form is the same as that of the impedance of an electrical capacitance ($\bar{Z} = 1/j\omega C$). The dimensions and units of the impedances are the same as those of a mechanical resistance, since they are all defined by the same equation, $\bar{Z} = \tilde{f}/\tilde{v}$.

The concept of a mechanical impedance makes it possible to introduce the same simplification into the theory of mechanical systems as the concept of electrical impedances does into that of electrical systems. The problem is split into two parts: the computation or measurement of the masses, the resistances, and the compliances; and the evaluation of a system of linear network equations. Today, no one would be inclined to compute an electrical network with the aid of Maxwell's equations. Similarly, there is no justification for computing a mechanical system by starting with the fundamental differential equations of an elastic continuum and applying boundary conditions.

All the computations that follow will be performed in terms of the mechanical impedances. The expressions obtained in this way are exact and more general than one would normally expect. They can be interpreted as Laplace transforms and can be easily transformed into general solutions.

Mechanical Circuit Diagrams

Two masses moving together: (1) Force-voltage analogy. If two masses M_1 and M_2 are compounded into one unit, as shown in Figure 1.23, the total mass is M_1+M_2, and Newton's law states that

$$f=M_1\frac{dv}{dt}+M_2\frac{dv}{dt}=(M_1+M_2)\frac{dv}{dt} \tag{1.164}$$

The force that is required to drive both masses with a prescribed velocity is greater than the force that would be required to drive either mass with the same velocity. The system composed of the two masses is stiffer, i.e., harder to move, than either of the individual masses; therefore, the impedances add, and the masses are defined as being connected in series. The mechanical circuit is represented in Figure 1.23. Equation 1.164 corresponds to the

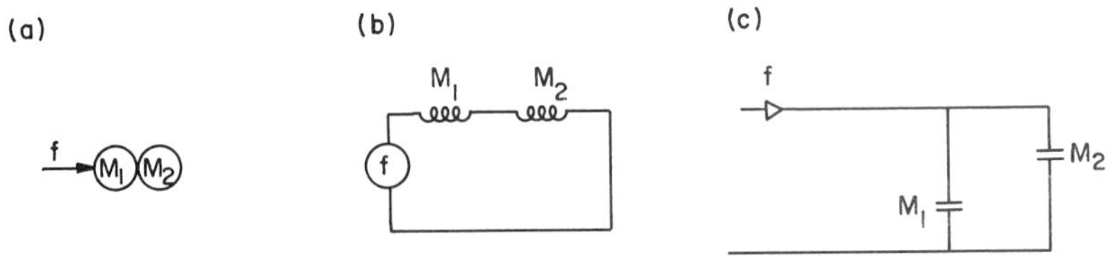

Fig. 1.23 Two masses moving together; *a*, representative sketch; *b*, mechanical diagram; *c*, dual circuit.

electrical mesh equation: the sum of the voltages around a closed circuit is zero. In mechanical language, the resulting mechanical force (external force plus reactions) on an element of the system is zero, or action equals reaction. If, for harmonic motion, the differentiations are replaced by $j\omega$,

Equation 1.164 becomes:

$$\tilde{f}=(j\omega M_1+j\omega M_2)\tilde{v} \tag{1.165}$$

The corresponding equation for electrical components is:

$$\tilde{u}=(j\omega L_1+j\omega L_2)\tilde{\imath} \tag{1.166}$$

The magnitudes $j\omega M_1$ and $j\omega M_2$ are the mechanical impedances of the masses M_1 and M_2; they add up to the resultant mechanical impedance:

$$\bar{Z}=j\omega M_1+j\omega M_2 \tag{1.167}$$

in the same way that the impedances of two inductances add in an electrical series connection.

(2) *Force-current analogy*. In the dual electrical configuration, the force corresponds to an electrical current, and the masses are represented by the symbols that correspond to electrical capacitances (Fig. 1.23*c*). The network equation is now in the node form:

$$\tilde{f}=j\omega(M_1+M_2)\tilde{v} \tag{1.168}$$

which is the differential equation of the system and consequently is identical with Equation 1.167, which has been derived on the basis of the force-voltage analogy.

The corresponding equation for the electrical elements is

$$\tilde{\imath}=j\omega(C_1+C_2)\tilde{u} \tag{1.169}$$

The capacitances representing the masses are connected in parallel (as they appear in Fig. 1.23*c*).

External forces of equal magnitude acting between two masses: (1) Force-voltage analogy. Frequently, attractive forces (or repulsive forces) act between two masses, as indicated in Figure 1.24. To derive a basic understanding of this problem, let it be decomposed into two similar problems, in which two forces of the same magnitude but of opposite direction act

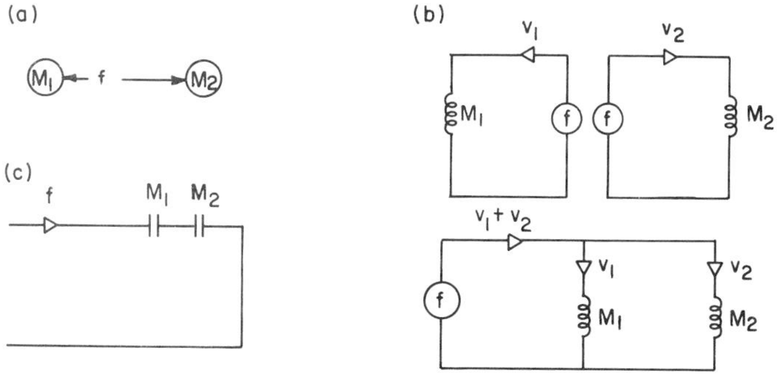

Fig. 1.24 Force acting between two masses; *a*, representative sketch; *b*, mechanical diagram; *c*, dual circuit.

independently on two masses. The two separate circuits are shown in Figure 1.24*b*. In the resulting circuit, the force that acts on each mass is the same, but the velocities are added. The sum of the two velocities can be interpreted as the relative velocity of the two masses. The current that is generated by the source represents the relative velocity between the two masses, and the currents through the masses represent their velocities. Thus, two masses are in parallel, if the forces that act on them are of the same magnitude, but opposite in direction.

(*2*) *Force-current analogy*. The dual circuit for this case is shown in Figure 1.24*c*. Since the same force acts on both masses, the same current flows through the capacitances in the electrical analogue. The two capacitances representing the two masses are in series, and the network equation becomes:

$$\tilde{v}=\tilde{v}_1+\tilde{v}_2=\left(\frac{1}{j\omega M_1}+\frac{1}{j\omega M_2}\right)\tilde{f}$$

$$\left[\tilde{u}=\tilde{u}_1+\tilde{u}_2=\left(\frac{1}{j\omega C_1}+\frac{1}{j\omega C_2}\right)\tilde{\imath}\right] \tag{1.170}$$

Force acting on the two ends of a spring: (1) Force-voltage analogy. This example is similar to the preceding one, except that the force now acts on the two ends of a spring. The deflection of the spring would be the same, if one end were fixed in space and the force acted on the other end, because of the principle that action equals reaction. The relative velocity of the ends of the spring is represented by the circuit in Figure 1.25*b*, where the spring appears as a series impedance that has to be overcome by the driving force. The circuit equations are:

$$\tilde{f}=\frac{1}{K}\tilde{\xi}_{\text{rel}}=\frac{1}{K}(\tilde{\xi}_1+\tilde{\xi}_2)=\frac{1}{K}\frac{(\tilde{v}_1+\tilde{v}_2)}{j\omega}$$

$$\tilde{v}_{\text{rel}}=\tilde{v}_1+\tilde{v}_2=j\omega K\tilde{f} \tag{1.171}$$

where v_{rel} is the relative velocity between the ends of the spring, i.e., the velocity of compression of the spring.

(*2*) *Force-current analogy*. In the dual network (Fig. 1.25*c*), the current flows through the compliance; since both ends of the spring transmit the same force and no current is conducted away by a shunt branch, the velocity is given by:

$$\tilde{f}=\frac{\tilde{v}}{Z_K}=\frac{\tilde{v}}{j\omega K}$$

$$\left(\tilde{\imath}=\frac{\tilde{u}}{j\omega L}\right) \tag{1.172}$$

Point-mass compliance vibrator. (*1*) *Force-voltage analogy*. The mechanical series-resonant circuit consists of a mass and a spring (Fig. 1.26*a*). One end of the spring is clamped to an infinite mass, and the other end is attached to the mass M. The external force acts on the mass M. A resistance has been introduced that is proportional to the velocity of the mass. The network is

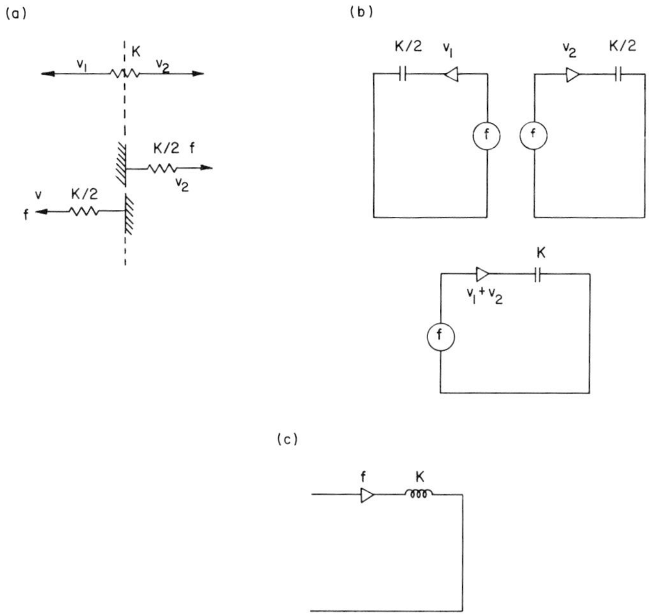

Fig. 1.25 Force acting between the two ends of a spring; *a*, representative sketch; *b*, mechanical diagram; *c*, dual circuit.

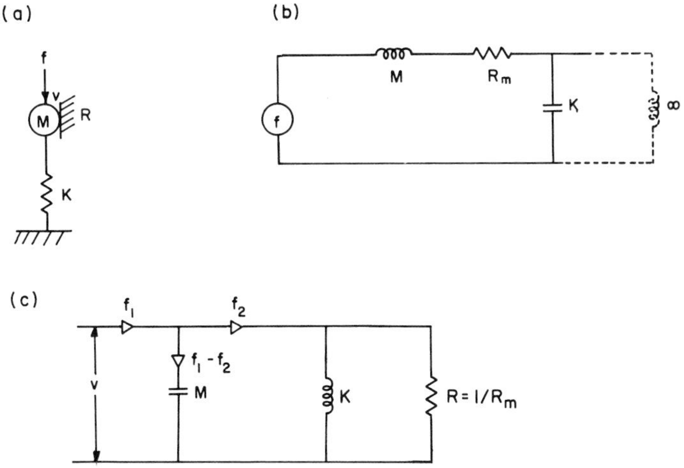

Fig. 1.26 Mechanical resonant circuits (force drives mass); *a*, representative sketch; *b*, circuit diagram; *c*, dual circuit.

a series-resonant circuit (Fig. 1.26*b*), and the circuit equation is:

$$f = M\frac{d}{dt}v + Rv + \int \frac{vdt}{K} \tag{1.173}$$

or, for a harmonic force,

$$\tilde{f} = \left(j\omega M + R + \frac{1}{j\omega K}\right)\tilde{v} \tag{1.174}$$

(*2*) *Force-current analogy.* The dual representation leads to the network shown in Figure 1.26*c*. Part of the force is used up in driving the mass, which, therefore, appears as a shunt; but the mass and the end of the spring next to the mass have the same velocity; therefore, the voltage that acts on the two elements in the electrical diagrams is the same.

Force applied at free end of spring: (2) *Force-voltage analogy.* If the force acts on the spring, the network becomes a parallel-resonant circuit (Fig. 1.27*a*). Since the spring transmits the force, there is no voltage drop across the electrical analogue (Fig. 1.26*b*). The spring, because of its compressibility, reduces the velocity that is transmitted. This decrease in velocity is represented by the current through the shunted capacitance in the electrical analogue. Since the "second end" or "terminal" of the mass is forceless, it is connected to ground potential.

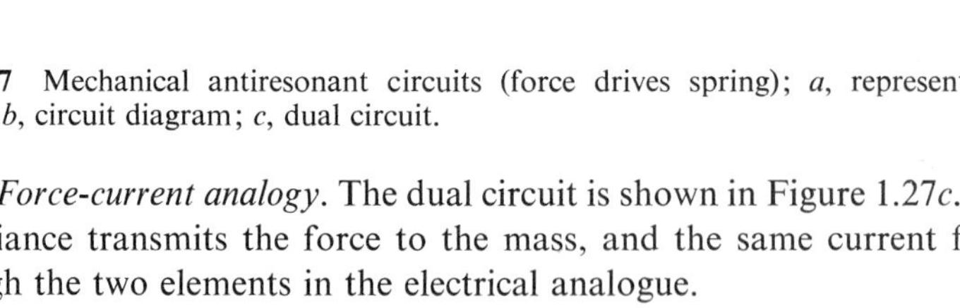

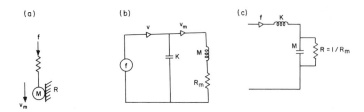

Fig. 1.27 Mechanical antiresonant circuits (force drives spring); *a*, representative sketch; *b*, circuit diagram; *c*, dual circuit.

(*2*) *Force-current analogy.* The dual circuit is shown in Figure 1.27*c*. The compliance transmits the force to the mass, and the same current flows through the two elements in the electrical analogue.

Two or more point-mass compliance vibrators driven by the same force generator: (*1*) *Force-voltage analogy.* The schematic diagram for a number of vibrators driven simultaneously by a force f is shown in Figure 1.28*a*. The electrical circuit can be constructed from its individual constituents: the force f_1 drives the first system, f_2 drives the second system, etc. The values of these forces are unknown, but their sum is equal to the total driving force. Hence,

$$f = f_1 + f_2 + f_3 \tag{1.175}$$

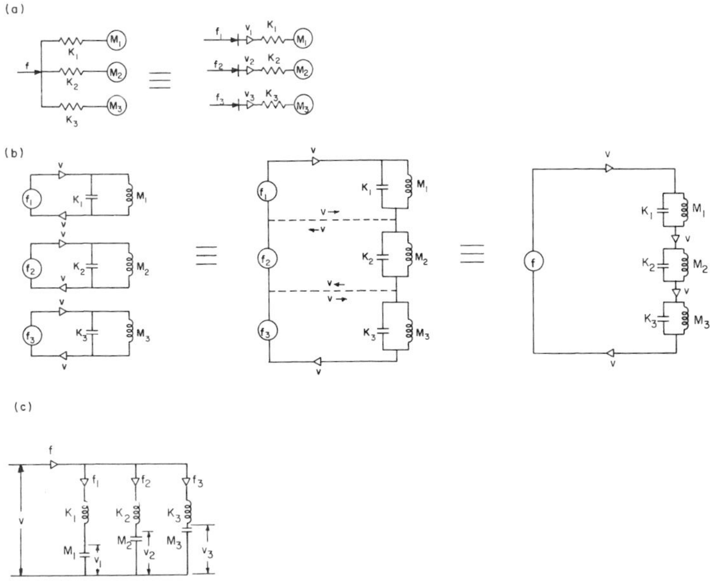

Fig. 1.28 Three resonant circuits driven by the same force generator; *a*, representative sketch; *b*, electrical circuit—left hand circuit electrically equivalent to middle circu it—the sources are independent of one another, and the same currents flow in the M_ν and K_ν—but the currents compensate in the dotted leads, so that they need not be included in the right-hand diagram): *c*, dual circuit.

The velocities of the left-hand ends of all the springs are equal:

$$v_1 = v_2 = v_3 \tag{1.176}$$

Consequently, the current that leaves the first tuned circuit is equal to the current that enters the second tuned circuit, and the two currents compensate one another. The same currents in the other horizontal branches compensate one another in a similar manner. Therefore, the circuits have to be drawn in series (Fig. 1.28*b*.) Because the point-mass spring systems are in series, the compliances shunt the masses. Consequently, the reference point for the compliances is no longer ground. This is an example of the loss of the external references in the voltage-current analogies.

(*2*) *Force-current analogy*. The condition that the left ends of all the springs have the same velocity leads to the dual circuit shown in Figure 1.28*c*.

Dumbbell-shaped vibrator: (*1*) *Force-voltage analogy*. The dumbbell vibrator consists of two masses at opposite ends of a thin connection piece that acts as a compliance (Fig. 1.29*a*). The vibrator may be driven magnetostrictively by a coil of wire around the connecting piece. This connecting piece can then be interpreted as a spring driven at its ends. The ends of the springs are loaded by the masses. The relative motion of the masses is represented by the circuit shown in Figure 1.24*b*; the motion of the ends of the spring, which generates the force that has to be overcome by the exciting force, is represented by the circuit shown in Figure 1.25*b*.

Figure 1.29*b* shows the diagram for the complete system. The external force has to overcome the compliance of the connecting link, and the current through K represents the relative velocity of the ends of this link. The velocity of compression is also the relative velocity of the two masses. Thus it is apparent that the compliance K lies in series with the force f; no further proof is needed. Since the ends of the two masses are free of force, they are at ground potential in the mechanical diagram.

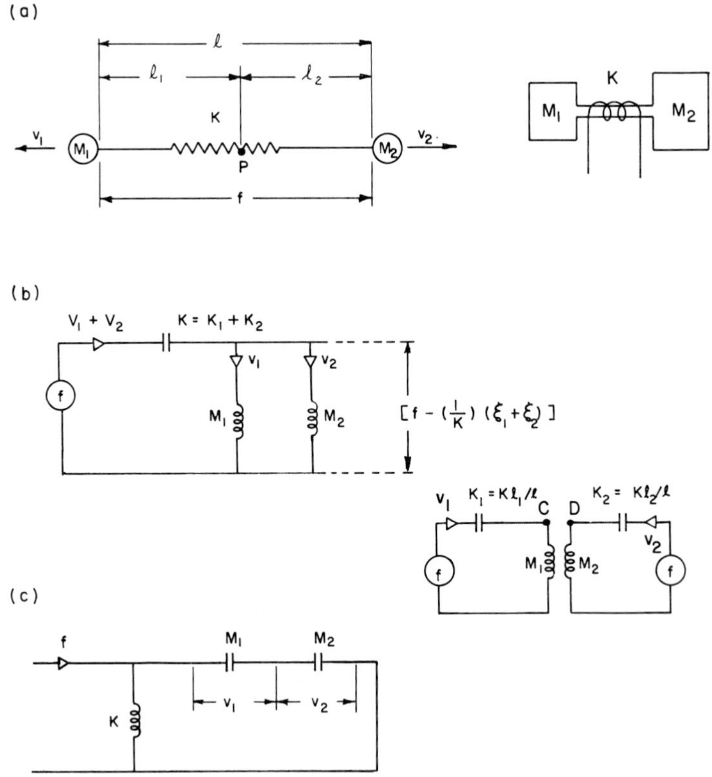

Fig. 1.29 Dumbbell vibrator; *a*, representative sketch; *b*, *left*, mechanical diagram, *right*, the two halves of the mechanical diagram; *c*, dual circuit.

The circuit can also be derived in an elementary manner. Since the two masses move in opposite directions, a point P in the spring is at rest. This point may be considered to be rigidly clamped, and the system can be decomposed into two parts (Fig. 1.29*b*); these two circuits (*right*) can be combined into one circuit (*left*), if C and D have the same potential, that is, if

$$\frac{\frac{1}{\omega K_1}}{\omega M_1} = \frac{\frac{1}{\omega K_2}}{\omega M_2} \tag{1.177}$$

or

$$K_1 M_1 = K_2 M_2 \tag{1.178}$$

Since the spring is assumed to be massless, the ends exert the same force on the two masses (principle of action and reaction). Hence,

$$M_1 \ddot{\xi}_1 = M_2 \ddot{\xi}_2 \tag{1.179}$$

or

$$\frac{M_1}{M_2} = \frac{\ddot{\xi}_2}{\ddot{\xi}_1} = \frac{\xi_2}{\xi_1} \tag{1.180}$$

If ϵ is the elongation of the spring per unit length,

$$\xi_1 = \epsilon l_1 \qquad \text{and} \qquad \xi_2 = \epsilon l_2 \tag{1.181}$$

and

$$\frac{l_1}{l_2} = \frac{\xi_1}{\xi_2} = \frac{M_2}{M_1} \tag{1.182}$$

Hence,

$$\frac{K l_1 M_1}{l} = \frac{K l_2 M_2}{l} \qquad \text{or} \qquad K_1 M_1 = K_2 M_2 \tag{1.183}$$

Thus, Equation 1.178 is satisfied, and C and D can be combined without changing voltages or currents. The two compliances are in parallel, and their resultant is:

$$K_1 + K_2 = K\left(\frac{l_1}{l} + \frac{l_2}{l}\right) = K \tag{1.184}$$

and the diagrams shown in Figure 1.29*b* are equivalent.

(*2*) *Force-current analogy*. In the dual circuit (Fig. 1.29*c*), the same force acts on the two ends of the spring, and the same force acts on the two masses. This circuit is obtained by compounding the two elementary circuits shown in Figures 1.24*c* and 1.25*c*.

Simple Lever: (1) Force-voltage analogy. The lever in its simplest form consists of a weightless bar resting on an immovable fulcrum (Fig. 1.30*a*). The balance of moments around the fulcrum leads to the equation:

$$f_1 l_1 + f_2 l_2 = 0 \tag{1.185}$$

Because the lever is rigid,

$$\frac{v_1}{l_1} = \frac{v_2}{l_2} = \omega \tag{1.186}$$

where ω is the angular velocity of rotation around the fulcrum. In the

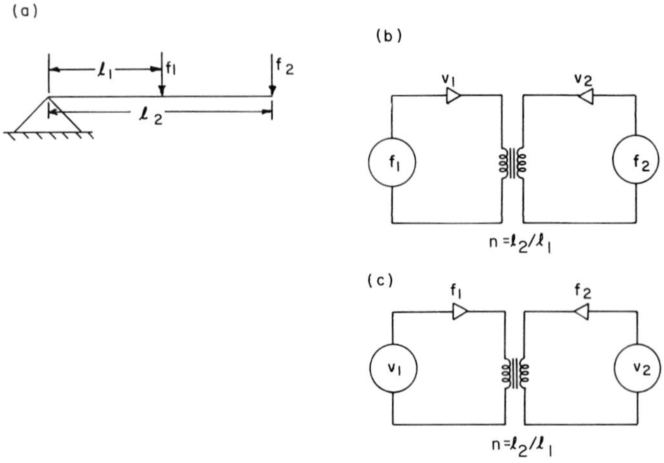

Fig. 1.30 Simple lever; *a*, representative sketch; *b*, force-current analogy; *c*, force-voltage analogy.

force-voltage analogy, these relations take the form:

$$u_1 l_1 + u_2 l_2 = 0 \qquad \text{or} \qquad \frac{u_1}{u_2} = -\frac{l_2}{l_1} \tag{1.187}$$

and

$$\frac{i_1}{l_1} = \frac{i_2}{l_2} = \text{const} \tag{1.188}$$

These relations can be represented by an ideal transformer of the turns ratio $l_2 : l_1$ (Fig. 1.30*b*).

(2) *Force-current analogy*. Correspondingly, we have

$$i_1 l_1 + i_2 l_2 = 0 \qquad \text{or} \qquad i_1 = -\frac{l_2}{l_1} i_2 \tag{1.189}$$

and

$$\frac{u_1}{l_1} = \frac{u_2}{l_2} \qquad \text{or} \qquad \frac{u_1}{u_2} = \frac{l_1}{l_2} \tag{1.190}$$

These relations are represented by a transformer of the turns ratio $l_1 : l_2$ (Fig. 1.30*c*).

Floating lever. An ideal floating lever (Fig. 1.31*a*) can be conceived as a bar that rests on a fulcrum 0, the fulcrum yielding under force. The following equations apply:

$$f_1 + f_2 + f_0 = 0 \tag{1.191}$$

(equilibrium of moments around fulcrum):

$$f_1 l_1 + f_2 l_2 = 0 \tag{1.192}$$

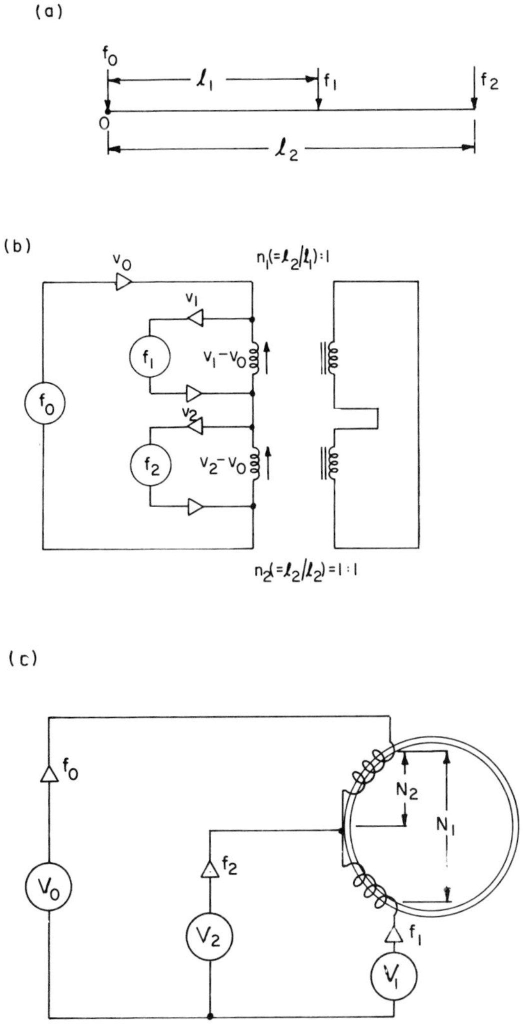

Fig. 1.31 Floating lever; *a*, representative sketch; *b*, *left*, force-voltage analogy, *c*, force-current analogy.

(because the lever is rigid):

$$\frac{v_1 - v_0}{l_1} = \frac{v_2 - v_0}{l_2} = \omega \tag{1.193}$$

where ω is the angular velocity around the point of attack of f_0. Equation 1.192 can be replaced by the energy principle by multiplying its first term by the left-hand side, its second term by the right-hand side of Equation 1.193:

$$f_1(v_1 - v_0) + f_2(v_2 - v_0) = 0$$

or

$$f_1 v_1 + f_2 v_2 - (f_1 + f_2) v_0 = 0 \tag{1.194}$$

and, because of Equation 1.191:

$$f_1 v_1 + f_2 v_2 + f_0 v_0 = 0 \tag{1.195}$$

We shall try to use ideal transformers to represent the equations with electrical networks. The energy-balance equation (1.195), then, is automatically satisfied, and we are left with Equations 1.191 and 1.193.

(*1*) *Force-voltage analogy.* If the force-voltage analogy is used, Equation 1.191 can be realized by two ideal transformers whose primaries are connected in series. To enforce Equation 1.193, the secondaries have to be connected in series, as shown in Figure 1.31*b*. Because the two transformers are ideal,

$$v_s = (v_1 - v_0) n_1 \qquad \text{and} \qquad v_s = (v_2 - v_0) n_2 \tag{1.196}$$

or

$$(v_1 - v_0) n_1 = (v_2 - v_0) n_2 \tag{1.197}$$

Hence, by comparison with Equation 1.193:

$$n_1 = \frac{\alpha}{l_1} \qquad \text{and} \qquad n_2 = \frac{\alpha}{l_2} \tag{1.198}$$

Since α is arbitrary, we may make it equal to l_2 and

$$n_1 = \frac{l_2}{l_1} \qquad \text{and} \qquad n_2 = 1 \tag{1.199}$$

If more than three forces act on the lever, additional transformers of the transformation ratio $n_\nu = l_2/l_\nu$ have to be included in the circuit.

(2) Force-current analogy. The equivalent circuit for the force-current analogy is best derived with the aid of a ring transformer (Fig. 1.31*c*); it satisfies the node equations:

$$i_1 + i_2 + i_0 = 0 \tag{1.200}$$

and because the flux is the same through all the windings, the equation:

$$\frac{u_2 - u_0}{N_2} = \frac{u_1 - u_0}{N_1} \tag{1.201}$$

where N_2 and N_1 are the number of turns, as indicated (Fig. 1.31*c*). Hence, by comparison with Equation 1.193:

$$\frac{N_2}{N_1} = \frac{l_2}{l_1} \tag{1.202}$$

By adding more windings, so that

$$N_1 : N_2 \ldots : N_n = l_1 : l_2 \ldots : l_n \tag{1.203}$$

the diagram can easily be generalized for more forces.

Recommended Reading

Complex Notation and Symbolic Methods

BERANEK, L. L., *Acoustics,* McGraw-Hill, Inc., New York, 1954.

BISHOP, R. E. D., AND D. C. JOHNSON, *The Mechanics of Vibration,* Cambridge University Press, New York, 1960.

CHURCHILL, R. V., *Fourier Series and Boundary Value Problems,* McGraw-Hill, Inc., New York, 1941.

CRAFTON, P. A., *Shock and Vibrations in Linear Systems,* Harper & Row, Publishers, New York, 1961.

HANSEN, H. M., AND P. F. CHENEA, *Mechanics of Vibrations,* John Wiley & Sons, Inc., New York, 1952.

LIGHTHILL, M. J., *Introduction to Fourier Analysis and Generalised Functions,* Cambridge University Press, New York, 1959.

MCLACHLAN, N. W., *Theory of Vibrations,* Dover Publications, Inc., New York, 1951.

Electrical Networks

Introductory

FITZGERALD, A. E., *Basic Electrical Engineering,* McGraw-Hill, Inc., New York, 1945.

GUILLEMIN, E. A., *Communication Networks,* John Wiley & Sons, Inc., New York, 1935, vol. I.

KERCHNER, R. M., AND G. F. CORCORAN, *Alternating-Current Circuits,* John Wiley & Sons, Inc., New York, 1943.

Advanced

BLOCH, A., "On methods for the construction of networks dual to non-planar networks," *Proc. Phys. Soc.* (London), **58** (1946), 677–94.

BODE, H. W., *Network Analysis and Feedback Amplifier Design,* D. Van Nostrand Company, Inc., Princeton, N.J., 1945.

BRENNER, E., AND M. JAVID, *Analysis of Electric Circuits,* McGraw-Hill, Inc., New York, 1959.

FOSTER, R. M., "A reactance theorem," *Bell System Tech. J.*, **3** (1924), 259.

GUILLEMIN, E. A., *Communication Networks,* John Wiley & Sons, Inc., New York, 1935, vol. II.

———, *The Mathematics of Circuit Analysis,* John Wiley & Sons, Inc., New York, 1949.

———, *Synthesis of Passive Networks,* John Wiley & Sons, Inc., New York, 1957.

LEY, B. J., LUTZ, S. G., AND C. F. REHBERG, *Linear Circuit Analysis,* McGraw-Hill, Inc., New York, 1959.

MARTIN, T. L., JR., *Electronic Circuits,* Prentice-Hall, Inc., Englewood Cliffs, N. J., 1956.

Stewart, J. L., *Circuit Theory and Design,* John Wiley & Sons, Inc., New York, 1956.

Storer, J. E., *Passive Network Synthesis,* McGraw-Hill, Inc., New York, 1957.

Sturley, K. R., *Radio Receiver Design,* John Wiley & Sons, Inc., New York, 1947.

Tellegen, B. D. H., "Geometrische Konfigurationen und Dualität von elektrischen Netzwerken," *Phillips Tech. Rdsch.,* **5** (1940), 332–38.

Van Valkenburg, M. E., *Network Analysis,* Prentice-Hall, Inc., Englewood Cliffs, N.J., 1955.

Electromechanical Analogies

Bauer, B. B., "Transformer couplings for equivalent network synthesis," *J.A.S.A.,* **25** (1953), 837–40.

Beranek, L. L., *Acoustics,* McGraw-Hill, Inc., New York, 1954.

Bloch, A., "Electromechanical analogies and their use for the analysis of mechanical and electromechanical systems," *J. Inst. Elec. Engrs.* (London), **92** (1945), 157–69.

———, "On methods for the construction of networks dual to non-planar networks," *Proc. Phys. Soc.* (London), **58** (1946), 677–94.

Darrieus, M., "Les modèles mécaniques en électrotechnique: Leur application aux problèmes de stabilité," *Bull. Soc. Franç. Elec.,* **96** (1929), 794–809.

Firestone, F. A., "A new analogy between mechanical and electrical systems," *J.A.S.A.,* **4** (1933), 249–67.

———, "The mobility method of computing the vibration of linear mechanical and acoustical systems: Mechanical and electrical analogies," *J. Appl. Phys.,* **9** (1938), 373–87.

———, "Twixt earth and sky with rod and tube: The mobility and classical impedance analogies," *J.A.S.A.,* **28** (1956), 1117.

Hähnle, W., "Die Darstellung elektromechanischer Gebilde durch rein elektrische Schaltbilder," *Wissen. Veröff. Siemens-Konzern,* **11** (1932), 1–23.

Koenig, H. E., and W. A. Blackwell, *Electromechanical System Theory,* McGraw-Hill, Inc., New York, 1961.

Le Corbeiller, P., and Ying-Wa Yueng, "Duality in mechanics," *J.A.S.A.,* **24** (1952), 643–48.

Mason, W. P., "Electrical and mechanical analogies," *Bell System Tech. J.,* **20** (1941), 405–14.

Olson, H. F., *Dynamic Analogies,* D. Van Nostrand Company, Inc., Princeton, N. J., 1943.

Rayleigh, Lord, *The Theory of Sound,* Macmillan and Co., Ltd., London, 1894; reprinted by Dover Publications, Inc., New York, 1945; vol. II.

Raymond, F., "Analogies électriques et mécaniques," *Rev. gén. élec.*, **61** (1952), 465–75.

Tellegen, B. D. H., "The gyrator: A new electric element," *Phillips Res. Rep.*, **3** (1948).

Trent, H. M., "An alternative formulation of the laws of mechanics" (Am. Soc. Mech. Eng. Paper No. 51, 1951), *J. Appl. Mech.* (1952), 147–53

———, "Isomorphisms between oriented linear graphs and lumped physical systems," *J.A.S.A.*, **27** (1955), 500–27.

II / THE POINT-MASS SPRING SYSTEM

In the preceding chapter, methods for dealing efficiently with vibratory systems have been summarized. The main task of this chapter is to study the point-mass compliant element vibrator. This vibrator is of considerable importance because of the frequency of its appearance in the physical world. Furthermore, as will be shown in Chapter VII, the behavior of a vibrator of any degree of complexity can be described by a sum of terms, each of which represents the solution for a simple point-mass compliant element vibrator. Let it be emphasized here that a thorough understanding of the theory in this chapter is imperative for the study of more complex vibratory systems.

The Differential Equation of a Series-Resonant System

The tuned electrical circuit is the fundamental electrical oscillator, and the point-mass spring system is the fundamental mechanical vibrator; both obey similar differential equations. The methods to be used are those of electrical network theory; therefore, we shall start with the electrical circuit equations and rewrite them for the mechanical systems.

An electrical tuned circuit consists of an inductance, a capacitance, and a resistance connected in series; it usually is driven by a voltage generator, as shown in Figure 2.1. The differential equation is:

$$L\frac{di}{dt}+Ri+\frac{1}{C}q=u \tag{2.1}$$

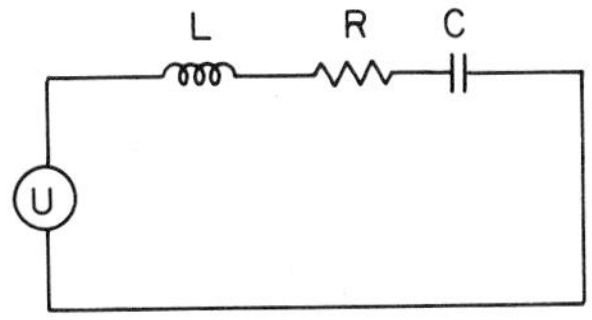

Fig. 2.1 Electrical series-resonant circuit.

where $i = dq/dt$. The first coefficient is made unity by dividing the equation by L:

$$\frac{di}{dt} + 2\delta i + \omega_0^2 q = \frac{1}{L} u \tag{2.2}$$

where $\omega_0^2 = 1/LC$ is the square of the radial frequency of the resonance maximum of the velocity amplitude and $\delta = R/2L$ is the decay constant. The corresponding mechanical vibrator is a point-mass spring system, as shown in Figure 2.2. Its differential equation is:

$$M\frac{dv}{dt} + Rv + \frac{1}{K}\xi = f \tag{2.3}$$

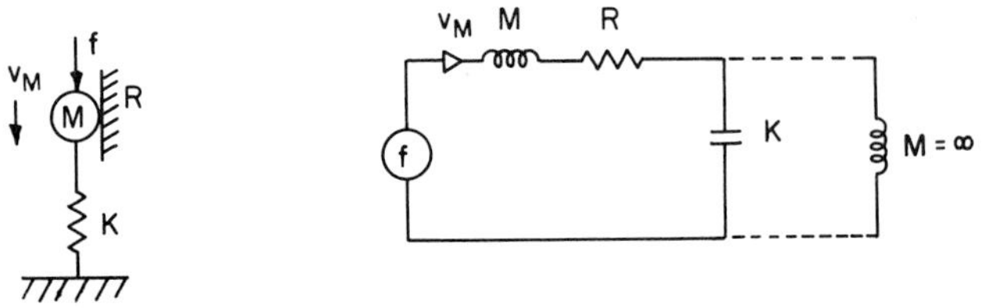

Fig. 2.2 Point-mass compliance (series-resonant) vibrator.

Equation 2.3 for the mechanical vibrator can be obtained from Equation 2.1 simply by replacing the electrical magnitudes L, C, R, q, i, and u by the corresponding mechanical magnitudes M, K, R, ξ, v, and f. The fundamental equations are of the same form, and mathematically there is no need to distinguish between electrical and mechanical systems. If we differentiate with respect to t and divide by M we obtain:

$$\frac{d^2v}{dt^2} + \frac{R}{M}\frac{dv}{dt} + \frac{1}{KM}v = \frac{1}{M}\frac{df}{dt} \tag{2.4}$$

or

$$\frac{d^2v}{dt^2} + 2\delta\frac{dv}{dt} + \omega_0^2 v = \frac{1}{M}\frac{df}{dt} \tag{2.5}$$

where

$$\delta = \frac{R}{2M} \quad \text{and} \quad \omega_0^2 = \frac{1}{MK} \tag{2.6}$$

The parameters M, R, and K in the above differential equation are of secondary interest. A system is primarily characterized by the effort required to drive it; that is, by the force per unit mass, by its resonant frequency, and by its damping. The mass has been eliminated in the above equations by dividing by it. The coefficients of dv/dt and v then represent the resistance $R/M = 2\delta$ and the stiffness $1/MK = \omega_0^2$ per unit mass, and the force term on the right represents the force per unit mass of the system.

The Complex Solution

The complete solution consists of the sum of the solutions of the homogeneous differential equation (when the force term on the right-hand side is set equal to zero) and of the inhomogeneous equation (when the force term on the right-hand side is retained and the steady state is reached). The solution of the homogeneous equation describes either the decay of the vibration after the external force has been removed or the building up of the vibration after the external force has been applied to the system.

Experimental results show that the solution of the homogeneous differential equation is an exponentially decaying vibration, i.e.,

$$\tilde{v} = \bar{V}e^{pt} \tag{2.7}$$

In fact, the solution to a homogeneous differential equation with constant coefficients is always of this form (Eq. 2.7).

The parameter p is similar to the same variable in the theory of the Laplace transform. It will be considered to be complex even if it appears without a bar, and this will be the only exception permitted in the notation. If the right-hand side of Equation 2.5 is made zero, and if Equation 2.7 is substituted as a trial solution, the following equation results:

$$(p^2 + 2\delta p + \omega_0^2)\bar{V}e^{pt} = 0 \tag{2.8}$$

If the factor outside the parentheses were zero, there would be no motion; however, this is a trivial solution and is ignored. To preserve the equality, the expression in the parentheses must vanish, and p becomes a root of the so-called characteristic equation:

$$p^2 + 2\delta p + \omega_0^2 = 0 \tag{2.9}$$

Its roots are given by

$$p = -\delta \pm \sqrt{\delta^2 - \omega_0^2} = -\delta \pm \sqrt{-(\omega_0^2 - \delta^2)} = -\delta \pm j\sqrt{\omega_0^2 - \delta^2} = -\delta \pm j\omega_0^* \tag{2.10}$$

where

$$\omega_0^* = \sqrt{\omega_0^2 - \delta^2} \tag{2.11}$$

Subcritically Damped Decaying Vibrations

In the theory of vibrators, we are predominantly interested in lightly damped systems. Since δ then is much smaller than ω_0, $\delta^2 - \omega_0^2$ has been written as $-(\omega_0^2 - \delta^2)$, and the -1 under the root has been taken as a factor j in front of the root. If the above value p is substituted into Equation 2.7, the complex solution becomes:

$$\tilde{v} = \bar{V}e^{(-\delta \pm j\omega_0^*)t} \tag{2.12}$$

where $\bar{V} = Ve^{j\varphi}$ is the integration constant. Thus, the constant δ, which is $\frac{1}{2}$ the resistance per unit mass (see Eq. 2.6), is identified with the decay constant of the system. The real solution then is given by the real (or the imaginary) part of the complex solution:

$$v = Re[\tilde{v}] = Re[e^{-\delta t} V e^{j(\varphi \pm \omega_0{}^* t)}] = V e^{-\delta t} \cos(\varphi \pm \omega_0{}^* t)$$
$$= V e^{-\delta t} \cos(\omega_0{}^* t \pm \varphi) \tag{2.13}$$

The phase angle φ may be arbitrarily selected, and its sign may be positive or negative; since $\cos \omega t = \cos(-\omega t)$, the negative sign in the parentheses is superfluous. The complex solution represents a vector that rotates in the positive angular direction (counterclockwise), and the magnitude of this vector decreases exponentially with time. The real solution, which is the projection of this vector on the real or the imaginary axis, is a sinusoid with an amplitude that decreases exponentially with time. The frequency $\omega_0{}^*$ of the decaying vibrations is called the natural frequency, because it represents the frequency of the vibration when the system has been excited and let go. If damping is small, and the resistance R is constant, this natural frequency is only slightly smaller than the resonant frequency ω_0.

It is of interest to compare the preceding derivations with the standard or classical derivation of the solution. In the standard theory of differential equations, only real solutions are of concern. The solution

$$v = \bar{A} e^{(-\delta + j\omega_0{}^*)t} + \bar{B} e^{(-\delta - j\omega_0{}^*)t} = e^{-\delta t}[(\bar{A} + \bar{B}) \cos \omega_0{}^* t + j(\bar{A} - \bar{B}) \sin \omega_0{}^* t]$$
$$= e^{-\delta t}(C \cos \omega_0{}^* t + D \sin \omega_0{}^* t) \tag{2.14}$$

is real if the constants $\bar{A}$ and $\bar{B}$ are real and equal, or conjugate complex; the constants $\bar{C}$ and $\bar{D}$ are consequently real; and the two signs for ω_0 have to be retained. Without the two signs for ω_0, the two terms would be proportional to one another, and there would be only one integration constant instead of two. In contrast, if complex notation is used, only one complex integration constant $\bar{V}$ is needed, and the complex solution is:

$$\tilde{v} = \bar{V} e^{-\delta t + j\omega_0{}^* t} \tag{2.15}$$

where

$$\bar{V} = V e^{j\varphi} = V \cos \varphi + jV \sin \varphi = V \angle \varphi \tag{2.16}$$

The complex constant $\bar{V}$ is equivalent to two integration constants: the real part and the imaginary part, or the magnitude and the phase angle.

Supercritically Damped Decaying Vibrations

For large damping, $\omega_0{}^*$ may be considerably smaller than the resonant frequency ω_0, or it may even be imaginary. If $\omega_0{}^2$ is smaller than δ^2, $\omega_0{}^{*2}$ becomes imaginary, and the velocity decays without vibration exponentially with time. Since there is no vibration, a significant complex solution does not exist, and the integration constants can be assumed to be real. Since $\delta^2 > \omega_0{}^2$, the two signs that occur in the expression for p

$$p = -\delta \pm \sqrt{\delta^2 - \omega_0{}^2} \tag{2.17}$$

lead to independent solutions, and the complete solution is given by:

$$v = Ae^{(-\delta+\sqrt{\delta^2-\omega_0^2})t} + Be^{(-\delta-\sqrt{\delta^2-\omega_0^2})t} \tag{2.18}$$

The vibration is said to be aperiodically damped. For $\omega_0^* = 0$, the two solutions become identical and reduce to a simple exponential:

$$\xi = Ae^{-\delta t} \tag{2.19}$$

where $\delta = \omega_0$. A second independent solution can then be found by differentiating Equation 2.19 with respect to the parameter δ:

$$\xi = -Ate^{-\delta t} \tag{2.20}$$

Differentiation with respect to a parameter is equivalent to forming the difference between two solutions. The expression that results is linearly independent of (not proportional to) the original solution (because of the factor t) and still satisfies the original differential equation.

Figure 2.3 illustrates the decay of the vibration for a motion that is generated by an impulsive force for subcritical damping (a) and for supercritical damping (b), the system being initially at rest. Figure 2.4 represents similar curves for a system that is initially deflected and released. The curves in Figure 2.4 show that the system comes to rest most rapidly when the damping is 0.6 of the critical damping. From a practical point of view, this value of damping will usually be preferable to critical damping.

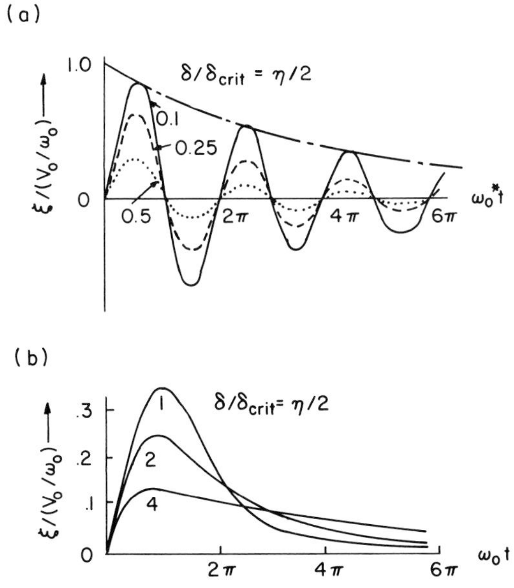

Fig. 2.3 Natural vibration of a system started from rest, with a short pulse; a, subcritical damping; b, supercritical damping.

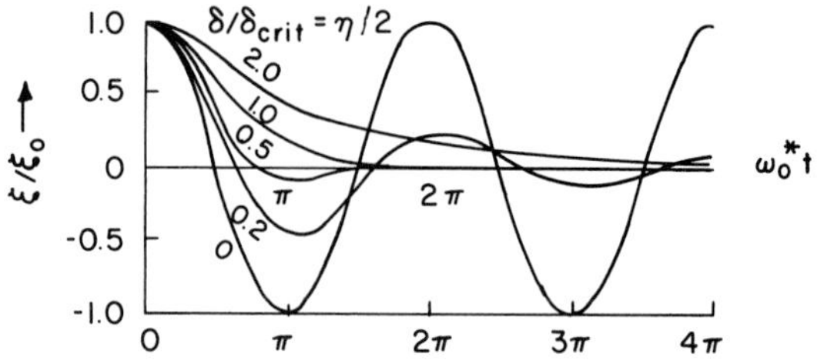

Fig. 2.4 Natural vibration of a system deflected and released without initial velocity, at various values of damping.

Forced Vibrations

The inhomogeneous differential equation (the force term on the right-hand side being retained) describes the effect of the driving force, and its solution is called the "forced" solution. Since we are predominantly interested in periodic vibrations, it will be assumed that the driving force varies harmonically. The simplest solution of the inhomogeneous equation is the strictly periodic or steady-state solution. This solution describes the motion of a system long after the driving force has been applied. The frequency of this motion is obviously the same as the frequency of the force, and d/dt can be replaced by $j\omega$. In this way, the differential equation (2.3) is reduced to the following algebraic equation:

$$\left(j^2\omega^2 M + j\omega R + \frac{1}{K}\right)\tilde{\xi} = \tilde{f} \tag{2.21}$$

or to

$$\left(j\omega M + R + \frac{1}{j\omega K}\right)\tilde{v} = \tilde{f} \tag{2.22}$$

because $j\omega\tilde{\xi} = \tilde{v}$. The solution is:

$$\tilde{v} = \frac{\tilde{f}}{R + j\omega M + \dfrac{1}{j\omega K}} = \frac{\tilde{f}}{\bar{Z}} \tag{2.23}$$

where

$$\tilde{f} = \bar{F}e^{j\omega t} = Fe^{j(\omega t + \varphi_F)} \quad \text{and} \quad \bar{F} = Fe^{j\varphi_F} \tag{2.24}$$

and $\bar{Z}$ is the mechanical impedance of the system:

$$\bar{Z} = R + j\omega M + \frac{1}{j\omega K} \tag{2.25}$$

The steady-state solution could have been derived from the circuit diagram (Fig. 2.2) without computation by dividing the driving force by the sum of the impedances in the one-mesh circuit.

Equation 2.25 for the impedance $\bar{Z}$, then, contains two terms that involve the frequency. It can be transformed into an equation that contains only one term that involves the frequency, as follows:

$$\bar{Z} = R + j\omega M - \frac{j}{\omega K} = R + j\omega M\left(1 - \frac{1}{\omega^2 MK}\right) = R + j\omega_0 M\left(\frac{\omega}{\omega_0}\right)\left(1 - \frac{\omega_0^2}{\omega^2}\right)$$

$$= R + j\omega_0 M\left(\frac{\omega}{\omega_0} - \frac{\omega_0}{\omega}\right) = R + j\omega_0 M\underline{\nu} \tag{2.26}$$

where $\omega_0 = 1/\sqrt{MK}$, as before, and

$$\underline{\nu} = \frac{\omega}{\omega_0} - \frac{\omega_0}{\omega} \tag{2.27}$$

is a nondimensional frequency variable, which is just as convenient a variable as the frequency ω itself.

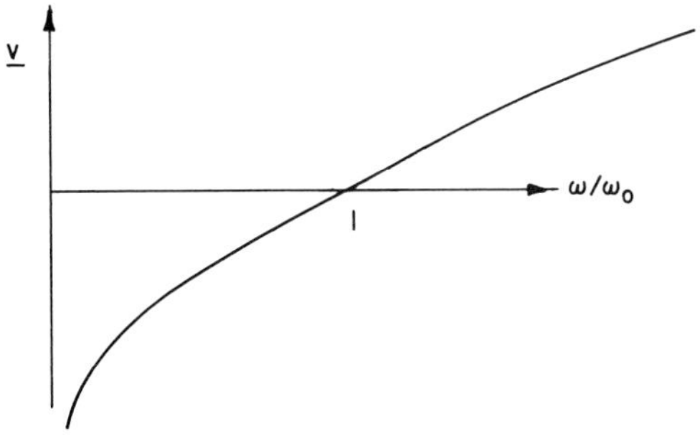

Fig. 2.5 Frequency variable $\underline{\nu}$ as a function of ω/ω_0.

The introduction of the frequency variable $\underline{\nu}$ makes it possible to condense the terms containing the frequency ωM and $1/\omega K$ into a single term. Figure 2.5 shows a plot of $\underline{\nu}$ as a function of ω. At very low frequencies,

$$\underline{\nu} = \frac{\omega}{\omega_0} - \frac{\omega_0}{\omega} \cong -\frac{\omega_0}{\omega} \tag{2.28}$$

At very high frequencies, $\underline{\nu}$ becomes proportional to the frequency

$$\underline{\nu} \cong \frac{\omega}{\omega_0} \tag{2.29}$$

At the resonant frequency, $\underline{\nu}$ is zero. In the vicinity of the resonant frequency, $\underline{\nu}$ is equal to twice the relative deviation of the frequency from the resonant frequency:

$$\underline{\nu} = \frac{\omega}{\omega_0} - \frac{\omega_0}{\omega} = \frac{\omega^2 - \omega_0^2}{\omega\omega_0} = \frac{(\omega + \omega_0)(\omega - \omega_0)}{\omega\omega_0} \doteq \frac{2\omega_0 \triangle\omega}{\omega\omega_0} = \frac{2\triangle\omega}{\omega} \doteq \frac{2\triangle\omega}{\omega_0} \tag{2.30}$$

where $\triangle\omega = \omega - \omega_0$, and

$$\omega + \omega_0 \doteq 2\omega_0 \tag{2.31}$$

Outside the resonance range, the resistance R is usually small in comparison to $\omega_0 M\underline{v}$ and can be neglected. Equation 2.26 then reduces to:

$$\bar{Z} \doteq j\omega_0 M\underline{v} \tag{2.32}$$

Within the resonance range, the resistance is very important, and it is expedient to write Equation 2.26 in the following form:

$$\bar{Z} = R + j\omega_0 M\underline{v} = R(1 + jQ\underline{v}) = R\sqrt{1 + Q^2\underline{v}^2}\, e^{j\varphi_Z} \tag{2.33}$$

where

$$Q = \frac{\omega_0 M}{R} \tag{2.34}$$

and φ_Z is the phase angle of the mechanical impedance given by:

$$\tan \varphi_Z = Q\underline{v} \qquad \text{or} \qquad \cos \varphi_Z = \frac{1}{\sqrt{1 + Q^2 v^2}} = \frac{R}{Z} \tag{2.35}$$

The resistance now appears as a multiplier. The magnitude Q is the quality factor; it represents the ratio of the mass reactance $\omega_0 M$ of the system at the resonant frequency to the loss resistance. The reciprocal of the quality factor $\eta = Q^{-1}$ is called the loss factor. The loss factor represents the tangent of the acute angle between the impedance $\bar{Z} = R + j\omega_0 M$ (of the loss element) and the imaginary axis (Fig. 2.6). The greater the losses (or the resistance), the greater this angle becomes; therefore, it is called the loss angle, and the loss factor η is the tangent of the loss angle. Usually φ is small, and

$$\eta = \tan \varphi \doteq \varphi \tag{2.36}$$

Since

$$\omega_0 M = \frac{1}{\omega_0 K} \tag{2.37}$$

the quality factor can also be represented as the ratio of the reactance of the compliance at the resonant frequency to the loss resistance:

$$Q = \frac{\omega_0 M}{R} = \frac{1}{\omega_0 K R} \tag{2.38}$$

If the loss resistance is constant, the quality factor is a function of the resonant frequency of the system.

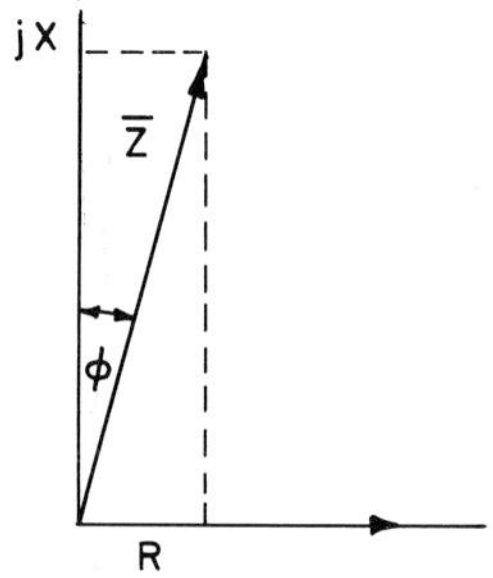

Fig. 2.6 Loss angle of the impedance.

The Real Solution

The simplest way to obtain the real solution is to express the complex solution in its polar form:

$$\tilde{v}=\frac{\tilde{f}}{\bar{Z}}=\frac{Fe^{j\omega t+j\varphi_F}}{Ze^{j\varphi_Z}}=\frac{F}{Z}e^{j(\omega t+\varphi_F-\varphi_Z)} \tag{2.39}$$

where

$$\bar{Z}=Ze^{j\varphi_Z} \quad \text{and} \quad \bar{F}=Fe^{j\varphi_F} \tag{2.40}$$

and

$$\tan\varphi_Z=\frac{\omega M-\dfrac{1}{\omega K}}{R}=\frac{\omega_0 M \underline{v}}{R}=Q\underline{v} \tag{2.41}$$

The magnitude of $\bar{Z}$ can be written in the following three forms:

$$Z=|\bar{Z}|=\left|R+j\left(\omega M-\frac{1}{\omega K}\right)\right|=\sqrt{R^2+\left(\omega M-\frac{1}{\omega K}\right)^2} \tag{2.42}$$

$$=|R+j\omega_0 M\underline{v}|=\sqrt{R^2+(\omega_0 M)^2\underline{v}^2} \tag{2.43}$$

$$=|R(1+jQ\underline{v})|=R\sqrt{1+Q^2\underline{v}^2} \tag{2.44}$$

The real solution for the velocity is obtained by discarding the imaginary part of the exponential in Equation 2.39:

$$v=Re(\tilde{v})=\frac{F}{Z}\cos(\omega t+\varphi_F-\varphi_Z) \tag{2.45}$$

The complex solution for the displacement amplitude is given by:

$$\tilde{\xi}=\frac{\tilde{v}}{j\omega}=\frac{\tilde{F}}{j\omega\bar{Z}}=\frac{F}{\omega Z}e^{j(\omega t+\varphi_F-\varphi_Z-\frac{\pi}{2})} \tag{2.46}$$

and the real solution is:

$$\xi=Re(\tilde{\xi})=\frac{F}{\omega Z}\cos\left(\omega t+\varphi_F-\varphi_Z-\frac{\pi}{2}\right)=\frac{F\cos\left(\omega t+\varphi_F-\varphi_Z-\dfrac{\pi}{2}\right)}{\sqrt{\left(\dfrac{1}{K}-\omega^2 M\right)^2+\omega^2 R^2}} \tag{2.47}$$

The solution depends on the damping, and the peak in the frequency curve is finite. Figure 2.7*a* shows the frequency curve of the displacement amplitude, and Figure 2.7*b*, the frequency curve of the phase angle α (Eqs. 2.41 and 2.47) of the displacement relative to that of the force. At low frequencies, the amplitude is equal to the static amplitude, and the phase angle of the amplitude is the same as that of the force. The amplitude curve passes through a resonance maximum, provided that $\delta<\delta_{\text{crit}}$; and the phase angle becomes $-90°$ at the resonant frequency. For very high frequencies, the amplitude decreases in inverse proportion to the square of the frequency, and its phase angle lags behind that of the force by 180°.

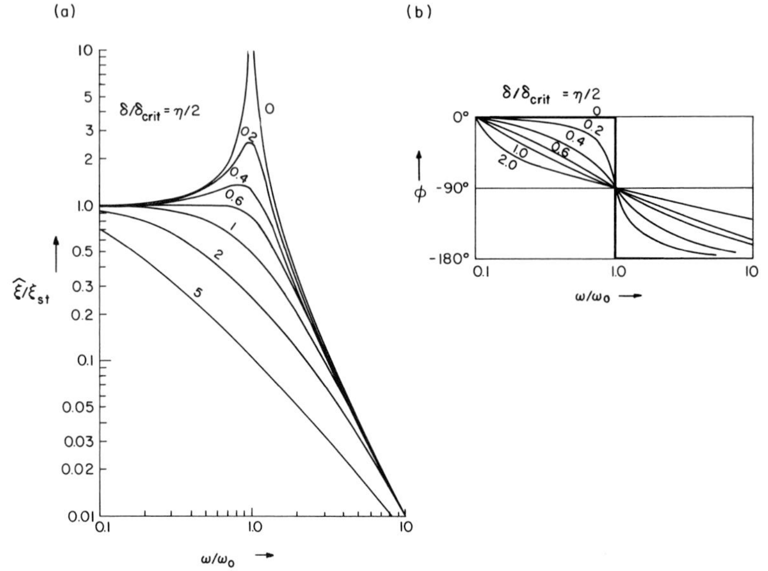

Fig. 2.7 Response of a point-mass spring system to a sinusoidal driving force; *a*, displacement amplitude; *b*, phase of the displacement with respect to the driving force. Parameter is the damping relative to the critical damping $\delta/\delta_{crit} = \eta/2$.

The corresponding curves for the velocity amplitude are plotted in Figure 2.8. The velocity amplitude is zero at zero frequency, and all the velocity amplitude curves have a maximum at the same frequency ω_0, irrespective of the damping. The frequency ω_0 is a characteristic parameter of the systems and is designated as the resonant frequency; it is the frequency of the maximum value of the velocity amplitude. In contrast, the maxima of the displacement amplitudes occur at frequencies that depend on the damping. The displacement amplitude is $1/\omega$ times the velocity amplitude; multiplication by $1/\omega$ raises the curves at the lower frequencies and lowers them at the higher frequencies, and the peaks of the frequency curves of the amplitude move toward the lower frequencies to a degree that is greater for greater damping. The resonant frequency is identical with the frequency of the natural vibrations of the system, if the system has no damping. Because of the simplicity of the resonance curve for the velocity amplitude, the velocity is a more convenient variable than the displacement. This is no disadvantage in the study of acoustics, since the velocity is also the significant variable in analyzing the sound radiation of a vibrator.

The situation is very similar in network theory, where the currents, and not the charges, are always the variables.

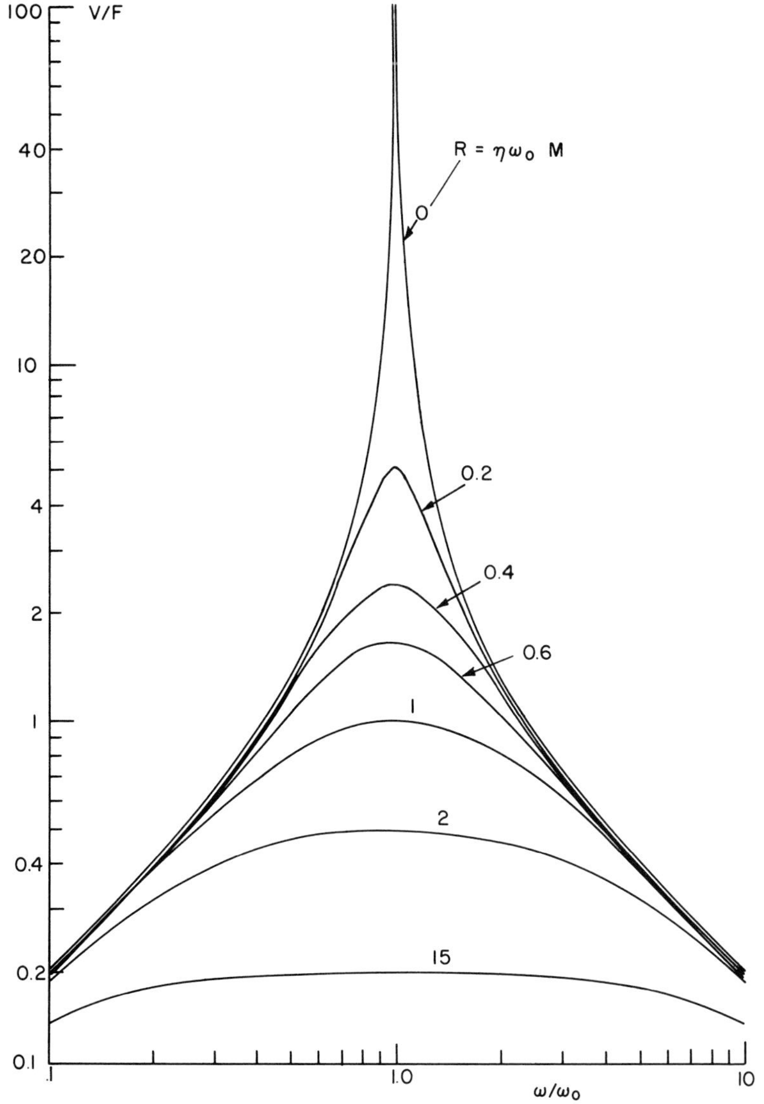

Fig. 2.8 Velocity amplitude of a point-mass spring system as a function of the frequency of the driving force, at various values of damping.

Locus of the Impedance in the Complex Plane

The locus of the impedance in the complex plane, when the frequency is varied from $\omega=0$ to $\omega=\infty$, is a line that extends from $-\infty$ to $+\infty$, parallel to the imaginary axis at a distance R from it. The impedance is represented by a vector that starts at the origin and ends at the line, at a point that is determined by the frequency. At the resonant frequency ω_0, the imaginary part of the impedance is zero, and $\bar{Z}=R$. The imaginary part becomes $-j\,\infty$ as the frequency approaches zero, and $+\infty$ as the frequency becomes infinite (Fig. 2.9).

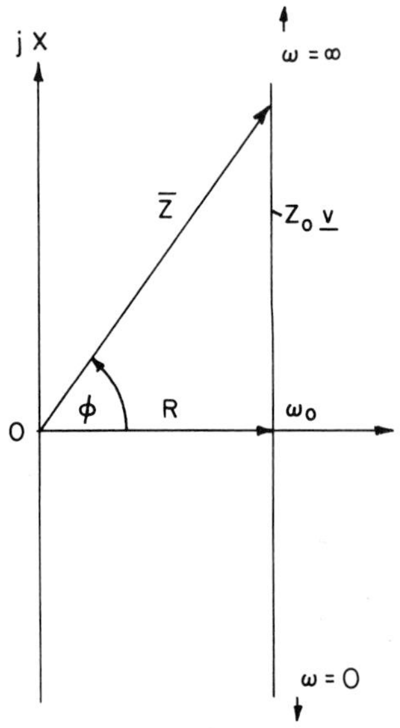

Fig. 2.9 Locus of the impedance in the complex plane of a series-resonant circuit.

The velocity is proportional to the admittance $\bar{Y}$, which is the reciprocal of the impedance:

$$\bar{Y}=\frac{1}{\bar{Z}}=\frac{1}{\bar{Z}}\cdot\frac{R}{R}=\frac{1}{R}\cdot\frac{R}{Ze^{j\varphi_Z}}=\left(\frac{1}{R}\cos\varphi_Z\right)e^{-j\varphi_Z} \tag{2.48}$$

where $R/Z=\cos\varphi_Z$ is the cosine of the angle between the impedance vector and the real axis. The angle φ_Z varies from $-\pi/2$ to $+\pi/2$ as the frequency varies from 0 to $+\infty$. If plotted as a function of φ_Z, the magnitude $(1/R)\cos\varphi_Z$ describes the circumference of a circle. The end point of the admittance vector describes a similar circle, but because of the factor $e^{-j\varphi_Z}$, the locus of its points is the mirror image of the first circle with respect to the real axis. As the frequency is increased, the head of the admittance vector moves along this circle in a clockwise sense (Fig. 2.10).

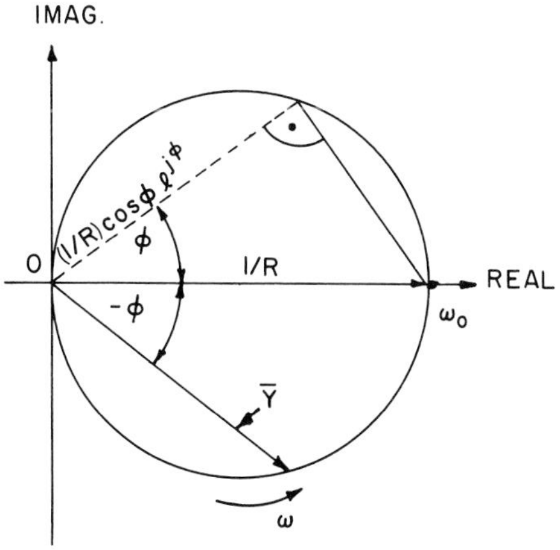

Fig. 2.10 Locus of the admittance in the complex plane of a series-resonant circuit.

Band Width, Decay Factor, and Logarithmic Decrement

The frequency curve of a complex mechanical vibrator usually exhibits many resonance peaks. If the peaks are separable, the shape of the frequency curve in the immediate vicinity of a resonance peak is always very similar to that of a simple mass compliance system. If the band width is defined as the width of the resonance curve in the immediate region of the peak, at a height not very much lower than that of the peak, the formulas that apply to the point-mass compliance system become applicable. A very suitable definition of the band width is based on the half-energy points. The half-energy band width, then, is the width of the resonance peak above a height of $1/\sqrt{2}$ (or 0.707) times that of the maximum, as indicated in Figure 2.11. Since the vibrational energy of a linear system is proportional to the square of the velocity amplitude, at the limits of the band width the velocity amplitude decreases to $1/\sqrt{2}$ of its value at the resonant frequency, and the vibrational energy is one half that at the resonant frequency.

The band width of a resonance curve is a measure of the damping of the system. To derive an expression for the damping, the height of the resonance peak

$$V_m = \frac{F}{R} \tag{2.49}$$

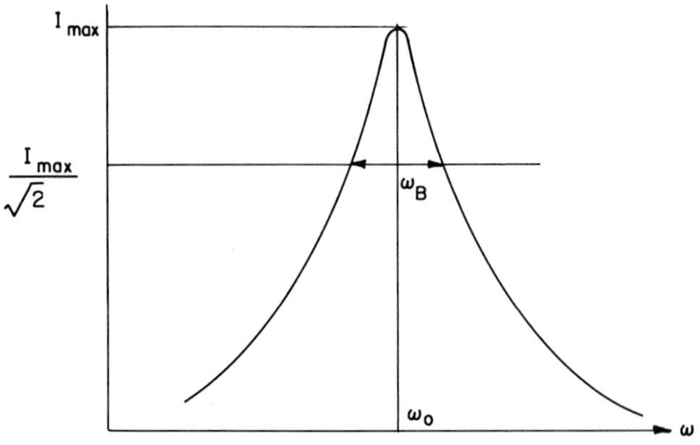

Fig. 2.11 Definition of band width.

is compared with the height of the resonance curve at the frequency limits of the band width. The height V of the resonance curve at any frequency is given by:

$$V=\frac{F}{R|1+jQ\underline{\nu}|}=\frac{F}{R\sqrt{(1+Q^2\underline{\nu}^2)}} \tag{2.50}$$

and the ratio V/V_m becomes:

$$\frac{V}{V_m}=\frac{1}{\sqrt{(1+Q^2\underline{\nu}^2)}} \tag{2.51}$$

By definition, this ratio is $1/\sqrt{2}$ for the limits of the band width. Hence,

$$\frac{1}{\sqrt{2}}=\frac{1}{\sqrt{(1+Q^2\underline{\nu}^2)}} \quad \text{or} \quad Q\underline{\nu}=\pm 1 \quad \text{and} \quad \underline{\nu}=\pm\frac{1}{Q} \tag{2.52}$$

The last equation can be solved for the frequencies that correspond to the two limits of the band width; they are given by:

$$\underline{\nu}=\underline{\nu}_1=\frac{1}{Q} \quad \text{and} \quad \underline{\nu}=\underline{\nu}_2=-\frac{1}{Q} \tag{2.53}$$

and the band width becomes:

$$\underline{\nu}_1-\underline{\nu}_2=\frac{\omega_1^2-\omega_2^2}{\omega_0^2}=\frac{(\omega_1+\omega_2)(\omega_1-\omega_2)}{\omega_0^2}\cong\frac{2\omega_0(\omega_1-\omega_2)}{\omega_0^2}=\frac{2}{Q} \tag{2.54}$$

or

$$\frac{\omega_1-\omega_2}{\omega_0}=\frac{1}{Q}=\eta \tag{2.55}$$

We have assumed that $\omega_1+\omega_2\doteq 2\omega_0$ and that Q and R are constant; this assumption is always admissible in the resonance range if the circuits are not overdamped. Thus, the relative band width is numerically equal to the loss factor $1/Q$ of the system.

Another measure for the energy absorption is the decay constant δ, which describes the rate of decay of the vibration amplitude of the system after the force has been removed. This decay constant is given by:

$$\delta = \frac{R}{2M} = \frac{\omega_0 R}{2\omega_0 M} = \frac{\omega_0 \eta}{2} \tag{2.56}$$

where

$$\eta = \frac{R}{\omega_0 M} = \omega_0 KR \tag{2.57}$$

is the loss factor of the system at its resonant frequency. Many modern instruments measure the logarithm of the amplitude, which is

$$\ln V = \ln V_0 e^{-\delta t} = \ln V_0 - \delta t \tag{2.58}$$

The decay curve then becomes a straight line, and the slope of this line is the decay constant:

$$\frac{\partial \ln V}{\partial t} = -\delta \text{ [Nepers per second]} \tag{2.59}$$

The decay time t_e is the time interval during which the amplitude decreases to $1/e$ times its initial value; it is given by:

$$\frac{V}{V_0} = \frac{V_0 e^{-\delta t_e}}{V_0} = e^{-1} \tag{2.60}$$

or

$$t_e = \frac{1}{\delta} = \frac{2}{\omega_0 \eta} = \frac{2Q}{\omega_0} \tag{2.61}$$

This relation (Eq. 2.61) shows that the decay time is proportional to the quality factor.

The logarithmic decrement Λ is defined as the logarithm of the ratio of successive maxima (Fig. 2.12):

$$\Lambda = \ln \frac{V_1}{V_2} = \ln \frac{V_0 e^{-\delta t_1}}{V_0 e^{-\delta t_2}} = \ln e^{\delta(t_2 - t_1)} = \delta(t_2 - t_1)$$
$$= \delta \frac{2\pi}{\omega_0{}^*} \cong \delta \cdot \frac{2\pi}{\omega_0} = \pi\eta \tag{2.62}$$

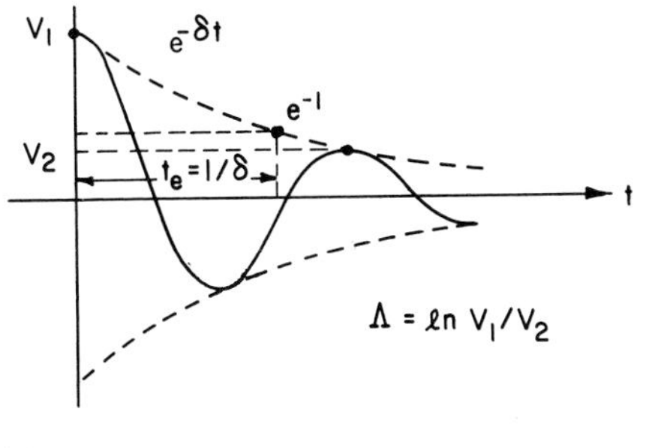

Fig. 2.12 Definition of logarithmic decrement.

On the right-hand side of the equation, $t_2 - t_1$ is the period $2\pi/\omega_0^*$ of the decaying vibration, and ω_0^* is the natural radial frequency. If damping is small (as in most cases of practical interest), $1/\omega_0^*$ may be replaced by $1/\omega_0$, where ω_0 is the resonant frequency, and the logarithmic decrement is π times the loss factor. The logarithmic decrement is a magnitude that is very rarely used today. In practical cases, the decay constant or the loss factor is much more useful.

Equation 2.61 was derived on the basis of the natural logarithm. Unity, then, implies a decay of the amplitude to $1/e$ of its initial value, two, a decay to $1/e^2$ of the initial value, and so on. This unit is called the Neper. Frequently, the decibel scale is used. This scale is obtained by forming the logarithm of the ratio of the powers or the energies to the base 10 (to obtain the Bell scale) and by multiplying the result by 10. The decibel scale represents a power ratio, and 10 dB. represent a power ratio of 1:10; 20 dB., a power ratio of $1{:}10^2 = 1{:}100$. The power can be expressed in terms of the amplitudes; in fact, the power is always proportional to the square of the amplitude. In the power ratio, the factor of proportionality cancels out, and the logarithm of a square is twice the logarithm of the linear quantity: power and amplitude are proportional to one another, and the factor of proportionality is 2. The power ratio can, therefore, be expressed just as well in terms of the amplitudes, but to obtain the decibel scale the multiplying factor is 20. Thus, we have $10 \log_{10}$ (power ratio)$=$ $20 \log_{10}$ (amplitude ratio), if decibels are used as the unit. The Neper scale is a logarithmic amplitude scale. The conversion factor between decibels and Nepers is derived as follows: let the amplitude ratio be ξ/ξ_0; then,

$$\frac{\xi}{\xi_0} = e^{ln(\xi/\xi_0)} \tag{2.63}$$

as is verified easily by taking the natural logarithm left and right. If the logarithm is formed to the base 10, and the result multiplied by 20:

$$20 \log_{10}\frac{\xi}{\xi_0} = 20 \log_{10} e^{ln(\xi/\xi_0)} = 20\, ln\frac{\xi}{\xi_0} \cdot \log_{10} e \tag{2.64}$$

In words, the ratio ξ/ξ_0 expressed in decibels is equal to

$$20 \log_{10} e = 8.69 \tag{2.65}$$

times the ratio ξ/ξ_0 expressed in Nepers. Thus, 1 Neper$=$8.69 dB.

Mechanical Parallel-Resonant Circuit

The only difference between a mechanical series-resonant circuit and a mechanical parallel-resonant circuit is the manner in which it is driven by the external force. In the series-resonant circuit, the force drives the mass;

in the antiresonant circuit (Fig. 2.13), the force drives the spring.

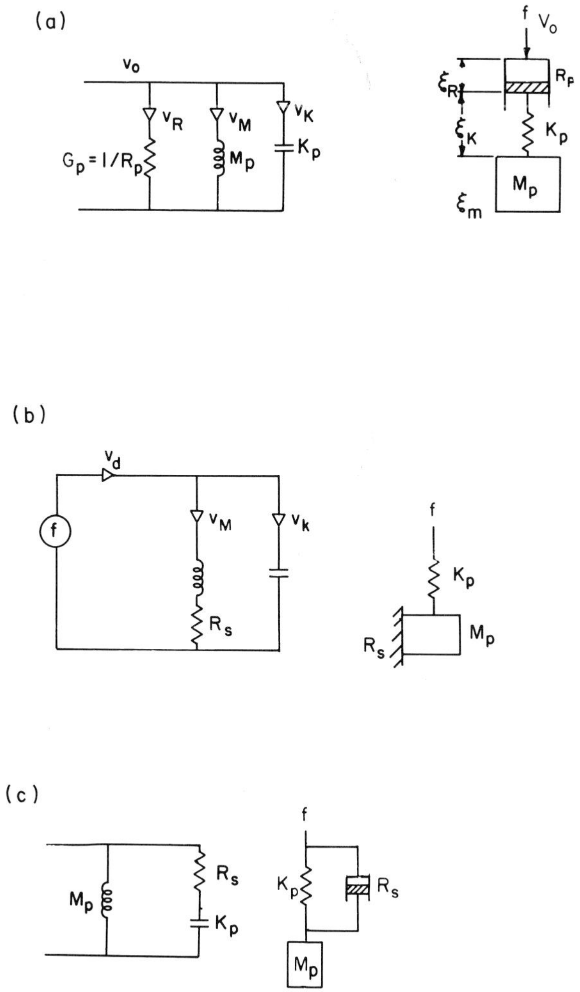

Fig. 2.13 Antiresonant circuit; *a*, loss resistance parallel to tuned circuit; *b*, loss resistance in series with inductance; *c*, loss resistance in series with capacity.

The antiresonant or parallel-resonant circuit (Fig. 2.13*a*) is the dual of the series-resonant circuit shown in Figure 2.1. The three elements in series in the series-resonant circuit are now in parallel. The mass is replaced by a compliance; the compliance, by a mass; and the resistance, by a conductance. Equivalent relations apply to the mechanical diagram. The results obtained for the velocity or the current in the series-resonant circuit now apply to the force or the voltage of the parallel-resonant circuit. Since the impedance of a series-resonant circuit can be condensed to the simple expression of Equation 2.26, it must be possible to obtain a similarly simple result for the admittance of the parallel-resonant circuit because of the dual properties. Since the three branches are in parallel, the admittances add:

$$Y_p = G_p + j\omega K_p + \frac{1}{j\omega M_p} = G_p + j\omega K_p\left(1 - \frac{1}{\omega^2 M_p K_p}\right)$$
$$= G_p\left(1 + \frac{j\omega_0 K_p}{G_p}\underline{\nu}\right) = G_p(1 + jQ_p\underline{\nu}) \tag{2.66}$$

where

$$\omega_0^2 = \frac{1}{K_p M_p} \quad \text{and} \quad \underline{\nu} = \frac{\omega}{\omega_0} - \frac{\omega_0}{\omega} \tag{2.67}$$

and

$$Q_p = \frac{\omega_0 K_p}{G_p} = \frac{1}{\omega_0 K_s R_s} = Q_s \tag{2.68}$$

is the quality factor of the system. The term Q_s is obtained with the aid of Equation 1.75.

The differential equations of the parallel resonator can be deduced from the picture of the system or from the circuit diagram (Fig. 2.13*a*), as follows: the dashpot and spring fully transmit the applied force to the driven mass; therefore,

$$f = f_R = f_K = f_M \qquad (u = u_R = u_C = u_L) \tag{2.69}$$

The forces that actuate the three elements are given by:

$$f_R = v_R R \quad f_K = \frac{\xi_R}{K} \quad f_M = M\ddot{\xi} \quad \left(u_R = Ri \quad u_C = \frac{q}{C} \quad u_L = L\ddot{q}\right) \tag{2.70}$$

Thus, three differential equations are needed to analyze the system in the classical manner. In contrast, the mechanical circuit diagram implicitly contains the boundary condition that the force on the spring be the same as that on the mass or that on the resistance, and the solution can be read directly from the diagram.

The antiresonant frequency of the circuit is defined as the frequency at which the current flowing into the parallel-resonant circuit is a minimum. This frequency is found most readily with the aid of the circuit shown in Figure 2.13*a*. The current is a minimum if the inductive and the capacitive currents compensate one another, that is, if

$$\tilde{\imath}_C + \tilde{\imath}_L = \frac{\tilde{u}}{\frac{1}{j\omega C}} + \frac{\tilde{u}}{j\omega L} = j\tilde{u}\left(\omega C - \frac{1}{\omega L}\right) = 0 \tag{2.71}$$

And the antiresonant frequency ω_p is given by the same expression as the series-resonant frequency:

$$\omega_p^2 = \omega_0^2 = \frac{1}{LC} \tag{2.72}$$

The impedance at the antiresonant frequency reduces to that of the parallel resistance:

$$(Z)_{\omega=\omega 0}=R_p \tag{2.73}$$

Frequently, the loss resistance is in series with the inductance (Fig.2.13*b*) or in series with the capacitance (Fig. 2.13*c*). The simplest method to obtain the antiresonant impedance and the antiresonant frequency is to transform the series combination into a parallel combination with the aid of the results derived in Chapter I. The impedance of the parallel-resonant circuit at the resonant frequency then becomes equal to the equivalent parallel resistance R_p of the series combination, as given by Equation 1.77:

$$R_p=X_s^2\frac{(1+\eta^2)}{R_s}\doteq\frac{X_s^2}{R_s}=Q_sX_s=Q_s^2R_s=\frac{\omega_0L}{R_s}\omega_0L=\frac{L_s}{CR_s} \tag{2.74}$$

since

$$Q=\frac{\omega_0L}{R}=\frac{1}{\omega_0CR}=\frac{1}{\eta} \quad \text{and} \quad \omega_0^2=\frac{1}{LC} \tag{2.75}$$

The effective reactance of the series combinations is given by Equation 1.79:

$$X_p=X_s(1+\eta^2) \tag{2.76}$$

and the exact value of the antiresonant frequency ω_p is given by:

$$X_p+X_p''=X_s(1+\eta^2)+X_p''=0 \tag{2.77}$$

where X_p'' is the reactance of the branch of the parallel-resonant circuit that does not contain the resistance. If $X_s=\omega_pL$ is the reactance of an inductance and $X_p''=-1/\omega_pC$ is the reactance of a capacitance, Equation 2.77 becomes:

$$\omega_pL(1+\eta^2)=\frac{1}{\omega_pC} \quad \text{or} \quad \omega_p^2=\frac{1}{(1+\eta^2)LC}=\frac{\omega_0^2}{1+\eta^2} \tag{2.78}$$

where

$$\omega_0^2=\frac{1}{LC} \tag{2.79}$$

is the antiresonant frequency of the circuit without resistance. If X_s is the reactance of a condenser and X_p'' that of an inductance, we obtain in a similar manner:

$$\omega_p^2=\omega_0^2(1+\eta^2) \tag{2.80}$$

Thus the series resistance changes the resonant frequency slightly. The distribution of the current between the two branches of the series-resonant circuit has already been discussed in Chapter I.

Resonant System as Amplitude, Force, or Voltage or Current Transformer

The resonance amplitude of a series-resonant system is proportional to the quality factor:

$$|\hat{\xi}| = \frac{F_0}{\omega_0 R} = \frac{F_0 K}{\omega_0 R K} = \xi_{st} Q \tag{2.81}$$

where

$$\xi_{st} = F_0 K \tag{2.82}$$

is the static deformation of the system under a force F_0. Since ξ is also the amplitude of the compliant element, the force that acts on this element is:

$$\frac{\xi}{K} = F_0 Q \tag{2.83}$$

Similarly, for an electrical circuit, the voltage at resonance across the capacitor or inductor is proportional to Q:

$$U = I\omega L = \frac{U_0}{R}\omega L = U_0 Q \tag{2.84}$$

where U_0 is the voltage applied to the series-resonant circuit. The circuit acts like a voltage transformer.

For an electrical parallel-resonant circuit consisting of the elements Z_1 and Z_2, the current through the reactive element Z_1 is:

$$I_1 = I_0 \cdot \frac{|\bar{Z}_2|}{|\bar{Z}_1 + \bar{Z}_2|} = \frac{I_0 \omega_0 L}{R} = I_0 Q \tag{2.85}$$

where i_0 is the current that flows into the antiresonant circuit and

$$\bar{Z}_1 + \bar{Z}_2 = R \quad \text{and} \quad Z_1 \doteq Z_2 \doteq \frac{1}{\omega_0 C} \doteq \omega_0 L \tag{2.86}$$

Similarly, for a mechanical antiresonant system

$$V_1 = Q V_0 \tag{2.87}$$

where V_1 is the velocity of the mass, and V_0, the velocity of the driven end of the spring (Fig. 2.13*c*).

The resonant amplitude of a series-resonant system is Q times greater than the static amplitude. For quartz, Q is about 10^6. Because of the great elastic strains, driving a quartz resonator with 0.4 v. may break it. For an antiresonant system, the situation is very similar, except that the driving point (terminals) and the observation point are interchanged.

Energy and the Dissipation of Energy by a Point-Mass Spring Vibrator

The energy equation is usually obtained as a first integral of the equations of motion. To derive this first integral, the equation of motion for the series-resonant circuit is multiplied by $\dot{\xi}$:

$$M\dot{\xi}\ddot{\xi}+R\dot{\xi}^2+\lambda\xi\dot{\xi}=f\dot{\xi} \tag{2.88}$$

which, when integrated with respect to time t, gives:

$$\frac{1}{2}M(\dot{\xi}_2{}^2-\dot{\xi}_1{}^2)+\int_0^t R\dot{\xi}^2dt+\frac{1}{2}\lambda(\xi_2{}^2-\xi_1{}^2)=\int_0^t f\frac{d\xi}{dt}dt=\int_{\xi_1}^{\xi_2} fd\xi \tag{2.89}$$

The first term represents the kinetic energy; the third, the potential energy. The second term denotes the energy dissipated in the resistance R, and the right-hand side of the equation represents the work performed by the external force f. In the absence of dissipation and of external forces, the energy E of the system is constant:

$$E=\frac{1}{2}Mv^2+\frac{1}{2}\lambda\xi^2=\text{const}=\frac{1}{2}MV^2=\frac{1}{2}\lambda\hat{\xi}^2 \tag{2.90}$$

At the instant when $\xi=0$, all the energy is kinetic; and when $v=0$, all the energy is potential. The constant is, therefore, equal to the maximum kinetic or maximum potential energy that the system can have, and the two energies are the same. The work performed by the force per period T of the vibration in driving the system is equal to the energy dissipated in the resistance:

$$W=\int_0^T Rv^2dt=\int_0^T RV^2\cos^2(\omega t+\varphi)dt=\frac{1}{2}RV^2T \tag{2.91}$$

This equation is equivalent to the well-known expression for the electrical work, i.e.,

$$W=\frac{1}{2}RI^2T \tag{2.92}$$

where I is the current amplitude. If the effective values are substituted, $I_{\text{eff}}=I/\sqrt{2}$, and the factor 1/2 drops out. The same result can be derived with the aid of the solution of the differential equation by directly evaluating the expression $<fv>$. If the external force is:

$$f=F\cos\omega t \tag{2.93}$$

the velocity will be given by:

$$v=V\cos(\omega t-\varphi) \tag{2.94}$$

where

$$\tan \varphi = \frac{X}{R} \quad \text{and} \quad \cos \varphi = \frac{R}{Z} \tag{2.95}$$

and φ is the phase angle of the mechanical impedance of the system. The work per period T then becomes:

$$W = \int_0^T f d\xi = \int_0^T f \frac{d\xi}{dt} dt = \int_0^T f v \, dt$$

$$= \int_0^T F \cos \omega t \, V \cos (\omega t + \varphi) \, dt$$

$$= \frac{FV}{2} \int_0^T [\cos (2\omega t + \varphi) + \cos \varphi] \, dt = \frac{FV}{2} T \cos \varphi \tag{2.96}$$

since the integral of the cosine vanishes over an integral number of periods. If the value for φ given by Equation 2.95 is substituted—and with the relation $F = VZ$ and $\eta = 1/Q = R\omega K$—the above result simplifies to:

$$W = T \cdot \frac{FV}{2} \frac{R}{Z} = T \cdot \frac{1}{2} R V^2 = \pi \eta \frac{V^2}{\omega^2 K} = \pi \lambda \eta \hat{\xi}^2 \tag{2.97}$$

where

$$R = \frac{\eta}{\omega K} \quad \text{and} \quad \lambda = \frac{1}{K} \tag{2.98}$$

Thus, the work in each period of the vibration is proportional to the loss factor η. This work is represented by the area enclosed by the force deformation curve in the f-ξ plane (Fig. 2.14). For harmonic vibrations, and in the range where Hooke's law is obeyed, this curve is always an ellipse, and

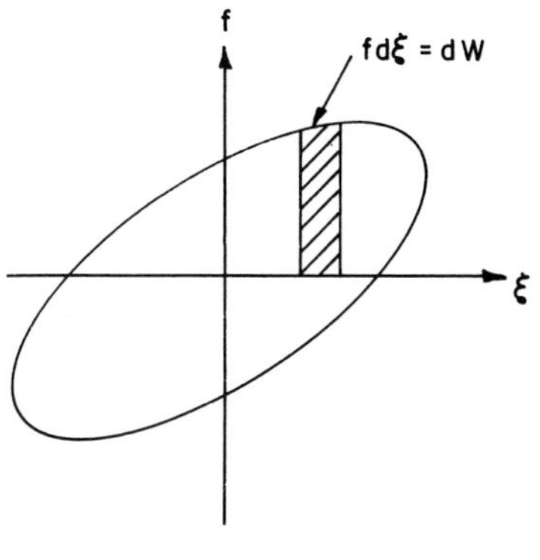

Fig. 2.14   Dissipation ellipse in the f-ξ plane.

its area measures the energy dissipated per cycle. To prove this, let $x = A\cos\omega t$ and $y = A\cos(\omega t+\phi) = A\cos\omega t\cos\phi - A\sin\omega t\sin\phi$. If $\cos\omega t$ and $\sin\omega t$ are eliminated in the second equation with the aid of the first equation, we obtain:

$$y = x\cos\phi - A\sqrt{1-\frac{x^2}{A^2}}\sin\phi \tag{2.99}$$

If the first term on the right is transferred to the left and the equation squared, we obtain the equation of an ellipse:

$$x^2 + y^2 - 2xy\cos\phi = A^2\sin^2\phi \tag{2.100}$$

If new axes inclined at an angle α with respect to the old ones are introduced:

$$\begin{aligned} x &= x'\cos\alpha + y'\sin\alpha \\ y &= -x'\sin\alpha + y'\cos\alpha \end{aligned} \tag{2.101}$$

the above equation becomes:

$$x'^2(1+\cos\phi\sin 2\alpha) + y'^2(1-\cos\phi\sin 2\alpha) + x'y'(\cos^2\alpha - \sin^2\alpha) = A^2\sin^2\phi \tag{2.102}$$

The term $x'y'$ vanishes if $\alpha = \pi/4$. Hence,

$$x'^2(1+\cos\phi) + y'^2(1-\cos\phi) = A^2\sin^2\phi \tag{2.103}$$

The axes of the ellipse are:

$$a = \frac{A\sin\phi}{\sqrt{1+\cos\phi}} \quad \text{and} \quad b = \frac{A\sin\phi}{\sqrt{1-\cos\phi}} \tag{2.104}$$

and the area of the ellipse is:

$$\pi ab = \frac{\pi A^2\sin^2\phi}{\sqrt{1-\cos^2\phi}} = \pi A^2\sin\phi \doteq \pi A^2\eta \tag{2.105}$$

If the loss angle $\tan^{-1}\eta$ is zero, the ellipse degenerates into a straight line, and no mechanical energy is dissipated into heat; the energy supplied to the system during one half of the cycle is returned to the driver during the second half of the cycle. As η becomes greater and the ellipse becomes broader, more work is dissipated into heat. The mechanism of this energy dissipation does not enter into consideration.

Equation 2.97 shows that the loss factor, except for a factor $1/2\pi$, is equal to the ratio of the energy dissipated per cycle to the total energy of the system. Thus,

$$\frac{1}{E}\frac{dE}{dt} = \frac{\pi\lambda\eta\hat{\xi}^2}{\dfrac{\lambda\hat{\xi}^2}{2}} = 2\pi\eta \tag{2.106}$$

The logarithmic decrement $\Lambda = \pi\eta$ is equal to half this ratio.

Build-Up and Decay of Forced Sinusoidal Vibrations

Let the driving force be zero previous to the instant $t=0$, and let

$$f=Re(\bar{F}e^{j\omega t})=F\cos(\omega t+\varphi_F) \tag{2.107}$$

for $t>0$. The solution for the vibration velocity of a point-mass compliance system is given by the sum of the solutions for the homogeneous differential equation and for forced vibrations, i.e., by:

$$\bar{v}=\bar{V}_t e^{(-\delta+j\omega_0{}^*)t}+\frac{\bar{F}}{\bar{Z}}e^{j\omega t}=\bar{V}_t e^{(-\delta+j\omega_0{}^*)t}+\bar{V}_f e^{j\omega t} \tag{2.108}$$

where

$$\bar{V}_t=V_t e^{j\varphi_t} \qquad \bar{F}=Fe^{j\varphi_F} \qquad \bar{Z}=Ze^{j\varphi_Z} \qquad \tan\varphi_Z=Q\underline{v}$$

$$\bar{V}_f=V_f e^{j(\varphi_F-\varphi_Z)}=V_f e^{j\alpha}=\frac{\bar{F}}{\bar{Z}} \quad \text{and} \quad \alpha=\varphi_F-\varphi_Z \tag{2.109}$$

The first term represents the transient part of the solution, and the second, the forced vibration. The displacement is obtained by integrating the above expression:

$$\bar{\xi}=\int_0^t \bar{v}dt=\frac{\bar{V}_t}{-\delta+j\omega_0{}^*}e^{(-\delta+j\omega_0{}^*)t}+\frac{V_f e^{j\alpha}}{j\omega}e^{j\omega t} \tag{2.110}$$

In the denominator,

$$|-\delta+j\omega_0{}^*|=\sqrt{\delta^2+\omega_0{}^{*2}}\doteq\omega_0 \tag{2.111}$$

and the real solution becomes:

$$\begin{aligned} v&=Re(\bar{v})=V_t e^{-\delta t}\cos(\omega_0 t+\varphi_t)+V_f\cos(\omega t+\alpha)\\ \xi&=Re(\bar{\xi})=\hat{\xi}_t e^{-\delta t}\sin(\omega_0 t+\varphi_t)+\hat{\xi}_f\sin(\omega t+\alpha) \end{aligned} \tag{2.112}$$

where

$$\hat{\xi}_t=\frac{V_t}{\omega_0} \qquad \hat{\xi}_f=\frac{V_f}{\omega} \quad \text{and} \quad \tan\varphi_t=\frac{\omega_0}{\delta} \tag{2.113}$$

represent the initial displacement amplitude of the transient and the forced vibrations, respectively. The integration constants V_t and φ_t are determined by the initial conditions. If the system was at rest at $t=0$,

$$0=(v)_{t=0}=V_t\cos\varphi_t+V_f\cos\alpha \tag{2.114}$$

and

$$0=(\xi)_{t=0}=\xi_t\sin\varphi_t+\xi_f\sin\alpha \tag{2.115}$$

By using Equation 2.111 and expressing the displacements in terms of the velocities, the last two equations may be written as follows:

$$V_t\cos\varphi_t=-V_f\cos\alpha \tag{2.116}$$

and

$$V_t\sin\varphi_t=-V_f\frac{\omega_0}{\omega}\sin\alpha \tag{2.117}$$

The phase of the transient oscillation φ_t is obtained by dividing the second equation by the first:

$$\tan \varphi_t = \frac{\omega_0}{\omega} \tan \alpha \tag{2.118}$$

The velocity amplitude V_t of the transient oscillation is obtained by squaring and adding the two equations:

$$V_t^2 = V_f^2\left(\cos^2 \alpha + \frac{\omega_0^2}{\omega^2} \sin^2 \alpha\right) \tag{2.119}$$

or

$$\frac{V_t}{V_f} = \left(\cos^2 \alpha + \frac{\omega_0^2}{\omega^2} \sin^2 \alpha\right)^{\frac{1}{2}} \tag{2.120}$$

The displacement amplitude is given by:

$$\frac{\xi_t}{\xi_f} = \frac{\omega}{\omega_0} \cdot \frac{V_t}{V_f} = \left(\frac{\omega^2}{\omega_0^2} \cos^2 \alpha + \sin^2 \alpha\right)^{\frac{1}{2}} \tag{2.121}$$

where

$$\alpha = \varphi_F - \varphi_Z \tag{2.122}$$

The amplitude of the transient vibration that is generated when the external force is applied to the system is a function of the frequency ratio ω/ω_0, of the phase of the force φ_F when the motion is started, and of the phase φ_Z of the mechanical impedance.

The transient response of a point-mass compliance system is summarized in Table 2.1. If the force is applied at the instant of its maximum amplitude, the forced amplitude and the initial amplitude of the transient vibration are the same at all frequencies. The velocity amplitude of the transient oscillation is then greater than that of the forced vibrations at the lower frequencies. A force applied at its zero value generates a transient whose velocity amplitude is the same as that of the forced oscillation. The displacement amplitude of the transient then increases with increasing frequency.

When the force is removed, the forced vibration stops immediately, and velocity and displacement then decay to zero in the manner prescribed by the homogeneous solution. Thus,

$$\tilde{v} = \bar{V}_t e^{-\delta t + j\omega_0^* t} \tag{2.123}$$

and because of Equation 2.110:

$$\tilde{\xi} = \frac{\bar{V}_t}{-\delta + j\omega_0^*} e^{-\delta t + j\omega_0^* t} \doteq \frac{\bar{V}_t}{j\omega_0} e^{-\delta t + j\omega_0^* t} \tag{2.124}$$

The real solution of the decaying vibration is:

$$v = Re(\tilde{v}) = V_t e^{-\delta t} \cos(\omega_0^* t + \varphi_t) \tag{2.125}$$

and

$$\xi = Re(\tilde{\xi}) \doteq \frac{V_t}{\omega_0} e^{-\delta t} \sin(\omega_0^* t + \varphi_t) \tag{2.126}$$

Table 2.1 *The transient response of a point-mass compliance system.*

	Force Applied at Its Maximum Value $\varphi_F=0$			Force Applied at Its Zero Value $\varphi_F=-\frac{\pi}{2}$		
	$\omega\to 0$	$\omega=\omega_0$	$\omega\to\infty$	$\omega\to 0$	$\omega=\omega_0$	$\omega\to\infty$
Phase angle of mechanical impedance φ_Z	$-\frac{\pi}{2}$	0	$\frac{\pi}{2}$	$-\frac{\pi}{2}$	0	$\frac{\pi}{2}$
Phase of forced vibration $\alpha=\varphi_F-\varphi_Z$	$\frac{\pi}{2}$	0	$-\frac{\pi}{2}$	0	$-\frac{\pi}{2}$	$-\pi$
Phase of transient vibration φ_t	$\frac{\pi}{2}$	0	$-\frac{\pi}{2}$	0	$-\frac{\pi}{2}$	0
Ratio of transient to forced velocity amplitude V_t/V_f	$\frac{\omega_0}{\omega}$	1	$\frac{\omega}{\omega_0}$	1	1	1
Ratio of transient to forced displacement amplitude ξ_t/ξ_f	1	1	1	$\frac{\omega}{\omega_0}$	1	$\frac{\omega}{\omega_0}$

If at the instant the force is removed $v=v_0$ and $\xi=\xi_0$, and if this instant is selected as zero time $t=0$:

$$v_0=V_t\cos\varphi_t \tag{2.127}$$

and

$$\xi_0=\frac{V_t}{\omega_0}\sin\varphi_t \tag{2.128}$$

The two equations determine the integration constants V_t and φ_t:

$$\tan\varphi_t=\frac{\omega_0\xi_0}{V_0} \quad\text{and}\quad V_t=\sqrt{\omega_0^2\xi_0^2+V_0^2} \tag{2.129}$$

The vibration then decays exponentially with the natural frequency of the system, irrespective of how it was driven.

The preceding results show that the natural vibration of the system is excited when a periodic force is applied or removed from the system. Figure 2.15*a* shows the build-up of the forced vibration when the system is excited by a periodic force whose frequency is lower than the natural frequency of the system. The natural vibration decays exponentially with time. After a certain time, only the forced vibration is discernible. Excitation

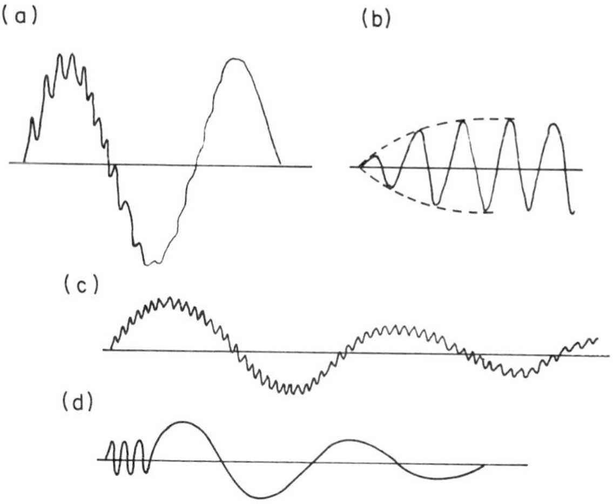

Fig. 2.15 Build-up and decay of the vibration of a tuned system excited by a periodic force; *a*, whose frequency is below the resonant frequency of the system; *b*, whose frequency is equal to the resonant frequency of the system; *c*, whose frequency is above the resonant frequency of the system; *d*, the decay of the natural vibration after the excitation has been cut off.

with the resonant frequency leads to the well-known curve that is shown in Figure 2.15*b* and that usually is reproduced in all the textbooks on vibrations. Figure 2.15*c* is of particular interest; it shows that a high-frequency force excites low-frequency transients with particularly high amplitudes. This phenomenon is important for musical instruments; it shows that low-frequency transients are excited in high-frequency music. Since these transients are imperative for the quality of a musical instrument, the musical instrument will sound inferior if its low-frequency response is inferior, even if a high-pitched tune is played.

After the excitation is stopped, the system decays in its natural vibration (Fig. 2.15*d*), regardless of what the frequency of its excitation was.

The Three Fundamental Types of Friction

Fluid Friction (constant loss resistance)

The preceding derivations have been performed on the assumption that the loss resistance is constant and that the friction force is proportional to the velocity. This is typical of fluid friction. The frequency of the natural vibrations was found to decrease with damping, and the vibrations decayed aperiodically when the damping exceeded critical damping.

Solid Friction (loss resistance decreasing in inverse proportion to the frequency)

In mechanical systems, the compliance is usually the element that dissipates vibrational energy into heat, and the loss resistance is no longer arbitrarily variable, but becomes a property of the compliance and of the frequency. The loss resistance of the compliance is independent of the other elements of the tuned system, since it is generated by the compliance alone and does not depend on whether the compliance is actuated by a moving mass or by a force directly applied to it. If the compliance generates the losses, the following definition for the quality factor is preferable to that given by Equation 2.34:

$$Q' = \frac{\frac{1}{\omega K}}{R} = \frac{1}{\omega K R} \tag{2.130}$$

The quality factor Q' depends only on the material of which the compliant element is constructed and represents a material constant. In general, Q' will be a function of the frequency. Experimental results show that for most solids the quality factor Q' is approximately constant in the audio-frequency range; the loss resistance then decreases in inverse proportion to the frequency:[1]

$$R = \frac{1}{\omega K Q'} = \frac{\text{const}}{\omega} \tag{2.131}$$

Since such a loss resistance is characteristic for elastic deformation of most solids, this type of internal friction is called solid friction. For solid friction (constant Q'), the following expression for the mechanical impedance is convenient:

$$\begin{aligned} \bar{Z} &= R + j\omega M + \frac{1}{j\omega K} = R + \frac{j}{\omega K}(\omega^2 M K - 1) \\ &= R + \frac{j}{\omega K}\left(\frac{\omega^2}{\omega_0^2} - 1\right) \\ &= R\left[1 + \frac{j}{\omega K R}\left(\frac{\omega^2}{\omega_0^2} - 1\right)\right] \\ &= R(1 + jQ'v') \end{aligned} \tag{2.132}$$

where

$$Q' = \frac{1}{\omega K R} = \text{const} = \frac{\omega_0}{\omega}\frac{1}{\omega_0 K R} = \left(\frac{\omega_0}{\omega}\right) Q \tag{2.133}$$

[1] See Eq. 2.38. The steady-state solutions (Eq. 2.23) represent the vibration of the system for a sinusoidally varying force, regardless of whether the parameters M, R, and λ are constants or depend on the frequency. But the solution of the homogeneous differential equation depends on the frequency variation of the parameters of the system, as will be shown later.

$$R=\frac{1}{\omega K Q'}=\frac{R_0\omega_0}{\omega} \quad \text{and} \quad R_0=\text{const}=\frac{1}{\omega_0 K Q} \tag{2.134}$$

$$\nu'=\frac{\omega^2}{\omega_0{}^2}-1=\frac{\omega}{\omega_0}\left(\frac{\omega}{\omega_0}-\frac{\omega_0}{\omega}\right)=\frac{\omega}{\omega_0}\nu \tag{2.135}$$

and Q and ν are the parameters given by Equations 2.34 and 2.27. In the resonance range $\omega \cong \omega_0$, both Q and Q' and ν and ν' are practically equal, so that there is no need to distinguish between the different definitions of these magnitudes. Furthermore,

$$Q\nu \equiv Q'\nu' \tag{2.136}$$

at all frequencies. But regardless of whether the parameters Q' and ν' or Q and ν are used, the resistance R that occurs as a factor in Equation 2.33 or 2.132 for the impedance is the resistance at the actual frequency of the vibration.

Most of the network computations are based on the assumption of a constant R. The variables Q and ν are, then, the proper ones. Most of the mechanical equations are based on the assumption of solid friction, that is, on the assumption of a loss resistance that decreases in inverse proportion to the frequency. The variables Q' and ν' are, then, the proper ones. Since most formulas contain only the product $Q\nu$, and since $Q\nu = Q'\nu'$, the type of friction need not be specified, and the primes will usually be dropped for the sake of a simple notation.

In the resonance range, the frequency response curve for a system with solid friction is very similar to that for a system with liquid friction ($R=$ constant). But because the resistance $R=R_0\omega_0/\omega$ is inversely proportional to the frequency, the velocity amplitude is smaller at the lower frequencies than that for a system governed by fluid friction, for we have:

$$\tilde{\xi}=\frac{\tilde{f}}{\dfrac{R\omega_0}{\omega}+j\omega M+\dfrac{1}{j\omega K}}=\frac{j\omega\tilde{f}K}{1+j\omega_0 K R_0-\omega^2 MK}=\frac{j\omega\tilde{f}K}{1-\dfrac{\omega^2}{\omega_0{}^2}+j\eta_0} \tag{2.137}$$

and

$$\tilde{\xi}=\frac{\tilde{f}K}{1-\dfrac{\omega^2}{\omega_0{}^2}+j\eta_0} \tag{2.138}$$

which differs by the term $j\eta_0$ (instead of $jR\omega K$) in the denominator from the expression for fluid friction.

In contrast to fluid friction, the decaying vibration has a natural frequency that is greater than the resonant frequency. This is proved by solving the differential equation for a decaying vibration:

$$M\ddot{\xi}+\frac{R_0\omega_0}{\omega}\dot{\xi}+\frac{1}{K}\xi=0 \tag{2.139}$$

This equation contains the frequency. Hence, it applies only to strictly periodic vibrations. However, if damping is not very great, $\dot{\xi}$ can be replaced by $j\omega_0{}^*\ddot{\xi}=j\omega_0\ddot{\xi}$ in the friction term, and the equation simplifies to:

$$\ddot{\xi}+\frac{1}{MK}(1+j\omega_0 R_0 K)\xi=0 \qquad \text{or to} \qquad \ddot{\xi}+\frac{1}{MK}(1+j\eta)\xi=0 \tag{2.140}$$

The assumption that the resistance is inversely proportional to the frequency or that the loss factor is exactly constant can never be absolutely correct, because (as will be shown later) the loss factor represents the imaginary part of an analytic function and must depend on the frequency. However, this assumption represents a very good approximation in many practical cases. The transition to Equation 2.140, then, is equivalent to applying a perturbation method. It seems that this equation is a better approximation than the starting equation (2.139), provided that the loss factor is constant in the frequency range of interest. This will become clearer in the next chapter. We shall, therefore, postulate this equation or consider it as an equation that defines the properties of ideal solid friction. The trial solution (Eq. 2.7), then, leads to:

$$p^2+\omega_0{}^2(1+j\eta)=0 \tag{2.141}$$

or

$$\begin{aligned} p&=\pm j\omega_0\sqrt{1+j\eta}\\ &=\pm\frac{j\omega_0}{2}\left[(1+\sqrt{1+\eta^2})+\frac{j\eta}{1+\sqrt{1+\eta^2}}\right]\\ &=j\omega_0\left[\left(1+\frac{\eta^2}{8}\right)+j\frac{\eta}{2}\right]+\ \ldots \end{aligned} \tag{2.142}$$

The second form of the right-hand side is obtained by evaluationg the square root in an exact manner; the third, by series development. The frequency of the decaying vibrations

$$\omega_0{}^*=\omega_0\left(1+\frac{\eta^2}{8}\right) \tag{2.143}$$

is greater than the resonant frequency, and the decay constant is

$$\delta=\omega_0\frac{\eta}{2} \tag{2.144}$$

as it is for fluid friction. Aperiodic vibrations do not occur, regardless of how great the damping may be.

The solution for the decaying vibration can also be derived by an exact process. Equation 2.139 applies to strictly periodic vibrations. If we replace the zero on the right by a constant periodic force, multiply left and right by $e^{j\omega t}$ and integrate over frequency space, the right hand side turns into a pulse that is generated at t=0. At the left, $\ddot{\xi}(\omega)$ and $\xi(\omega)$ are transformed into $\ddot{\xi}$(t) and ξ(t), and the middle term represents a spectral function that contains two factors in the integrand; this integral can be written as a convolution integral

$$\int \dot{\xi}(\omega)R(\omega)e^{j\omega t}dt = \int \dot{\xi}(t'-t)\, r(t')dt' \tag{2.145}$$

of the two time functions, whose spectra are given by $\dot{\xi}(\omega)$ and $R(\omega)$ respectively. A trial solution can then be derived by solving Equation 2.139 for a constant periodic force on the right hand side, and interpreting $\xi(\omega)$ as the Fourier component of the displacement if the system is excited by an infinitely short pulse. Fourier integration then leads to the above decaying solution, and to Equation 2.143. That this is indeed the solution then is proved by substitution into the transformed equation.

Constant or Coulomb Friction

This type of friction occasionally occurs in heavy machinery, but it is seldom encountered in simple vibrators. Coulomb friction is proportional to the weight of the moving part, but is independent of its velocity. The differential equation of motion, then, is:

$$m\ddot{\xi} + \lambda(\xi \pm \Delta) = f \tag{2.146}$$

where the friction term Δ is approximately constant (if the mass moves) and is infinite until the force on the body exceeds a certain limiting value. The sign of Δ is such that it always opposes the motion. Coulomb friction is not discussed in this book, and none of the formulas apply to it.[2]

[2] Coulomb friction is much harder to handle in mathematical computations; it is frequently replaced by an equivalent velocity-proportional friction. A very good representation of Coulomb friction is given by L. S. Jacobson and R. S. Ayre, *Engineering Vibrations* (New York, 1958), chap. 5.

Recommended Reading

BERANEK, L. L., *Acoustics,* McGraw-Hill, Inc., New York, 1954.

BICKLEY, W. C., AND A. TALBOT, *An Introduction to the Theory of Vibrating Systems,* Oxford University Press, Inc., New York, 1961, chaps. 1–4.

CHURCH, A. H., *Elementary Mechanical Vibrations,* Pitman Publishing Corporation, New York, 1948, chaps. 1–6.

DEN HARTOG, J. P., *Mechanical Vibrations,* McGraw-Hill, Inc., New York, 1947, chaps. 1–2.

GARDNER, M. F., AND J. L. BARNES, *Transients in Linear Systems,* John Wiley & Sons, Inc., New York, 1942

GEIGER-SCHEEL, *Handbuch der Physik: Akustik,* vol. VIII.

HANSEN, H. M., AND P. F. CHENEA, *Mechanics of Vibration,* John Wiley & Sons, Inc., New York, 1952.

HARMS-WIEN, *Handbuch der experimental Phystik, Akustik,* vol. XVIII, part 2.

HARRIS, C. M., AND C. E. CREDE, *Shock and Vibration Handbook,* McGraw-Hill, Inc., New York, 1961, vol. I.

JACOBSON, L. S., AND R. S. AYRE, *Engineering Vibrations,* McGraw-Hill, Inc., New York, 1951, chap. 1.

KÁRMÁN, T. VON, AND M. A. BIOT, *Mathematical Methods in Engineering,* McGraw-Hill, Inc., New York, 1940.

KIMBAL, A. L., *Vibration Prevention in Engineering,* John Wiley & Sons, Inc., New York, 1946, chaps. 1–4.

MYKLESTAD, N. O., *Vibration Analysis,* McGraw-Hill, Inc., New York, 1944, chaps. 1–4.

POESCHL, T., "Das Anlaufen eines einfachen Schwingers," *Ing. Archiv.,* **4** (1933), 98–102.

RAYLEIGH, LORD, *The Theory of Sound,* Macmillan and Co., Ltd., London, 1894, vol. I.

TIMOSHENKO, S., *Vibration Problems in Engineering,* D. Van Nostrand Company, Inc., Princeton, N.J., 1937.

TRIMMER, J. D., *Response of Physical Systems,* John Wiley & Sons, Inc., New York, 1950, chap. 4.

ZOLLICH, H., "Pruefung von Messgeraeten zur Aufzeichnung sich rasch veraendernder," *Grössen. Wissen. Abhandl. Siemens-Konzern,* **1** (1920), 24–63.

III / LOSS FACTOR, COMPLEX MASS, AND COMPLEX ELASTIC CONSTANTS

In discussing friction we usually distinguish between external velocity-proportional friction and internal friction. Constant or Coulomb friction is not considered here.

Loss Factor for External Velocity-Proportional Friction

External friction is the friction that is determined by displacement and time derivatives—e.g., sliding friction, the friction generated by a dashpot, or the reaction of the system to sound radiation. External friction is usually dependent on the mass, but it is independent of the compliance of the system. It can be represented by a resistance R_e, which, in general, is frequency-dependent. For periodic motion, the loss resistance R_e due to external friction can be combined with the mass of the system to form a complex mass $\bar{M}$.[1] Since

$$\frac{\partial \xi}{\partial t} = \frac{1}{j\omega}\frac{\partial^2 \xi}{\partial t^2} \tag{3.1}$$

the differential equation for the motion of the system of mass M_0 can be written as follows:

$$\begin{aligned}\left(M_0\frac{d^2\xi}{dt^2} + R_e\frac{d\xi}{dt}\right) + \frac{1}{K}\xi &= M_0\left(1 - j\frac{R_e}{\omega M_0}\right)\frac{d^2\xi}{dt^2} + \frac{1}{K}\xi \\ &= M_0(1 - j\eta_M)\frac{d^2\xi}{dt^2} + \frac{1}{K}\xi = f\end{aligned} \tag{3.2}$$

or

$$\bar{M}\frac{d^2\xi}{dt^2} + \frac{1}{K}\xi = f \tag{3.3}$$

where

$$\eta_M = \frac{R_e}{\omega M_0} \qquad \text{and} \qquad \bar{M} = M_0(1 - j\eta_M) \tag{3.4}$$

[1] For a point-mass compliance system, the loss resistance due to external friction can also be lumped with the elastic-restoring force by writing the friction term in the form $R_e \cdot \partial\xi/\partial t = j\omega R_e\, \xi$. But a similar procedure would not be permissible for systems with continuously distributed parameters, where the elastic-restoring force is proportional to the curvature of some other more complex function of the amplitude.

Since η_M is almost always a small quantity, its square can be neglected, and

$$M = |\bar{M}| = |M_0(1 - j\eta_M)| = M_0 \sqrt{1+\eta_M{}^2} \doteq M_0 \tag{3.5}$$

The real part of $\bar{M}$ and its absolute value are the same, except for squares and higher powers of η_M; the subscript zero of $M_0 \doteq M$ can be dropped for the sake of a simpler notation. The magnitude η_M may be defined as the loss factor due to external friction, and the magnitude $\bar{M}$, as the complex mass of the system. The loss factor, then, is a very convenient parameter for describing the vibrational behavior of the system. Introducing the loss factor of an element is merely another way of expressing the loss resistance in a dimensionless manner.

Loss Factor for Internal Friction

In contrast to external friction, internal friction is generated by the deformation of compliant elements. The corresponding loss resistances are functions of the compliant elements, and it becomes expedient to combine them with the compliances in the equation of motion, as follows:

$$M\frac{d^2\xi}{dt^2} + \frac{1}{K}\xi + R\frac{d\xi}{dt} = M\frac{d^2\xi}{dt^2} + \frac{1}{K}(1 + j\omega RK)\xi = M\frac{d^2\xi}{dt^2} + \frac{1}{K}(1 + j\eta)\xi = \tilde{f} \tag{3.6}$$

or

$$M\frac{d^2\xi}{dt^2} + \bar{\lambda}\xi = \tilde{f} \tag{3.7}$$

where

$$\bar{\lambda} = \frac{1}{K}(1 + j\eta) = \lambda_0(1 + j\eta) \tag{3.8}$$

is the complex spring constant and

$$\eta = \omega KR = \frac{1}{Q} \tag{3.9}$$

is its loss factor. The magnitude

$$\bar{\lambda} = \frac{1}{K} + j\omega R = \frac{1}{K}(1 + j\omega KR) = \lambda_0(1 + j\eta) \tag{3.10}$$

plays the same role in the dissipative system as the stiffness constant in the ideal nondissipative system; it can be interpreted as the complex stiffness of the system. Its real part $\lambda_0 = 1/K$ describes the stiffness; its imaginary part is proportional to the loss factor $\eta = \omega KR$, as defined in the preceding chapter.

Equation 3.10 shows that for strictly periodic vibrations the loss resistance and the stiffness constant can be condensed into a single complex stiffness constant, the real part of which describes the stiffness, and the imaginary part, the loss factor of the system. The real part and the imaginary part of the complex stiffness constant can be easily determined experimentally by constructing a point-mass compliant element system and measuring its resonant frequency and band width. The real part of the stiffness constant is proportional to the square of the resonant frequency; the imaginary part, to the relative band width of the resonance curve.

No new physical concept has been introduced. All we have gained up to this point is a condensed notation. The loss resistance has been lumped with the elastic constant. The reader should convince himself that the real part of the steady-state solution that is obtained in this way is identical with the standard classical solution.

Complex Elastic Constant

In the preceding discussion, resistance and compliance are constants that are independent of each other; they depend on the properties and on the size of the system. Because of the assumption of strictly harmonic motion, displacement and velocity are proportional to one another, and it becomes possible to combine the two independent constants to one complex constant, which is called the complex stiffness constant of the system.

The losses are not generally due to dashpots, whose magnitudes can be randomly varied, but are generated by the internal friction of the compliant elements; loss resistance and stiffness are no longer independent of one another, but are determined by the elastic and dissipative properties of the material that is used for the compliant elements. Since the stiffness constant is proportional to the elastic modulus, elastic and dissipative properties of the compliant elements can be described by a complex elastic modulus:

$$\bar{\lambda} = \lambda_0(1 + j\eta) \doteq \lambda(1 + j\eta) \tag{3.11}$$

+terms in η^2 and higher powers of η. The magnitude η is usually small as compared to 1, and λ_0 and $|\bar{\lambda}| = \lambda_0 \sqrt{1+\eta^2} = \lambda$ are substantially the same, so that the subscript zero (to denote real part) can be dropped for the sake of a simpler notation. A similar simplification has already been used in Equation 3.5 for the complex mass.

The stiffness constant is defined as the ratio of the total force that acts on the compliant element to the deflection of this element that is produced by this force. If the compliant element is a rod of cross section σ and length l, the stiffness constant is:

$$\bar{\lambda} = \frac{\tilde{f}}{\tilde{\xi}} = \frac{\tilde{f}}{\dfrac{\tilde{f} l}{\sigma \bar{\lambda}_E}} = \frac{\sigma \bar{\lambda}_E}{l} = \frac{\sigma \lambda_E}{l}(1 + j\eta_E) = \lambda_0(1 + j\eta_E) \tag{3.12}$$

where σ denotes the cross section of the rod $\sigma\lambda_E/l=\lambda_0$; $\bar{\lambda}_E$ is Young's modulus, and η_E is the loss factor for deformations that are described by Young's modulus.

Equation 3.12 shows that the loss factor of the compliant rod is the same as that of the elastic constant of the material of which the compliant rod is made. Thus, by introducing a complex elastic constant, the losses of the system can be expressed in terms of a constant of the elastic material used for the compliant elements.

Because of the phase angle of the complex elastic constant, the stress leads the strain. To prove this, let the elastic constant be written as a complex exponential: Since $e^x=1+x+\ldots$,

$$\bar{\lambda}=\lambda_0(1+j\eta)\doteq\lambda_0 e^{j\eta} \tag{3.13}$$

where squares and higher powers of η have been neglected. The ratio of the stress to the strain then becomes:

$$\frac{\tilde{f}}{\tilde{\xi}}=\frac{\bar{F}e^{j\omega t}}{\bar{\xi}e^{j\omega t}}=\frac{\hat{F}e^{j(\omega t+\varphi_F)}}{\hat{\xi}e^{j(\omega t+\varphi_\xi)}}=\bar{\lambda}=\lambda_0 e^{j\eta} \tag{3.14}$$

or

$$\tilde{f}=\bar{F}e^{j(\omega t+\varphi_F)}=\lambda_0\hat{\xi}e^{j(\omega t+\eta+\varphi_\xi)} \tag{3.15}$$

In the last two formulas, ξ is written to represent the strain. For a simple compliant element, the strain is proportional to the displacement. Since the exponents, left and right, must be the same,

$$\varphi_F=\varphi_\xi+\eta \tag{3.16}$$

and the stress leads the deformation by an angle that is equal to the loss factor η. Since η also is the phase angle between force and displacement, Equation 2.97 applies, and η also describes the energy that is dissipated into heat per cycle of the vibration.

The physical significance of a complex elastic constant may be derived as follows: A "real" elastic constant expresses the ratio of a certain type of stress to the corresponding strain when equilibrium is reached. During periodic motion, stresses and strains change periodically. The complex elastic constant can, therefore, be defined as the ratio of the rotating vectors that represent the periodically varying stress to the strain.

However, the stresses are usually complicated functions of the strains and of the history of the motion. The history of the motion is known, if the stresses and the strains are given as functions of the time. If certain conditions are fulfilled, these functions can be developed into Taylor series:

$$f(t)=f(0)+tf'(0)+\frac{t^2}{2}f''(0)\ldots \tag{3.17}$$

where

$$f^\nu(0)=\left[\frac{\partial^\nu f(t)}{\partial t^\nu}\right]_{t=0} \tag{3.18}$$

and t is the variable. Provided that the series converges, the Taylor coefficients $f^{\nu}(0)$ contain complete information about the motion from $t=0$ to any value of t for which the series will converge. The Taylor coefficients $f^{\nu}(0)$ are, therefore, representative of the history of the function. For harmonic motion, the history of the motion is well known—it is a harmonic variation—and the Fourier series always converges. The relationship that the stresses $\sigma(t)$ and their history are a function of the strains $\epsilon(t)$ and their history can, therefore, be written in the following form:

$$f_1(\sigma, \sigma', \sigma'') = f_2(\epsilon, \epsilon', \epsilon'', \ldots) \tag{3.19}$$

The quantity σ now represents the stress, and the primes represent derivatives with respect to time. As long as Hooke's law, which we assume to hold also for the derivatives, is satisfied, the above functions can be replaced by their Taylor series, and the nonlinear terms can be neglected:

$$\sigma + \alpha_1\sigma' + \alpha_2\sigma'' + \ldots = \lambda^{(0)}(\epsilon + \beta_1\epsilon' + \beta_2\epsilon'' \ldots) \tag{3.20}$$

The Taylor coefficients α_1, α_2, $\lambda^{(0)}$, and β_1, β_2 . . . can be interpreted as the elastic constants of the substance. In general, a substance that contains N molecules has 3 N degrees of freedom and consequently may have as many as 3 N elastic constants. Mathematically, Equation 3.20 represents a linear differential equation for the time variation of the strains if the stresses are prescribed or for the time variation of the stresses if the strains are prescribed.

For the ideal elastic fluid, all the α_ν and β_ν are zero, and the stresses become proportional to the strains:

$$\sigma = \lambda^{(0)}\epsilon \tag{3.21}$$

If only the coefficient of the first time derivative on the right is different from zero

$$\sigma = \lambda^{(0)}\left(\epsilon + \beta\frac{\partial\epsilon}{\partial t}\right) \tag{3.22}$$

fluid friction results. If the Taylor coefficients of the first time derivative on the left and on the right of Equation 3.20 are different from zero, the relaxation equation is obtained:

$$\sigma + \alpha_1\frac{\partial\sigma}{\partial t} = \lambda^{(0)}\left(\epsilon + \beta_1\frac{\partial\epsilon}{\partial t}\right) \tag{3.23}$$

If the first two time derivatives, left and right, are retained:

$$\sigma + \alpha_1\frac{\partial\sigma}{\partial t} + \alpha_2\frac{\partial^2\sigma}{\partial t^2} = \lambda^{(0)}\left(\epsilon + \beta_1\frac{\partial\epsilon}{\partial t} + \beta_2\frac{\partial^2\epsilon}{\partial t^2}\right) \tag{3.24}$$

then the elastic constant exhibits a resonancelike dispersion range. In general, all the Taylor coefficients are different from zero. However, for periodic motion, $\partial/\partial t$ may be replaced by $j\omega$, and the ratio $\bar{\lambda}$ of the stress $\tilde{\sigma}$ to the strain $\tilde{\epsilon}$ becomes a complex function of the frequency:

$$\bar{\lambda}=\frac{\tilde{\sigma}}{\tilde{\epsilon}}=\lambda^{(0)}\frac{1+j\omega\beta_1-\omega^2\beta_2-j\omega^3\beta_3+\omega^4\beta_4+\dots}{1+j\omega\alpha_1-\omega^2\alpha_2-j\omega^3\alpha_3+\omega^4\alpha_4+\dots}=\lambda_0(\omega)[1+j\eta(\omega)] \quad (3.25)$$

where $\lambda_0(\omega)$ and $\lambda_0(\omega)\cdot\eta(\omega)$ are abbreviations for the real and the imaginary parts.

Thus, for periodic motion, the infinite number of elastic constants of the elastic continuum (describing the elastic aftereffects) can be condensed into a complex function of the frequency. This function $\bar{\lambda}(\omega)$ is defined as the complex elastic constant. The use of a complex elastic constant is limited to harmonic vibrations.

For decaying vibrations,

$$\frac{\partial}{\partial t}=j\omega-\delta=j(\omega+j\delta) \quad (3.26)$$

and the frequency ω in the argument of the complex elastic constant has to be replaced by $\omega+j\delta$. However, if $\eta^2\ll 1$ and $\delta^2\ll 1$, the same elastic constant may be used in computations for decaying vibrations. This is proved by the Taylor development:

$$\begin{aligned}\bar{\lambda}(\omega+j\delta)&=\bar{\lambda}(\omega)+j\delta\cdot\frac{\partial\bar{\lambda}(\omega)}{\partial\omega}+\dots\\&=\lambda_0\left[1+j\left(\eta+\delta\frac{\partial\log\lambda_0(\omega)}{\partial\omega}\right)\right]+\text{second-order terms in }\eta\text{ and }\delta\\&=\lambda_0\left[1+j\eta\left(1+\frac{\omega}{2}\frac{\partial\log\lambda_0(\omega)}{\partial\omega}\right)\right]+\dots\end{aligned} \quad (3.27)$$

where δ has been replaced by $\omega\eta/2$. Unless $\lambda_0(\omega)$ changes greatly with frequency (as in a dispersion region), the derivative on the right is negligible.

For harmonic motion, the history of the motion is unique and is represented by a sinusoidal or a decaying sinusoidal function, regardless of whether the damping is due to velocity-proportional friction, elastic lags, or any other phenomena; as a consequence, the friction constant is a unique function of the frequency, irrespective of the origin of the friction. Thus, provided that the motion is strictly harmonic, any kind of friction can be accounted for by assuming a frequency-dependent loss resistance or loss factor η or, more simply, by assuming a complex elastic constant or a complex mass. This procedure is exact as long as the phenomenon is strictly periodic. The real part of the elastic constant usually changes very little with frequency. But the loss factor frequently varies considerably with frequency. Figure 3.1 shows the loss factor of various materials as a function of the frequency.

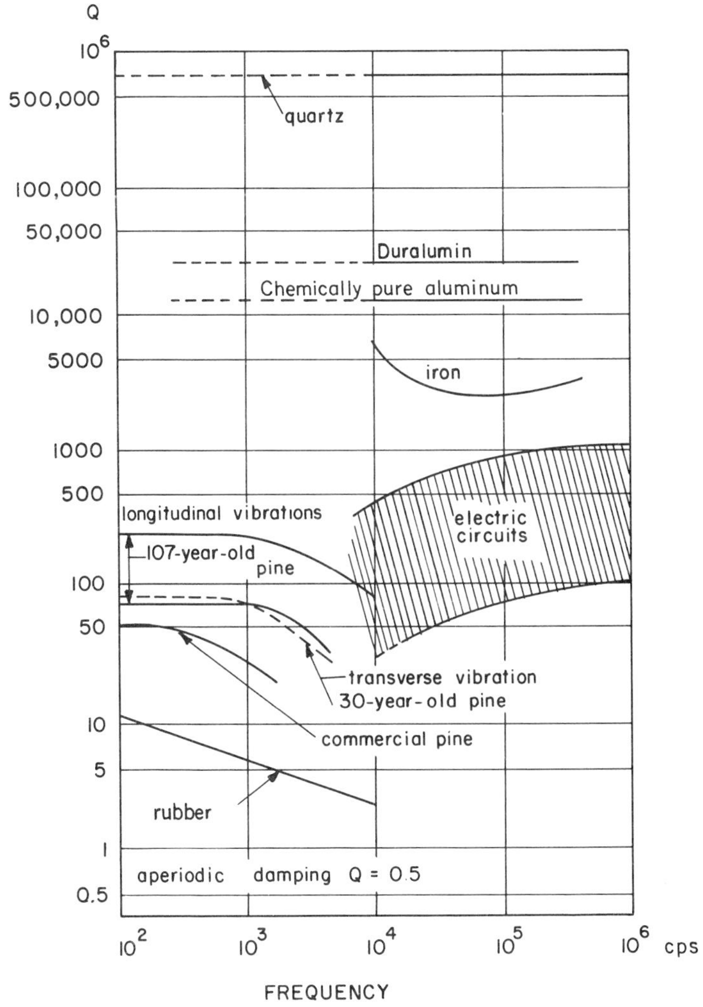

Fig. 3.1 Comparison of the quality factors of different substances with those of turned electrical circuits.

Transformation of the Solution for the Nondissipative System into That for the Dissipative System

The introduction of the complex elastic constant makes it possible to neglect losses in all formal computations, as if the system were ideal, and to correct for the losses by assuming a complex stiffness constant. For example, the velocity of a point-mass spring system that is excited by a periodic force is:

$$\bar{V}=\frac{\bar{F}}{j\omega M+\frac{1}{j\omega K}}=\frac{\bar{F}}{j\omega M+\frac{1}{j\omega K_0}(1+j\eta)}=\frac{\bar{F}}{j\omega M+\frac{1}{j\omega K_0}+\frac{\eta}{\omega K_0}} \tag{3.28}$$

which is the same as Equation 2.23 because

$$R=\frac{\eta}{\omega K_0} \tag{3.29}$$

If the elastic constant has been expressed by the resonant frequency with the aid of the relation

$$\omega_0^2=\frac{1}{MK_0} \tag{3.30}$$

then ω_0^2 has to be replaced by

$$\bar{\omega}_0^2=\frac{1}{M\bar{K}}=\omega_0^2(1+j\eta) \tag{3.31}$$

and the solution becomes

$$\bar{V}=\frac{\bar{F}}{j\omega M\left(1-\frac{\bar{\omega}_0^2}{\omega^2}\right)}=\frac{\bar{F}}{j\omega M\left(1-\frac{\omega_0^2}{\omega^2}\right)+\frac{\eta\omega_0^2 M}{\omega}} \tag{3.32}$$

Since $\omega_0^2 M\eta/\omega=\eta/\omega K=R$, and since $M\omega_0^2/\omega=1/\omega K$, the two solutions (Eqs. 3.32 and 3.28) are the same.

The same method may be used to obtain the solution for the decaying vibration of a tuned circuit. Without damping,

$$\tilde{v}=V_0 e^{j\omega_0 t} \tag{3.33}$$

and with damping,

$$\tilde{v}=V_0 e^{j\bar{\omega}_0 t} \tag{3.34}$$

where

$$\bar{\omega}_0=\frac{1}{\sqrt{KM}}=\omega_0\sqrt{(1+j\eta)}=\omega_0\left(1+j\frac{\eta}{2}+\ldots\right)=\omega_0+j\delta \tag{3.35}$$

In the exact solution, the frequency of the decaying vibration is ω_0^* instead of ω_0. But since the complex elastic constant represents only a first-order approximation for decaying vibrations, it is senseless to retain terms in η^2 in the Taylor development of Equation 3.35 and to distinguish between ω_0 and ω_0^*. The solution then becomes:

$$\tilde{v}=V_0 e^{-\delta t+j\omega_0 t}=V_0 e^{-\omega_0\eta t/2+j\omega_0 t} \tag{3.36}$$

and, except for terms in η^2, the result is identical with Equation 2.12.

Various Complex Elastic Constants of Isotropic Materials

Since "rigid body" rotations and "rigid body" translations do not generate elastic forces, the only motions that are of interest in the theory of elasticity are those that occur during deformations. The relations between the forces and the deformations are governed by the elastic constants. An elastic constant is defined as the ratio of the stress to the strain:

$$\text{elastic constant} = \frac{\text{stress}}{\text{strain}} \tag{3.37}$$

Fundamentally, there are two types of deformation: volume changes or dilatations and shear deformations. The volume changes depend on the dilatation modulus; the shear deformations, on the shear modulus. These two moduli are independent of one another. Correspondingly, there are two types of internal friction that are also independent of one another; and a distinction must be made between friction generated by volume changes and friction generated by shear deformations. The friction that accompanies either type of deformation can be fully taken into account by introducing complex elastic constants in a manner similar to that used to introduce complex stiffness constants. The only difference is that the stiffness constant represents the ratio of the total deformation to the total force, whereas the modulus describes the stiffness of the compliant elements per unit length and unit cross section. The loss factor of the elastic constant, then, represents the loss factor of the compliance of the system for the type of motion that is described by the elastic constant.

Any deformation, irrespective of its complexity, can be made up of dilatation and of shear motion; correspondingly, any complex elastic constant can be made up of some combination of the fundamental elastic moduli for dilatation and shear. For instance, Young's modulus λ_E, which describes the deformation of thin rods, is given by:

$$\lambda_E = \frac{G(3L+2G)}{G+L} \tag{3.38}$$

where $L = L_0(1+jl)$ is Lamé's dilatation modulus and $G = G_0(1+jg)$ is the shear modulus. This formula and all the others that are derived in the theory of elasticity apply also to the complex elastic constants, so that their loss factors can be computed as a function of the loss factors g and l for shear motion and for dilatation, respectively. The relations among the various elastic constants are summarized in Table 3.1. Table 3.2 gives the real parts and the loss factors of some of the more important elastic constants.

Table 3.1 *The relations between the various elastic constants and their loss factors.**

Deformation	Real Part of Elastic Constant	Loss Factor η	Minimum of the Coefficient of g	Loss Factor for		
				$m_0=2$	$m_0=3.4$	$m_0=\infty$
Shear or torsional	G_0		1	g	g	g
Longitudinal or bending of thin rods (Young's modulus)	$\lambda_{e0}=\frac{2G_0(m_0+1)}{m_0}$	$\frac{(m_0^2+2)g+(m_0-2)l}{m_0(m_0+1)}$	$0.9(m_0=4.46)$	g	$0.91g+0.09l$	g
Compression (bulk modulus)	$\lambda_{k0}=\frac{L_0}{3}(m_0+1)$	$\frac{(m_0-2)g+3l}{m_0+1}$	$0(m_0=2)$	l	$0.32g+0.68l$	g
Transverse vibration of thin plates (plate modulus)	$\lambda_{b0}=\frac{\lambda_{e0}m_0^2}{m_0^2-1}$	$\frac{m_0^2-2m_0+2)g+(m_0-2)l}{m_0(m_0-1)}$	$0.58(m=3.4)$	g	$0.83g+0.17l$	g
Longitudinal waves (elastic constant in wave equation for solids)	$\lambda_{s0}=\rho c_0^2=L_0(m_0-1)$	$\frac{(m_0-2)g+l}{m_0-1}$	$0(m=2)$	l	$0.58g+0.42l$	g

* $m=1/\nu$; ν=Poisson's contraction.

Table 3.2 *Relations among elastic constants**.

Constant	λ_E	ν	λ_k	μ	λ
λ_E, ν	λ_E	ν	$\frac{\lambda_E}{3(1-2\nu)}$	$\frac{\lambda_E}{2(1+\nu)}$	$\frac{\lambda_E\nu}{(1+\nu)(1-2\nu)}$
λ_E, λ_k	λ_E	$\frac{3\lambda_k-\lambda_E}{6\lambda_k}$	λ_k‡	$\frac{3\lambda_k\lambda_E}{9\lambda_k-\lambda_E}$	$\frac{3\lambda_k(3\lambda_k-\lambda_E)}{9\lambda_k-\lambda_E}$
λ_E, μ	λ_E	$\frac{\lambda_E-2\mu}{2\mu}$	$\frac{\mu\lambda_E}{3(3\mu-\lambda_E)}$	μ	$\frac{\mu(\lambda_E-2\mu)}{3\mu-\lambda_E}$
λ_E, λ	λ_E	$\frac{2\lambda}{\lambda_E+\lambda+\dagger}$	$\frac{\lambda_E+3\lambda+\dagger}{6}$	$\frac{\lambda_E-3\lambda+\dagger}{4}$	λ
ν, λ_k	$3\lambda_k(1-2\nu)$	ν	λ_k	$\frac{3\lambda_k(1-2\nu)}{2(1+\nu)}$	$\frac{3\lambda_k\nu}{1+\nu}$
ν, μ	$2\mu(1+\nu)$	ν	$\frac{2\mu(1+\nu)}{3(1-2\nu)}$	μ	$\frac{2\mu\nu}{1-2\nu}$
ν, λ	$\frac{\lambda(1+\nu)(1-2\nu)}{\nu}$	ν	$\frac{\lambda(1+\nu)}{3\nu}$	$\frac{\lambda(1-2\nu)}{2\nu}$	λ
λ_k, μ	$\frac{9\lambda_k\mu}{6\lambda_k+\mu}$	$\frac{3\lambda_k-2\mu}{6\lambda_k+2\mu}$	λ_k	μ	$\lambda_k-\frac{2}{3}\mu$
λ_k, λ	$\frac{9\lambda_k(\lambda_k-\lambda)}{3\lambda_k-\lambda}$	$\frac{\lambda}{3\lambda_k-\lambda}$	λ_k	$\frac{3}{2}(\lambda_k-\lambda)$	λ
μ, λ	$\frac{\mu(3\lambda+2\mu)}{\lambda+\mu}$	$\frac{\lambda}{2\lambda+2\mu}$	$\frac{3\lambda+2\mu}{3}$	μ	λ

* From C. E. Pearson, *Theoretical Elasticity* (Cambridge, Mass., 1959).
† $\sqrt{\lambda_E^2+9\lambda^2+2\lambda\lambda_E}$.
‡ $\lambda_k=\lambda+\frac{2}{3}\mu$.

Fundamental Types of Elastic Behavior and Internal Friction

The Ideal Elastic Substance without Internal Friction

For the ideal elastic substance, the stresses are proportional to the strains, and any change in stress is instantly followed by a corresponding change in strain, and vice versa. However, such a behavior is physically unrealistic. The substances consist of molecules, and every time the stress or strain is changed, the internal equilibrium of the substance is disturbed, and a certain amount of time is required for a new state of equilibrium to be reached. The ideal elastic substance has no internal friction.

Fluid Friction

The classical internal friction is fluid friction. The loss resistance is constant, and the frictional force is proportional to the velocity. The loss factor is:

$$\eta = \omega KR \tag{3.39}$$

and the energy losses per cycle, which are proportional to the loss factor (Eq. 2.97), increase proportionally to the frequency (Fig. 3.2); they are given by:

$$W_T = \frac{\pi\eta\hat{\xi}^2}{K} = \pi\omega R\hat{\xi}^2 \tag{3.40}$$

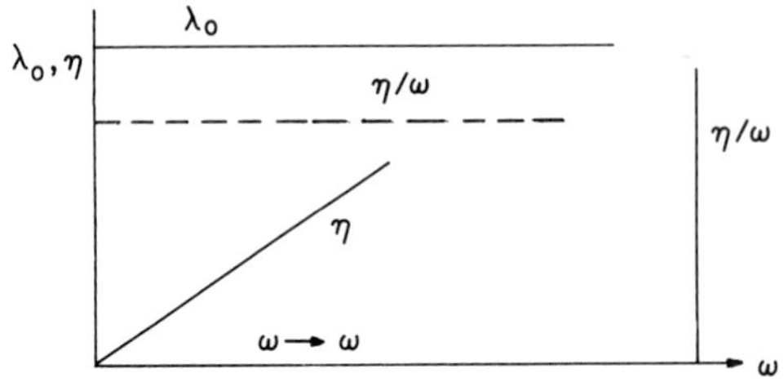

Fig. 3.2 Elastic constant (real part) and loss factor for fluid friction.

Mechanical Hysteresis

Mechanical hysteresis is similar to magnetic hysteresis, and the stress, instead of being proportional to the strain, describes a hysteresis loop. For small deformations (like small magnetic fields), the hysteresis loop turns into an ellipse, and hysteresis becomes a lag phenomenon. The strain that is produced by a given stress lags in phase behind the stress. Hysteresis is usually characterized by the residual deformation of the compliant element when the force is removed. For ideal hysteresis, the ratio of the residual deformation ξ_r to the maximum deformation $\hat{\xi}$ is independent of the velocity and independent of the time duration of the preceding deformations. Let this ratio be defined as the hysteresis constant:

$$\eta_H = \frac{\xi_r}{\hat{\xi}} \tag{3.41}$$

If the external force is periodic, i.e.,

$$f = F\cos\omega t \tag{3.42}$$

the deformation is periodic and lags by a phase angle α behind the force. Displacement and velocity are given by:

$$\begin{aligned} \xi &= \hat{\xi}\cos(\omega t - \alpha) \\ \dot{\xi} &= -\omega\hat{\xi}\sin(\omega t - \alpha) = \omega\hat{\xi}\cos\left(\omega t + \frac{\pi}{2} - \alpha\right) \end{aligned} \tag{3.43}$$

The force is zero whenever $\omega t = (2\nu + 1)\frac{\pi}{2}$, where $\nu = 0, 1, 2, 3, \ldots$. The residual deformation, therefore, is:

$$\xi_r = \hat{\xi} \cos\left[(2\nu+1)\frac{\pi}{2} - \alpha\right] = \pm \hat{\xi} \sin \alpha \tag{3.44}$$

and

$$\eta_H = \pm \frac{\xi_r}{\hat{\xi}} = \sin \alpha \doteq \alpha \tag{3.45}$$

or

$$\alpha = \sin^{-1} \eta_H \doteq \eta_H \tag{3.46}$$

The last equation determines the angle of lag of the deformation with respect to the driving force as a function of the residual deformation. The complex elastic constant is, as usual, given by the ratio between force and deformation:

$$\frac{Fe^{j\omega t}}{\hat{\xi} e^{j(\omega t - \alpha)}} = \frac{F}{\hat{\xi}} e^{j\alpha} = \lambda e^{j\alpha} \doteq \lambda e^{j\eta_H} = \lambda (1 + j\eta_H + \ldots) \tag{3.47}$$

because of Equation 3.45. The last form of the right-hand side is obtained by Taylor development, without retaining the squares and higher powers of η_H. Hysteresis factor and loss factor are identical as long as $\eta_H^2 \ll 1$, and the phase lag of the displacement behind the driving force is practically equal to this factor. Figure 3.3 shows a plot of λ_0 and η for ideal hysteresis.

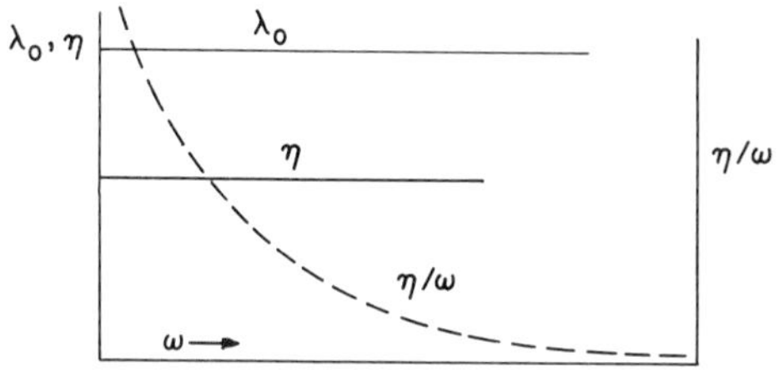

Fig. 3.3 Elastic constant and loss factor in mechanical hysteresis.

Constancy of loss factor corresponds to ideal mechanical hysteresis, provided that the stiffness constant does not vary with frequency. If the stiffness constant varies with frequency, we may be confronted with a complex relaxation or elastic lag phenomenon (see below).

Plastic Flow

At very low frequencies, materials frequently flow. The residual deformation then is proportional to the time T that the force is active, and the loss factor becomes proportional to the period of the vibration:

$$\eta = \text{const} \cdot T = \frac{p}{\omega} \tag{3.48}$$

where p is a constant. If this relation holds, the damping mechanism is defined as ideal plastic flow. Figure 3.4 shows the loss factor for plastic flow.

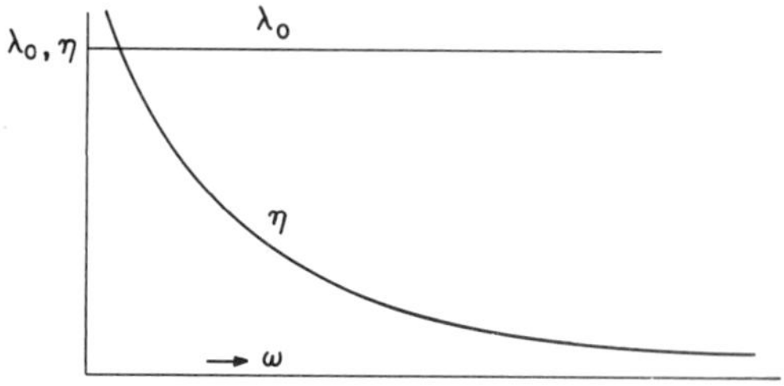

Fig. 3.4 Loss factor and stiffness constant in plastic flow.

Relaxation

One more phenomenon—relaxation—is important. All bodies are made up of molecules, and every deformation disturbs the internal equilibrium. The deformation is, therefore, always a function of the time. The simplest differential equation that satisfies this requirement is:

$$\xi + \tau_\xi \frac{\partial \xi}{\partial t} = Kf \tag{3.49}$$

If a constant force is applied to the system, the solution becomes:

$$\xi = f \cdot K(1 - e^{-t/\tau_\xi}) \tag{3.50}$$

The deformation then approaches its final value exponentially with time; the constant τ_ξ is the so-called relaxation time of the strain. Similar considerations must be applied to the internal stress. If the system is deformed, the internal stress must also approach its final value with a time constant τ_f, the relaxation time of the stress. A time derivative similar to that on the left-hand side of Equation 3.49 must, therefore, be added on the right-hand side of the differential equation:

$$\xi + \tau_\xi \frac{\partial \xi}{\partial t} = K\left(f + \tau_f \frac{\partial f}{\partial t} \right) \tag{3.51}$$

If the system is suddenly deformed by giving the left-hand side of the above equation a constant value, the stresses adjust exponentially:

$$f = f_0(1 - e^{-t/\tau_f}) \tag{3.52}$$

For periodic phenomena, $\partial/\partial t = j\omega$, and thus the relaxation equation (3.51) reduces to:

$$\bar{\lambda} = \frac{\tilde{f}}{\tilde{\xi}} = \frac{(1 + j\omega\tau_\xi)}{K(1 + j\omega\tau_f)} = \frac{1}{K}\left[\frac{(1 + \omega^2\tau_\xi\tau_f) + j\omega(\tau_\xi - \tau_f)}{1 + \omega^2\tau_f{}^2}\right] \tag{3.53}$$

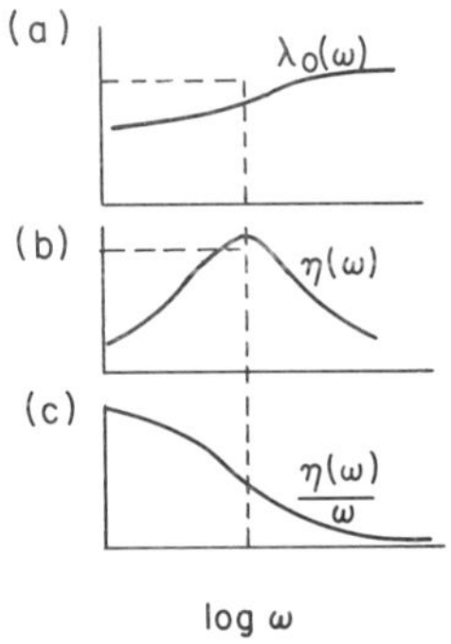

Fig. 3.5 A simple relaxation phenomenon; *a*, stiffness (real part of complex elastic constant); *b*, loss factor; *c*, internal friction constant.

Figure 3.5 shows a plot of both the real and the imaginary part of the elastic constant as a function of the frequency. In contrast to the preceding examples, the real part of the elastic constant now is strongly frequency-dependent. The real part of the elastic constant is constant at low frequencies, increases at higher frequencies, passes through a point of inflection, and then reaches a constant value at very high frequencies. At very high frequencies, the material has no time to relax and becomes stiffer. The loss factor increases proportionally to the frequency at low frequencies, as in ideal fluid friction, then passes through a maximum, and at very high frequencies becomes inversely proportional to the frequency. Many gases exhibit simple relaxation phenomena of this type. However, in some cases, two or more relaxation phenomena are superimposed on one another. Solids, like rubber, exhibit a continuous relaxation time spectrum that varies from long to short times. Some metals, like iron and brass, exhibit relaxation spectra because of the heat currents that are set up in their crystallites by vibrational stresses.

Typical Frictional Behavior of Solids

At very low frequencies, plastic flow usually masks all other types of internal dissipation, since its loss factor is inversely proportional to the frequency. Figure 3.6 shows examples of plastic flow in metals at very low frequencies; they represent measurements performed with transversely vibrating bars of different metals. The increase of the loss factor that is shown in these curves at higher frequencies is caused by thermal relaxation. At the instant one face of the bar is extended and cooled, the other is compressed and heated, and vice versa. Heat currents are set up between the two faces of the bar, and vibrational energy is transformed into heat.

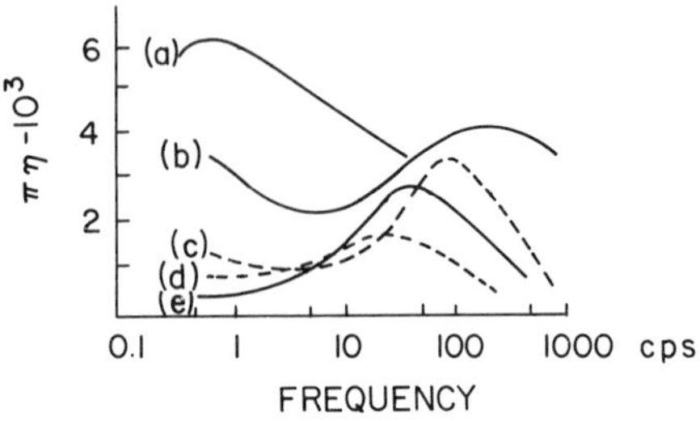

Fig. 3.6 Examples of plastic flow in metals at low frequencies; *a*, glass (d. = 1.25 mm.); *b*, silver (d. = 1.01 mm.); *c*, aluminum (d. =); *d*, steel; *e*, brass (from Bennewitz and Rötger, 1937)

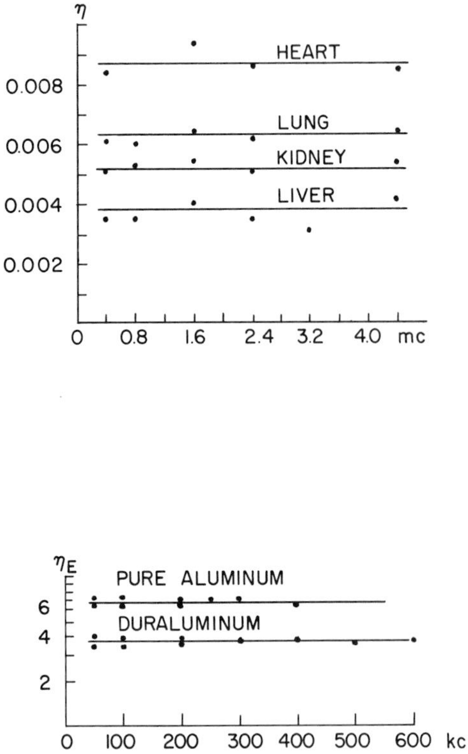

Fig. 3.7 Examples of predominating hysteresis;

At audio-frequencies, hysteresis is usually the predominating component of internal friction in solids, and the loss factor is independent of the frequency. Figure 3.7 shows examples of predominating hysteresis. Figure 3.8 represents measurements on wood. The low-frequency portions of the

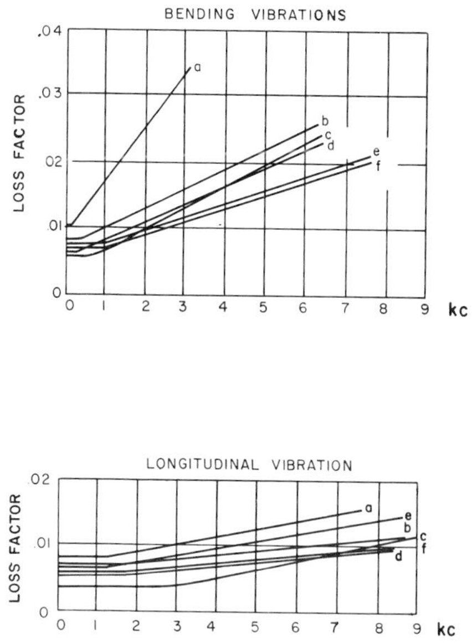

Fig. 3.8 The mechanical loss factors of wood as a function of curing; *above*, bending vibrations; *below*, longitudinal vibrations; *a*, unseasoned wood; *b*, 3-month-old wood; *c*, 17-year-old wood; *d*, kiln-dried (3-month-old) wood; *e*, 10-year-old wood; *f*, 30-year-old wood.

curves are due to hysteresis; as the frequency increases, fluid friction (relaxation) predominates. Figure 3.9 represents the frequency curve of the loss factor of carbon dioxide. This shape is typical for relaxation in gases. In this curve the effect of two distinct relaxation phenomena can be recognized. Figure 3.10 represents the loss factor of iron, which can be shown to be generated primarily by the heat currents in the crystallites of the metal. Each little crystal generates its own relaxation phenomenon, and its relaxation time depends on the diameter of the crystal. Figure 3.11 shows the frequency curve of the real part of the elastic constant and that of the loss factor of rubber. Because of the increase of the real part of the elastic constant with frequency, the form of this curve is due to the relaxation (elastic aftereffects) rather than hysteresis.

Let us now return to Figure 3.1, which shows a comparison of the loss factors of some frequently used elastic substances with those obtained from electrical circuits; this comparison shows that much more sharply tuned systems are possible with mechanical elements than with electrical components, particularly at the lower frequencies.

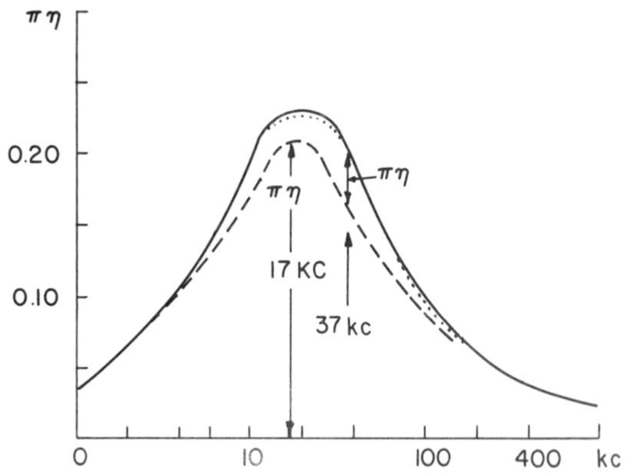

Fig. 3.9 Loss factor of carbon dioxide and its decomposition into two separate relaxation phenomena. From Fricke (1940) and Pielemeyer (1943).

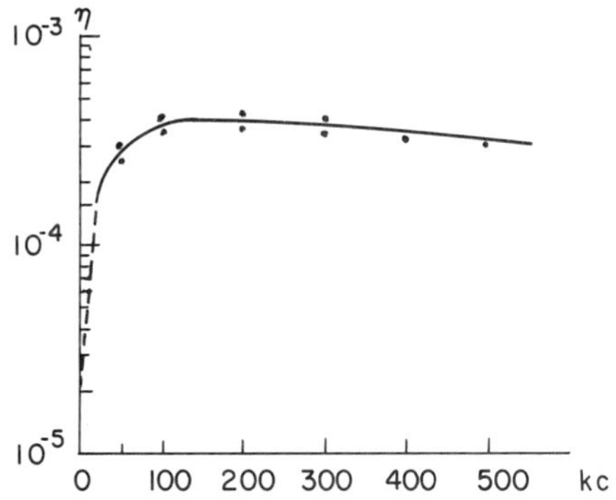

Fig. 3.10 Loss factor of steel.

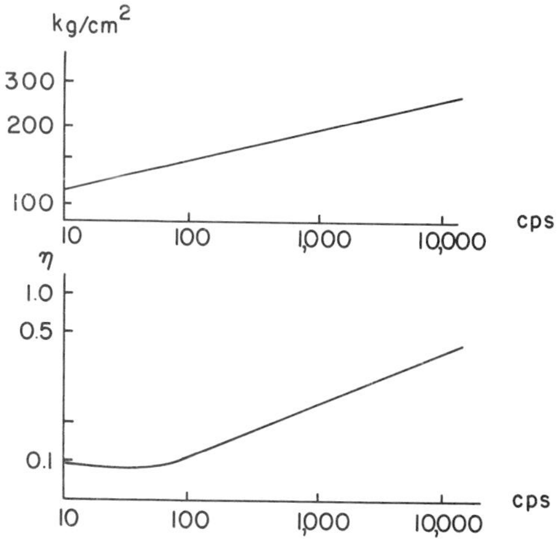

Fig. 3.11 Young's modulus and the loss factor of rubber as a function of the frequency. From W. Kuhl (1953). The horizontal portion of the curve for the loss factor is generated by a particular distribution of relaxation times and not by hysteresis, as follows from the strong frequency dependence of the modulus.

Recommended Reading

ALFREY, T., *The Mechanical Behavior of High Polymers*, Interscience, New York, 1948.

BLAND, D. R., *The Theory of Linear Viscoelasticity*, Pergamon Press, Inc., New York, 1960.

BÖHME, H., "Dynamisches Verhalten von Schalldaemmstoffen," *Akustische Zeits,* **2** (1937).

CHESAPEAKE INSTRUMENT CORPORATION, "Dynamic mechanical properties of materials for noise and vibration control," C. I. C. Report No. 101, Contract No. Nonr 2678100, Office of Naval Research, Washington, D. C., Jan. 1, 1960, 2 vols.

DEN HARTOG, J. P., "Forced vibrations with combined Coulomb and viscous friction," *Trans. A. S. M. E.,* **53** (1931); also in *Mechanical Vibrations,* McGraw-Hill Inc., New York, 1947.

EXNER, R., *Kautschuk U. Gummi,* **9**, W. T. 2 (1956).

EXNER, M. L., Schalldaemmung durch Gummi: Stahlfedern," *Acustica,* **2** (1952), 213–21.

——— AND W. BÖHME, "Messung der Korperschalldaemmung bei Biegewellen," *Acustica,* **3** (1953), 105–10.

FERRY, J. D., *Viscoelastic Properties of Polymers,* John Wiley & Sons, Inc., New York, 1961.

HENKEY, H., "Elastic behavior of vulcanized rubber," *Trans. A. S. M. E.*, **55** (1933).

KOLSKY, H., AND Y. Y. SHI, "The validity of model representation for linear viscoelastic behavior," Brown University Report to the Office of Naval Research, Nonr 562(14)/5, Jan. 1958.

KOSTEN, C. W., "Berechnung von Federungselementen aus Gummi," *Verein Deutscher Ingenieur Zeitschrift,* **50** (1942).

———AND C. ZWIKKER, "Qualities of sponge rubber as a material for vibration and shock damping," *Physica,* **4** (1937).

KUHL, W., AND E. MEYER, "Dynamical properties of rubber and rubberlike materials in a large frequency range," Report of the 1948 Summer Symposium of the Acoustics Group, The Physical Society, London.

LAZAN, B. J., in *Structural Damping,* ed. by J. E. Ruzicks, The American Society of Mechanical Engineers, New York, 1959, Sect. 1, pp. 1–34.

LEHMBERG, W. H., "Mechanical properties and uses of wool felt," *Mech. Eng.*, **67** (1945).

LEIGH-DUGMORE, C. H., in *The Applied Science of Rubber,* ed. by W. J. S. Naunton, Edward Arnold (Publishers) Ltd., London, 1961, chap. 7, pp. 475–505.

MADDEN, B. C., "Effectiveness of shear-stressed rubber compounds in isolating machimery vibration," *Trans. A.S.M.E.,* (1943).

MASON, W.P., *Physical Acoustics,* Academic Press, New York, 1965, vols. II–IV.

MINDLIN, R. D., STUBNER, F. W., AND H. L. COOPER, "Response of damped elastic systems to transient disturbances," *Proc. Soc. Exp. Stress Anal.,* **5** (1947).

PAYNE, A. R., in *The Rheology of Elastomers,* ed. by P. Mason and N. Wookey, Pergamon Press, Inc., New York, 1958, pp. 86–110.

SKUDRZYK, E. J., *Die Grundlagen der Akustik,* Springer Verlag, Vienna, 1954, pp. 762–849.

SMITH, J. F. D., "Rubber mountings, " *Trans. A.S.M.E.*, **60** (1938).

SNOWDON, J. C., "Rubberlike materials: Their internal damping and role in vibration isolation," *J. Sound Vib.,* **2** (1965), 175–93.

TYZZER, F. G., AND H. C. HARDY, "The properties of felt in the reduction of noise and vibration," *J.A.S.A.*, **19** (1947).

YIN, T. P., "The frequency-temperature dependence of the damping characteristics of several elastomers," Gordon Research Conferences, Elastomers, July 16, 1962.

ZELLER, W., "Eigenschaften von Buna-Gummi für die Anwendung in der Schwingungstechnik," *Verein Deutscher Ingenieur Zeitschrift*, **49** (1941).

ZENER, C., *Elasticity and Inelasticity of Metals,* The University of Chicago Press, Chicago, 1948.

IV / LUMPED PARAMETER SYSTEMS

Examples of Simple Point-Mass Compliance Vibrators

Vibrating systems frequently exhibit a number of resonances that are widely spaced in frequency and are practically independent of one another. In the frequency range near each resonance, the system behaves as if it were a simple point-mass compliance vibrator. Such systems can be analyzed in a simple manner, as illustrated by the following examples.

Phonograph Cartridge

The phonograph cartridge affords a very instructive example of the behavior of a more complex point-mass compliant element system and of the concepts of driving point and transfer impedance. Following through, in one particular case, with the derivation of the mechanical diagram and complete calculation of its elements will greatly clarify the use of the electro-mechanical analogies. Force-voltage analogues will be used.

The moving-coil magnetic cartridge consists of a needle or stylus, an armature, which is surrounded or held in position by rubber or some other damping material, and a permanent magnet (Fig. 4.1*a*). The excursions ξ and the velocity of the stylus are prescribed by the record grooves. In the mechanical diagram (Fig. 4.1*b*), the record is represented by a velocity generator. The compliance of the grooves K_g reduces the velocity of the needle; therefore, it appears as a shunt branch in the mechanical circuit diagram. The compliance of the grooves has a strong resistive component that helps to damp the antiresonances of the pickup. These losses can be accounted for by a parallel resistance R_g. The compliance of the needle, which reduces the velocity transmitted to the armature, is represented by the shunted capacity K_N. The force generated by the grooves is transmitted almost without reduction to the armature. In fact, the mass of the needle can be neglected because of its smallness, or it can be added to the mass M_A of the armature. The armature compresses the rubber and drives the magnet and the pickup arm M_M. The velocity transmitted to the magnet M_M is less than that transmitted to the armature, and the compliance of the rubber appears as a shunt branch in the diagram. The mass M_M also includes the equivalent mass of the tone arm (which is given by the ratio

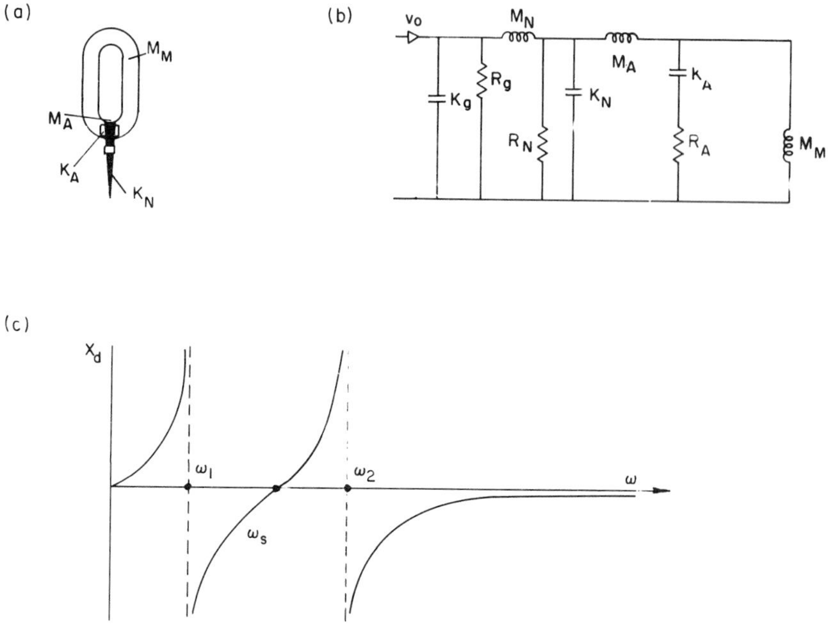

Fig. 4.1 The phonograph pickup; *a*, elements of the pickup; *b*, mechanical circuit diagram($K_A=50 \cdot 10^{-6}$ m./Newton; $K_N=3 \cdot 10^{-6}$m./Newton; $M_A=3 \cdot 10^{-4}$kg, $M_M=0.1$ kg). *c*, frequency curve of driving-point reactance.

of its inertia around the pivot to the square of the distance from it). To simplify writing, the compliance K_N can be considered to include the groove compliance K_g, and the resistance R_g can be included in the resistance R_N. In the moving-coil cartridges, the armature carries a coil. In the variable-reluctance type, the coil is wound around the magnet, and the armature moves in an air gap, thus varying the reluctance of the magnetic circuit.

The output voltage of the cartridge is proportional to the relative velocity between the armature and the magnet, that is, to the compressional velocity of the rubber. This velocity is represented by the current through the compliance K_A.

During playback, wear of the record is proportional to the force that the stylus exerts on the grooves. This force is equal to the product of the mechanical impedance of the cartridge and the velocity amplitude transcribed on the recording. The record is usually cut in such a way that constant velocity amplitude also represents constant voltage (except for frequencies below 350 cps; see below). For constant loudness, wear is proportional to the mechanical impedance Z of the phonograph cartridge as seen from the stylus.

The equivalent electric circuit has four independent reactive elements; consequently, it has five resonances (Fig. 4.1*c*).[1] The resonance at zero frequency is a series resonance, because the inductances have no impedance, i.e., they are short circuits at this frequency. The second resonance ω_1 is an antiresonance (M_M vibrating against K_A); the third ω_s, a series resonance (M_A vibrating against K_A); and the fourth ω_2, an antiresonance (M_A vibrating against K_N; K_A representing a negligible impedance at this frequency). The fifth resonance, at infinite frequency, is, again, a series resonance because of the vanishing impedance $1/\omega K_N$ of the needle compliance K_N. Figure 4.1*c* shows the frequency curve of the input reactance of the circuit as seen from the needle. At zero frequency, the masses $M_N+M_A+M_M$ form a short circuit, and the velocity of the needle is fully transmitted to the magnet. At very low frequencies, the mass of the needle and armature can be neglected, and the diagram reduces to the parallel circuit shown in Figure 4.2*a*, which is equivalent to the circuit in Figure 4.2*b*, if the series resistance R_A is transformed into a parallel resistance where

$$R_{pA}=\frac{\omega_1^2 M_M^2}{R_A}=\omega_1 M_M Q(\omega_1) \tag{4.1}$$

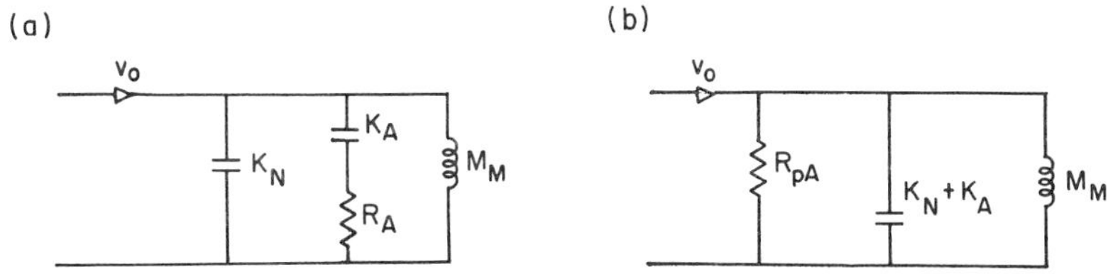

Fig. 4.2 The equivalent circuit at low frequencies; *a*, parallel circuit; *b*, equivalent circuit if the series resistance R_A is transformed into a parallel resistance.

$Q(\omega_1)$ being the quality factor of the armature compliance at the frequency ω_1. The antiresonant frequency is given by:

$$\omega_1^2=\frac{1}{M_M(K_A+K_N)} \tag{4.2}$$

and the impedance at the antiresonance is

$$Z_1=R_{pA}=\omega_1 M_A Q(\omega_1) \tag{4.3}$$

[1] See Foster's theorem, p. 32.

The compression velocity v_K is computed with the aid of Equation 1.63. It is given by:

$$V_K = \frac{V_0 j\omega M}{R + j\omega M + \dfrac{1}{j\omega K}} \tag{4.4}$$

At the resonant frequency, this reduces to:

$$V_K = \frac{V_0 j\omega M}{R_A} = V_0 jQ(\omega_1) \tag{4.5}$$

Above the first antiresonance, the impedance ωM_M of the magnet becomes much greater than that of the compliance $(1/\omega K_A)$, and M_M can be neglected. In the mid-frequency range, the compliance of the needle is still negligible, and the diagram simplifies to the series-resonant circuit shown in Figure 4.3*a*. Its resonant frequency is:

$$\omega_S = \frac{1}{\sqrt{M_A K_A}} \tag{4.6}$$

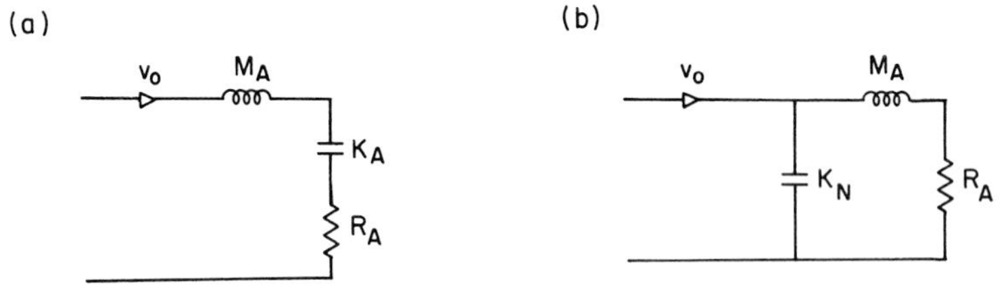

Fig. 4.3 The equivalent circuit in the range of the mid-frequencies (*a*) and at high frequencies (*b*).

and the magnitude of the mechanical impedance at this resonance becomes:

$$Z = R_s \doteq \frac{\omega_S M_A}{Q(\omega_s)} \tag{4.7}$$

Because there is no parallel branch, the velocity of the needle is the same as the relative velocity between the armature and the magnet, and

$$v_A = v_K = v_0 \tag{4.8}$$

As long as the simplifications in the diagram are permissible, the output voltage is independent of the frequency. This mid-frequency range represents the useful range of the cartridge. At still higher frequencies, the compliance of the needle and the grooves must be taken into account; but the impedance of the armature compliance K_A can be neglected, and the diagram reduces to a parallel-resonant circuit (Fig. 4.3*b*). To simplify writing, K_N will be understood to represent the sum of the compliances of the needle and the grooves. The second antiresonant frequency is:

$$\omega_2 = \frac{1}{\sqrt{M_A K_N}} \tag{4.9}$$

The mechanical impedance at resonance is computed as follows:

$$Z_2 = \frac{X^2}{R_A} = Z(\omega_2) = \frac{\omega_2{}^2 M_A{}^2}{R_A} = \frac{\omega_2{}^2 M_A}{\dfrac{1}{\omega_2 K_A Q_A}} = \omega_2{}^3 M_A{}^2 K_A Q_A(\omega_2)$$

$$= \frac{\omega_2{}^2 Q_A(\omega_2)}{\omega_s{}^2} \omega_2 M_A \tag{4.10}$$

where

$$Q_A = \frac{1}{\omega_2 K_A R_A} \quad \text{and} \quad M_A K_A = \frac{1}{\omega_s{}^2} \tag{4.11}$$

and the resulting quality factor of the M_A, K_N, R_A circuit is:

$$Q(\omega_2) = \frac{\omega_2{}^2}{\omega_s{}^2} Q_A(\omega_2) \tag{4.12}$$

The ratio of the impedances at the high antiresonant frequency of the pickup to that of the low antiresonant frequency is:

$$\frac{Z(\omega_2)}{Z(\omega_1)} = \left(\frac{K_A}{K_N}\right)^{\frac{3}{2}} \frac{Q_A(\omega_2)}{Q(\omega_2)} \left(\frac{M_A}{M_M}\right)^{\frac{1}{2}} \tag{4.13}$$

The voltage output is proportional to the velocity of the armature, because the magnet is at rest at high frequencies:

$$\tilde{v}_A = Q(\omega_2)\tilde{v}_0 \tag{4.14}$$

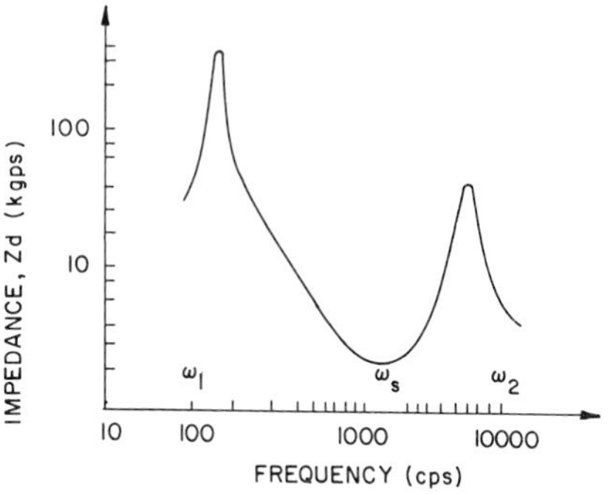

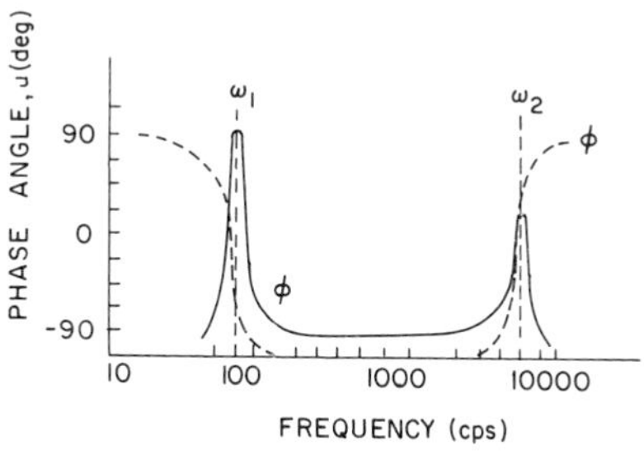

Fig. 4.4 Frequency curves of phonograph cartridge; *a*, frequency curve of driving-point impedance (absolute values, with damping included); *b*, frequency curve of phase angle ϕ and of pickup voltage.

Figure 4.4*a* shows the frequency curve of the magnitude of the mechanical impedance as viewed from the needle, and Figure 4.4*b* shows the frequency curve of the output voltage (in this curve the loss resistances have been taken into account). The voltage output of the pickup is proportional to the relative velocity of the armature with respect to the magnet. This velocity, which is represented by the current in the shunt K_A, is described by a transfer impedance; Foster's theorem does not apply, and the frequency curve of this voltage (Fig. 4.4*b*) differs greatly from that of the mechanical admittance of the system. The series resonance that occurs in the input admittance has been replaced by a shallow trough. The output voltage is zero both at very low and at very high frequencies and is proportional to Qv_0 at the two parallel-resonant frequencies, where the Q for the lower frequency is that of the rubber and the Q for the higher frequency is the modified value. In the frequency range between the two parallel resonances—that is, in the frequency range of the shallow trough of the admittance curve—the output voltage is practically constant. This range represents the useful frequency range of the pickup.

Thus, the antiresonance in the driving-point impedance has been replaced by a shallow trough in the frequency curve of the transfer admittance. It is this shallow trough that ensures a practically frequency-independent output voltage. A horizontal frequency curve could not result if the output voltage were proportional to the driving-point admittance.

In phonograph recordings, the low-frequency amplitudes are considerably reduced in order to counteract the increase in amplitude of the natural sounds with decreasing frequency. In the pickups for mechanical reproduction and in the early electromagnetic cartridges, the low-frequency resonance was used to increase the low-frequency response of the system. This resonant frequency was at approximately 70 cps, and it represented the lower limit of the transmission range. Modern cartridges have a considerably greater armature compliance, and their low-frequency resonance occurs somewhere below 20 cps. The frequency curve is horizontal above 30 cps, and the low-frequency response must be increased with the aid of electrical networks, but this is easily done.

The series resonance has no effect on the frequency response of the cartridge. The upper antiresonance ω_2 is generated by the mass of the armature and the compliance of the needle. In the earlier cartridges this resonance occurred at about 7 kc.; it accentuated the scratch noise produced by the needle and had to be eliminated by a scratch-removing filter. The mass of the armature in modern pickups is less than one tenth that of earlier versions (some models have been reduced by a factor of 100), and the old-fashioned steel needle has been replaced by a very short sapphire or diamond needle. Because of the decreased mass, the upper resonant frequency is usually in the region of 12 to 20 kc. The mechanical antiresonances cause considerable wear on the records. With $M_M=0.1$ kg., the mass impedance at the lower parallel-resonant frequency of 70 cps is 44 kg. per second. The antiresonance increases the impedance to Q times this value. If Q is assumed to be 3, this impedance becomes 3.44 kg. per second. The maximum amplitude that occurs in 78-rpm recordings is about 125μ; the alternating force on the stylus is $vZ=\omega\xi Z=7.25$ Newtons or 725 gm. weight. If the diameter of the point of the stylus is assumed to be about 75 μ (0.003″), the pressure on the point of the stylus reaches 20,000 kg. wt. per square centimeter. Thus, it is not at all surprising that the records exhibited considerable wear. This wear led to scratch noises in the frequency range of the parallel resonances. The low-frequency noises were usually inaudible, but the high-frequency needle noise was always disturbing. In the modern pickups the mechanical impedance at the lower resonant frequency is less than one tenth that of older models; furthermore, the lower resonant frequency is below the audible range. Because the high-frequency resonance is beyond the audible range, record wear is much less perceptible. Wear on the stylus increases the radius of curvature of its point and results in a loss of the high frequencies. A sapphire needle must be replaced after about 100 hours of play, and a diamond needle, after about 1,000 hours.

Design of a Pickup

Figure 4.1*a* shows an early type of pickup; its fundamental resonant frequency is 70 cps, and the mass M_M is O.1 kg. The compliance of the armature is:

$$70=\frac{1}{2\pi\sqrt{0.1K_A}} \qquad (4.15)$$

or $K_A=5\cdot10^{-5}$ m. per Newton. This compliance, which consists of a layer of rubber on each side of the armature, has a total area σ of 0.1 sq. cm. and a thickness h of 2.5 mm. If Young's modulus λ_E of rubber is assumed as $0.5\cdot10^7$ Newtons per square meter,

$$K_A=\frac{\xi}{f}=\frac{h}{\lambda_E\sigma}=\frac{2.5\cdot10^{-3}}{0.5\cdot10^7\cdot0.1\cdot10^{-4}}=5\cdot10^{-5}\text{m. per Newton} \qquad (4.16)$$

which is the same as the value determined from the resonant frequency. The needle is analogous to a cylindrical beam that is pointed at one end. The maximum bending moment occurs at the clamp. The tapering of the beam has practically no effect on its stiffness, and the compliance of the needle is given with sufficient accuracy by the formula for the cantilever:

$$\xi=\frac{fl^3}{3\,\lambda_E J} \qquad (4.17)$$

where ξ=deflection, f=force, λ_E=Young's modulus, J=second moment of cross section ($J=\pi d^4/64$), l=length of beam, and d=diameter of beam. Young's modulus of steel is 2×10^{11} Newtons per square meter. For a typical needle, l is $\frac{2}{3}$ cm., and its diameter is 1.35mm.; the compliance K_N of the needle is:

$$K_N = \frac{\xi}{f} = \frac{64\, l^3}{3\, \lambda_E \pi d^4} = \frac{(\frac{2}{3})^3 \cdot 10^{-6} \cdot 64}{3 \cdot 2 \cdot 10^{11}\, \pi (0.135)^4 \cdot 10^{-8}}$$

$$= 3 \cdot 10^{-6} \text{ m. per Newton} \tag{4.18}$$

If the mass of the armature is assumed to be about 0.3 gm., the upper resonant frequency becomes:

$$\frac{\omega_2}{2\pi} = \frac{1}{2\pi \sqrt{3 \cdot 10^{-4} \cdot 3 \cdot 10^{-6}}} = 5{,}000 \text{ cps} \tag{4.19}$$

The frequency of the series resonance can be computed in a similar manner:

$$\frac{\omega_S}{2\pi} = \frac{1}{2\pi \sqrt{K_A M_A}} = \frac{1}{2\pi \sqrt{5 \cdot 10^{-5} \cdot 3 \cdot 10^{-4}}} = 1{,}300 \text{ cps} \tag{4.20}$$

The value of Q_A for the rubber is about 10 at 70 cps and 2 at 5 kc. A measurement of width of the resonant curve of the pickup results in a value for Q that is about one third as large. This smaller value is probably due to several factors: the nonrigid contact of the needle with the groove, the relatiely great loss resistance of the groove compliance, and the bearing friction in the pickup arm. The frequency curves shown in Figures 4.4*a* and 4.4*b* of the mechanical impedance and of the output voltage have been computed with the numerical values shown in Figure 4.1*b*.

Modern Variable-Reluctance Cartridge

In modern variable-reluctance cartridges, the needle has been replaced by a short sapphire or diamond stylus. The armature is a thin strip of iron that guides the flux from one pole of a permanent magnet through the variable gap to the other pole. The needle is practically rigid, and the compliance of the armature ($2 \cdot 10^{-3}$ m. per Newton) is about 40 times greater than that of the classical case described above. The effective mass of the cartridge and pickup arm varies from 30 to 50 gm. If 40 gm. is assumed as an average value, the fundamental resonant frequency becomes:

$$\frac{\omega_2}{2\pi} = \frac{1}{2\pi} \frac{1}{\sqrt{2 \cdot 10^{-3} \cdot 4 \cdot 10^{-2}}} = 17.7 \text{ cps} \tag{4.21}$$

Electromechanical Filter

At lower frequencies, mechanical filters have a much better frequency resolution than electrical filters and are frequently used in electrical circuits. The simplest mechanical filter is a dumbbell vibrator with a moving coil at each mass (Fig. 4.5).

The external force drives the mass M. Because of the compression of the

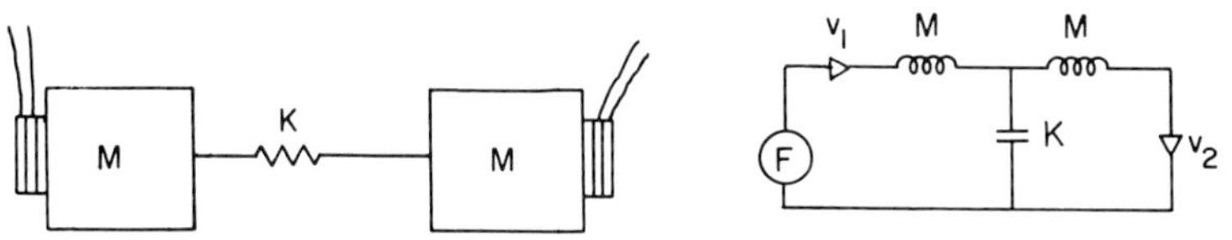

Fig. 4.5 Dumbbell vibrator used as electrical filter.

spring, the velocity of the second mass is smaller. This loss of velocity is accounted for by the shunt capacity in the diagram. The force that acts on the mass is the same as that exerted by the first mass on the spring. Therefore, the two masses are connected in series. The moving coils are placed in the air gaps of two permanent magnets. By passing an a.c. current through one of the coils, the vibrator is driven like an electrodynamic loudspeaker. The other moving coil acts as a microphone and measures the velocity of one side of the system. The driving coil produces a force that is given (in Newtons) by the product of the current (in amperes), the length of the wire on the coil (in meters), and the flux density in the air gap (in volt-seconds per square meter or Gauss $\times 10^{-4}$; thus,

$$F = IlB \tag{4.22}$$

The velocity amplitude of the mass is:

$$\bar{V} = \frac{\bar{F}}{\bar{Z}} = \frac{Bl\bar{I}}{R(1+jQ\nu)} \tag{4.23}$$

If the generator coil is of similar construction, its open-circuit output voltage is:

$$\bar{U} = Bl\bar{V} = \frac{B^2l^2\bar{I}}{R(1+jQ\nu)} = B^2l^2\bar{I}\frac{Q}{\omega_0 M\ (1+jQ\nu)} \tag{4.24}$$

The quality factor of steel is about 10^4. To estimate the sensitivity of such a filter, let the resistance R_i of the driving coil be 10 ohms; the mass M, 0.1 kg.; and the frequency ω_0, 1,000 radians per second. If the flux density is 10,000 Gauss (1 volt-second per square meter) and the length of the wire on the coil is 1 m., the ratio of the output voltage U to the input voltage IR_i is:

$$\frac{U}{IR_i} = \frac{B^2l^2}{R_i}\frac{Q}{\omega_0 M|1+jQ\nu|} = \frac{100}{|1+jQ\nu|} \tag{4.25}$$

At the resonant frequency, $\nu = (\omega/\omega_0 - \omega_0/\omega) = 0$, and the open-circuit voltage output of the filter is 100 times greater than the driving voltage; the filter also acts like a step-up transformer.

If the secondary is loaded, and if the secondary loop impedance is R, a current u/R is generated. This current gives rise to a force $Bli = Blu/R = [(Bl)^2/R]\ \nu$ (because $u = Blv$). This force is proportional to the velocity, and it opposes the motion. The term $(Bl)^2/R$ may be interpreted as a loss resistance that is caused because of the production of electrical power in the output coil. Because of this resistance, the loss factor $1/Q$ of the filter is reduced to the value:

$$\frac{1}{Q'}=\frac{\dfrac{\omega_0 M}{Q}+\dfrac{(Bl)^2}{R}}{\omega_0 M}=\frac{1}{Q}+\frac{(Bl)^2}{R\omega_0 M} \tag{4.26}$$

If $R=10$ ohms, and $\omega_0 M=100$, and $B=10{,}000$ Gauss or 1 volt-second per square meter, the effective Q of the rod becomes:

$$Q'=\frac{10\cdot 100}{1}=1{,}000 \tag{4.27}$$

which is ten times smaller than the Q of the steel. This example shows that the load resistance of the output coil must be large if a narrow band width is desired.

The selectivity of a one-circuit filter is not great. If a sharper filter with a more rectangular transmission curve is required, two or more tuned systems must be coupled. Figure 4.6 shows a mechanical band-pass filter made up of two loosely coupled vibrators. One would expect this system to behave similarly to an electrical band-pass filter built of two loosely coupled tuned circuits; however, this is not so. The mechanical system contains more independent reactive elements than the electrical system and

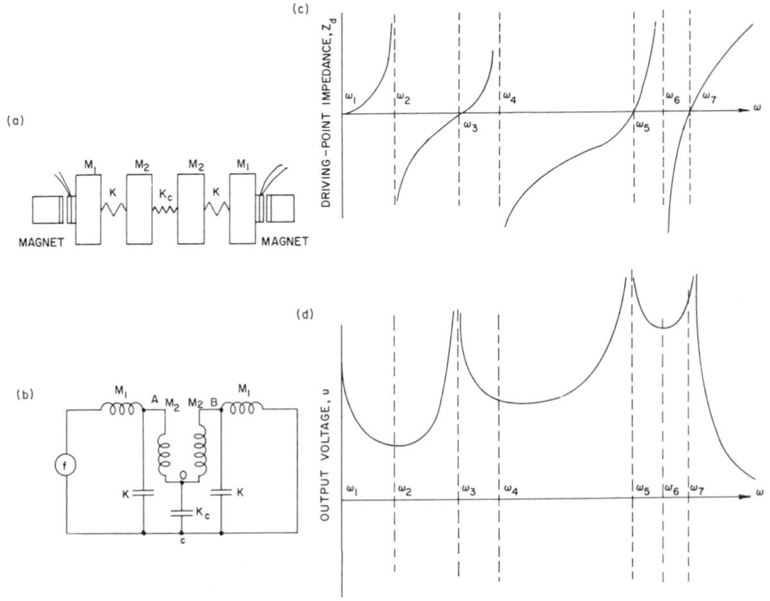

Fig. 4.6 Mechanical band-pass filter; *a*, mechanical system; *b*, mechanical circuit diagram; *c*, frequency curves of the driving-point impedance; *d*, frequency curves of the output voltage.

exhibits eight resonances as compared to the five resonances of the electrical band-pass filter. Figure 4.6*c* shows the driving-point impedance of the mechanical filter. The output voltage of the filter is determined by the velocity of the outermost mass. The corresponding transfer impedance has shallow troughs instead of antiresonances; the frequency curves of the output voltage are shown in Figure 4.6*d*.

Unless special precautions are taken in the design of the filter, the shallow trough at the frequency ω_4 will usually destroy the effectiveness of the filter below its supposed cutoff point. To reduce this deficiency, coupling between the two filter halves must be very loose. For the same reason it seems to be of advantage to have the masses M_1 and M_2 nearly equal. The resonances and antiresonances, their band width and the height of the troughs, can be analyzed in a manner similar to that used above for the phonograph pickup. This analysis is more difficult to perform because of the loose coupling of the two systems. The resulting coupled modes have similar resonant frequencies, and it is difficult to recognize which of the elements affects a particular mode and which can be neglected.

For the frequency range near the transmission region, the circuit can be simplified. The star M_2, K_c, M_2 (Fig. 4.6*b*) can be transformed into a mesh, as shown in Figure 4.7, and the admittances between *AB*, *AC*, and *BC* become:

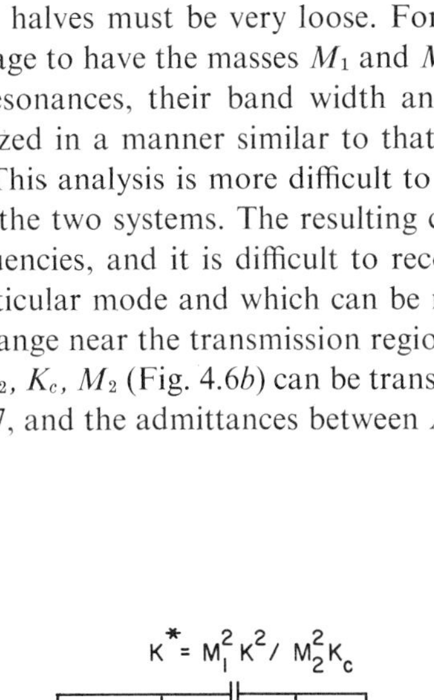

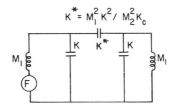

Fig. 4.7 Equivalent circuit simplified by star-mesh transformation.

$$\bar{Y}_{AB} = \frac{\bar{Y}_a \bar{Y}_b}{\bar{Y}_a + \bar{Y}_b + \bar{Y}_c} = \frac{\dfrac{1}{(j\omega M_2)^2}}{\dfrac{2}{j\omega M_2} + j\omega K_c} \tag{4.28}$$

$$\bar{Y}_{AC} = \bar{Y}_{BC} = \frac{\bar{Y}_b \bar{Y}_c}{\bar{Y}_a + \bar{Y}_b + \bar{Y}_c} = \frac{K_c M_2}{\dfrac{2}{j\omega M_2} + j\omega K_c} \tag{4.29}$$

The mass impedance $j\omega M_2$ is always very large as compared to the coupling impedance $1/j\omega K_c$, so that coupling is reduced to the required small value. The first term in the denominator can then be neglected, and the above expressions simplify to:

$$\bar{Y}_{AB}=\frac{j}{\omega^3 M_2{}^3 K_c}=\frac{j\omega}{\omega^4 M_2{}^2 K_c}=\frac{j\omega M_1{}^2 K}{M_2{}^2 K_c}\cdot K=j\omega K^* \tag{4.30}$$

$$\bar{Y}_{AC}=\bar{Y}_{BC}=\frac{1}{j\omega M_2} \tag{4.31}$$

where

$$\omega^2=\frac{1}{M_1 K} \quad \text{and} \quad K^*=\frac{M_1{}^2 K^2}{M_2{}^2 K_c} \tag{4.32}$$

The admittance Y_{BC} can be neglected, because it is small as compared to the admittance of the compliance K. The admittance $\bar{Y}_{AB}$ can be interpreted as that of a compliance in the narrow transmission range of the filter. The band-pass filter thus reduces to a filter of the standard type and can be computed as outlined in the textbooks.

Matching of a Resonance Transducer

The transducer shown in Figure 4.8 serves to transmit sound vibrations into the ground. The element K_i is a nickel rod, driven magnetostrictively. The loss resistance of K_i is determined by the loss factor of the nickel:

$$R_i=\frac{\eta}{\omega K_i} \tag{4.33}$$

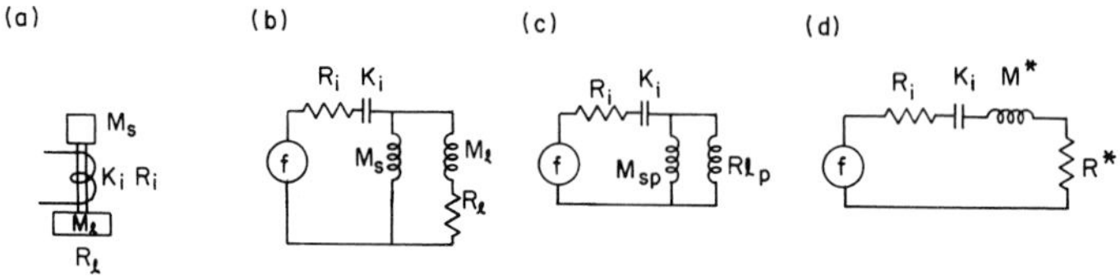

Fig. 4.8 Matching of a resonance transducer; *a*, mechanical sketch; *b*, electromechanical diagram; *c*, series resistance transformed into parallel resistance and parallel connection of inductances replaced by single inductance; *d*, parallel connection of $R_{sp}M_{sp}$ transformed into series connection R^*M^*.

The magnetostrictive force has to extend the nickel rod. Therefore, the compliance K_i appears as a series element. The two ends of the compliant nickel rod (which is assumed massless) exert the same force on the two masses, which in turn are free to move. The force that is not balanced by the restoring force of the rod drives the two masses. Therefore, the two masses lie at the same potential in the diagram and are in series with the compliance K_i. Since the other ends of the mass symbols are force-free, they are at ground potential. We thus obtain the mechanical diagram of Figure 4.8*b*. The mass M_s vibrates in air. The mass M_l vibrates in contact with the resistance R_l; it represents the radiation resistance of the ground. To find the condition for optimum sound radiation into the ground, the series combination $M_l R_l$ is transformed into a parallel combination M_{lp} R_{lp}:

$$M_l \doteq M_{lp}$$

$$R_{lp} = \omega^2 \frac{M_l^2}{R_l} \tag{4.34}$$

If the ground impedance is high, M_s will usually be very small, and the shunt M_{lp} can be neglected. The diagram then simplifies to that of Figure 4.8*c*. The parallel combination $M_s R_{lp}$ is transformed again into a series combination $R^* M^*$, where

$$M^* \doteq M_s$$

$$R^* = \frac{\omega^2 M_s^2 R_l}{\omega^2 M_l^2} = \frac{M_s^2 R_l}{M_l^2} \tag{4.35}$$

For matching,

$$\omega M^* = \frac{1}{\omega K_i} \tag{4.36}$$

or

$$\omega^2 = \frac{1}{M^* K_i} \doteq \frac{1}{M_s K_i} \tag{4.37}$$

and

$$R_i = \frac{\eta}{\omega K_i} = R^* = \frac{R_l M_s^2}{M_l^2} \tag{4.38}$$

or

$$\eta = \frac{\omega K_i M_s^2 R_l}{M_l^2} = \frac{R_l M_s}{\omega M_l^2} \tag{4.39}$$

Thus, for optimum sound generation into the ground,

$$\omega M_l \doteq \frac{R_l}{\eta} \qquad \text{and} \qquad M_s = \frac{1}{\omega^2 K_i} \tag{4.40}$$

Lumped Parameter Systems with *n* Degrees of Freedom

Solution and Partial-Fraction Development

The theory represented in the preceding sections gives insight into systems with one degree of freedom and into systems built from simple tuned point masses that are coupled in a simple manner. It is obvious that the theory of lumped parameter systems contains the theory of filters, of chains of filters built in one, two, and three dimensions, and of coupled systems of any complexity. Our task now is to investigate complex lumped parameter systems and to determine whether predictions of their vibrational behavior can be made.

The simplest way to deal with a lumped parameter system is to represent it by its electromechanical diagram and to use the methods developed in the theory of electrical networks. The mechanical system can always be represented by a system of network equations of the form of Equation 1.127 or 1.138, but resistances now have to be included. The determinant solution can be decomposed in partial fractions, as shown in Chapter I. Because of the resistances, the roots of the determinant (the natural frequencies) become conjugate complex, and since they must represent decaying vibrations, their real part must be negative. As a consequence, the corresponding coefficients in the partial-fraction development become conjugate complex, and the contribution of every conjugate pair can be condensed to a single term. The solution can be represented by a circuit diagram similar to that of the reactance network, except that the individual circuits now contain resistances and are of the form shown in Figure 4.9.[2]

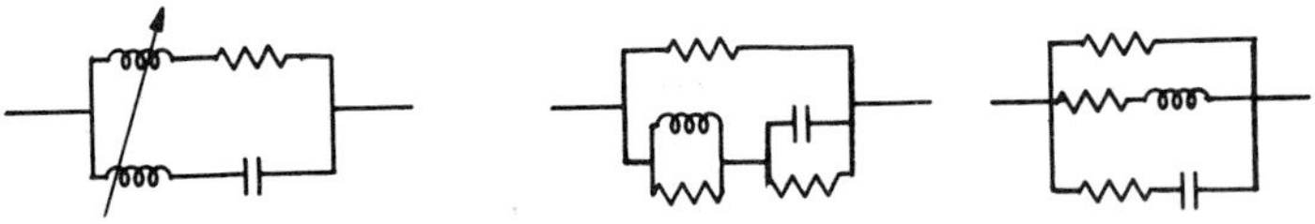

Fig. 4.9 Elementary tuned circuits in the partial-fraction development of a resistive network.

Resistance-Compensated Lumped Parameter Systems

In general, a lumped parameter system in which resistances, compliances, and masses can be selected in an arbitrary manner is of very complex nature. It is considerably more complex than a continuous system in which mass, compliance, and resistance are continuously distributed. In fact, a lumped parameter system corresponds to a continuous system that may be mass-loaded at various points and may consist of various parts coupled together. As a consequence, the lumped parameter system is very hard to deal with mathematically. In communication theory it has long been the practice to simplify the computation of filters by resistance compensation. The resistances are increased until all the inductances have the same loss factor. The computations then become relatively simple.

In mechanical systems, the compliances generate the losses, and the masses are dissipationless; therefore, resistance-compensated mechanical systems are systems in which the compliances all have the same loss factors.

[2] For a detailed derivation of this result, see H. W. Bode, *Network Analysis and Feedback Amplifier Design* (Princeton, N. J., 1945).

Such a resistance-compensated system can be conceived as the limiting case of a homogeneous system. The discontinuous system can be derived from the continuous system by so shaping a block of material into springs and masses that the compliance of the masses and the masses of the compliant parts are negligible in the frequency range of interest, which is below the resonant frequencies of the elements that represent the point masses and the springs. The masses and compliances may have arbitrarily chosen values, but the loss resistances are no longer arbitrarily variable. Since all the springs are made of the same material, they have the same loss factor. The n-dimensional analogue of a continuous system is, therefore, a mass spring system in which all the springs have the same loss factor.

If the loss factors of all compliances are the same, the equations of motion simplify to equations of the following form:

$$\left(j\omega M_{11}+\frac{\lambda_{11}\,(1+j\eta)}{j\omega}\right)\tilde{v}_1-\frac{\lambda_{12}}{j\omega}\,(1+j\eta)\,\tilde{v}_2+\ldots=\tilde{f}_1 \tag{4.41}$$

The computations can then be performed as if the system were dissipationless, and the losses can be taken into account by multiplying finally all stiffnesses by the factor $(1+j\eta)$; or, if the compliances hav been replaced by squares of the natural frequencies (which are linear functions of the compliances), the natural frequencies will have to be multiplied by the factor $\sqrt{1+j\eta}$.

Orthogonality Relations

For a system with continuously distributed mass and compliance, the amplitude is a continuous function of the location of the vibrating point. For a lumped parameter system, the vibration amplitude is specified only for the various point masses of the system.

The velocity amplitude distribution v_1/v_n, $v_2/v_n \ldots v_{n-1}/v_n$ (where v_i is the velocity of the ith mass), for a particular mode, can be normalized by prescribing the maximum kinetic energy of the system. If the kinetic energy for the rth mode of the system is E^r (where r is a superscript and not the symbol for raising to the power r), and if this kinetic energy is wholly stored in the n point masses and not in the coupling impedances, then,

$$\frac{1}{2}\sum_{i=1}^{n} M_i\left(v_i{}^r\right)^2=E^r \tag{4.42}$$

or, written in full,

$$\frac{1}{2}\left[M_1\left(v_1{}^r\right)^2+M_2\left(v_2{}^r\right)^2+\ldots\, M_n\left(v_n{}^r\right)^2\right]=E^r \tag{4.43}$$

where $v_i{}^r$ is the velocity of the ith point mass for the rth mode of vibration.

The solutions

$$v_1^r,\ v_2^r,\ v_3^r,\ \ldots\ v_n^r \qquad \text{and} \qquad r=1,\ 2,\ 3,\ \ldots\ n \tag{4.44}$$

that correspond to the normal modes are orthogonal. An elementary proof of the orthogonality condition when springs are the only coupling elements can be derived as follows. The equations of motion for the rth mode are:

$$\sum_{\nu=1}^{n} \lambda_{i\nu}\ \xi_\nu^r = -M_i \frac{d^2\xi_i^r}{dt^2} \qquad \text{and} \qquad i=1,\ \ldots\ n \tag{4.45}$$

or, written in terms of the velocities, since all variations occur with a radial frequency ω_r,

$$\sum_{\nu=1}^{m} \lambda_{i\nu} v_\nu^r = \omega_r^2\ M_i v_i^r \tag{4.46}$$

If each equation is multiplied by v_{is} (i$=1, \ldots n$) and the resulting equations are added, we obtain:

$$\sum_\nu \sum_r \lambda_{i\nu} v_\nu^r v_i^s = \omega_r^2 \sum_i M_i v_i^r v_i^s \tag{4.47}$$

If we had started with the equations of motion for the sth mode, we should have obtained the analogous result:

$$\sum_\nu \sum_r \lambda_{i\nu} v_\nu^s v_i^r = \omega_s^2 \sum_i M_i v_i^r v_i^s \tag{4.48}$$

The left sides of the last two equations are identical. If we subtract one side of the equation from the other, we get

$$(\omega_r^2 - \omega_s^2) \cdot \sum_i M_i v_i^r v_i^s = 0 \tag{4.49}$$

or

$$\sum_i M_i v_i^r v_i^s = 0 \tag{4.50}$$

since

$$\omega_r^2 - \omega_s^2 \neq 0 \tag{4.51}$$

if the system is not degenerate.[3] Because this condition (Eq. 4.50) is satisfied, the natural modes are all independent of one another, and the kinetic energy of the system is equal to the sum of the kinetic energies of all the

[3] The important conclusion here is the occurrence of the masses in the orthogonality condition (Eq. 4.50). A similar condition will be derived later (pp. 237–38) for continuous inhomogeneous systems.

natural modes. This is proved as follows. If the modes r and s are excited:

$$2E=\sum_{\lambda=1}^{n} M_\nu \left(v_\nu{}^r+v_\nu{}^s\right)^2=\sum_{\nu=1}^{n} M_\nu \left(v_\nu{}^r\right)^2+\sum_{\nu=1}^{n} M_\nu \left(v_\nu{}^s\right)^2+2\sum_{\nu=1}^{n} M_\nu v_\nu{}^r v_\nu{}^s$$

$$=\sum_{\nu=1}^{n} M_\nu \left(v_\nu{}^r\right)^2+\sum_{\nu=1}^{n} M_\nu \left(v_\nu{}^s\right)^2=2E^r+2E^s \tag{4.52}$$

As a consequence of the orthogonality condition, the energy matrix (E) is represented by the following diagonal matrix:

$$(E)=\begin{vmatrix} M_1\, 0\, 0\, 0\, \ldots\, 0 \\ 0\, M_2\, 0\, 0\, \ldots\, 0 \\ \cdots\cdots \\ \cdots\cdots \\ 0\, 0\, 0\, 0\, \ldots\, 0\, M_n \end{vmatrix} \tag{4.53}$$

If the coupling impedances also include masses (mutual inductances), then the kinetic energy is represented by:

$$\sum_i \sum_j M_{ij} v_i{}^r v_j{}^r = 2E^r \tag{4.54}$$

and the orthogonality condition becomes:

$$\sum_i \sum_j M_{ij} v_i{}^r v_j{}^s = 0 \tag{4.55}$$

where $r \neq s$. The proof is performed in a manner similar to that above for springs as coupling elements.

Since the average or maximum kinetic energy of a linear mass compliance system is the same as the average or maximum potential energy, the matrix of the potential energy for the normal modes of vibration is also diagonal.

If loss resistances are present, the energy becomes a function of time, and the various natural modes decay with different decay rates. The natural modes can then be normalized only for a particular instant of time. But the orthogonality conditions hold at all times, since all $v_i{}^r$ are proportional to $e^{-\delta_r t}$, all $v_j{}^s$ are proportional to $e^{-\delta_s t}$, and the decay factors can be divided out.

Static Coupling and the Influence Coefficients

In the preceding sections, the velocities or the currents were the primary variables. Impedances and velocities, or currents, turned out to be very convenient quantities. All the theorems that have been derived during the study of electrical networks were directly applicable to mechanical systems.

Many mechanical structures are coupled only by compliant elements. The vibration problem can then be reduced to the static case by means of the influence coefficients. Because of Hooke's law, the displacement ξ_i at a point i of the system is proportional to the force f_k that acts at a point k of the system:

$$\xi_i = K_{ik} f_k \tag{4.56}$$

The "compliance" influence coefficient K_{ik} represents the deflection at point i generated by a unit force at point k if all other forces are zero. If more forces f_r act on the system,

$$\xi_i = \sum_k K_{ik} f_k \tag{4.57}$$

If the coupling masses (inductances) M_{ik} and the coupling resistances R_{ik} are zero, the preceding equations can be generalized for periodic motion by writing the differential equations of the system in the form:

$$\sum_i K_{ik}^{-1} \xi_i = f_k - M\ddot{\xi}_k - R\dot{\xi}_k = f_k' \tag{4.58}$$

where f_k' is the total force that acts at the kth mass point, if friction and inertia force are considered as negative driving forces (as in d'Alembert's principle). In Equation 4.58, the K_{ik}^{-1} represent the elements of the inverted K_{ik} matrix. The differential equations can then be written in matrix form, and solutions can be derived by matrix methods.

Sometimes the stiffness influence coefficients λ_{ik} are more convenient. They are defined by the equation:

$$f_i = \lambda_{ik} \xi_k \tag{4.59}$$

They represent the force that is generated at point i, if point k experiences unit deflection and if all other points are clamped rigidly. Again, inertia and resistance force may be included in the driving force by replacing f_i by $f_i' = f_i - M\ddot{\xi}_i - R\dot{\xi}_i$.

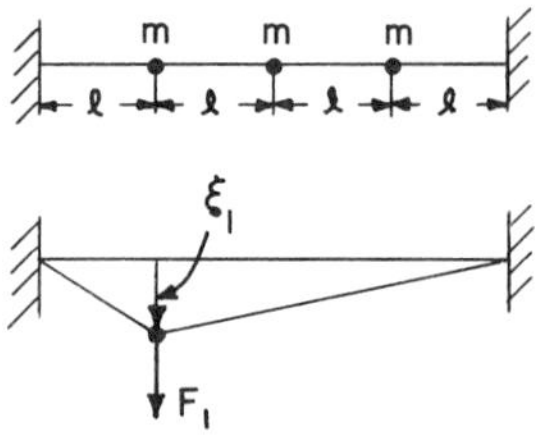

Fig. 4.10 The influence coefficients for a string.

Let us consider the example in Figure 4.10 in more detail. The tension in the string is T; the vertical component of the tension is $(\xi_1/l)T$ in the part of the string to the left of m_1 and $(\xi_1/3l)T$ in the part to the right of m_1. The sum of the vertical components must be equal to the applied force F_1:

$$F_1=\frac{\xi_1}{l}T+\frac{\xi_1}{3l}T=\frac{4T}{3l}\xi_1 \tag{4.60}$$

and the influence number K_{11} is given by:

$$K_{11}=\frac{\xi_1}{F_1}=\frac{3}{4}\frac{l}{T} \tag{4.61}$$

The deflections of the masses m_2 and m_3 generated by the force F_1 applied to m_1 are $\xi_2=2\xi_1/3$ and $\xi_3=\xi_1/3$ (Fig. 4.10), and the influence numbers are:

$$\begin{aligned}K_{21}&=\frac{\xi_2}{F_1}=\frac{2}{3}\cdot\left(\frac{3}{4}\frac{l}{T}\right)=\frac{1}{2}\frac{l}{T}\\ K_{31}&=\frac{\xi_3}{F_1}=\frac{1}{3}\cdot\left(\frac{3}{4}\frac{l}{T}\right)=\frac{1}{4}\frac{l}{T}\end{aligned} \tag{4.62}$$

Far-Coupled Systems

For the point-mass spring systems, the solutions derived with the aid of the influence coefficients are equivalent to the network solutions of the problem. However, the influence coefficients make it possible to deal with systems of greater complexity, such as those whose compliant elements are of a higher degree of complexity, like beams or beam structures. Such systems can no longer be represented by simple networks because of the complicated boundary conditions that have to be satisfied for deflection, slope, bending moment, and the shear force at the points of discontinuity. The deflection of a beam, for instance, depends in a rather complex manner on the loads that are distributed along its length. In the example of a beam supported at its ends and loaded with two masses (Fig. 4.11), we have:

$$\begin{aligned}\xi_1&=K_{11}\left(f_1-M_1\frac{d^2\xi_1}{dt^2}\right)+K_{12}\left(f_2-M_2\frac{d^2\xi_2}{dt^2}\right)\\ \xi_2&=K_{21}\left(f_1-M_1\frac{d^2\xi_1}{dt^2}\right)+K_{22}\left(f_2-M_2\frac{d^2\xi_2}{dt^2}\right)\end{aligned} \tag{4.63}$$

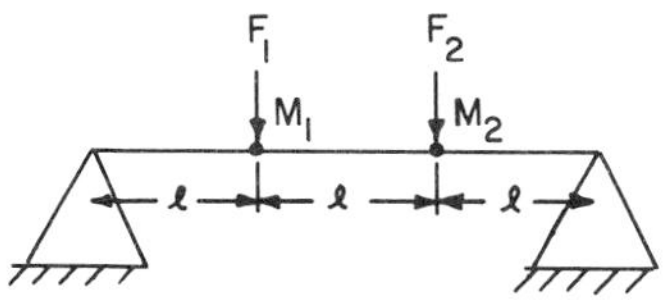

Fig. 4.11 Simple supported beam with two masses.

For periodic forces, these equations, rearranged, become:

$$\begin{aligned}(1-K_{11}\omega^2 M_1)\,\tilde{\xi}_1 - K_{12}\omega^2 M_2\tilde{\xi}_2 &= K_{11}\tilde{f}_1 + K_{12}\tilde{f}_2\\ -K_{21}\omega^2 M_1\tilde{\xi}_1 + (1-K_{22}\omega^2 M_2)\,\tilde{\xi}_2 &= K_{21}\tilde{f}_1 + K_{22}\tilde{f}_2\end{aligned} \tag{4.64}$$

With the formulas from standard engineering tables for beams supported at their ends we find (Fig 4.11) that

$$K_{11}=\frac{\xi_1}{F_1}=\frac{\xi_2}{F_2}=K_{22}=\frac{4l^3}{9\lambda_E I} \quad \text{and} \quad K_{12}=\frac{\xi_1}{F_2}=\frac{\xi_2}{F_1}=K_{21}=\frac{2l^3}{9\lambda_E I} \tag{4.65}$$

The above equations can easily be solved. The method applies to any number of masses.

Systems like those shown in Figure 4.11 are called far-coupled systems, in contrast to close-coupled systems. In a far-coupled system, each vibrator (each mass) is not only coupled with its neighbor, but cross-coupled with some or all of the other vibrators (masses). In the example of Figure 4.11, cross-coupling is caused by the beam. The beam sections are not independent of one another, but satisfy the condition of continuity for deflection, slope, and bending moment. Because of these conditions of continuity,

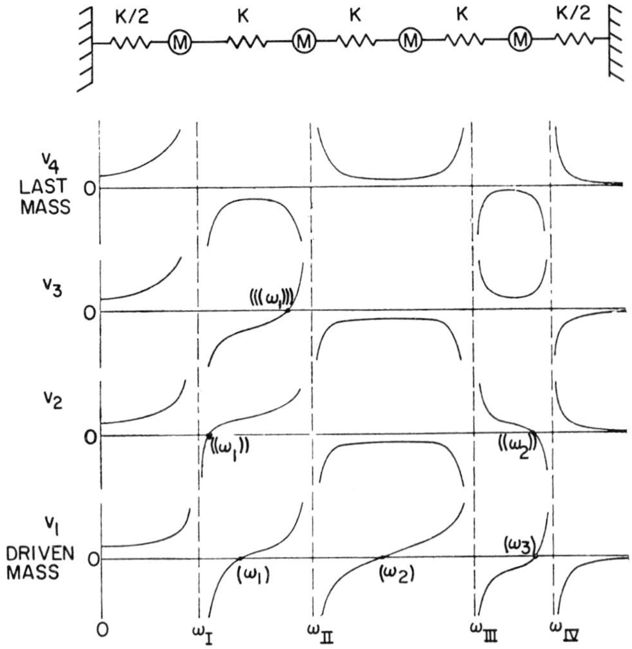

Fig. 4.12 Frequency curves of the motion of four coupled point masses. From L. S. Jacobson and R. S. Ayre, *Engineering Vibrations* (New York, 1958).

motion is transmitted from one end of the beam to the other, and all the masses attached to the beam are coupled regardless of their position.

Close-Coupled Systems with Many Masses

Systems that consist of masses and springs (Figs. 4.12 and 4.13) are called close-coupled; the first vibrator is coupled with the second, the second with the third, etc. Only adjacent meshes in the mechanical diagrams are coupled, and the determinant of the network equation consists only of the diagonal and of a diagonal line above and below the diagonal. The network equations are particularly simple.

To illustrate the physical behavior of systems consisting of masses coupled by compliant elements, let us consider the special case of four masses coupled by springs (Fig. 4.12). The mesh equations then become:

$$\begin{aligned}
\bar{z}_{11}\tilde{v}_1 - \bar{z}_{12}\tilde{v}_2 - \quad 0 \quad - \quad 0 \quad &= \tilde{f}_1 \\
-\bar{z}_{21}\tilde{v}_1 + \bar{z}_{22}\tilde{v}_2 - \bar{z}_{23}\tilde{v}_3 - \quad 0 \quad &= \tilde{f}_2 \\
0 \quad - \bar{z}_{32}\tilde{v}_2 + \bar{z}_{33}\tilde{v}_3 - \bar{z}_{34}\tilde{v}_4 &= \tilde{f}_3 \\
0 \quad - \quad 0 \quad - \bar{z}_{43}\tilde{v}_3 + \bar{z}_{44}\tilde{v}_4 &= \tilde{f}_4
\end{aligned} \tag{4.66}$$

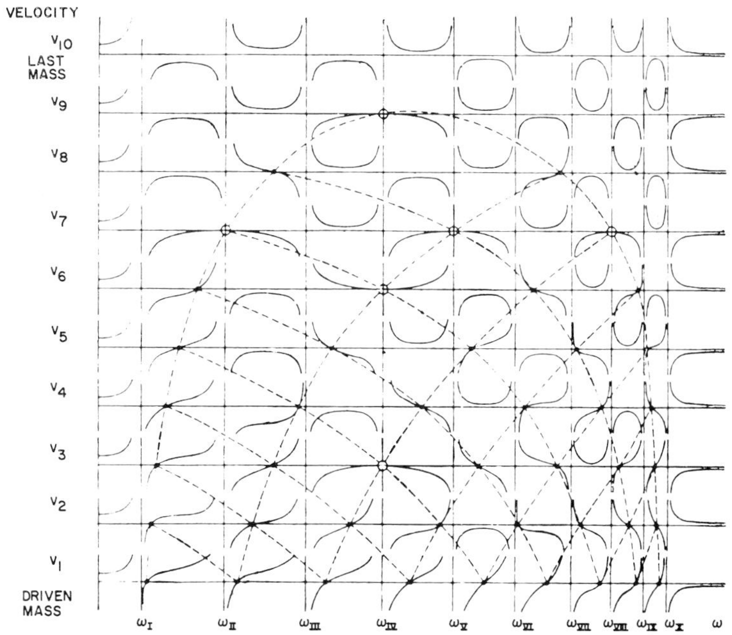

Fig. 4.13 Frequency curves of the motion of ten coupled point masses. From L. S. Jacobson and R. S. Ayre, *Engineering Vibrations* (New York, 1958).

where

$$\bar{Z}_{11}=j\omega M+\frac{1}{\frac{j\omega K}{2}}+\frac{1}{j\omega K}=\bar{Z}_{44}$$

$$\bar{Z}_{12}=\frac{1}{j\omega K}$$

$$\bar{Z}_{22}=\bar{Z}_{33}=j\omega M+\frac{2}{j\omega K} \tag{4.67}$$

and $\bar{Z}_{ij}=\bar{Z}_{ji}$, as discussed in Chapter I.

Equations such as those above are always solved by applying Cramer's rule. The evaluation of determinants of higher order is usually very laborious. One of the most valuable procedures for evaluating determinants is the method of using one element as a "pivot" and reducing the order of the determinant step by step until we are left with determinants of the second order. If the determinant below is of nth order, and if α_1 is the so-called pivot, the determinant can be transformed into one of the order $n-1$ by the following self-explanatory operation:[4]

$$\begin{vmatrix} \alpha_1\ b_1\ c_1 \ldots \\ \alpha_2\ b_2\ c_2 \ldots \\ \alpha_3\ b_3\ c_3 \ldots \\ \cdots\cdots \\ \alpha_n\ b_n\ c_n \ldots \end{vmatrix} = \frac{1}{\alpha_1^{\,n-2}} \begin{vmatrix} \alpha_1 b_2-\alpha_2 b_1, & \alpha_1 c_2-\alpha_2 c_1, & \ldots \\ \alpha_1 b_3-\alpha_3 b_1, & \alpha_1 c_3-\alpha_3 c_1, & \ldots \\ \cdots & \cdots & \cdots \\ \alpha_1 b_n-\alpha_n b_1, & \alpha_1 c_n-\alpha_n c_1, & \ldots \end{vmatrix} \tag{4.68}$$

For the four-mass system's determinant $\varDelta$ of order 4, we have

$$\begin{aligned}\varDelta=&\frac{1}{\bar{Z}_{11}^2(\bar{Z}_{11}\bar{Z}_{22}-\bar{Z}_{12}^2)}\\ &\times\begin{vmatrix}(\bar{Z}_{11}\bar{Z}_{22}-\bar{Z}_{12}^2)\bar{Z}_{11}\bar{Z}_{33}; & -\bar{Z}_{11}^2\bar{Z}_{23}^2; -(\bar{Z}_{11}\bar{Z}_{22}-\bar{Z}_{12}^2)\bar{Z}_{34}\bar{Z}_{11} \\ -(\bar{Z}_{11}\bar{Z}_{22}-\bar{Z}_{12}^2)\bar{Z}_{11}\bar{Z}_{34}; & (\bar{Z}_{11}\bar{Z}_{22}-\bar{Z}_{12}^2)\bar{Z}_{11}\bar{Z}_{44}\end{vmatrix}\\ =&\bar{Z}_{11}\bar{Z}_{22}\bar{Z}_{33}\bar{Z}_{44}-(\bar{Z}_{12}^2\bar{Z}_{33}\bar{Z}_{44}+\bar{Z}_{23}^2\bar{Z}_{44}\bar{Z}_{11}+\bar{Z}_{34}^2\bar{Z}_{11}\bar{Z}_{22})+\bar{Z}_{12}^2\bar{Z}_{34}^2\end{aligned} \tag{4.69}$$

If we assume that only the force $\tilde{f}_1$ is other than zero, the solution becomes:

$$\tilde{v}_1=\frac{1}{\varDelta}(\bar{Z}_{22}\bar{Z}_{33}\bar{Z}_{44}-\bar{Z}_{23}^2\bar{Z}_{44}-\bar{Z}_{34}^2\bar{Z}_{22})\,\tilde{f}_1$$

$$\tilde{v}_2=\frac{1}{\varDelta}(\bar{Z}_{12}\,(\bar{Z}_{33}\bar{Z}_{44}-\bar{Z}_{34}^2)\,\tilde{f}_1$$

$$\tilde{v}_3=\frac{1}{\varDelta}\bar{Z}_{12}\bar{Z}_{23}\bar{Z}_{44}\,\tilde{f}_1$$

$$\tilde{v}_4=\frac{1}{\varDelta}\bar{Z}_{12}\bar{Z}_{23}\bar{Z}_{34}\,\tilde{f}_1 \tag{4.70}$$

The determinant $\varDelta$ is a polynomial of fourth degree in ω^2. It has four zeros of ω^2 and is finite at all finite frequencies. The zeros of $\varDelta$ represent the

[4] For more details, see L. S. Jacobson and R. S. Ayre, *Engineering Vibrations* (New York, 1958), pp. 371–74.

resonances; the zeros of the factor at the right-hand side of Δ^{-1} represent the antiresonances. For v_1, this factor is of third degree in ω^2; for v_2, of second degree; and for v_3, of first degree. The factor at the right-hand side of Δ^{-1} for v_4 contains only coupling impedances and has no zeros at all. The velocity v_4 of the mass farthest away from the driven mass exhibits finite minima at frequencies between any two resonant frequencies. The determinant, and consequently also v_4, changes sign every time the frequency is increased above a resonant frequency. The transfer impedance, then, is alternately a mass impedance and a compliance impedance. The magnitude v_1 measures the driving-point admittance and obeys Foster's theorem; between any two resonances there is an antiresonance, and the slope of the frequency curve is always positive. The magnitudes v_2, v_3, and v_4 are proportional to the transfer admittance. As the distance from the driven point increases, more shallow troughs in the frequency curve replace the antiresonances that occurred in the frequency curve for the driven point. The velocity curve of the outermost mass exhibits no antiresonance at all; all minima are flat, as shown in Figure 4.12. Figure 4.13 shows a similar computation for a system with ten point masses.

The curves illustrate a number of important features that are encountered in most vibrators. The resonant frequencies are independent of the point of observation and of the force distribution, since the factor $1/\Delta$ occurs in all the solutions v_i. The zeros of the velocity represented by the antiresonances depend on the point of observation and on the force distribution as shown in Figures 4.12 and 4.13. They occur at frequencies that are different for each mass. For close-coupled systems, the number of antiresonances (zeros) decreases to zero as we pass from the driven point to the extreme points of the system. This observation also leads to the conclusion that in the partial-fraction development of the transfer impedance for the outermost point mass, successive terms always have opposite signs if the system is close-coupled.

Rayleigh's Principle

The hardest problem in dealing with systems of more than two degrees of freedom is the solution of the determinant equation $D=0$ for the natural frequencies. Once the natural frequencies are known, the amplitude distributions can easily be computed by substituting each natural frequency in turn into the equations of motion and then solving them in the standard way by Cramer's rule. In computing the natural frequencies, damping can usually be neglected, since it affects the result only by the factor $1 \pm \delta^2$, where δ is the decay constant. Very good approximations for the values of the natural frequencies, particularly for that of the fundamental frequency, can be obtained with the help of Rayleigh's principle and the Rayleigh-Ritz method. Rayleigh's principle centers on the fact that the maximum potential energy of a vibrator is equal to its maximum kinetic energy. In a dissipationless system that is not driven by an external force, the total energy E is constant:

$$E = E_p + E_k \tag{4.71}$$

where E_p is the potential energy and E_k is the kinetic energy. A natural mode may then be defined as a vibration during which all points of the system move synchronously; they attain their maximum deflections and their minimum deflections at the same time. At the instant of the maximum, the velocity becomes zero, the kinetic energy vanishes, and the potential energy becomes equal to the total energy of the system. The potential energy vanishes when the system passes through its equilibrium configuration, and the kinetic energy becomes equal to the total energy of the system. Thus, the maximum potential energy and the maximum kinetic energy are equal to the total energy of the system.

The potential energy is a quadratic function of the displacements, and the kinetic energy is a quadratic function of the velocities. It is proved in the theory of matrices that it is always possible to introduce new variables in such a way that the potential energy and the kinetic energy simultaneously contain only the squares of the amplitudes q_ν and of the velocities $\dot{q}_\nu$. Each q_ν now is a combination of the old co-ordinates and represents a particular mode of vibration; it is called a normal co-ordinate. If the normal co-ordinates are introduced as variables, the expressions for the kinetic and the potential energy become:

$$\begin{aligned} 2E_k &= a_1\dot{q}_1^2 + a_2\dot{q}_2^2 + \ldots\ a_n\dot{q}_n^2 \\ 2E_p &= c_1 q_1^2 + c_2 q_2^2 + \ldots\ c_n q_n^2 \end{aligned} \tag{4.72}$$

If only the νth mode is excited, all but q_ν and $\dot{q}_\nu$ are zero, and

$$\begin{aligned} 2E_k &= a_\nu \dot{q}_\nu^2 \\ 2E_p &= c_\nu q_\nu^2 \end{aligned} \tag{4.73}$$

Since the modes represent sinusoidal vibrations,

$$\dot{q}_\nu^2 = -\omega_\nu^2 q_\nu^2 \tag{4.74}$$

and since the maximum kinetic energy and the maximum potential energy are equal,

$$a_\nu \omega_\nu^2 q_\nu^2 = c_\nu q_\nu^2 \tag{4.75}$$

or

$$\omega_\nu^2 = \frac{c_\nu}{a_\nu} \tag{4.76}$$

We now assume a fictitious constrained mode[5] of frequency ω^*, in which all the co-ordinates vary in step with one another:

$$q = q_1 + q_2 + \ldots\ q_n \tag{4.77}$$

[5] This is a mode that would be enforced on the system only by additional constraints that would force the motion by external means to be of the type described here.

and

$$\dot{q}_\nu^2 = -\omega^{*2} q_\nu^2 \tag{4.78}$$

Since the maxima of the potential energy E_p and of the kinetic energy E_k must be equal under all circumstances:

$$\frac{(E_k)_{\max}}{(E_p)_{\max}} = 1 = \frac{\sum a_\nu \omega^{*2} \hat{q}_\nu^2}{\sum c_\nu \hat{q}_\nu^2} \tag{4.79}$$

or

$$\omega^{*2} = \frac{\sum c_\nu \hat{q}_\nu^2}{\sum a_\nu \hat{q}_\nu^2} = \frac{\sum a_\nu \omega_\nu^2 \hat{q}_\nu^2}{\sum a_\nu \hat{q}_\nu^2} = \frac{\sum \omega_\nu^2 A_\nu^2}{\sum A_\nu^2} \tag{4.80}$$

where

$$A_\nu = a_\nu \hat{q}_\nu^2 \tag{4.81}$$

Equation 4.80 gives the period of the vibration. The magnitudes

$$\frac{A_\nu}{\sqrt{\sum A_\nu^2}} = \cos\theta_\nu \tag{4.82}$$

can be interpreted as the direction cosines of a vector $A_1, A_2, \ldots A_n$, since

$$\frac{A_1^2}{\sum A_\nu^2} + \frac{A_2^2}{\sum A_\nu^2} + \ldots + \frac{A_n^2}{\sum A_\nu^2} = 1 = \cos\theta_1^2 + \cos^2\theta_2^2 + \ldots + \cos^2\theta_n \tag{4.83}$$

Equation 4.80 can, therefore, be written as follows:

$$\begin{aligned} \omega^{*2} &= \omega_1^2 \cos\theta_1^2 + \omega_2^2 \cos^2\theta_2 + \ldots + \omega_n^2 \cos^2\theta_n \\ &= \omega_1^2 + (\omega_2^2 - \omega_1^2)\cos^2\theta_2 + \ldots (\omega_n^2 - \omega_1^2)\cos^2\theta_n \end{aligned} \tag{4.84}$$

where $\cos^2\theta_1$ has been substituted from Eq. 4.83. If ω_1 is the smallest natural frequency, then all the terms in the last equation are positive. The smallest value that ω^* can have is, therefore, ω_1. If, on the other hand, ω_1 denotes the highest natural frequency, then all the terms except the first are negative, and ω^* is smaller than the highest natural frequency. Thus, ω^* must lie between the greatest and the smallest values ω_ν. Equation 4.80 gives the period of the vibration when the motion is constrained to the form represented by Equation 4.77. It is evident from Equation 4.84 that the period is stationary (i.e., is a maximum or minimum, or a point of inflection) when all but one of the coefficients q_ν^2 vanish, that is to say, when the type of mode excited coincides with one of those natural to the system and no constraint is needed.

This result may be used to compute the period of vibration with the aid of approximations to the normal modes. We make an estimate of the amplitude distribution $A_1\ A_2 \ldots A_n$ and interpret the deviation of the amplitude distribution from the correct values as a consequence of a hypothetical constraint; the frequency of the constrained motion then is given by:

$$\omega^{*2} = \frac{2E_p}{2E_k} = \frac{c_{11}A_1^2 + c_{22}A_2^2 + \ldots c_{12}A_1A_2 + \ldots}{a_{11}A_1^2 + a_{22}A_2^2 + \ldots a_{12}A_1A_2 + \ldots} \tag{4.85}$$

If the assumed mode approximates one of the normal modes, the corresponding q_ν will be large as compared with the amplitudes q_ν generated by the constraints, so that ω^{*2} and the square of the angular frequency of the dominant mode will differ by quantities of the order of the squares of the small normal co-ordinates. This approximation to the angular frequency is of much greater accuracy than the approximation to the modal configuration, since the square, and not the linear value of the correction, enters the result.

The value of the angular frequency thus computed can be substituted into the equations of motion, and a second-order approximation can be derived for the ratios $A_1 : A_2 : A_3 : \ldots$. These new values can again be used to compute more accurate values for ω^*, and so on. The corrections usually converge very rapidly, and the procedure gives excellent results after one or two iterations.

As an example, let the vibrating system be a simple string, and let the deflection be approximated by:

$$\xi = \left[1 - \left(\frac{2x}{l}\right)^n\right] \cos \omega t \tag{4.86}$$

where $n \geq 1$. Kinetic energy and potential energy become:[6]

$$E_k = \frac{1}{2} \int_{-\frac{1}{2}l}^{\frac{1}{2}l} \rho \dot{\xi}^2 dx = \frac{\rho\, n^2 l \omega^2 \sin^2 \omega t}{(n+1)(2n+1)} \tag{4.87}$$

and

$$E_p = \frac{1}{2} T \cdot \int_{-\frac{1}{2}l}^{\frac{1}{2}l} \left(\frac{d\xi}{dx}\right)^2 dx = \frac{2n^2 T \cos^2 \omega t}{(2n-1)l} \tag{4.88}$$

where T is the tension. Hence,

$$\omega^2 = \frac{2(n+1)(2n+1)}{2n-1} \frac{T}{\rho l^2} \tag{4.89}$$

If $n=1$, the vibration amplitude is the same as if the mass were concentrated at the middle point of the string, and $\omega^2 = 12T/\rho l^2$. If $n=2$, the form is parabolic, and $\omega^2 = 10\, T/\rho l^2$. The true value of ω^2 is $\pi^2 T/\rho l^2$, which is 0.99361 times that given by the approximation $n=2$.

The Rayleigh principle is just as efficient for computing the periods of lumped parameter systems, but the computations are not quite so impressive because of the greater complexity of the terms in comparison to the simple integrals for the string.

The Rayleigh method works particularly well for the first mode of complex lumped systems. The higher modes are usually computed by the

[6] E.g., see pp. 143–44.

Rayleigh-Ritz method, which makes use of the fundamental frequency as determined by the Rayleigh method and of the orthogonality of the natural functions.[7]

Recommended Reading

BICKLEY, W. G., AND A. TALBOT, *An Introduction to the Theory of Vibrating Systems,* Oxford University Press, London, 1961.

DEN HARTOG, J.P., *Mechanical Vibrations*, McGraw-Hill Inc., New York, 1947.

JACOBSEN, L.S., AND R. S. AYRE, *Engineering Vibrations*, McGraw-Hill, Inc., New York, 1958.

KÁRMÁN, T. V., AND M. A. BIOT, *Mathematical Methods in Engineering*, McGraw-Hill, Inc., New York, 1940.

KINSLER, L. E., AND A. R. FREY, *Fundamentals of AdouwBidw*, John Wiley Sons, Inc., New York, 1962.

MYKLESTAD, N. O., *Fundamentals of Vibration Analysis*, McGraw-Hill, Inc., New York, 1956.

RAYLEIGH, LORD, *The Theory of Sound*, Dover Publications, Inc., New York, 1945.

WHITTAKER, E. T., *A Treatise on the Analytical Dynamics of Particles and Rigid Bodies*, Dover Publications, Inc., New York, 1944.

[7] This method is described in detail by T. von Kármán and M. A. Biot, *Mathematical Methods in Engineering* (New York, 1940), pp. 352–64, and by G. Temple and W. G. Bickley, *Rayleigh's Principle* (New York, 1956).

V / CONTINUOUS SYSTEMS

In a strict sense, all mechanical systems are continuous—a continuous system being one in which mass and compliance are distributed evenly over the entire system. The mass in the point-mass spring system is not actually a point mass, but always takes up a finite volume and exhibits an infinite number of natural modes of vibration. However, the natural frequencies of these modes are usually much higher than the frequency range of interest in point-mass spring systems. Similarly, the compliant elements are of finite dimensions and, consequently, have a finite mass. Therefore, compliant elements also have an infinite number of natural modes of vibration. The natural frequencies of these modes are similarly much higher than the frequency range of interest in point-mass spring systems. If elements that essentially represent masses are combined with elements that are predominantly compliances, a system is evolved that has some of its resonances at relatively low frequencies (the resonances we are interested in) and has the remaining resonances at very high frequencies. At the lower frequencies, such a system behaves much the same as a system that is made up of ideal dimensionless point masses and massless springs. Such a system is defined as a lumped system. Thus, each element of a lumped system is itself a continuous system, but the lowest natural frequencies of these elements are much higher than the resonant frequencies of the lumped system of which they are components.

This chapter represents a thorough study of the transversely vibrating string and the longitudinally vibrating rod without and with internal friction. After the point-mass compliant element system, these two vibrators represent the next most highly organized vibratory system, and the theory governing their behavior already contains most of the elements that occur in the study of complex vibratory systems.

Transversely Vibrating String

Differential Equation

The simplest continuous vibrating system is a transversely vibrating string. Such a string is specified by its length l, its mass per unit length m, and its tension T. If the vibration amplitude is small, as will be assumed in the following, the tangential displacement of the string is zero, and the tension along the string is of constant magnitude. But because of the displacement, the tension changes direction along the string. The net force acting on an element of length ds of the string is the vector difference of the tensions at both ends, as illustrated in Figure 5.1. The net force is a restoring force whose direction is opposite to that of the displacement ξ. This restoring force is given by:

$$-2T\sin\left(\frac{1}{2}\frac{\partial\theta}{\partial x}dx\right) = -T\frac{\partial\theta}{\partial x}dx \tag{5.1}$$

The force that accelerates the element ds, that is the inertia force, is $mdx\,\partial^2\xi/\partial t^2$, since $dx \doteq ds$.

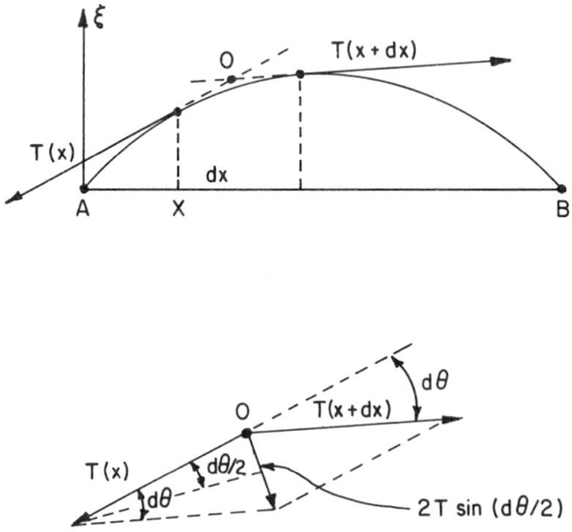

Fig. 5.1 Derivation of the differential equation of the string.

The differential equation of motion is obtained by eliminating θ with the aid of the relation:

$$\tan\theta = \frac{\partial\xi}{\partial x} \doteq \theta \tag{5.2}$$

and equating the inertia force to the restoring force:

$$mdx\frac{\partial^2\xi}{\partial t^2} = Tdx\frac{\partial^2\xi}{\partial x^2} \tag{5.3}$$

or

$$\frac{1}{c^2}\frac{\partial^2\xi}{\partial t^2} - \frac{\partial^2\xi}{\partial x^2} = 0 \tag{5.4}$$

where $c^2 = T/m$. The last equation is the one-dimensional wave equation, and c^2 is the square of the propagation velocity of progressive waves along the string, as is proved below.

Progressive Wave Solution

The solution of the wave equation (5.4) may be represented by two progressive waves of the form:

$$\xi = f_1(ct-x) + f_2(ct+x) \tag{5.5}$$

as is shown by substituting the last expression into the differential equation (5.4). This solution can be derived by introducing the new variables $u=ct+x$ and $v=ct-x$, which transform the equation into its characteristic form:

$$\frac{\partial^2 \xi}{\partial u \partial v} = 0 \tag{5.6}$$

Thus, the variable ξ is a function either of u alone or of v alone (or it is the sum of such functions), and the general solution is of the form given by Equation 5.5.

The function $f_1\,(ct-x)$ depends only on the combination $u=ct-x$ of the variables and does not change if $u=ct-x$ maintains the same value. The condition $ct-x=\text{const}$ is equivalent to:

$$\frac{d}{dt}(ct-x) = 0 \tag{5.7}$$

or to:

$$c - \frac{dx}{dt} = 0 \qquad \text{or} \qquad \frac{dx}{dt} = c \tag{5.8}$$

The x-co-ordinate of the points for which the function $f\,(x-ct)$ has the same value (i.e., for which the deflection is constant) propagates in the positive x-direction with the velocity c. Similarly, the x-co-ordinate of the points for which the function $f\,(ct+x)$ has a constant value propagates in the negative x-direction with the velocity c. The first function represents a wave traveling in the positive x-direction; the second, a wave traveling in the negative x-direction. The solution is complete, since it contains two arbitrary functions. The solution (Eq. 5.5) is particularly suited for studying wave propagation, i.e., for studying the spreading of an initial disturbance over the system.

For periodic vibrations, Equation 5.5 is written as follows:

$$\xi = f_1\left[\frac{c}{\omega}(\omega t - kx)\right] + f_2\left[\frac{c}{\omega}(\omega t + kx)\right] \tag{5.9}$$

where

$$k = \frac{\omega}{c} = \frac{2\pi f}{c} = \frac{2\pi}{\lambda} \tag{5.10}$$

is the wave number and $\lambda = c/f$ is the wave length, i.e., the distance the vibration travels during one period. Since f_1 and f_2 are arbitrary functions of the argument $ct \pm kx = (c/\omega)\,(\omega t \pm kx) = \text{const}\,(\omega t \pm kx)$, the periodic progressive wave solution is necessarily of the form:

$$\xi = A\cos\frac{\omega}{c}(ct-x) + B\cos\frac{\omega}{c}(ct+x) = A\cos(\omega t - kx) + B\cos(\omega t + kx) \tag{5.11}$$

or of the form:

$$\xi = (Ae^{-jkx} + Be^{+jkx})\, e^{j\omega t} \tag{5.12}$$

Standing Wave Solution and Natural Modes of the String

The systems of interest in the theory of vibration are frequently small as compared to the wave length, and the waves are reflected many times during each period. No traveling waves can then be distinguished. In theory, the above solution is still useful, but it is expedient to replace it by a standing wave solution that is made up of a sum of particular integrals of the form:

$$\xi = X(x) \cdot T(t) \tag{5.13}$$

If Equation 5.13 is substituted in the differential equation,

$$\frac{1}{c^2} X(x) \frac{\partial^2 T(t)}{\partial t^2} = T(t) \frac{\partial^2 X(x)}{\partial x^2} \tag{5.14}$$

or

$$\frac{1}{c^2 T} \frac{\partial^2 T}{\partial t^2} = \frac{1}{X} \frac{\partial^2 X}{\partial x^2} \tag{5.15}$$

The left-hand side of this equation is a function of t, and the right-hand side is a function of x. But a function of the independent variable t can never be equal (for all values of t) to a function of the independent variable x (for all values of x). The only possibility is that the left- and right-hand sides of Equation 5.15 are equal to a constant. If this constant is assumed as a positive square δ^2, particular integrals that are exponentially increasing or decreasing result. Such solutions usually are of little interest. But a very useful particular integral is obtained if this constant is written as a negative square $-k^2$:

$$\frac{1}{c^2 T} \frac{\partial^2 T}{\partial t^2} = \frac{1}{X} \frac{\partial^2 X}{\partial x^2} = -k^2 \tag{5.16}$$

In this way, solutions that represent harmonic vibrations are selected, as will be shown. The differential equation (5.16) can be split into the two equations:

$$\frac{\partial^2 X}{\partial x^2} = -k^2 X \tag{5.17}$$

and

$$\frac{\partial^2 T}{\partial t^2} = -k^2 c^2 T = -\omega^2 T \tag{5.18}$$

where $\omega^2 = k^2 c^2$. These equations are similar to those representing point-mass compliance systems. The solutions are:

$$X = A\cos(kx + \varphi_x) \tag{5.19}$$

and

$$T = B\cos(\omega t + \varphi_t) \tag{5.20}$$

The solution of the wave equation is given by the product XT, that is, by:

$$\xi = XT = C\cos(kx + \varphi_x)\cos(\omega t + \varphi_t) \tag{5.21}$$

where $C = AB$. The factor $X(x)$ represents the amplitude distribution and is the same at all times. The factor $T(t)$ states that all points move in step or in unison; the displacement increases or decreases with time by the same factor $T(t)$. The displacements no longer propagate. The deflections of all the points of the string attain their maxima at the same time and their minima at the same time. The solution obtained is called a standing wave or natural vibration. Thus, the special solution (Eq. 5.13) helped us to select, from the infinite number of different types of solutions of the wave equation, solutions of the form of standing vibrations.

Undamped string. The vibration of a mechanical system is determined only if the system is isolated, so that it is completely under control; no energy must leave or enter the system through its boundaries—that is, no work must be done on or by the boundaries. Since work is equal to the product of force and displacement, either the boundaries must be motionless (clamped rigidly), i.e., $\xi = 0$, or the force at the boundaries must vanish. For a string or a longitudinally vibrating rod, the force at any point is proportional to $\partial\xi/\partial x$; if the boundary is free, $\partial\xi/\partial x$ must vanish at the boundary.

It is natural to try to generate the general solution from building blocks that have a physical meaning, such as those given by Equation 5.21. We shall not be satisfied if only the sum of all the particular integrals satisfies the boundary conditions, but shall favor solutions in which the individual terms themselves satisfy the boundary conditions. Every one of these terms or building blocks will be a solution by itself and will describe a possible motion of the system. Each term will be of the form:

$$\xi_\nu(x, t) = A_\nu \cos(k_\nu x + \varphi_{\nu x})\cos(k_\nu ct + \varphi_{\nu t}) \tag{5.22}$$

where $\omega_\nu = k_\nu c$ is the angular frequency of the vibration $\xi_\nu\,(x, t)$.

For a clamped string, the deflection ξ vanishes at the ends $x = 0$ and $x = l$ for all values of t, or:

$$A_\nu \cos(\varphi_{\nu x})\cos(\omega_\nu t + \varphi_{\nu t}) = A_\nu \cos(k_\nu l + \varphi_{\nu x})\cos(\omega_\nu t + \varphi_{\nu t}) = 0 \tag{5.23}$$

Hence,

$$\varphi_{\nu x} = \frac{\pi}{2} \qquad k_\nu l = \nu\pi \qquad \text{and} \qquad \nu = 1, 2, 3, \ldots \tag{5.24}$$

Thus, every term of the solution is of the form:

$$\xi_\nu(x, t) = \xi_\nu(x) \cos(\omega_\nu t + \varphi_{\nu t}) \tag{5.25}$$

where

$$\xi_\nu(x) = A_\nu \sin\frac{\nu\pi x}{l} \quad \text{and} \quad \omega_\nu = k_\nu c = \frac{\nu\pi c}{l} \tag{5.26}$$

The motion described by $\xi_\nu(x, t)$ is called a natural vibration of the system. The natural vibrations represent the simplest form of vibrations that the system is capable of performing in the absence of external forces. The natural vibrations represent a motion that preserves itself indefinitely. The first factor $\xi_\nu(x)$ depends on x, and not on t; it describes the amplitude distribution along the string. The second factor is independent of x and depends only on the time t; it represents a sinusoidal time variation of the space pattern of the vibration. The functions $\xi_\nu(x)$ are called the natural functions, or the modes, of vibration of the system; the frequencies ω_ν are called the natural (angular) frequencies of the system. Each natural function $\xi_\nu(x)$ describes the space variation of the amplitude of the vibration when the system vibrates at the corresponding natural frequency ω_ν. For other than the natural frequencies $\omega = \omega_\nu$, the homogeneous (i.e., force-free) equation

$$\frac{\partial^2 \xi_\nu}{\partial x^2} + \frac{\omega_\nu^2}{c^2}\xi_\nu = 0 \tag{5.27}$$

has no other but the trivial solution $\xi_\nu = 0$. Thus, the natural functions are defined as the nontrivial periodic solutions of the homogeneous differential equation (5.27); they represent periodic vibrations of the force-free system that persist indefinitely.

A more general solution can be constructed by adding the natural vibrations of the system with their corresponding amplitudes A_ν:

$$\xi(x, t) = \sum_\nu \xi_\nu(x) \cos(\omega_\nu t + \varphi_\nu)$$

$$= \sum_\nu A_\nu \sin\frac{\nu\pi x}{l} \cos(\omega_\nu t + \varphi_\nu) \qquad \text{where } \nu = 1, 2, 3, \ldots \tag{5.28}$$

This solution would be of value if it were general enough to deal with the cases of practical interest. Indeed, the above solution is the most general solution that can be obtained. This is proved with the aid of the theorems of Fourier. It can be adapted to any initial conditions $t=0$ for the displacement $\xi(x, 0) = \xi_0(x)$ and for the velocity $\dot{\xi}(x, 0) = \dot{\xi}_0(x)$ at $t=0$. The first condition yields the relation:

$$\xi(x, 0) = \sum_\nu \xi_\nu(x) \cos\varphi_\nu = \sum_\nu (A_\nu \cos\varphi_\nu) \sin\frac{\nu\pi x}{l}$$

$$= \sum_\nu \alpha_\nu \sin\frac{\nu\pi x}{l} \tag{5.29}$$

where

$$\alpha_\nu = A_\nu \cos \varphi_\nu \tag{5.30}$$

The second condition yields the relation:

$$\dot{\xi}(x, 0) = \sum \xi_\nu(x)\omega_\nu \sin \varphi_\nu = \sum A_\nu \omega_\nu \sin \varphi_\nu \sin \frac{\nu\pi x}{l}$$
$$= \sum \beta_\nu \omega_\nu \sin \frac{\nu\pi x}{l} \tag{5.31}$$

where

$$\beta_\nu = A_\nu \sin \varphi_\nu \tag{5.32}$$

The series on the right-hand side of both equations (5.29 and 5.31) can be reduced to one single term. In the case of the former equation, this is done by multiplying both sides by sin $(\mu\pi x/l)$ and integrating over the system:

$$\int_0^l \xi(x, 0) \sin \frac{\mu\pi x}{l} dx = \sum_\nu \alpha_\nu \int_0^l \sin \frac{\nu\pi x}{l} \sin \frac{\mu\pi x}{l} dx \tag{5.33}$$

The integrals on the right are zero if $\nu \neq \mu$:

$$\int_0^l \sin \frac{\nu\pi x}{l} \sin \frac{\mu\pi x}{l} dx = \frac{1}{2} \int_0^l \left\{ \cos \left[(\nu - \mu) \frac{\pi x}{l}\right] - \cos \left[(\nu + \mu) \frac{\pi x}{l}\right] \right\} dx$$
$$= \frac{1}{2} \left[\frac{\sin (\nu - \mu)\pi}{(\nu - \mu)\frac{\pi}{l}} - \frac{\sin (\nu + \mu)\pi}{(\nu + \mu)\frac{\pi}{l}} \right] = 0 \tag{5.34}$$

But the integral for $\mu = \nu$ is different from zero and is positive:

$$\int_0^l \sin^2 \frac{\nu\pi x}{l} dx = \frac{1}{2} \int_0^l \left(1 - \cos \frac{2\nu\pi x}{l}\right) dx = \frac{1}{2}\left(l - \frac{\sin 2\nu\pi}{\frac{2\nu\pi}{l}}\right) = \frac{1}{2} l \tag{5.35}$$

The fundamental property of the natural functions that is expressed by Equations 5.34 and 5.35 can be stated in a more condensed form:

$$\int_0^l \xi_\nu(x)\xi_\mu(x) dx = \begin{cases} 0 \text{ if } \nu \neq \mu \\ \neq 0 \text{ if } \nu = \mu \end{cases} \tag{5.36}$$

This so-called orthogonality condition will be derived later in a more general manner. As a consequence of the orthogonality condition, all the terms on the right-hand side of Equation 5.33 vanish except when $\nu = \mu$, and the equation simplifies to:

$$\int_0^l \xi(x, 0) \sin \frac{\nu\pi x}{l} dx = \alpha_\nu \int_0^l \sin^2 \frac{\nu\pi x}{l} dx = \frac{\alpha_\nu l}{2} \tag{5.37}$$

or

$$A_\nu \cos \varphi_\nu = \frac{2}{l} \int_0^l \xi(x, 0) \sin \frac{\nu \pi x}{l} dx \tag{5.38}$$

Equation 5.31 for the initial velocity is dealt with in a similar manner by multiplying it by sin ($\mu\pi x/l$) and integrating again over the length of the string. The mixed terms $\mu \neq \nu$ vanish because of the orthogonality condition, and

$$\omega_\nu \beta_\nu = \frac{2}{l} \int_0^l \dot{\xi}_\nu(x, 0) \sin \frac{\nu \pi x}{l} dx \tag{5.39}$$

By squaring Equations 5.30 and 5.32 and adding, we obtain:

$$\alpha_\nu^2 + \beta_\nu^2 = A_\nu^2 (\cos^2 \varphi_\nu + \sin^2 \varphi_\nu) = A_\nu^2 \tag{5.40}$$

Dividing Equation 5.32 by Equation 5.30 yields:

$$\frac{\beta_\nu}{\alpha_\nu} = \tan \varphi_\nu \tag{5.41}$$

The constants A_ν and φ_ν are thus determined. The theorems of Fourier ensure that the system of natural functions $\xi_\nu(x)$ is complete and that the series on the right-hand sides of Equations 5.29 and 5.31 do indeed represent the initial amplitude and the initial velocity.

For the fundamental natural vibration of the string, $\nu = 1$, and

$$\xi_1 = A_1 \sin \frac{\pi x}{l} \qquad \omega_1 = k_1 c = \frac{\pi c}{l} \qquad f_1 = \frac{\omega_\nu}{2\pi} = \frac{c}{2l} \tag{5.42}$$

where f_1 is the frequency and

$$T_1 = \frac{1}{f_1} = \frac{2l}{c} \tag{5.43}$$

is the period. The last form of the right-hand side shows that the period of the fundamental vibration is equal to the time it takes a progressive wave to travel from one end of the string to the other and back, that is, to travel twice the length of the string. In fact, the standing wave

$$A_\nu \sin \frac{\nu \pi x}{l} \cos \omega_\nu t = \frac{A_\nu}{2} \left[\sin \left(\omega_\nu t + \frac{\nu \pi x}{l}\right) - \sin \left(\omega_\nu t - \frac{\nu \pi x}{l}\right) \right] \tag{5.44}$$

can be decomposed into two progressive waves. For the fundamental vibration, each progressive component runs through one complete cycle (to the other end and back), so that the original state is restored after one period. The progressive components that make up the standing wave are continuously reflected at the ends of the string, and the period of the natural vibration is the time it takes the system to pass through one complete cycle. For the second harmonic,

$$\xi_2 = A_2 \sin\frac{2\pi x}{l}\cos(\omega_2 t + \varphi_2)$$

$$\omega_2 = \frac{2\pi}{l}c \qquad \text{and} \qquad f_2 = 2\frac{c}{2l} = 2f_1$$

$$T_2 = \frac{1}{2}\cdot\frac{2l}{c} = \frac{1}{2}T_1 \tag{5.45}$$

as though the string consisted of two independent sections, each section of a length one half that of the original string. The fundamental frequency of each section, then, is twice as great and is the frequency of vibration of the complete string. For the third natural frequency, three half-waves are distributed over the string, and the frequency of the vibration is three times the fundamental frequency of the original string.

Damped string. Up to this point, damping has not been considered. It was shown in Chapter III that the internal dissipation of the material, regardless of its cause, leads to a phase lag φ ($\tan\varphi = \eta$) between stress and strain and that this phase lag is accounted for by the differential equation if the elastic constant λ is replaced by the complex elastic constant:

$$\bar{\lambda} = \lambda_0(1 + j\eta) \tag{5.46}$$

In the case of the string, the tension assumes the role of the elastic constant:

$$\bar{T} = T_0(1 + j\eta)$$

$$\bar{c}^2 = \frac{\bar{T}}{m} = c_0^2(1 + j\eta) \tag{5.47}$$

where

$$c_0^2 = \frac{T_0}{m} \tag{5.48}$$

and the differential equation becomes:

$$\frac{\partial^2 \xi}{\partial t^2} = c_0^2(1 + j\eta)\frac{\partial^2 \xi}{\partial x^2} = \bar{c}^2\frac{\partial^2 \xi}{\partial x^2} \tag{5.49}$$

The introduction of a complex elastic constant is equivalent to restricting the motion to progressive or standing, periodic or decaying periodic, vibrations of the form:

$$\xi_\nu = \xi_\nu(x, t) = \hat{\xi}_\nu(x)e^{-\delta_\nu t + j\omega_\nu{}^* t} \tag{5.50}$$

Substitution in the complex wave equation (5.49) yields the relation:

$$(-\delta_\nu + j\omega_\nu{}^*)^2\hat{\xi}_\nu e^{-\delta_\nu t + j\omega_\nu{}^* t} = c_0^2(1 + j\eta)\frac{\partial^2 \hat{\xi}_\nu}{\partial x^2}e^{-\delta_\nu t + j\omega_\nu{}^* t} \tag{5.51}$$

which is equivalent to two equations, obtained by canceling the time and phase factors and by equating the real and imaginary parts:

$$(-\omega_\nu{}^{*2} + \delta_\nu{}^2)\hat{\xi}_\nu = c_0^2\frac{\partial^2 \hat{\xi}_\nu}{\partial x^2} \qquad \text{[real parts]} \tag{5.52}$$

and

$$-2\delta_\nu\omega_\nu{}^*\hat{\xi}_\nu = c_0{}^2\eta\frac{\partial^2\hat{\xi}_\nu}{\partial x^2} \quad \text{[imaginary parts]} \tag{5.53}$$

Equation 5.52 is of the same form as Equation 5.27 of the nondissipative system if $\omega_\nu{}^{*2}-\delta_\nu{}^2$ is replaced by $\omega_\nu{}^2$:

$$-\omega_\nu{}^2\hat{\xi}_\nu = c_0{}^2\frac{\partial^2\hat{\xi}_\nu}{\partial x^2} \tag{5.54}$$

where

$$\omega_\nu{}^2 = \omega_\nu{}^{*2}-\delta_\nu{}^2 \tag{5.55}$$

The magnitudes ω_ν are determined by the boundary conditions. If the magnitudes ω_ν have been determined, the frquencies $\omega_\nu{}^*$ of the decaying vibrations (Eq. 5.50) are given by:

$$\omega_\nu{}^{*2} = \omega_\nu{}^2+\delta_\nu{}^2 \tag{5.56}$$

Because solid friction (η=const) was assumed, this frequency is higher than the resonant frequency ω_ν.[1] Comparison of Equations 5.54 and 5.27 shows that the amplitude distribution of the natural vibrations is unaffected by the damping and that the *eigen* values $\omega_\nu{}^2$ and the natural functions are the same as for a nondissipative system. The natural functions form a complete set of orthogonal functions, which can be used to represent the solution of the dissipative system just as well as that of the nondissipative system at any particular instant. It is almost obvious that the dissipative system must have the same natural functions as the corresponding undamped system—we may take a photograph of an instantaneous vibration of the damped system and produce an undamped system that has the same initial amplitude and velocity distribution. Since every instantaneous state of the damped system can also be an initial state of the undamped system, any motion that the damped system is capable of performing can be represented by the natural functions of the undamped system. Any physically possible state of the undamped system, then, can be represented by the natural functions of the damped system, and vice versa; every amplitude and velocity distribution of the undamped system can also be considered as an initial state of the damped system. Consequently, the natural functions of both systems must be the same. However, the frequencies of the free vibrations are influenced by the damping (Eq. 5.56), and the natural modes of the dissipative systems decay with time.

The decay constant follows from Equation 5.53, if $\partial^2\hat{\xi}/\partial x^2$ is eliminated with the aid of Equation 5.52 and $\omega_\nu{}^*$ is computed by Equation 5.56; it is given by:

$$\delta_\nu = -\frac{c_0{}^2\eta}{2\omega_\nu{}^*}\frac{1}{\hat{\xi}_\nu}\frac{\partial^2\hat{\xi}_\nu}{\partial x^2} = -\frac{\eta(-\omega_\nu{}^{*2}+\delta_\nu{}^2)}{2\omega_\nu{}^*} = \frac{\eta}{2}\frac{\omega_\nu{}^2}{\sqrt{\omega_\nu{}^2+\delta_\nu{}^2}}$$

$$= \frac{\omega_\nu\eta}{2} + \text{terms with higher powers in } \eta \tag{5.57}$$

[1] See also Eq. 2.142.

which is essentially identical with Equation 2.144 for the point-mass compliance system.

The complete solution for the free vibrations, then, is:

$$\xi(x,t)=\sum_{\nu}\hat{\xi}_{\nu}(x)\cos(\omega_{\nu}t+\phi_{\nu})\cdot e^{-\omega_{\nu}\eta t/2+j\omega_{\nu}^{*}t}=\sum_{\nu}\xi_{\nu}(x)g_{\nu}(t) \tag{5.58}$$

where

$$\hat{\xi}_{\nu}(x)=A_{\nu}\cos(k_{\nu}x+\psi_{\nu}) \quad \text{and} \quad g_{\nu}(t)=e^{-\omega_{\nu}\eta t/2+j\omega_{\nu}^{*}t} \tag{5.59}$$

The constants k_{ν}, ω_{ν}, and ψ_{ν} are derived from the boundary conditions; the constants A_{ν} and φ_{ν}, from the initial condition of the system.

The computations above have been performed on the assumption of solid damping, that is, of an approximately constant loss factor η. As a consequence, damping increases the absolute value of the stiffness constant and, consequently, also increases the natural frequencies of the system; and the vibrations—regardless of how great the damping constant η is—never become aperiodically damped. Similar computations can be performed on the assumption of velocity-proportional friction or of a complex mass of the string. The magnitudes ω_{ν}^{*}, then, are:

$$\omega_{\nu}^{*}=\sqrt{\omega_{\nu}^{2}-\delta_{\nu}^{2}} \tag{5.60}$$

where

$$\delta_{\nu}=\frac{R}{2M} \tag{5.61}$$

and aperiodic vibrations are possible whenever $\omega_{\nu}<\delta$.

Forced Vibration of the String

In the preceding computations, no external force was acting on the system; the system had been assumed to be initially excited and then released. If a driving force

$$f(x,t)=F(x)\cos(\omega t+\varphi_{F}) \tag{5.62}$$

acts on the unit length of the string, the differential equation (5.3) becomes:

$$m\left(\frac{\partial^{2}\xi}{\partial t^{2}}-c^{2}\frac{\partial^{2}\xi}{\partial x^{2}}\right)=F(x)\cos(\omega t+\varphi_{F}) \tag{5.63}$$

In the steady state, the frequency of the forced vibrations is necessarily the same as the frequency of the force; thus,

$$\xi=\hat{\xi}(x)\cos(\omega t+\varphi) \tag{5.64}$$

and the equation for the forced vibration simplifies to:

$$m\left[-\omega^{2}\hat{\xi}(x)-c^{2}\frac{\partial^{2}\hat{\xi}}{\partial x^{2}}(x)\right]\cos(\omega t+\varphi)=F(x)\cos(\omega t+\varphi_{F}) \tag{5.65}$$

The bracketed term is independent of t; the equation is valid for all values of x and all values of t, only if $\varphi=\varphi_F$ and if:

$$m\left[-\omega^2\xi(x)-c^2\frac{\partial^2\xi}{\partial x^2}(x)\right]=F(x) \tag{5.66}$$

As pointed out above, any amplitude and velocity distribution that can be excited by an external force can also occur as an initial state of the system. For instance, when the force is suddenly removed this instant may be considered as the initial instant of the free motion. Consequently, $\xi\,(x, t)$ can always be expressed as a sum of the natural functions of the system:

$$\xi(x,0)=\xi(x)=\sum_\nu \xi_\nu(x)=\sum_\nu A_\nu \sin\frac{\nu\pi x}{l} \tag{5.67}$$

The natural functions obey the relation:

$$\frac{\partial^2\xi_\nu}{\partial x^2}=-A_\nu\left(\frac{\nu\pi}{l}\right)^2\sin\frac{\nu\pi x}{l}=\frac{-\omega_\nu^{\ 2}}{c^2}A_\nu\sin\frac{\nu\pi x}{l}=\frac{-\omega_\nu^{\ 2}}{c^2}\xi_\nu \tag{5.68}$$

which can be obtained by straightforward differentiation and with the aid of the relation:

$$\omega_\nu^{\ 2}=k_\nu^{\ 2}c^2=\left(\frac{\nu\pi}{l}\right)^2c^2 \tag{5.69}$$

or directly from the differential equation for the natural functions (Eq. 5.54). If Equation 5.67 is introduced into Equation 5.66, we obtain:

$$m\left[-\omega^2\sum_\nu\xi_\nu(x)-\sum_\nu c^2\frac{\partial^2\xi_\nu(x)}{\partial x^2}\right]=\sum_\nu m(-\omega^2+\omega_\nu^{\ 2})A_\nu\sin\frac{\nu\pi x}{l}=F(x) \tag{5.70}$$

The sum on the left-hand side of the equation can again be reduced to a single term by multiplying by a particular natural function sin $(\nu\pi x/l)$ and by integrating over the system:

$$\sum_\mu m(-\omega^2+\omega_\mu^{\ 2})\int_0^l A_\mu\sin\frac{\mu\pi x}{l}\sin\frac{\nu\pi x}{l}dx=\int_0^l F(x)\sin\frac{\nu\pi x}{l}dx \tag{5.71}$$

Because of the orthogonality condition (Eq. 5.36), the terms with $\nu\neq\mu$ vanish, and the result simplifies to:

$$m(-\omega^2+\omega_\nu^{\ 2})\frac{A_\nu l}{2}=\int_0^l F(x)\sin\frac{\nu\pi x}{l}dx=\kappa_\nu F_0 \tag{5.72}$$

The right-hand side is known, if the force distribution $F\,(x)$ is given; it is expressed here as the product of two factors, F_0 and κ_ν. The factor F_0 measures the magnitude of the force distribution, and κ_ν is a function of the space distribution of the force and of the natural functions of the system. We may, for instance, interpret F_0 as the total force that acts on the system by defining it in the following manner:

$$F_0=\int_0^l F(x)dx \tag{5.73}$$

The second factor κ_ν is then given by:

$$\kappa_\nu=\frac{1}{F_0}\int_0^l F(x)\sin\frac{\nu\pi x}{l}dx \tag{5.74}$$

This factor expresses the fraction of the total driving force that is available for the excitation of a particular mode $\xi_\nu(x)$, and the constant κ_ν is called the excitation constant. Equation 5.72 determines A_ν:

$$A_\nu=\frac{\kappa_\nu F_0}{\frac{1}{2}M(\omega_\nu^2-\omega^2)} \tag{5.75}$$

where $M=ml$ is the total mass of the string. If this value is substituted in Equations 5.67 and 5.64, the solution for the forced vibration becomes:

$$\xi=\sum_\nu\frac{\kappa_\nu F_0\sin\frac{\nu\pi x}{l}}{M_\nu(\omega_\nu^2-\omega^2)}\cdot\cos(\omega t+\varphi_F) \tag{5.76}$$

and

$$\dot{\xi}=j\omega\xi=\sum_\nu\frac{\kappa_\nu F_0\sin\frac{\nu\pi x}{l}}{j\omega M_\nu\left(1-\frac{\omega_\nu^2}{\omega^2}\right)}e^{j(\omega t+\varphi_F)} \tag{5.77}$$

where

$$M_\nu=\frac{1}{2}M \quad \text{and} \quad \omega_\nu^2=\frac{1}{M_\nu K_\nu} \quad \text{or} \quad K_\nu=\frac{1}{\omega_\nu^2 M_\nu} \tag{5.78}$$

The abbreviation $M_\nu=\frac{1}{2}M$ may be interpreted as the equivalent mass, or mode mass, of the system for vibrations in the νth mode, and K_ν, as the equivalent compliance.

The solution (Eq. 5.77) is made up of an infinite number of terms. Every term is of the same form as the solution for the point-mass compliance system, except for a constant multiplier that depends on the point of observation x and on the position of the external force x_F. Every term corresponds to one natural mode of vibration, and the natural frequency of the mode (damping neglected) takes the place of the natural frequency of the point-mass compliance system.

The examples of an external force acting at a point of the system—that is, of a point force and of a force uniformly distributed over the system with constant intensity—are of special interest. A point force is represented mathematically by a force distribution that is zero everywhere except in the immediate vicinity of the point of attack of the force. At this point, the force has a large peak, as indicated in Figure 5.2. To simplify the notation and to avoid unnecessary subscripts, F will denote the set of co-ordinates x_F, y_F, and z_F of the driven point. Thus, the integrand of Equation 5.74 is zero, except in the immediate vicinity of the point $x=F$. We may, therefore, replace x in the factor sin $(\nu\pi x/l)$ by F and write this factor in front of the integral, since it no longer is a function of x:

$$\kappa_\nu = \frac{1}{F_0} \sin \frac{\nu\pi F}{l} \int_0^l F(x)dx = \sin \frac{\nu\pi F}{l} \tag{5.79}$$

where

$$\int_0^l F(x)dx = \int F_0\delta(x-F)dx = F_0 \tag{5.80}$$

Equation 5.76 then becomes:

$$\xi = F_0 \sum_\nu \frac{\sin \frac{\nu\pi F}{l} \sin \frac{\nu\pi x}{l}}{M_\nu(\omega^2{}_\nu - \omega^2)} e^{j(\omega t + \varphi F)} \tag{5.81}$$

We note the symmetry of the solution with respect to the co-ordinate x_F of the point force F and the co-ordinate x of the point of observation. A force acting at F produces the same deflection at the point x as the same force would produce at $x=F$, if the force would act at x. This is a special instance of the so-called reciprocity principle.

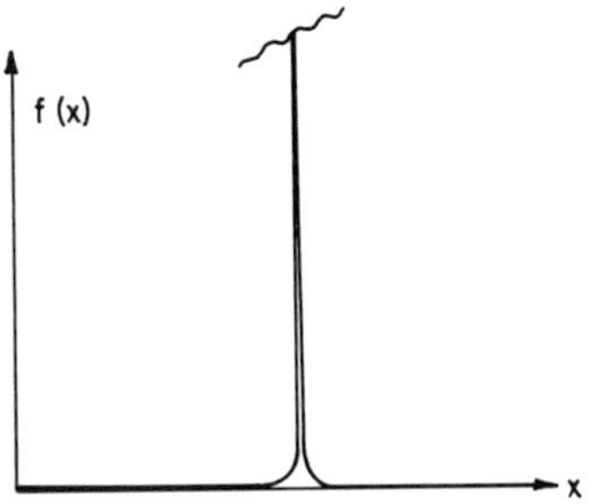

Fig. 5.2 A point force as the limiting case of a continuous force distribution.

When the driving point coincides with the point of observation, the numerators of all the terms in Equation 5.81 are positive; the contribution of each term is, then, positive below and negative above its resonant frequency (Fig. 1.17). The curve obtained by adding the contributions of the various modes (terms) exhibits peaks at the resonances and deep minima at the antiresonances of the system (Foster's theorem). If the driving point does not coincide with the point of observation, sin $(\nu\pi F/l)$ and sin $(\nu\pi x/l)$ may have opposite signs, some of the terms become negative, some, or all, of the antiresonances may be replaced by simple minima (as pointed out in Chapter I), and Foster's theorem no longer applies.

For a force that is distributed with constant intensity:

$$F(x)=\frac{F_0}{l} \tag{5.82}$$

and

$$\kappa_\nu=\frac{1}{F_0}\int_0^l \frac{F_0}{l}\sin\frac{\nu\pi x}{l}dx=\left(\frac{-\cos\dfrac{\nu\pi x}{l}}{l\dfrac{\nu\pi}{l}}\right)_0^l$$

$$=\begin{cases}\dfrac{2}{\nu\pi} & \nu=1,3,5,\ldots\\ 0 & \nu=2,4,6,\ldots\end{cases} \tag{5.83}$$

A constant force distribution excites only odd-order modes, and

$$\xi=\sum_\nu \frac{4\,F_0\sin\dfrac{\nu\pi x}{l}}{\nu\pi M(\omega_\nu^2-\omega^2)}\cos(\omega t+\varphi_F) \qquad \nu=1,3,5,\ldots \tag{5.84}$$

Because of the factor ν in the denominator, such a force excites the higher-order modes to a much lesser extent than does a point force.

Forced Vibration of a Damped String

If friction is neglected, the differential equation (5.66) and its solution (Eq. 5.77) are entirely real. Friction is taken into account by introducing a complex elastic constant. For the string, this constant is represented by the tension $\bar{T}$ or the sound velocity $\bar{c}$:

$$\bar{c}^2=c_0^2(1+j\eta)=\frac{\bar{T}}{m} \tag{5.85}$$

Equation 5.63 then contains complex coefficients, and complex notation must be introduced:

$$-m\omega^2\bar{\xi}+T_0(1+j\eta)\frac{\partial^2\bar{\xi}}{\partial x^2}=\bar{F}(x)e^{j\omega t} \tag{5.86}$$

where $\bar{F}(x)=F(x)e^{j\varphi_F}$. The differential equation can be solved in the same manner as that discussed above, by expanding the solution into natural functions:

$$\bar{\xi}=\sum\bar{\xi}_\nu(x)=\sum A_\nu\sin\frac{\nu\pi x}{l} \tag{5.87}$$

These natural functions obey the differential equation of the homogeneous nondissipative system:

$$-m\omega_\nu^2\hat{\xi}_\nu + T_0\frac{\partial^2\hat{\xi}_\nu}{\partial x^2} = 0 \tag{5.88}$$

This equation is of great value, since it gives the result of the differential operator $\partial^2/\partial x^2$ that acts on a natural function $\hat{\xi}_\nu$:

$$T_0\frac{\partial^2\hat{\xi}_\nu}{\partial x^2} = m\omega_\nu^2\hat{\xi}_\nu \tag{5.89}$$

This result could, again, have been derived by direct differentiation of the various terms of Equation 5.87, but it is more convenient to obtain it from the homo geneous differential equation (5.88) of the nondissipative system. The differential equation (5.86) can now be written in the following form:

$$-m\omega^2\sum_\nu \hat{\xi}_\nu + T_0(1+j\eta)\sum_\nu \frac{\partial^2\hat{\xi}_\nu}{\partial x^2} = \bar{F}(x) \tag{5.90}$$

The x-derivatives can still be eliminated with the aid of the homogeneous equation (5.89):

$$\sum_\nu \left[-m\omega^2 + (1+j\eta)m\omega_\nu^2\right]\hat{\xi}_\nu = \bar{F}(x) \tag{5.91}$$

Because of dissipation, force and displacement need no longer be in phase, and complex amplitudes $\hat{\xi}_\nu\ (x)$ and $\bar{F}(x)$ have been introduced in the above equations.

The sum on the left-hand side is again reduced to a single term by multiplying both sides by $\sin\ (\nu\pi x/l)$ and integrating over the system. The result of this integration is:

$$m\left[-\omega^2 + (1+j\eta)\omega_\nu^2\right]\frac{1}{2}lA_\nu = \int_0^l \bar{F}(x)\sin\frac{\nu\pi x}{l}dx = \kappa_\nu\bar{F}_0 \tag{5.92}$$

where

$$\kappa_\nu = \frac{1}{F_0}\int_0^l F(x)\sin\frac{\nu\pi x}{l}dx \tag{5.93}$$

and

$$F_0 = \int_0^l F(x)dx \tag{5.94}$$

represents the total force that acts on the string. The solution of Equation

5.91 now becomes:

$$\bar{V}_\nu = \dot{\xi}_\nu = j\omega A_\nu \sin\frac{\nu\pi x}{l} = j\omega \cdot \frac{\kappa_\nu F_0 \sin\frac{\nu\pi x}{l}}{[-\omega^2+\omega_\nu^2(1+j\eta)]M_\nu}$$

$$= F_0 \frac{\kappa_\nu \sin\frac{\nu\pi x}{l}}{j\omega M_\nu + R_\nu + \frac{1}{j\omega K_\nu}}, \tag{5.95}$$

where

$$M_\nu = \frac{ml}{2} \qquad R_\nu = \frac{\eta\omega_\nu^2}{\omega} M_\nu \qquad K_\nu = \frac{1}{\omega_\nu^2 M_\nu} \tag{5.96}$$

and the complete solution is:

$$\dot{\xi}(x) = \sum_\nu \dot{\xi}_\nu(x) = F_0 \sum_\nu \frac{\kappa_\nu \sin\frac{\nu\pi x}{l}}{j\omega M_\nu + R_\nu + \frac{1}{j\omega K_\nu}} \tag{5.97}$$

The only differences between this solution and the solution of the dissipationless system (Eq. 5.77) are that ω_ν^2 has been replaced by $\omega_\nu^2(1+j\eta)$ in the first form of the right-hand side of Equation 5.95 and that the resistance R_ν has been added to the impedance $j\omega M_\nu + 1/j\omega K_\nu$ in the denominator of the second form of the right-hand side.

Longitudinally Vibrating Rod

Differential Equation

A thin longitudinally vibrating rod satisfies a differential equation similar to that of a transversely vibrating string. Let the cross-sectional area of the rod be σ, and let x be the co-ordinate in the direction of the rod. Figure 5.3 shows an infinitely short element of such a rod. The resultant force on this element in the positive x-direction is:

$$\sigma\left[p_{xx}(x) - p_{xx}(x+dx)\right]\frac{dx}{dx} = -\sigma\frac{\partial p_{xx}(x)}{\partial x}dx \tag{5.98}$$

where $p_{xx}(x)$ (the stress with reversed sign) is the force per unit area on the cross section in the x-direction. This force can be expressed as a function of the deformation with the aid of Young's modulus λ_E, where

$$\lambda_E = \frac{\text{stress}}{\text{strain}} = \frac{p_{xx}}{-\frac{\partial\xi}{\partial x}} \qquad \text{or} \qquad p_{xx} = -\lambda_E\frac{\partial\xi}{\partial x} \tag{5.99}$$

Newton's law that the resultant force on an elementary volume is equal to

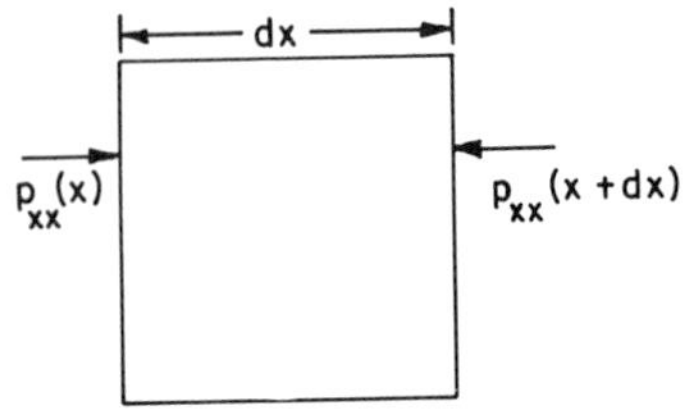

Fig. 5.3 Derivation of differential equation for the longitudinal vibrations of a rod.

the product of its mass and its acceleration leads to the equation:

$$-\sigma\frac{\partial\tilde{p}_{xx}}{\partial x}=\bar{\lambda}_E\sigma\frac{\partial^2\xi}{\partial x^2}=\rho\sigma\frac{\partial^2\xi}{\partial t^2}\quad\text{or}\quad\frac{\partial^2\xi}{\partial x^2}=\frac{1}{\bar{c}^2}\frac{\partial^2\xi}{\partial t^2}\tag{5.100}$$

where $\bar{c}^2=\bar{\lambda}_E\sigma/m=\bar{\lambda}_E/\rho$ is the square of the propagation velocity; this is deduced by comparison with Equation 5.4.

If dissipation is to be taken into account, and if the motion is periodic, λ_E and c^2 must be considered complex constants:

$$\bar{\lambda}_E=\lambda_{0E}(1+j\eta)\qquad\text{and}\qquad\bar{c}^2=\frac{\bar{\lambda}_E}{\rho}=c_0^2(1+j\eta)\tag{5.101}$$

The magnitude m represents the mass per unit length of the rod; ρ, the density of the rod.

Rayleigh's Correction for Lateral Inertia

Because of Poisson's contraction ν, the rod also deforms in the radial direction. This "lateral motion" has no effect on the potential energy, since no force counteracts it (the radial stress vanishes at the cylindrical surface of the rod, and consequently is also very small inside). Because of the lateral motion, the kinetic energy of the rod is:

$$E_k'=\rho\int_0^l dx\int_0^r\frac{1}{2}V_r^2 2\pi r dr=\rho\pi\nu^2\int_0^l dx\int r^2\left(\frac{\partial\dot{\xi}}{\partial x}\right)^2 rdr$$

$$=\rho\frac{\pi r^2\cdot r^2\nu^2}{4}\int_0^l dx\left(\frac{\partial\dot{\xi}}{\partial x}\right)^2\tag{5.102}$$

where V_r is proportional to the rate of change of the longitudinal strain and Poisson's contraction ν:

$$V_r=\nu r\frac{\partial\dot{\xi}}{\partial x}\tag{5.103}$$

Since the relation $\dot{\xi}_x=v_x=V_x\cos kx$ (or $=V_x\sin kx$) varies sinusoidally along the rod, and since we are assuming either that $\xi_x=0$ or that $\partial\xi/\partial x=0$

are the boundary conditions at $x=0$ and $x=l$:

$$E_k'=\rho\pi r^2\frac{r^2}{8}\nu^2k^2l\dot{\xi}_x^2 \tag{5.104}$$

The kinetic energy of the longitudinal motion is:

$$E_k=\pi r^2\rho\frac{1}{4}\dot{\xi}_x^2 l \tag{5.105}$$

Thus, the lateral motion increases the kinetic energy by the factor:

$$\alpha=\frac{E_k+E'_k}{E_k}=1+\frac{1}{2}\nu^2k^2l^2\frac{r^2}{l^2}=1+\frac{\Delta m}{m} \tag{5.106}$$

This increase in kinetic energy is taken into account as a first-order correction by replacing the mass m by $m\alpha$ in the differential equation of the rod. This correction is known as Rayleigh's correction for lateral inertia. Figure 5.4 shows the classical solution *(curve 6)*, the classical solution with the radial inertia term *(curve 5)*, and more accurate solutions that will be derived in Chapter XIV.

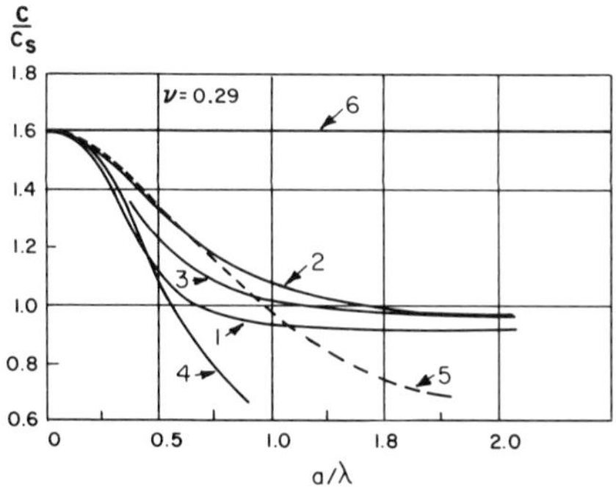

Fig. 5.4 Longitudinal wave velocities of first mode of motion according to:
(1) Exact Pochhammer solution (after Davies)
(2) κ correction (after Mindlin and Hermann)
(3) κ and κ_1 correction (after Mindlin and Hermann)
(4) radial inertia correction (after Mindlin and Hermann)
(5) Classical theory with Rayleigh radial inertial term added (after Davies)
(6) Classical first approximation

Natural Mode Solution

The theory outlined above applies to a rod just as well as it applies to a string, and the solutions for a clamped rod are formally identical with those for a string. The solution for a rod with its ends free is obtained by replacing the natural functions of the string by the natural functions for the rod with free ends:

$$\xi_\nu=A_\nu\cos\frac{\omega_\nu}{c}x=A_\nu\cos\frac{\nu\pi}{l}x \qquad \text{where} \qquad \nu=0, 1, 2, 3, \ldots \tag{5.107}$$

which satisfy the boundary conditions that the stress

$$p_{xx} = -\lambda_E \frac{\partial \hat{\xi}_\nu}{\partial x} = \frac{\nu\pi}{l} \lambda_E A_\nu \sin \frac{\nu\pi x}{l} \tag{5.108}$$

is zero at the ends $x=0$ and $x=l$ of the rod. The natural frequencies are, therefore, given by:

$$k_\nu = \frac{\nu\pi}{l} \qquad \text{and} \qquad \omega_\nu = k_\nu c = \frac{\nu\pi}{l} c \tag{5.109}$$

The term ξ_0 ($\nu=0$) is essential in this solution. It represents a constant periodic motion of the center of gravity of the rod, as if the rod were ideally rigid. The characteristic parameters for this term are:

$$\omega_0 = 0 \qquad \kappa_0 = \frac{1}{F_0} \int F(x) \frac{A_0}{A_0} dx = 1$$

$$\xi_0 = A_0 = \frac{F_0 e^{j(\omega t + \varphi_F)}}{M(\omega_0^2 - \omega^2)} = \frac{F_0 e^{j(\omega t + \varphi_F)}}{-\omega^2 M} \tag{5.110}$$

and the motion ξ_0 described by it is given by:

$$\dot{\xi}_0 = \frac{F_0 e^{j(\omega t + \varphi_F)}}{j\omega M} \tag{5.111}$$

The series solution for the forced vibration (Eq. 5.97), then, takes the form:

$$\dot{\hat{\xi}}(x) = \frac{F_0}{j\omega M} + F_0 \sum_\nu \frac{\kappa_\nu \cos \frac{\nu\pi x}{l}}{R_\nu + j\omega M_\nu + \frac{1}{j\omega K_\nu}} \qquad \nu = 0, 1, 2, 3, \ldots \tag{5.112}$$

For a point force that acts at $x=F$, Equation 5.79 applies:

$$\kappa_\nu = \frac{1}{F_0} \cos \frac{\nu\pi F}{l} \int_0^l F(x) dx = \cos \frac{\nu\pi F}{l} \tag{5.113}$$

Solution for Forced Vibration in Closed Form

For a periodic point force, a solution may be derived in closed form. This solution is based on the progressive wave solution of the wave equation (5.100):

$$\dot{\xi} = \dot{\xi}_0 [e^{-j(\bar{k}x - \omega t)} + \bar{R} e^{j(\bar{k}x + \omega t)}] \tag{5.114}$$

where

$$\bar{k} = \frac{\omega}{c_0 \sqrt{(1 + j\eta)}} = \frac{\omega}{c_0} (1 - \frac{j\eta}{2} + \ldots) \tag{5.115}$$

The integration constant $\bar{R}$ can be interpreted as the relative magnitude and phase of the reflected wave. If the rod is driven at $x=0$ by a force $Fe^{j\omega t}$, the boundary condition at $x=0$ is:

$$\bar{F}=-\bar{\lambda}_E\sigma\frac{\partial\xi}{\partial x}=-\sigma\bar{\lambda}_E\hat{\xi}_0(-j\bar{k}+j\bar{k}\bar{R}) \tag{5.116}$$

or

$$\hat{\xi}_0=\frac{j\bar{F}}{\sigma\bar{\lambda}_E\bar{k}(1-\bar{R})} \tag{5.117}$$

If the second end is free, the stress must vanish at $x=l$, or

$$0=\left(\frac{\partial\hat{\xi}}{\partial x}\right)_{x=l}=\hat{\xi}_0(-j\bar{k}e^{-j\bar{k}l}+\bar{R}j\bar{k}e^{+j\bar{k}l}) \tag{5.118}$$

or

$$\bar{R}=e^{-2j\bar{k}l} \tag{5.119}$$

If the energy losses are neglected, $\bar{k}$ is real, the magnitude $R=1$, and its phase $\varphi_r=2kl$, corresponding to the delay generated by the wave in traveling from the driver to the other end of the rod and back. If the above values for $\tilde{\xi}_0$ and $\bar{R}$ are entered into Equation 5.114, the displacement and the velocity become:

$$\tilde{\xi}=\frac{jFe^{j(\omega t+\varphi_F)}\,[e^{-j\bar{k}x}+e^{+j\bar{k}(x-2l)}]}{\sigma\bar{\lambda}_E\bar{k}(1-e^{-2j\bar{k}l})}$$

$$\tilde{v}=\dot{\tilde{\xi}}=j\omega\tilde{\xi}=\frac{Fe^{j(\omega t+\varphi_F)}\,[e^{-j\bar{k}x}+e^{j\bar{k}(x-2l)}]}{\bar{Z}_c(1-e^{-2j\bar{k}l})}$$

$$=\frac{Fe^{j(\omega t+\varphi_F)-j\bar{k}l}}{\bar{Z}_c e^{-j\bar{k}l}}\cdot\frac{[e^{-j\bar{k}(x-l)}+e^{j\bar{k}(x-l)}]}{(e^{j\bar{k}l}-e^{-j\bar{k}l})}$$

$$=-j\frac{Fe^{j(\omega t+\varphi_F)}\cos\bar{k}(l-x)}{\bar{Z}_c\sin\bar{k}l} \tag{5.120}$$

where

$$\bar{\lambda}_E=\rho\bar{c}^2 \qquad \sigma\rho=m \qquad \bar{Z}_c=\bar{c}m \qquad \bar{k}=\frac{\omega}{\bar{c}} \qquad \bar{F}=Fe^{j\varphi_F} \tag{5.121}$$

Characteristic Impedance

For the driving point, $x=0$, and the driving-point velocity is given by:

$$\tilde{v}_d=\frac{-Fe^{j(\omega t+\varphi_F)}}{\bar{Z}_c}j\cot\bar{k}l \tag{5.122}$$

where

$$\bar{k}l=kl\left(1-\frac{j\eta}{2}\right)=\alpha-j\beta \tag{5.123}$$

At high frequencies, when damping is great and the length of the rod is large as compared to the wave length, $\alpha=\infty$ and $\beta=\infty$, and

$$\cot\bar{k}l=j\frac{e^{j\alpha+\beta}+e^{-j\alpha-\beta}}{e^{j\alpha+\beta}-e^{-j\alpha-\beta}}\doteq j\frac{e^{j\alpha+\beta}}{e^{j\alpha+\beta}}=j \tag{5.124}$$

The velocity of the driven end then becomes independent of the frequency and inversely proportional to the parameter $\bar{Z}_c$:

$$\tilde{v}_d = \frac{F}{\bar{Z}_c} \cdot e^{j(\omega t + \varphi_F)} \tag{5.125}$$

The parameter $\bar{Z}_c$ has the dimensions of an impedance; it represents the impedance of a rod that is driven by a point force and is of such a length that reflections from the free end are negligible. A direct proof of this statement is derived by solving the differential equation of the rod and by rejecting the term $Be^{jkx+j\omega t}$, which represents the reflected wave. The solution is then:

$$\tilde{\xi} = Ae^{-jkx+j\omega t} \tag{5.126}$$

The boundary condition at the driven[2] end determines the value of the integration constant A:

$$Fe^{j(\omega t+\varphi_F)} = -\bar{\lambda}_E\sigma\left(\frac{\partial\tilde{\xi}}{\partial x}\right)_{x=0} = j\bar{k}\bar{\lambda}_E\sigma Ae^{j\omega t} \tag{5.127}$$

and the solution is given by:

$$\bar{Z} = \frac{\bar{F}}{j\omega\tilde{\xi}} = \frac{j\bar{k}\bar{\lambda}_E\sigma \cdot \rho}{j\omega \cdot \rho} = \bar{c} \cdot m = \bar{Z}_c \tag{5.128}$$

The phase angle of the characteristic impedance $\bar{Z}_c = m\bar{c}$ of the rod is that of the sound velocity. This phase angle is very small and can be neglected in most cases. $\bar{Z}_c$, then, is real and turns into a kind of radiation resistance; it represents the energy transfer from the driver to the distant parts of the rod.

The quantity $\bar{Z}_c$ is the mechanical analogue of the impedance of an infinitely long electric line or of an electric line that is terminated by its wave or characteristic impedance so that no energy is reflected at the termination; it describes the velocity amplitude that is generated by the driving force and propagated into the system. The impedance $\bar{Z}_c$ represents a very important parameter in the theory of mechanical vibrations; it is called the characteristic impedance of the mechanical system.

Driving-Point Velocity

Equation 5.122 for the driving-point velocity can be derived directly by considering the sequence of waves that are generated at the driving point and reflected at the end of the rod. If attenuation is neglected in the case of a finite rod, the reflected amplitude is the same as the incident amplitude. The resultant amplitude at the driving point is equal to the sum of the amplitudes of the wave that has been reflected once and has traveled the distance $2l$ and of the wave that has been reflected twice and has traveled the

[2] The force is positive if it points in the positive x-direction. If such a force is applied to the end $x=0$, the rod near this end is compressed, and $\partial\xi/\partial x$ is negative. The left and right sides of Equation 5.127 must be positive or negative at the same time; hence, the negative sign.

distance $4l$ and of all the other waves that have been reflected more than twice. Each wave that is reflected is again reflected at the driving point; thus, the amplitude contribution of each reflected wave is doubled at the driving point. The amplitude at the driving point can therefore be computed by adding the incident wave and the infinite number of reflected waves that propagate in the rod:

$$\bar{V}=\frac{\bar{F}}{\bar{Z}_c}\left(1+2e^{-j2\bar{k}l}+2e^{-j4\bar{k}l}+\ldots\right)=\frac{\bar{F}}{j\bar{Z}_c}\cot\bar{k}l \tag{5.129}$$

It is easy to see that the series on the left-hand side is indeed the Taylor development of the function $-j\cot\bar{k}l$. The ratio

$$\frac{\bar{F}}{\bar{V}}=\bar{Z}_d=\bar{Z}_c j\tan\bar{k}l \tag{5.130}$$

represents the driving-point impedance of the rod; its inverse

$$\bar{Y}_d=\frac{1}{j\bar{Z}_c}\cot\bar{k}l=-j\frac{1}{\bar{Z}_c}\cot\bar{k}l \tag{5.131}$$

represents the driving-point admittance.

For very low frequencies, $\cot\bar{k}l \doteq 1/\bar{k}l$, and the driving-point admittance reduces to:

$$\bar{Y}=\frac{1}{j\bar{Z}_c\bar{k}l}=\frac{1}{jm\bar{c}\bar{k}l}=\frac{1}{j\omega M} \tag{5.132}$$

where $M=ml$ is the total mass of the rod. This value represents the motion of the center of gravity, as if the rod were perfectly rigid. As the frequency increases, the compliance of the rod becomes important and the driving-point response passes through a series of maxima (resonances) and minima (antiresonances), as shown in Figure 5.5*a*. The maxima and minima are given by the extreme values of the term $\cot\bar{k}l$. Since $\bar{k}$ is complex,

$$\bar{k}=\frac{\omega}{\bar{c}}=-\frac{\omega}{c_0\sqrt{1+j\eta}}=\frac{\omega}{c_0}\left(1-\frac{j\eta}{2}+\ldots\right)=k\left(1-\frac{j\eta}{2}\right) \tag{5.133}$$

where

$$k=k_0=\frac{\omega}{c_0} \tag{5.134}$$

The subscript zero is dropped in k_0 to simplify writing, and we have:

$$j\cot\bar{k}l=\frac{e^{j\bar{k}l}+e^{-j\bar{k}l}}{e^{j\bar{k}l}-e^{-j\bar{k}l}}=\frac{e^{jkl}e^{\eta kl/2}+e^{-jkl}e^{-\eta kl/2}}{e^{jkl}e^{\eta kl/2}-e^{-jkl}e^{-\eta kl/2}} \tag{5.135}$$

(See Eq. 5.129.) With the aid of the relations[3]

$$\begin{aligned}\sin(\alpha-j\beta)&=\sin\alpha\cosh\beta-j\cos\alpha\sinh\beta\\ \cos(\alpha-j\beta)&=\cos\alpha\cosh\beta+j\sin\alpha\sinh\beta\end{aligned} \tag{5.136}$$

[3] See p. XLI, Eqs. 63 and 64.

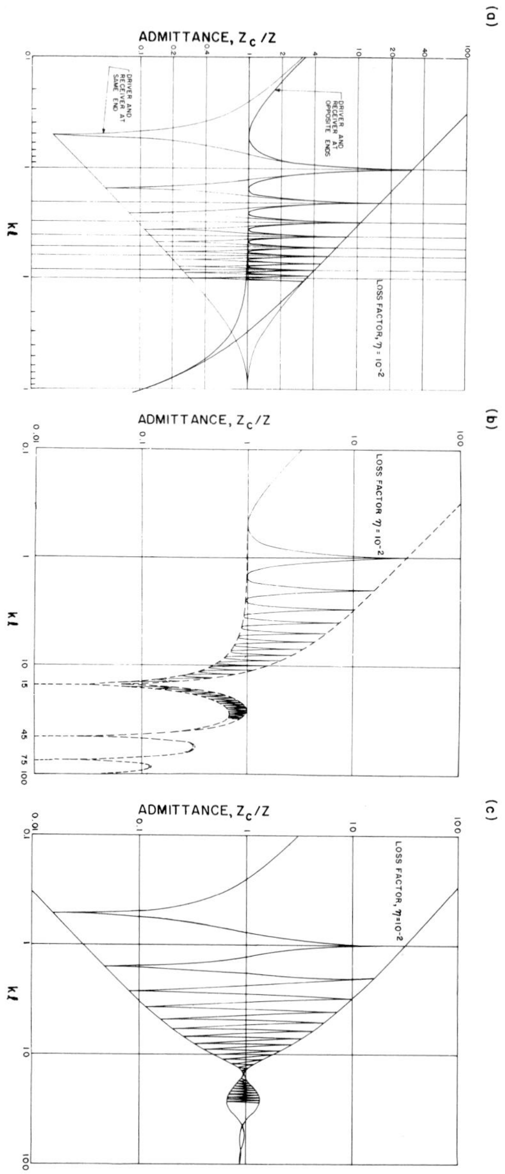

Fig. 5.5 Theoretical velocity response of a longitudinally vibrating rod for three receiver positions; *a*, driving-point admittance (thin curve), transfer admittance with respect to the free and of the rod; *b*, transfer admittance for a point $\frac{1}{30}$ the rod length from the free end; *c*, transfer admittance for a point $\frac{1}{30}$ the rod length from the driven end. Loss factor, $\eta = 10^{-2}$.

the alternate form is obtained:

$$\cot \bar{k}l = \frac{\cos kl \cosh\frac{\eta kl}{2} + j \sin kl \sinh\frac{\eta kl}{2}}{\sin kl \cosh\frac{\eta kl}{2} - j \cos kl \sinh\frac{\eta kl}{2}} \tag{5.137}$$

If damping is zero, the frequency of the peaks, i.e., the resonances, is given by:

$$\cot kl = \infty \qquad \text{and} \qquad kl = \nu\pi \qquad \text{where } \nu = 0, 1, 2, 3 \tag{5.138}$$

The frequency of the zeros, i.e., the antiresonances, is obtained for:

$$\cot kl = 0 \qquad \text{and} \qquad kl = (2\nu+1)\frac{\pi}{2} \qquad \text{where } \nu = 0, 1, 2, \ldots \tag{5.139}$$

Damping has very little or no effect on the resonant and antiresonant frequencies,[4] and the height of the peaks can be computed by substituting $kl=\nu\pi$ (Eq. 5.138) in Equation 5.137:

$$\bar{V}_l = \frac{\bar{F}}{j\bar{Z}_c} \coth\frac{\eta kl}{2} \doteq \pm\frac{\bar{F}}{m\bar{c}\frac{\eta \bar{k}l}{2}} = \pm\frac{\bar{F}}{\frac{ml}{2}\eta\omega} = \pm\frac{F}{R_\nu} \tag{5.140}$$

where $ml/2 = M_\nu$ and $\eta\omega M_\nu = R_\nu$, as in the lumped parameter theory (Eq. 5.95). The antiresonances are obtained by substituting $kl=(2\nu\pm1)\,\pi/2$ (Eq. 5.139) in Equation 5.137:

$$\bar{V} = \pm\frac{F}{Z_c}\tanh\frac{\eta kl}{2} = \pm\frac{F\frac{\eta\omega l}{2}}{m\bar{c}^2} = \pm F\frac{\eta\omega M_\nu}{m^2\bar{c}^2} = \pm\frac{FR_\nu}{\bar{Z}_c^{\,2}} \tag{5.141}$$

The ratio of the maxima to the minima is equal to the square of the characteristic impedance $\bar{Z}_c$, and the characteristic impedance $\bar{Z}_c$ represents the geometric mean between the resonance maxima and the antiresonance minima in the frequency curve of the driving-point velocity of the rod. If the curve is plotted to a logarithmic scale, the maxima are exactly as much above the level $F/\bar{Z}_c$ as the minima are below it. The magnitude of the fluctuations of $\cot jk\eta l$ decreases with increasing frequency. At high frequencies, the band width of the individual resonances $\omega_B \doteq \eta\omega$ becomes large as compared to the frequency difference between successive modes, $\omega_\nu - \omega_{\nu-1} = \varepsilon_\nu = c\pi/l = \omega_1$, where ω_1 is the fundamental frequency, and

$$\frac{\eta kl}{2} = \eta\frac{\omega}{c}\frac{l}{2} = \eta\frac{\pi\omega}{\frac{2\pi c}{l}} = \pi\eta\frac{\omega}{2\omega_1} = \pi\frac{\Delta\omega\omega}{\omega\omega_1} = \pi\frac{\Delta\omega}{\varepsilon_\nu} \gg 1 \tag{5.142}$$

The terms e^{-jkl} and $e^{-\eta kl/2}$ in Equation 5.135 become negligible, the cotangent reduces to 1, and the impedance $\bar{F}/\bar{V} = \bar{Z}$ becomes equal to the charac-

[4] E.g., see the solutions Eqs. 2.11 and 2.43 for the point-mass compliance system.

teristic impedance:

$$\frac{\bar{V}}{\bar{F}}=\frac{1}{\bar{Z}_d}=\frac{e^{jkl}e^{\eta kl/2}-0}{\bar{Z}_c e^{jkl}e^{\eta kl/2}+0}=\frac{1}{\bar{Z}_c} \tag{5.143}$$

The loss factor of the characteristic impedance (being equal to that of the sound velocity) is usually very small and can be neglected. Hence,

$$\bar{Z}_c=Z_c(1+\frac{j\eta}{2}+\ldots)\doteq Z_c \tag{5.144}$$

Figure 5.5*a* (*thin curve*) shows the computed result. The minima (antiresonances) are deeply depressed, and the characteristic impedance $\bar{Z}_c$ determines the line halfway between the peaks and the minima from the first resonance peak to the very high frequencies.

If the receiver is at the free end $x=l$ opposite the driver, the velocity at the end of the rod opposite the driver is given by Equation 5.120, and

$$\bar{V}=\frac{\bar{F}}{j\bar{Z}_c \sin \bar{k}l} \tag{5.145}$$

The ratio

$$\bar{Z}_t=\left(\frac{\bar{F}}{\bar{V}}\right)_{x=l}=j\bar{Z}_c \sin \bar{k}l \tag{5.146}$$

then represents a transfer impedance. The solution is very similar to that for the preceding case, up to the first resonance (Fig. 5.5*a, heavy line*). The velocity minima are flat; they are given by $\sin \bar{k}l \doteq \pm 1$, and the transfer impedance for the minima (except for the factor j) becomes equal to the characteristic impedance $\bar{Z}_c$.

As long as damping is small, the height of the maxima and minima of the velocity is approximately the same from one end of the rod to the other. However, at higher frequencies, when damping becomes large, the mean velocity would be expected to be smaller as the distance between the point of observation and the driving point is increased. This is indeed true for high frequencies (Fig. 5.5*a, heavy line*); the exact solution for the end of the rod then reduces to:

$$\left|Z_t\right|=\frac{1}{2}\left|Z_c\right|e^{-\eta kx/2} \tag{5.147}$$

The factor $\frac{1}{2}$ accounts for the doubling of the amplitude at the end of the rod because of the reflection of the incident wave. Figure 5.5*b* shows a curve for the transfer admittance when the receiver is displaced from the free end by a distance equal to 1/30 the length of the rod; most of the minima are shallow troughs, typical for reception at the free end of the rod, but a few have sharp antiresonances. Figure 5.5*c* shows the corresponding curve for the transfer admittance when the receiver is displaced from the driven end by the same distance (1/30 the length of the rod); most of the minima are now antiresonances, as they are for the driven end, but a few are shallow troughs.

Equivalence of Natural Mode and Classical Solutions

The natural mode solution (Eq. 5.97, with $\hat{\xi}=\cos \nu\pi x/l$ substituted for $\hat{\xi}=\sin \nu\pi x/l$ and the classical solution (Eq. 5.129) must lead to the same result. This indeed the case; the terms of the natural mode solution represent the partial-fraction development of the classical solution.

For instance, if the receiver is at the driven end, $x_F=0$, and the natural mode solution is given by:

$$\kappa_\nu=\cos \frac{\nu\pi F}{l}=1 \tag{5.148}$$

and

$$\begin{aligned}\frac{\bar{V}}{F_0}&=\left[\frac{1}{j\omega M}+\sum\frac{2\omega}{M(\eta\bar{\omega}_\nu{}^2+j(\omega^2-\bar{\omega}_\nu{}^2)}\right]\\ &=\frac{l}{jcM}\frac{1}{\bar{k}l}\left(1-2\sum\frac{1}{\dfrac{\nu^2\pi^2}{\bar{k}^2l^2}-1}\right)\\ &=\frac{1}{j\bar{c}m}\cot \bar{k}l=\frac{1}{j\bar{Z}_c}\cot \bar{k}l\end{aligned} \tag{5.149}$$

The expression in brackets represents the partial-fraction development of $\cot \bar{k}l$, and Equations 5.97 and 5.129 represent equivalent solutions.

The preceding derivations illustrate the vibratory properties of strings and rods. The results have been derived by methods that are especially formulated for these two types of vibrators. We may expect that these methods can be generalized for more complex systems and that they will yield valuable results. The following chapters will show that this is the case.

Longitudinally Vibrating Rod with Mass Loading

A mass-loaded rod can be thought of as a one-dimensional model for a joint between two mechanical systems. Such a rod also yields a considerable amount of information about coupled systems. The following computations are important enough to be reproduced here; they are an example of the method of analysis for complex vibrating systems.

Let us consider two rods of length l_1 and l_2 connected at a mass-loaded joint. The mass is assumed to be perfectly rigid, so that the velocities of its two faces are equal. The solution for the first section of the rod, from $x=0$ to $x=l_1$, is:

$$\hat{\xi}=A(e^{-jkx}+\bar{R}e^{+jkx}) \tag{5.150}$$

The section of the system to the right of the discontinuity may be described by an "acoustical" or "vibrational" impedance $\bar{Z}$, which is defined as the ratio of the pressure or force per unit area to the velocity (or as the mechanical impedance per unit area). The ratio of the force to the velocity, and consequently $\bar{Z}$, must be the same from the direction to the left and to the right of the joint. The amplitude at $x=l_1$, is:

$$(\hat{\xi})_{x=l_1}=A(e^{-jkl_1}+\bar{R}e^{+jkl_1}) \tag{5.151}$$

The force exerted by the rod of length l_1 on the system to the right of the face $x=l_1$ is:

$$\begin{aligned}\bar{F}&=-\lambda\sigma\left(\frac{\partial\hat{\xi}}{\partial x}\right)_{x=l_1}=jk\lambda\sigma\bar{A}(e^{-jkl_1}-\bar{R}e^{+jkl_1})\\&=j\omega\bar{A}\bar{Z}_c(e^{-jkl_1}-\bar{R}e^{jkl_1})\end{aligned} \tag{5.152}$$

where

$$\lambda_E=\rho c^2 \qquad k=\frac{\omega}{c} \qquad \text{and} \qquad k\lambda_E\sigma=\omega mc=\omega Z_c \tag{5.153}$$

The ratio of the force (Eq. 5.152) to the velocity (Eq. 5.150) to the left of the joint is:

$$\bar{Z}=\frac{\bar{F}}{\bar{V}}=\frac{j\omega\bar{A}Z_c(e^{-jkl_1}-\bar{R}e^{jkl_1})}{j\omega\bar{A}(e^{-jkl_1}+\bar{R}e^{jkl_1})}=\frac{Z_c(1-\bar{R}e^{2jkl_1})}{1+\bar{R}e^{2jkl_1}} \tag{5.154}$$

Let the normalized impedance to the right of the reflecting section at a distance l_1 from $x=0$ be $\bar{\zeta}$. Because the ratio of the force to the velocity must be the same left and right of the joint:

$$\frac{1-\bar{R}e^{2jkl_1}}{1+\bar{R}e^{2jkl_1}}=\frac{\bar{Z}}{\bar{Z}_c}=\bar{\zeta} \tag{5.155}$$

Hence,

$$\bar{R}=\frac{1-\bar{\zeta}}{1+\bar{\zeta}}e^{-2jkl_1} \tag{5.156}$$

The factor e^{-2jkl_1} corresponds to the time delay of the wave during its passage from $x=0$ to $x=l_1$ and back to $x=0$. The constant $\bar{A}$ in Equation 5.152 is determined by the boundary condition at $x=0$:

$$\bar{F}=-\lambda\sigma\left(\frac{\partial\xi}{\partial x}\right)_{x=0}=jk\bar{A}(1-\bar{R})\lambda\sigma=j\frac{\omega}{c}\rho c^2\sigma(1-\bar{R})\bar{A}=j\omega\bar{Z}_c(1-\bar{R})\bar{A} \tag{5.157}$$

If the resulting value of $\bar{A}$ is entered in Equation 5.152, and if the reflection factor is eliminated with the aid of Equation 5.156, Equation 5.150 becomes:

$$\bar{V}=\frac{\bar{F}\left(e^{-jkx}+\dfrac{1-\bar{\zeta}}{1+\bar{\zeta}}e^{jkx-2jkl_1}\right)}{\bar{Z}_c\left(1-\dfrac{1-\bar{\zeta}}{1+\bar{\zeta}}e^{-2jkl_1}\right)}=\frac{\bar{F}}{\bar{Z}} \tag{5.158}$$

or

$$\begin{aligned}\bar{V}\bar{Z}_c=\frac{\bar{Z}_c}{\bar{Z}}&=\frac{(1+\bar{\zeta})e^{-jkx}+(1-\bar{\zeta})e^{jkx-2jkl_1}}{(1+\bar{\zeta})-(1-\bar{\zeta})e^{-2jkl_1}}\\&=\frac{(1+\bar{\zeta})e^{-jkx+jkl_1}+(1-\bar{\zeta})e^{jkx-jkl_1}}{(1+\bar{\zeta})e^{jkl_1}-(1-\bar{\zeta})e^{-jkl_1}}\\&=\frac{\cos k(l_1-x)+j\bar{\zeta}\sin k(l_1-x)}{j\sin kl_1+\bar{\zeta}\cos kl_1}\end{aligned} \tag{5.159}$$

The impedance $\bar{Z}$ of the second section of the rod is equal to the sum of the impedances of the mass and the input impedance $\bar{Z}_c' j \tan k'l_2$ (see Eq. 5.130) of the second section of the rod, and the normalized impedance becomes:

$$\bar{\zeta} = \frac{1}{\bar{Z}_c}(j\omega M + j\bar{Z}_c' \tan k'l_2)$$
$$= j(kl_1\mu_1 + \gamma \tan k'l_2) \tag{5.160}$$

where

$$\mu = \frac{M}{ml_1} \quad \text{and} \quad \gamma = \frac{\bar{Z}_c'}{\bar{Z}_c} \tag{5.161}$$

The magnitude μ is the ratio of the mass attached to the rod to the mass of its first section; the magnitude γ is the ratio of the characteristic impedances of the two rod sections. If the above value of $\bar{\zeta}$ is introduced into Equation 5.159, the solution becomes:

$$\frac{\bar{Z}_c}{\bar{Z}} = \frac{\cos k(l_1 - x) - (kl_1\mu_1 + \gamma \tan k'l_2) \sin k(l_1 - x)}{j \sin kl_1 + j(kl_1\mu_1 + \gamma \tan k'l_2) \cos kl_1}$$
$$= \frac{\cos k(l_1 - x) \cos k'l_2 - \gamma \sin k(l_1 - x) \sin k'l_2 - kl_1\mu_1 \sin k(l_1 - x) \cos k'l_2}{j(\sin kl_1 \cos k'l_2 + kl_1\mu_1 \cos kl_1 \cos k'l_2 + \gamma \sin k'l_2 \cos kl_1)} \tag{5.162}$$

If the second section of the system is a rod of length l_2, and if $\bar{F}$ is the force the mass exerts on its end, the velocity of this end is (see Eq. 5.122):

$$\bar{V} = \frac{\bar{F}}{jZ_c' \tan k'l_2} \tag{5.163}$$

and the velocity of the other end is (see Eq. 5.145):

$$\bar{V}_l = \frac{\bar{F}}{j\bar{Z}_c \sin k'l_2} \tag{5.164}$$

Thus, the velocity of this free end is obtained from Equation 5.162 by substituting $x = l_1$ and by multiplying the velocity of the mass by $1/\cos k'l_2$. This term cancels the same term in the numerator, and

$$\bar{V}_{l_2} = \frac{\bar{F}}{j(\sin kl_1 \cos k'l_2 + kl_1\mu_1 \cos kl_1 \cos k'l_2 + \gamma \sin k'l_2 \cos kl_1)} \tag{5.165}$$

If the rod sections are of the same material and have the same cross section, $k = k_2'$ and $\gamma = 1$, and the solution for the driven section simplifies to:

$$\frac{\bar{Z}_c}{\bar{Z}} = \frac{\cos k(l - x) - kl_1\mu \sin k(l_1 - x)}{j(\sin kl + kl_1\mu \cos kl_1 \cos kl_2)} \tag{5.166}$$

where $l = l_1 + l_2$. At the driven end, $x = 0$, $\bar{Z} = \bar{Z}_d$, and

$$\frac{\bar{Z}_c}{\bar{Z}_d} = \frac{\cos kl - kl_1\mu \sin kl_1}{j(\sin kl + kl_1\mu \cos kl_1 \cos kl_2)} \tag{5.167}$$

For the free end, $x = l = l_1 + l_2$, $(\bar{V})_{x=l} = \bar{F}/\bar{Z}_t$, where $\bar{Z}_t$ is the transfer impedance for the free end, and

$$\frac{\bar{Z}_c}{\bar{Z}_t}=\frac{1}{j(\sin kl+kl_1\mu\cos kl_1\cos kl_2)} \tag{5.168}$$

Friction losses are taken into account by assuming that $\bar{k}=k\ (1-j\eta/2)$ is complex.

The first time that computations, such as those above, are made, it is almost impossible to avoid mistakes. But the result can be easily checked and errors traced by this procedure. First, let ω approach zero. The solution then must reduce to that of a rigid body driven by an external force. Errors in the sign and in the multiplying factors are easily traced this way. At high frequencies, when ω approaches infinity and damping is included, the solution for the driving point must reduce to the characteristic impedance of the driven section of the system, regardless of how complex the system may be. Finally, we increase to infinity the factors that describe discontinuties (like μ, γ) in the above example or decrease them to zero or change the co-ordinate of the discontinuities (l_2), making them coincide with the driving point ($l_1=0$) or with the extreme end of the system ($l_2=0$). The resonant frequencies are given by the zeros of the denominator; the antiresonances, by the zeros of the real part of the numerator.

Figure 5.6 shows the frequency curve of the velocity amplitude at the right-hand end of a rod, without mass loading and with mass loading at various positions. The rod is driven by a moving coil at its left end, and the driving force is independent of the frequency. This curve will be discussed in Chapter X, where it will be basic for illustrating coupled circuit behavior for complex vibratory systems. In measuring such curves, it is imperative

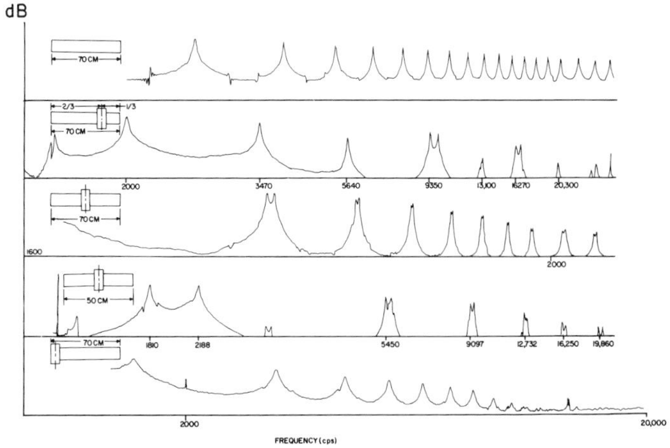

Fig. 5.6 Frequency response of the velocity amplitude at the right-hand end of a rod, with no mass loading and with mass loading in the positions shown. The rod is excited at its left end to longitudinal vibrations by a frequency-independent driving force.

that the rod be cut into two pieces and that the two pieces be connected by the mass loading. If the mass is only squeezed over the rod, the frequency curves become completely disturbed (Fig. 5.7). Because of the three-dimensional nature of the stress distribution in the rod, the stresses are transmitted at the higher frequencies through the mass loadings, as if the masses were absent, and the computed curves may differ considerably from the measurements; in order to avoid this, the rod must be cut into two parts that are cemented into the masses, so that the motion is transmitted only by the masses. Figure 5.8 shows a computed curve for two mass-loaded rods that are coupled by a compliant element. Theoretically determined frequency curves of vibrations, such as those in Figures 5.7 and 5.8, are very valuable for deriving and testing theorems applicable to complex vibratory systems.

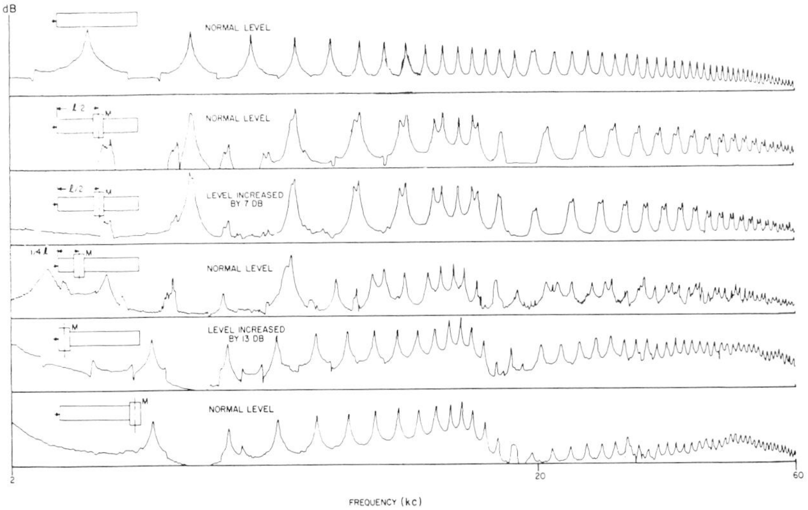

Fig. 5.7 Frequency response of the velocity amplitude at the right-hand end of a rod, with no mass loading and with mass loading squeezed over the rod and cemented to it. Because of the three-dimensional stress distribution in the rod, the vibration is transmitted through the masses, and the curves differ considerably from the computed ones.

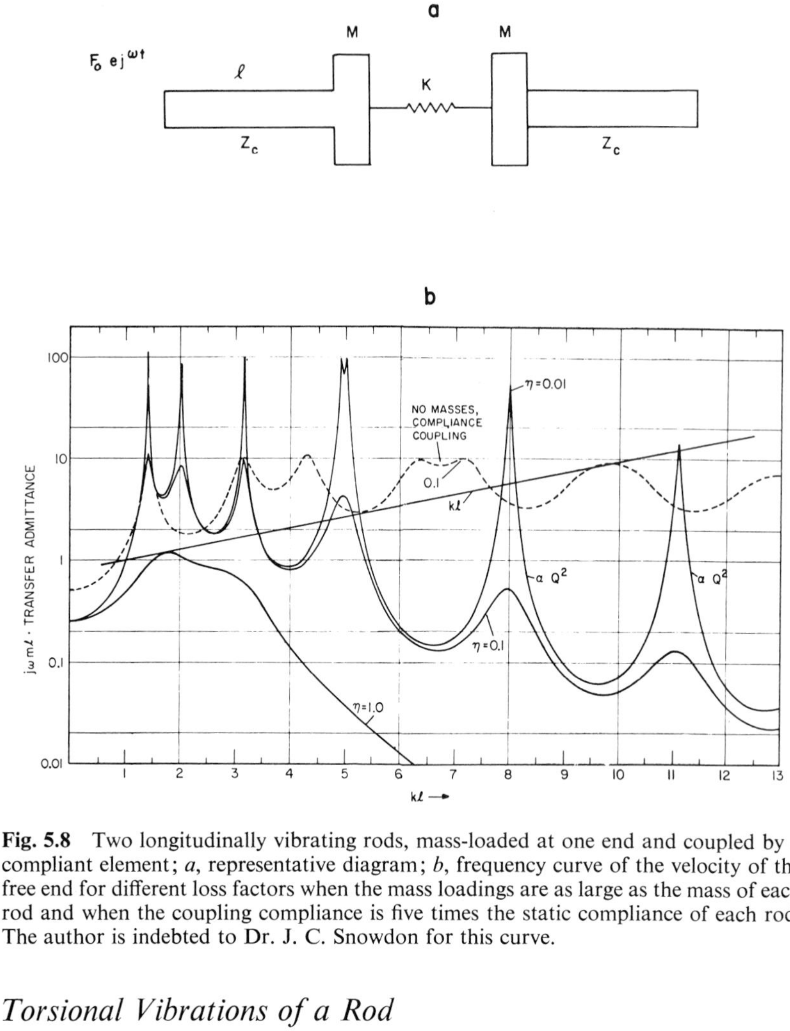

Fig. 5.8 Two longitudinally vibrating rods, mass-loaded at one end and coupled by a compliant element; *a*, representative diagram; *b*, frequency curve of the velocity of the free end for different loss factors when the mass loadings are as large as the mass of each rod and when the coupling compliance is five times the static compliance of each rod. The author is indebted to Dr. J. C. Snowdon for this curve.

Torsional Vibrations of a Rod

As can easily be shown, torque T and deflection θ of a shaft are connected by the equation:

$$T = -\lambda_{sh} J \frac{\partial \theta}{\partial x} \tag{5.169}$$

where λ_{sh} is the shear modulus, J is the inertia of the cross section around the central axis of the rod, and θ is the deflection in radians. When a rod is twisted, the torque changes with the distance along the rod because of the torsional vibration, and

$$T(x+dx) - T(x) = \frac{\partial T}{\partial x} dx = J \frac{\partial^2 \theta}{\partial t^2} \rho \cdot dx \tag{5.170}$$

If the torque is expressed in terms of the angular deformation,

$$\lambda_{sh}\frac{J\partial^2\theta}{\partial x^2}=mJ\frac{\partial^2\theta}{\partial t^2} \tag{5.171}$$

or

$$\frac{\partial^2\theta}{\partial x^2}=\frac{1}{c_s^2}\frac{\partial^2\theta}{\partial t^2} \tag{5.172}$$

where

$$c_s^2=\frac{\lambda_{sh}}{\rho} \tag{5.173}$$

Thus, the differential equation for torsional vibration of a rod is the same as that for longitudinal vibrations. But the propagation velocity of the torsional waves is determined by the shear modulus.

One-Dimensionally Excited Vibration Pattern and Communications Theory

The theory of one-dimensional vibrators (like strings, rods, one-dimensionally excited plates, or centrally excited plates) is very similar, or even identical with, the theory of electric lines and cables. A considerable amount of information has been derived by communications scientists in the last ten decades, and this information can be fully used in the theory of vibrations. The methods of communications theory are much more effective than those usually found in the journals or textbooks devoted to vibrations. In fact, communications theory contains much of what has been said about the rod in the preceding pages. Communications theory includes numerous results that could be applied almost directly to the rod, e.g., the curves for the locus of the impedance in a telephone line and for the locus of an ultra-high-frequency wave guide, the theory of small discontinuities, the theory of loaded lines, and the theory of filters. These theories, for instance, could readily be transformed into a form that would apply to mass-loaded rods or one-dimensionally vibrating plates with ribs.

We simply cannot afford to overlook this enormous amount of information, which is readily available for use in the field of vibrations. The purpose of the following sections is to open the door to this field and to show its connections with the theory of vibrations.

Longitudinally Vibrating Rods and Electric Lines

The theory of electric lines was very important in the early days of telegraphy and telephony, and considerable effort was expended in elaborating this theory and in dealing with the many special cases that arose in practice. The theory of loaded lines, the reflection at slight discontinuities, the input and transfer impedances, and many other aspects were investigated in great detail, and valuable equivalent electrical circuits have been developed.

The theory of a longitudinally vibrating rod is, for instance, identical with the theory of an electric line. A rod is characterized by its mass M, its compliance K, and its loss resistance R—all referred to unit length. A telephone line (Fig. 5.9) is characterized by its inductance L, its shunt capacity C, its series resistance R, and its leakage conductance G—all referred to unit length. In computations of the voltage drop per unit length, the decrease in the current because of the shunt capacity and leakage conductance can be neglected. Hence,

$$\frac{\partial u}{\partial x} = -L\frac{\partial i}{\partial t} - Ri \tag{5.174}$$

Similarly, in computations of the change of the current per unit length, the change in voltage over this length can be neglected. Hence,

$$\frac{\partial i}{\partial x} = -C\frac{\partial u}{\partial t} - Gu \tag{5.175}$$

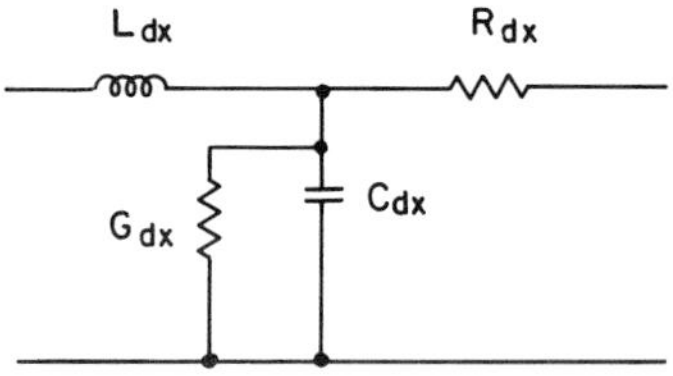

Fig. 5.9 Equivalent circuit of an element dx of an electric line.

In establishing the relation that corresponds to Eq. 5.174 for the rod, the compliance and the losses generated by it can be neglected. Hence,

$$f_2 - f_1 = \frac{\partial f}{\partial x}dx = -Mdx\frac{\partial v}{\partial t} - Rdxv \tag{5.176}$$

In computing the compression of an element of the rod, the change in force because of the inertia reaction can be neglected, and

$$\frac{\partial v}{\partial x} = -K\frac{\partial f}{\partial t} - Gf \tag{5.177}$$

where G represents a dashpotlike conductance.

If we eliminate the current (velocity) by differentiating Equation 5.174 with respect to x, Equation 5.175 with respect to t, we obtain the wave equations:

$$\frac{\partial^2 u}{\partial x^2} = \frac{1}{c^2}\frac{\partial^2 u}{\partial t^2} + r_1\frac{\partial u}{\partial t} + r_2 u \tag{5.178}$$

where

$$r_1=RC+GL \qquad r_2=RG \qquad \text{and} \qquad c^2=\frac{1}{LC} \tag{5.179}$$

and

$$\frac{\partial^2 f}{\partial x^2}=\frac{1}{c^2}\frac{\partial^2 f}{\partial t^2}+r_1\frac{\partial f}{\partial t}+r_2 f \tag{5.180}$$

where

$$r_1=RK+GM \qquad r_2=RG \qquad \text{and} \qquad c^2=\frac{1}{MK} \tag{5.181}$$

The magnitude c^2 is the propagation velocity. A similar equation is obtained for the current or the velocity. Thus, in the following we may write our equations either for the electrical or for the mechanical system. Since we are predominantly concerned with line theory, let the electrical system be considered here. For periodic variations, $\partial/\partial t=j\omega$, and Equations 5.174 and 5.175 become:

$$-\frac{\partial \tilde{u}}{\partial x}=(R+j\omega L)\tilde{i} \tag{5.182}$$

and

$$-\frac{\partial \tilde{i}}{\partial x}=(G+j\omega C)\tilde{u} \tag{5.183}$$

Hence,

$$\frac{\partial^2 \tilde{u}}{\partial x^2}=(R+j\omega L)(G+j\omega C)\tilde{u}=j\omega L\cdot j\omega C\left(1-j\frac{R}{\omega L}\right)\left(1-j\frac{G}{\omega C}\right)\tilde{u} \tag{5.184}$$

or

$$\frac{\partial \tilde{u}^2}{\partial x^2}=-k^2\tilde{u} \tag{5.185}$$

where

$$-\bar{k}^2=(R+j\omega L)(G+j\omega C) \tag{5.186}$$

and

$$\bar{k}=\sqrt{-(R+j\omega L)(G+j\omega C=)}\sqrt{\omega^2 LC\left(1-j\frac{R}{\omega L}\right)\left(1-j\frac{G}{\omega C}\right)}$$

$$=\sqrt{\omega LC}\left(1-\frac{j\eta}{2}\right)=k_0\left(1-\frac{j\eta}{2}\right) \tag{5.187}$$

where

$$k_0=\frac{\omega}{C} \qquad \text{and}$$

$$\eta=\frac{R}{\omega L}+\frac{G}{\omega C}+\text{squares and products of small quantities} \tag{5.188}$$

In taking the square root, the positive sign has to be selected, since only then will the solution describe waves whose amplitude decreases with distance.

The general solution of the wave equation (5.178) is of the form:

$$\tilde{u}=\tilde{A}\cos\bar{k}x+\tilde{B}\sin\bar{k}x=\tilde{u}_s\cos\bar{k}x+\tilde{B}\sin\bar{k}x \tag{5.189}$$

$$\tilde{i}=\tilde{C}\cos\bar{k}x+\tilde{D}\sin\bar{k}x=\tilde{i}_s\cos\bar{k}x+\tilde{D}\sin\bar{k}x \tag{5.190}$$

where $\tilde{u}_s$ and $\tilde{i}_s$ are the voltage and the current at the sending end $x=0$. Equation 5.182 yields the relation:

$$-\tilde{u}_s\bar{k}\sin\bar{k}x+\tilde{B}\bar{k}\cos\bar{k}x=-(R+j\omega L)(\tilde{i}_s\cos\bar{k}x+\tilde{D}\sin\bar{k}x) \tag{5.191}$$

Since this relation has to be satisfied for all values of x, the coefficients of the sine and the cosine must be the same, left and right:

$$\tilde{u}_s=\tilde{D}\frac{R+j\omega L}{\bar{k}}=j\bar{Z}_c\tilde{D} \tag{5.192}$$

$$\tilde{B}=-\tilde{i}_s\frac{R+j\omega L}{\bar{k}}=-j\tilde{i}_s\bar{Z}_c \tag{5.193}$$

where

$$\bar{Z}_c=j\frac{R+j\omega L}{\bar{k}}=\sqrt{\frac{R+j\omega L}{G+j\omega C}} \tag{5.194}$$

represents a very important parameter, the so-called characteristic impedance of the line. This characteristic impedance will turn out to represent the impedance of the sending end of the line, when it is infinitely long. If the losses are small,

$$\bar{Z}_c=\sqrt{\frac{L}{C}}\cdot\sqrt{\frac{1+j\eta_L}{1+j\eta_C}}=\sqrt{\frac{L}{C}}\left[1+j\frac{1}{2}(\eta_L-\eta_C)\right] \tag{5.195}$$

where

$$\eta_L=\frac{R}{\omega L}\quad\text{and}\quad\eta_C=\frac{G}{\omega C} \tag{5.196}$$

The corresponding mechanical analogue is obvious. If the losses generated in the masses (external friction) are negligible, this characteristic line impedance

$$\bar{Z}_C=\sqrt{M\sigma\lambda_E}\left[1+j\frac{\eta_K}{2}\right]=M\bar{c} \tag{5.197}$$

becomes equal to the characteristic impedance introduced in the preceding sections. The solution can then be written in the following form:

$$\tilde{u}=\tilde{u}_s\cos\bar{k}x-j\tilde{i}_s\bar{Z}_c\sin\bar{k}x \tag{5.198}$$

$$\tilde{i}=\tilde{i}_s\cos\bar{k}x+\frac{\tilde{u}_s}{j\bar{Z}_c}\sin\bar{k}x \tag{5.199}$$

For a very long line, $x\to\infty$, and

$$\cos\left[kx\left(1-\frac{j\eta}{2}\right)\right]=j\sin\left[kx\left(1-\frac{j\eta}{2}\right)\right]=\frac{e^{jkx+(\eta/2)kx}}{2} \tag{5.200}$$

Since voltage and current must remain finite,

$$\tilde{u}_s - \tilde{i}_s \bar{Z}_c = 0 \tag{5.201}$$

or

$$\left(\frac{\tilde{u}_s}{\tilde{i}_s}\right)_{x=\infty} = \bar{Z}_c \tag{5.202}$$

and Equation 5.199 reduces to:

$$\tilde{u} = \tilde{u}_s(\cos \bar{k}x - j \sin \bar{k}x) = \tilde{u}_s e^{-jkx-(\eta/2)kx} \tag{5.203}$$

We observe an oscillatory decaying curve. A similar result is obtained for the current.

Probably the most important magnitude in practical work is the input impedance $\bar{Z}_s$ of a line, which is terminated by a load impedance $\bar{Z}_l$. To compute this impedance, we set $x=l$ and divide Equation 5.198 by Equation 5.199:

$$\frac{\tilde{u}_l}{\tilde{i}_l} = \bar{Z}_l = \frac{\tilde{u}_s \cos \bar{k}l - j\tilde{i}_s \bar{Z}_c \sin \bar{k}l}{\tilde{i}_s \cos \bar{k}l + \dfrac{j\tilde{u}_s}{\bar{Z}_c} \sin \bar{k}l} = \frac{\dfrac{\tilde{u}_s}{\tilde{i}_s} - j\bar{Z}_c \tan \bar{k}l}{1 + \dfrac{\tilde{u}_s}{j\tilde{i}_s} \dfrac{1}{\bar{Z}_c} \tan \bar{k}l}$$

$$= \frac{\bar{Z}_s - j\bar{Z}_c \tan \bar{k}l}{1 - j\dfrac{\bar{Z}}{\bar{Z}_c} \tan \bar{k}l} \tag{5.204}$$

or

$$\frac{\bar{Z}_l}{\bar{Z}_c} = \frac{\dfrac{\bar{Z}_s}{\bar{Z}_c} - j \tan \bar{k}l}{1 - j\dfrac{\bar{Z}_s}{\bar{Z}_c} \tan \bar{k}l} \tag{5.205}$$

Solving for Z_s/Z_c, we get:

$$\frac{\bar{Z}_s}{\bar{Z}_c} = \frac{\dfrac{\bar{Z}_l}{\bar{Z}_c} + j \tan \bar{k}l}{1 + j\dfrac{\bar{Z}_l}{\bar{Z}_c} \tan \bar{k}l} \tag{5.206}$$

It is practical to introduce the normalized impedance by dividing through the characteristic impedance:

$$\zeta = \frac{\bar{Z}}{\bar{Z}_c} \tag{5.207}$$

The expression for the input impedance then simplifies to:

$$\zeta_s = \frac{\zeta_l + j \tan \bar{k}l}{1 + j\zeta_l \tan \bar{k}l} \tag{5.208}$$

for $l = \infty$; and Equation 5.206 reduces to:

$$\frac{\bar{Z}_s}{\bar{Z}_c} = \frac{\dfrac{\bar{Z}_l}{\bar{Z}_c} + 1}{1 + \dfrac{\bar{Z}_l}{\bar{Z}_c}} = 1 \tag{5.209}$$

because $\tan \bar{k}l \to 1/j$. As would be expected, the input impedance becomes equal to the characteristic impedance. Equation 5.209 gives the input impedance of a line as a function of its characteristic impedance and its termination impedance. The same formula applies for a longitudinally vibrating rod, if $\bar{Z}_c$ is replaced by the characteristic impedance $m\bar{c}$ of the rod.

The Electric Line as Matching Transformer

Impedance matching and impedance transformation constitute one of the foremost problems in practical work. The simplest impedance transformer is an ideal transformer; however, almost all four-terminal systems are impedance transformers. Impedance transformers are not always easily recognizable from the picture of the system, but they frequently become apparent when the system is excited by the troubles they cause. One of the most important impedance transformers is a one-dimensionally vibrating rod, or a one- or two-dimensionally vibrating plate that transmits the power from the driver to the main part of the vibrator.

The prototype of a more complex impedance transformer is the electric line (or a rod between driver and vibrator). If the line has a legnth of $\lambda/4$, it transforms a very large impedance into a very small one, or vice versa. If its length is $\lambda/2$, its input impedance is equal to its termination impedance. At other frequencies, its impedance transformation is between the two extremes.

If the length of the line is $\frac{1}{4}$ the wave length $[kl=(2\pi/\lambda)\ \lambda/4=\pi/2]$, $\tan kl \to \infty$; its input impedance is given by:

$$\bar{\zeta}_s=\frac{\bar{\zeta}_l+j\tan\bar{k}l}{1+j\bar{\zeta}_l\tan\bar{k}l}=\frac{1}{\bar{\zeta}_l} \quad \text{or} \quad \bar{Z}_s=\frac{\bar{Z}_c^{\,2}}{\bar{\zeta}_l} \tag{5.210}$$

Losses can be taken into account by writing:

$$kl\to\bar{k}l=k_0l-j\frac{\eta}{2}k_0l=\alpha-j\beta \tag{5.211}$$

and:[5]

$$\tan\bar{k}l=\tan(\alpha-j\beta)=\frac{\tan\alpha-\tan j\beta}{1+\tan\alpha\tan j\beta} \tag{5.212}$$

and if β is small,

$$\tan kl=\frac{\tan\alpha-j\beta}{1+j\beta\tan\alpha} \tag{5.213}$$

The input impedance of a $\lambda/4$ line ($k_0l=\pi/2$ and $\beta=\pi\eta/4$) with losses is thus given by:

$$\bar{\zeta}_s=\frac{\bar{\zeta}_l+\dfrac{1}{\beta}}{1+\dfrac{\bar{\zeta}_l}{\beta}}=\frac{1+\beta\bar{\zeta}_l}{\bar{\zeta}_l+\beta}=\frac{1+\dfrac{\pi}{4}\eta\bar{\zeta}_l}{\bar{\zeta}_l+\dfrac{\pi}{4}\eta} \tag{5.214}$$

[5] See Eq. 64, p. XLI.

where we have assumed that $\eta^2 \ll 1$. This result shows that the maximum impedance ratio that can be obtained with a $\lambda/4$ line (if $\bar{\zeta}_l \to 0$) is $1/\eta = Q$.

If the line has a length of an integral multiple of half a wave length

$$\bar{\zeta}_s = \bar{\zeta}_l \tag{5.215}$$

the input impedance is equal to the termination impedance of the line.

The Electric Line as Tuning Device

If the line is short-circuited at its terminals, $\bar{\zeta}_l = 0$; and its input impedance is given by:

$$\bar{\zeta}_s = j \tan \bar{k}l \qquad \text{or} \qquad \bar{Z}_s = j\bar{Z}_c \tan \bar{k}l \tag{5.216}$$

Figure 5.10 shows a representation of $\bar{Z}_i$ in the complex plane. It is a spiral whose diameter decreases because of the losses. The frequencies at which the spiral intersects the real axis at the left of its center are the resonant frequencies; those at the right of its center are the antiresonant frequencies. In the proximity of both sets of frequencies, the line (Fig. 5.10) can be replaced by the tangent, and this tangent is normal to the real axis. Figure 5.11*a* shows, for comparison, the input impedance of a series-resonant circuit; Figure 5.11*b*, that of a parallel-resonant circuit. Near the resonant frequencies, a line behaves like a series-resonant circuit; near the antiresonant frequencies, it behaves like a parallel-resonant circuit. To prove this

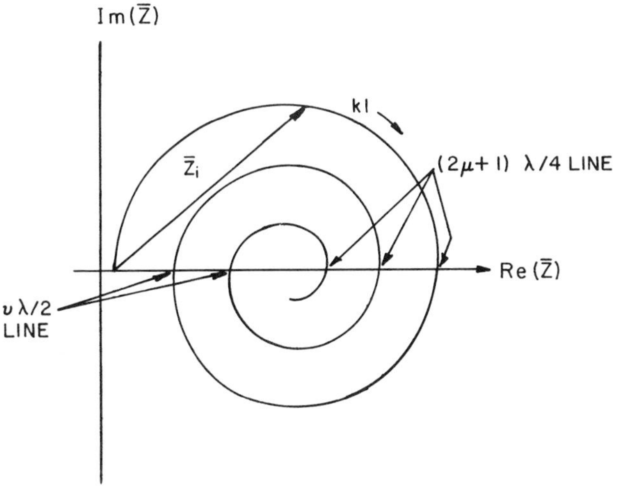

Fig. 5.10 Locus of the input impedance of an electric line whose terminals are short-circuited.

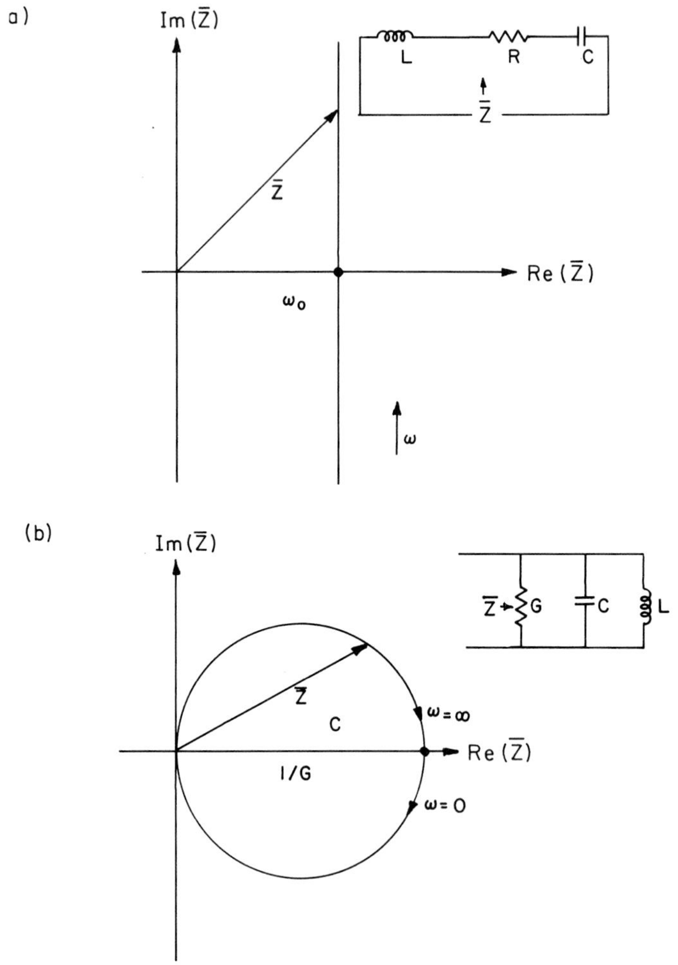

Fig. 5.11 Locus of the input impedance of a series-resonant circuit (*a*) and a parallel-resonant circuit (*b*).

statement, let $\Delta\omega$ represent a small frequency change, and let

$$\bar{k}l = \bar{k}_\nu l + \Delta\bar{k}_\nu l = k_\nu l\left(1+\frac{\Delta\omega l}{ck_\nu l}\right)\left(1-j\frac{\eta}{2}\right) = k_\nu l\left(1+\frac{\Delta\omega}{\omega_\nu}-j\frac{\eta}{2}\right)$$
$$= k_\nu l + \bar{\epsilon} \tag{5.217}$$

where

$$\bar{\epsilon} = k_\nu l\frac{\Delta\omega}{\omega_\nu} - jk_\nu l\frac{\eta}{2} \tag{5.218}$$

is a small magnitude. For the left-hand intersections of the spiral with the real axis:

$$k_\nu l = \nu\pi \qquad \text{where} \qquad \nu = 1, 2, 3, \ldots \tag{5.219}$$

and

$$j\bar{Z}_c \tan kl = j\bar{Z}_c \tan(\nu\pi + \bar{\epsilon}) = j\bar{Z}_c \tan \bar{\epsilon} = j\bar{Z}_c \bar{\epsilon}$$
$$= j\bar{Z}_c \nu\pi\left(\frac{\Delta\omega}{\omega_\nu} - j\frac{\eta}{2}\right) = \nu\pi\bar{Z}_c\frac{\eta}{2} + j\nu\pi Z_c\frac{1}{2}\left(\frac{2\Delta\omega}{\omega}\right) \tag{5.220}$$

This expression has to be compared with the impedance of a series-resonant circuit:

$$\bar{Z}_s = R_\nu + j\omega_\nu L + \frac{1}{j\omega C_\nu} = R_\nu + j\omega_\nu L\left(\frac{\omega}{\omega_\nu} - \frac{\omega_\nu}{\omega}\right) \tag{5.221}$$

where

$$\omega_\nu{}^2 = \frac{1}{L_\nu C_\nu} \qquad \text{and} \qquad C_\nu = \frac{1}{\omega_\nu{}^2 L_\nu} \tag{5.222}$$

But

$$\frac{\omega}{\omega_\nu} - \frac{\omega_\nu}{\omega} = \frac{(\omega + \omega_\nu)(\omega - \omega_\nu)}{\omega_\nu \omega} = \frac{2\Delta\omega}{\omega} \tag{5.223}$$

Hence,

$$\bar{Z}_s = R_\nu + j\omega_\nu L_\nu \frac{2\Delta\omega}{\omega} \tag{5.224}$$

This impedance is identical with that of the electric line, if

$$R_\nu = Z_c \cdot \frac{\eta\nu\pi}{2} \qquad \text{and} \qquad L_\nu = \frac{Z_c}{2_c} \tag{5.225}$$

where

$$\omega_\nu = \nu\omega_1 \qquad \omega_1 = \frac{\pi c}{l} \qquad \text{and} \qquad c = \frac{1}{\sqrt{LC}} \tag{5.226}$$

Near the antiresonances, i.e., near the right-hand intersections of the real axis with the spiral,

$$kl \approx \left(\mu + \frac{1}{2}\right)\pi \qquad \text{where} \qquad \mu = 0, 1, 2, \ldots \tag{5.227}$$

and

$$j\bar{Z}_c \tan \bar{k}l - j\bar{Z}_c \tan\left[\left(\mu + \frac{1}{2}\right)\pi\left(1 + \frac{\Delta\omega}{\omega} - j\frac{\eta}{2}\right)\right]$$
$$= \frac{-j\bar{Z}_c}{\tan\left[\left(\mu + \frac{1}{2}\right)\pi\left(\frac{\Delta\omega}{\omega} - j\frac{\eta}{2}\right)\right]}$$
$$= -j\bar{Z}_c \cot\left[\left(\mu + \frac{1}{2}\right)\pi\left(\frac{\Delta\omega}{\omega} - j\frac{\eta}{2}\right)\right]$$
$$= \frac{1}{\left[j\left(\mu + \frac{1}{2}\right)\pi\frac{\Delta\omega}{\omega} + \left(\mu + \frac{1}{2}\right)\pi\,\frac{\eta}{2}\right]\frac{1}{\bar{Z}_c}} \tag{5.228}$$

The impedance of a parallel-resonant circuit is given by:

$$\bar{Z} = \frac{1}{G_\mu + j\omega C_\mu + \frac{1}{j\omega L_\mu}} = \frac{1}{G_\mu + j\omega_\mu C_\mu\left(\frac{\omega}{\omega_\mu} - \frac{\omega_\mu}{\omega}\right)} = \frac{1}{G_\mu + j\omega_\mu C_\mu \frac{2\Delta\omega}{\omega}} \tag{5.229}$$

Equation 5.228 is identical with the expression for the impedance of a parallel-resonant circuit, if

$$G_\mu=\left(\mu+\frac{1}{2}\right)\frac{\eta}{2\bar{Z}_c} \qquad C_\mu=\frac{l}{2Z_cC} \qquad \text{and} \qquad \omega_\nu=\left(\mu+\frac{1}{2}\right)\frac{\pi c}{l} \tag{5.230}$$

Thus, a short-circuited electric line can be represented by a parallel-resonant circuit near any one of its antiresonances and by a series-resonant circuit near any one of its resonances. Below its series resonances, a short-circuited line has a predominantly inductive impedance; above them, a predominantly capacitive impedance. A short-circuited line, therefore, can be used as a capacitor or as an inductor, its quality factor being equal to the ratio of its reactive component to its resistive component. This ratio is greatest for the two points (Fig. 5.10) where the tangent from the origin touches the spiral. Near its antiresonances, the short-circuited line represents a large resistance, and the reactive component is relatively small.

Similar results are obtained for the open-circuited line, except that the frequencies for the resonances and antiresonances are interchanged. The impedance curve starts at the frequency zero with an antiresonance (Fig. 5.12), and the resonant frequencies are:

$$\omega_\nu=\left(\nu+\frac{1}{2}\right)\omega_1 \tag{5.231}$$

The antiresonances are

$$\omega_\nu=\nu\omega_1 \tag{5.232}$$

where, as before, $\omega_1=\pi c/l$. The same conclusions as those for the electric line apply to its mechanical analogue, the longitudinally vibrating rod.

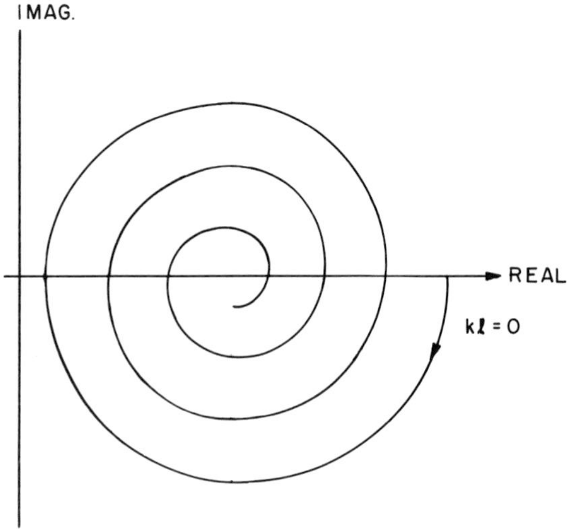

Fig. 5.12 Locus of the impedance of an open-circuited line.

Equivalent Networks

The electric line can be considered as a four-terminal network, whose input (sending end) and output (receiving end) quantities are connected by the following equations (see Eqs. 5.198 and 5.199):

$$\tilde{u}_r = \tilde{u}_s \cos kl - j\bar{Z}_s \tilde{i}_s \sin kl \tag{5.233}$$

$$\tilde{i}_r = \tilde{i}_s \cos kl + \frac{\tilde{u}_s}{j\bar{Z}_c} \sin kl \tag{5.234}$$

The corresponding equations for a symmetric four-terminal T-network (Fig. 5.13) are:

$$\tilde{u}_s = \tilde{i}_s (\bar{Z}_1 + \bar{Z}_2) - \bar{Z}_2 \tilde{i}_r \tag{5.235}$$

$$\tilde{u}_r = \tilde{i}_r (\bar{Z}_1 + \bar{Z}_2) - \tilde{i}_s \bar{Z}_2 \tag{5.236}$$

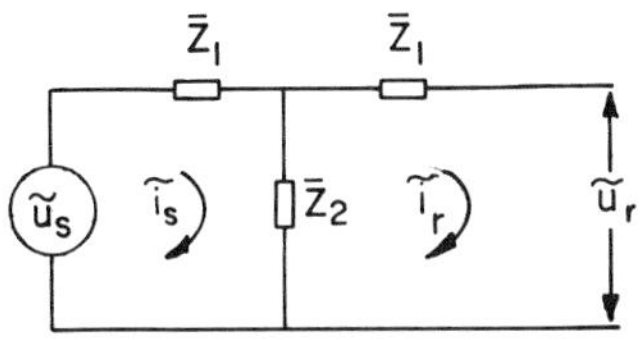

Fig. 5.13 Symmetric four-terminal T-network.

The former equation may be rearranged so that it is similar in form to Equation 5.234:

$$\tilde{i}_r = \tilde{i}_s \frac{\bar{Z}_1 + \bar{Z}_2}{\bar{Z}_2} - \frac{\tilde{u}_s}{\bar{Z}_2} \tag{5.237}$$

Equations 5.234 and 5.237 are identical, if

$$\frac{\bar{Z}_1 + \bar{Z}_2}{\bar{Z}_2} = 1 + \frac{\bar{Z}_1}{\bar{Z}_2} = \cos kl \tag{5.238}$$

and

$$\frac{1}{j\bar{Z}_c} \sin kl = \frac{-1}{\bar{Z}_2} \quad \text{or} \quad \bar{Z}_2 = \frac{\bar{Z}_c}{j \sin kl} \tag{5.239}$$

If $\bar{Z}_2$ is eliminated from the last two equations,

$$1 + \frac{\bar{Z}_1}{\bar{Z}_2} = 1 + \frac{j\bar{Z}_1}{\bar{Z}_c} \sin kl = \cos kl \tag{5.240}$$

or

$$j\frac{\bar{Z}_1}{\bar{Z}_c} \sin kl = j\frac{\bar{Z}_1}{\bar{Z}_c} \cdot 2 \sin\frac{kl}{2} \cos\frac{kl}{2} = \cos kl - 1 = -2 \sin^2\frac{kl}{2} \tag{5.241}$$

Hence,

$$\bar{Z}_1 = j\bar{Z}_c \tan\frac{kl}{2} \tag{5.242}$$

Because of the linearity of the two networks, these values for $\bar{Z}_1$ and $\bar{Z}_2$ also satisfy Equation 5.233. (*Proof.* If the above values for $\bar{Z}_1$ and $\bar{Z}_2$ are substituted in Equation 5.236, and if the receiver current is then eliminated with the aid of Equation 5.234, Equation 5.233 is reobtained.) We thus obtain the equivalent network of Figure 5.14*a*. The elements of the equivalent π-network (Fig. 5.14*b*) are obtained in a similar manner.

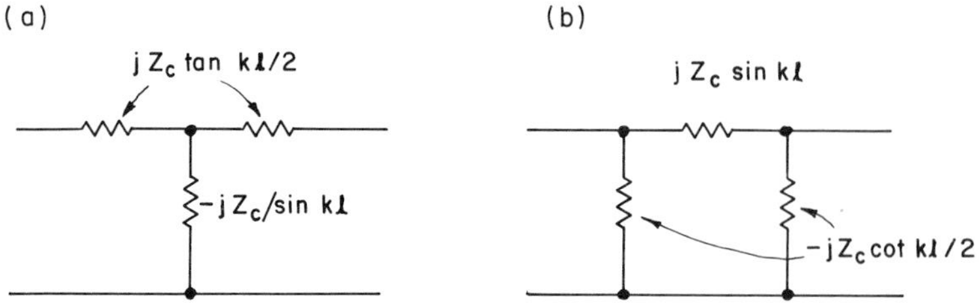

Fig. 5.14 Equivalent T-network (*a*) and equivalent π-network (*b*) of an electric line.

Equivalent Circuit of a Longitudinally Vibrating Piezoelectric Crystal

If the minute effect of the polarization of the crystal on the elastic constants is neglected, the vibration of a piezoelectric crystal is described by the wave equation:

$$\frac{1}{c^2}\frac{\partial^2 \xi}{\partial t^2} = \frac{\partial^2 \xi}{\partial x^2} \tag{5.243}$$

where $c^2 = \lambda_E/\rho$. (In the accurate formula, λ_E is replaced by $\lambda_E\ (1-\kappa^2)$, where κ is the so-called electromechanical coupling coefficient.[6] The solution is the same as that for a telephone line. The electric field generates a stress $k_2 dE$, where d is the thickness of the crystal and where $k_2 \cdot d$ is a piezoconstant of the crystal that acts on the left-hand face of the crystal (sending end of the line); the total force (the sum of the mechanical force $\bar{F}$ and the piezoelectric force $k_2\bar{U}$) is:

$$\bar{F} + k_2 \bar{U}_s \tag{5.244}$$

where $\bar{U}$ is the voltage across the faces of the crystal. The solution (Eqs. 5.198 and 5.199) now takes the form:

$$(\bar{F} + k_2\bar{U}_s) = (\bar{F}_s + k_2\bar{U}_s)\cos kx - j\bar{V}_s\bar{Z}_c \sin kx$$

$$\bar{V} = \bar{V}_s \cos kx + \frac{(\bar{F}_s + k_2\bar{U}_s)}{j\bar{Z}_c}\sin kx \tag{5.245}$$

[6] See W. P. Mason, *Electromechanical Transducers and Wave Filters* (Princeton, N. J., 1942), p. 202.

The force $k_2\bar{U}$ occurs between both ends of the transducer. It can, therefore, be represented by a secondary of a transformer of step-up ratio k_2 (Fig. 5.15). The capacitor C_0 represents the capacity of the crystal; this capacity loads the electric power source u.

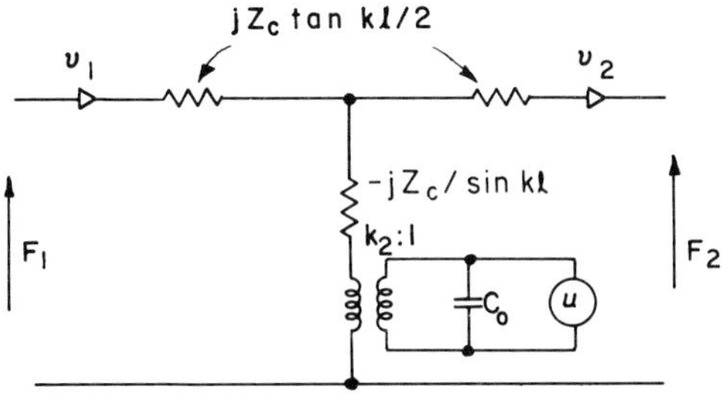

Fig. 5.15 Equivalent network of a longitudinally vibrating piezoelectric element.

If the crystal is clamped at one end, $V_1=0$, and the circuit degenerates to that of Figure 5.16, where

$$\bar{Z}=j\bar{Z}_c \tan\frac{kl}{2}-\frac{\bar{Z}_c}{j\sin kl}=-j\bar{Z}_c \cot\frac{kl}{2} \tag{5.246}$$

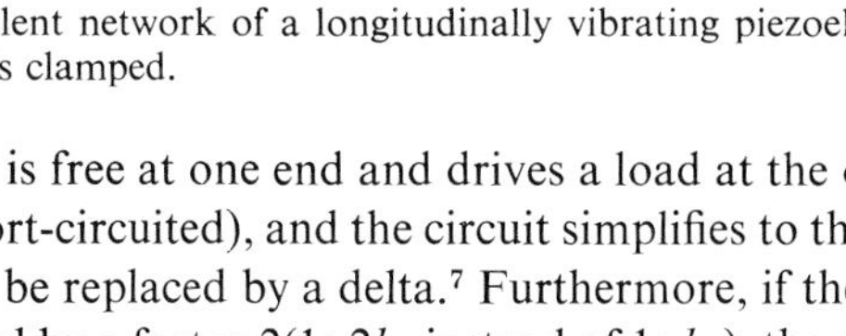

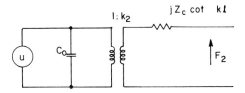

Fig. 5.16 Equivalent network of a longitudinally vibrating piezoelectric element, one surface of which is clamped.

If the crystal is free at one end and drives a load at the other, $\bar{F}_1=0$ (the input end is short-circuited), and the circuit simplifies to that of Figure 5.17 *a*. The star can be replaced by a delta.[7] Furthermore, if the transformation ratio is increased by a factor 2(1 : $2k_2$ instead of 1 : k_2), the equivalent circuit of Figure 5.17*b* results.

It is obvious that the crystal will be driven in a frequency range in which the series impedance $jZ_c \tan kl/2$ is as small as possible and the shunt impedance as large as possible. The impedance $jZ_c \tan kl/2$ is, then, equivalent to a series-resonant circuit; the impedance $jZ_c \cot kl$, to an antiresonant circuit (Fig. 5.17*c*). The shunt branch represents the effect of the motion of the center of gravity of the crystal. This shunt impedance can always be

[7] See pp. 20–21.

neglected if the crystal is driven near one of its resonant frequencies, for which

$$\cot\frac{kl}{2}=0 \qquad \frac{kl}{2}=\frac{2\pi l}{2\lambda}=\frac{\pi}{2} \qquad \text{or} \qquad l=\frac{\lambda}{2} \tag{5.247}$$

The shunt impedance, then, is infinite.

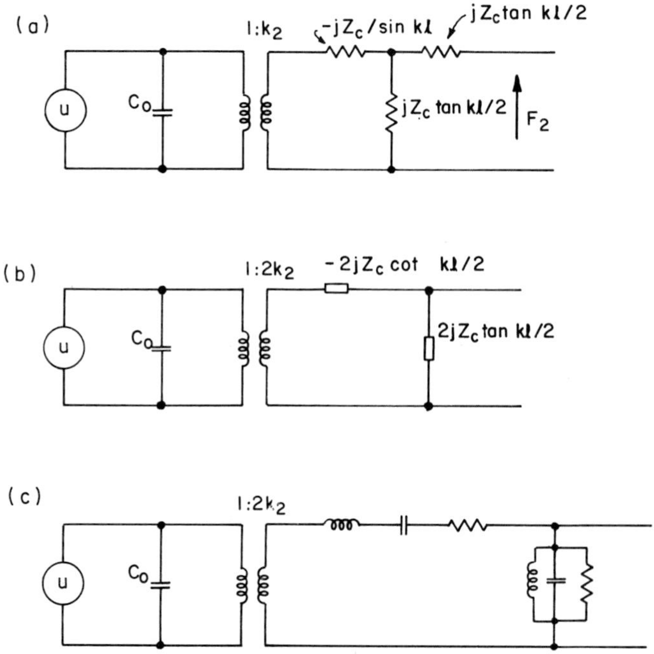

Fig. 5.17 Equivalent circuits of a piezoelectric element; *a*, free at one end and driving at the other; *b*, with star transformed into mesh; *c*, near a resonant frequency.

Recommended Reading[8]

BIESTERFELDT, H. J., LANGE, J. N., AND E. J. SKUDRZYK, "Vibrations of rods at frequencies below their radial resonance," *J.A.S.A.*, **32** (1960).

COURANT, R., AND D. HILBERT, *Methods of Mathematical Physics*, Interscience, New York, 1953, vol. II.

EXNER, M. L., "Schalldaemmung durch Gummi und Stahlfedern," *Acoustica*, **2** (1952), 213.

LINDSAY, R. B., "Filtration of elastic waves in solids," *J.A.S.A.*, **5** (1934), 196.

——— AND F. E. WHITE, "The theory of acoustic filtration in rods," *J.A.S.A.*, **2** (1932), 155.

LOVE, A. E. H., *The Mathematical Theory of Elasticity*, Dover Publications, Inc., New York, 1944.

MASON, W. P., *Electromechanical Transducers and Wave Filters*, D. Van Nostrand Company, Inc., Princeton, N.J., 1942.

RAYLEIGH, LORD, *The Theory of Sound*, Macmillan and Co., Ltd., London, 1894, *vol. I*.

REDWOOD, M., *Mechanical Wave Guides*, Pergamon Press, Inc., New York, 1960.

SNOWDON, J. C., "Longitudinal vibration of internally damped rods," *J.A.S.A.*, **36** (1964), 502.

[8] See also the references given at the end of the next chapter.

VI / TRANSVERSE VIBRATIONS OF BEAMS

The theory of the vibration of strings and of longitudinally excited rods is relatively simple. Sound propagation is one-dimensional, and the boundary conditions are similar to those for one-dimensional columns of fluids. Because of the great simplicity of their vibrations, such systems are very useful for deriving and illustrating the fundamental laws that apply to vibratory systems and for obtaining a first insight into the behavior of more complex vibrators.

Beams represent the next step in the study of complex vibratory systems. The beam may be considered to bridge the step between the very simple vibrators, such as strings and longitudinally vibrating rods, and the more complex vibrators, such as plates and all the other vibrators of higher complexity. Its differential equation is of fourth order; consequently, four boundary conditions have to be satisfied. Because of the additional boundary conditions, distortion terms are generated that increase the vibration amplitude of the ends of the beam by a factor of two if the ends of the beam are free. However, these terms decrease rapidly in amplitude with distance. Similar distortion terms occur in the solution for plates and for all other systems that are governed by a differential equation of higher than second order.

Differential Equation, Rotary Inertia, and Shear

Consider an elementary volume of a beam of length dx and of cross-sectional area σ (Fig. 6.1), and consider it to be cut out and exposed to the same forces that act on it when it is part of the beam. This elementary volume is exposed to a shear force $F(x+dx)$ that acts upward on its right-hand face (because of the forces on the right of it) and to a shear force $F(x)$ on its left-hand face that prevents it from being lifted up by the forces on the right. The resultant of the shear forces that act in the positive direction (upward) is:

$$F(x+dx)-F(x)=\frac{\partial F(x)}{\partial x}dx \tag{6.1}$$

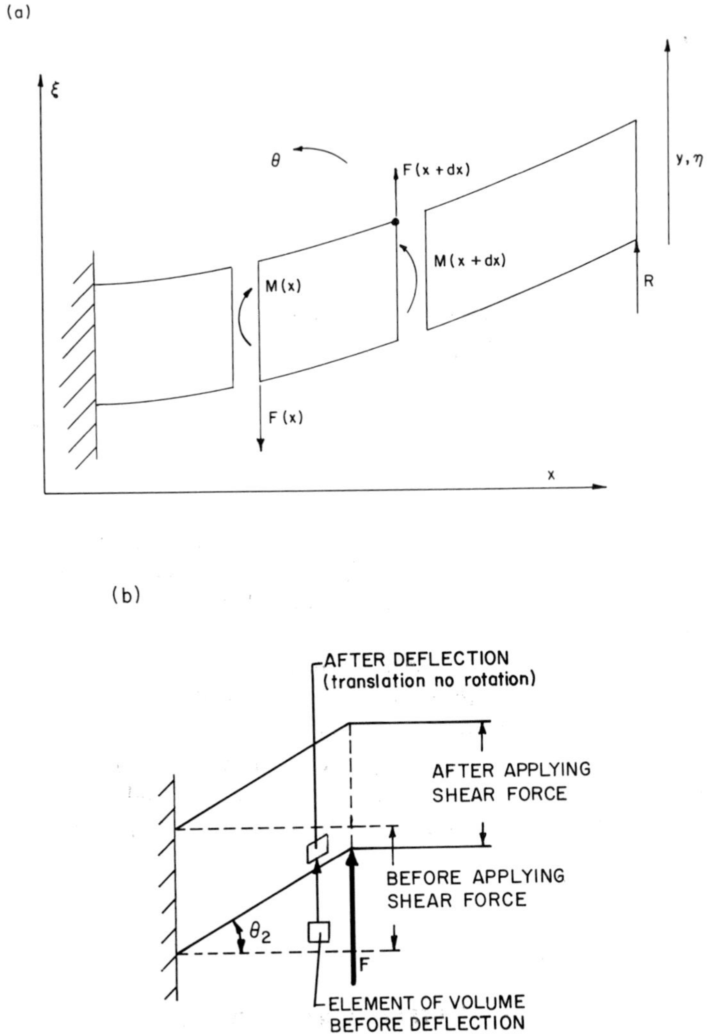

Fig. 6.1 Elementary volume of a beam; *a*, equilibrium of the elementary volume; *b*, the shear deformation, which moves the points of the beam upward, but does not generate rotation.

And the motion upward and downward of the elementary volume is governed by the differential equation:

$$\frac{\partial F}{\partial x}dx = mdx\frac{\partial^2 \xi}{\partial t^2} \tag{6.2}$$

The total deflection consists of two components:

$$\xi = \xi_1 + \xi_2 \tag{6.3}$$

The component ξ_1 is generated by the bending moment. The right-hand face of the elementary volume is bent upward in a counterclockwise sense by the bending moment that is due to the forces on the right-hand side of the beam. The elementary volume would revolve if it were not for a similar bending moment of opposite sense at the left-hand face. The resultant bending moment, which tends to turn the elementary volume in a counterclockwise sense, is:

$$M(x+dx)-M(x)=\frac{\partial M}{\partial x}dx \tag{6.4}$$

Angles are defined as positive if the vector that subtends this angle with the real axis rotates in a counterclockwise sense; correspondingly, bending moments are defined as positive if they tend to turn the elementary volume in a counterclockwise sense. The shear forces $F(x+dx)$ and $-F(x)$ exert a moment

$$dM=\frac{\partial M}{\partial x}dx=F(x)\,dx \tag{6.5}$$

that tends to rotate the elementary volume in a counterclockwise sense and that consequently is positive. If θ_1 is the angle of rotation, and if the moments are equated to the rotary inertia, the following equation results:

$$\frac{\partial M}{\partial x}dx+Fdx=\rho Jdx\,\ddot{\theta}_1 \tag{6.6}$$

or

$$\frac{\partial M}{\partial x}+F=\rho J\ddot{\theta}_1 \tag{6.7}$$

or

$$F=-\frac{\partial M}{\partial x}+\rho J\ddot{\theta}_1 \tag{6.8}$$

where ρ is the mass of the beam per unit volume and J is the moment of inertia of the cross section of the beam about an axis perpendicular to the plane of the vibration through the axis of the beam, and ρ is the density.

Lord Rayleigh was the first to take rotary inertia into account. Classical theory neglects rotary inertia and assumes that $J=0$. Equation 6.6 then reduces to:

$$\frac{\partial M}{\partial x}+F=0 \tag{6.9}$$

The magnitude $F(x+dx)$ in Figure 6.1*a* represents the shear force at the right-hand face of the elementary volume in the direction of the positive y-axis; the shear force at the left-hand face is $F(x)$. The relationship between the bending moment M and the deflection ξ_1 that is produced by this bending moment must now be established. It is usually assumed that the beam behaves as though it were made up of independent sheets that are capable of sliding one on top of the other (Bernoulli's theory of bending), as shown in Figure 6.2*a*. The extension of each sheet, then, is de-

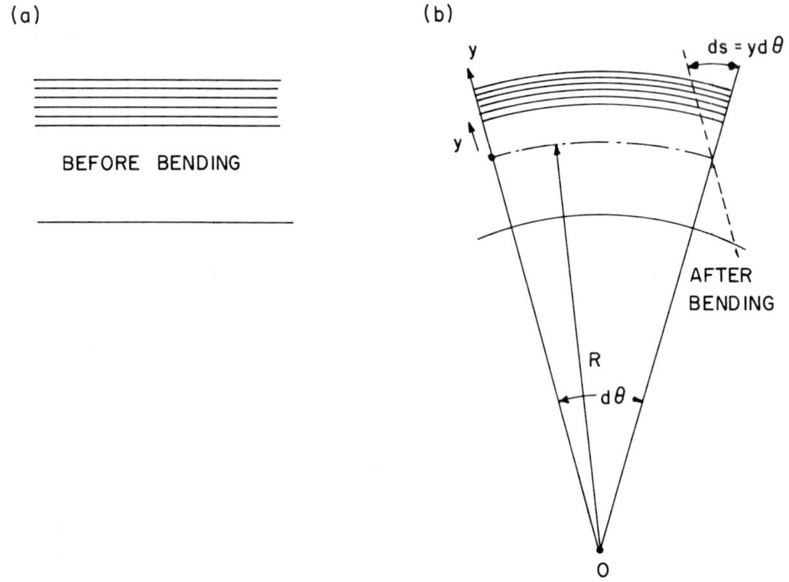

Fig. 6.2 Bernoulli's theory of bending; *a*, the fibers before bending; *b*, after bending.

scribed by Young's modulus λ_E:

$$\lambda_E = \frac{\text{stress}}{\text{strain}} \tag{6.10}$$

The strain is a result of the bending deformation. We assume that the elementary sheets are deformed as shown in Figure 6.2*b*, so that normals to the sheets are also normals after bending has taken place. Under this supposition,

$$ds = yd\theta_1 \tag{6.11}$$

But

$$\tan\theta_1 \doteq \theta_1 = \frac{\partial\theta_1}{\partial x} \quad \text{and} \quad d\theta_1 = \frac{\partial^2\xi_1}{dx^2}dx \tag{6.12}$$

Hence,

$$ds = \frac{y\partial^2\xi_1}{\partial x^2}dx \tag{6.13}$$

Since the stress is λ_E times the strain ds/dx, the bending moment generated by the elementary volume is:

$$\begin{aligned} M &= b\int \text{stress} \cdot y \cdot dy \\ &= b\int \frac{y\lambda_E\partial^2\xi_1}{\partial x^2} \cdot ydy = \lambda_E\frac{\partial^2\theta_1}{\partial x^2}b\int y^2dy \\ &= \lambda_E\frac{\partial^2\xi_1}{\partial x^2}J \end{aligned} \tag{6.14}$$

where J is the second moment of area of the cross section and b is the width of the beam.

The deflection observed is greater than ξ_1 because of the shearing of the beam (Eq. 6.3). Timoshenko included the shear force in the computations for the beam and postulated that the shear force causes a shear deflection that is given by:

$$\frac{\partial \xi_2}{\partial x}=\gamma\frac{F}{\sigma\lambda_{sh}} \tag{6.15}$$

where λ_{sh} is the shear modulus and γ is a factor that corrects for the non-uniform distribution of the shear stress over the cross section of the beam (see below). If the stresses were constant over the width of the beam, γ would be unity; for a circular beam, γ turns out to be 1.11. The last equation (6.15) is physically unrealistic and is valid only if the coupling between bending and shear is neglected. It states that if a concentrated force is applied to a beam that is clamped at its left end (Fig. 6.1*b*), the slope of the beam is constant at the left of the force, zero at the right, and discontinuous at the point of application of the force. The points of the beam move upward in a straight line, and each elementary volume is displaced vertically without being rotated about its center point. Thus, shear motion changes the slope of the beam, but does not generate rotation. The shear deflection increases the slope of the contour of the beam by the angle $\theta_2=\partial\xi_2/\partial x$; however, the shear motion is strictly in the direction of the shear force, and the elementary volume does not rotate during this motion. The following equations, then, apply to the beam:

$$\frac{\partial F}{\partial x}=m\frac{\partial^2 \xi}{\partial t^2} \qquad \text{(vertical motion)} \tag{6.16}$$

$$\frac{\partial M}{\partial x}+F=\rho J\ddot{\theta}_1 \qquad \text{(rotation)} \tag{6.17}$$

$$M=\lambda_E J\frac{\partial^2 \xi_1}{\partial x^2} \qquad \text{(bending moment)} \tag{6.18}$$

$$\frac{\partial \xi_2}{\partial x}=\gamma\frac{F}{\sigma\lambda_{sh}} \qquad \text{(shear deflection)} \tag{6.19}$$

$$\xi=\xi_1+\xi_2 \qquad \text{(total deflection)} \tag{6.20}$$

$$\theta_1=\frac{\partial \xi_1}{\partial x} \qquad \text{(rotation due to bending)} \tag{6.21}$$

The magnitudes θ_1, ξ_1, and ξ_2 must be eliminated, so that the main variable is the observable deflection ξ. Equations 6.18 to 6.21 yield:

$$M=\lambda_E J\frac{\partial^2 \xi_1}{\partial x^2}=\lambda_E J\left(\frac{\partial^2 \xi}{\partial x^2}-\frac{\partial^2 \xi_2}{dx^2}\right)=\lambda_E J\left[\frac{\partial^2 \xi}{\partial x^2}-\frac{\gamma}{\sigma\lambda_{sh}}\frac{\partial F}{\partial x}\right] \tag{6.22}$$

This value is substituted in Equation 6.17, and θ_1 is eliminated with the aid of Equations 6.19 and 6.20:

$$\lambda_E J\frac{\partial^3\xi}{\partial x^3}-\gamma\left(\frac{\lambda_E}{\lambda_{sh}}\right)J\frac{\partial^2 F}{\partial x^2}+F=\rho J\ddot{\theta}_1=\rho J\frac{\partial^2}{\partial t^2}\left(\frac{\partial\xi}{\partial x}-\frac{\partial\xi_2}{\partial x}\right)$$
$$=\rho J\frac{\partial^2}{\partial t^2}\left(\frac{\partial\xi}{\partial x}-\frac{\gamma F}{\sigma\lambda_{sh}}\right) \tag{6.23}$$

and F is eliminated with the aid of Equation 6.16:

$$\lambda_E J\frac{\partial^4\xi}{\partial x^4}-\gamma\left(\frac{\lambda_E}{\lambda_{sh}}\right)J\rho\frac{\partial^4\xi}{\partial x^2\partial t^2}+\frac{m\partial^2\xi}{\partial t^2}=\rho J\frac{\partial^4\xi}{\partial x^2\partial t^2}-\frac{m\rho J\gamma}{\sigma\lambda_{sh}}\frac{\partial^4\xi}{\partial t^4} \tag{6.24}$$

or divided by m and rearranged:

$$\alpha^4\frac{\partial^4\xi}{\partial x^4}+\frac{\partial^2\xi}{\partial t^2}-\beta\frac{\partial^4\xi}{\partial x^2\partial t^2}+\delta\frac{\partial^4\xi}{\partial t^4}=0 \tag{6.25}$$

where

$$\alpha^4=\frac{\lambda_E J}{m}\qquad \beta=\rho\alpha^4\left(\frac{1}{\lambda_E}+\frac{\gamma}{\lambda_{sh}}\right)\qquad\text{and}\qquad \delta=\frac{\rho^2\gamma\alpha^4}{\lambda_{sh}\lambda_E} \tag{6.26}$$

This is the complete equation for the bending vibrations of thin beams when rotary inertia and shear deflection are taken into account. It is based on the assumption of Bernoulli's theory of bending and on the assumption that shear and bending can be dealt with as if they were independent of each other. It represents a very good approximation to the exact theory of bending.[1]

A good method for checking the accuracy of the above beam equation is to compute the velocity c_B of bending waves and to compare it with the prediction of the rigorous theory.[2] For this purpose, the progressive wave solution

$$\xi=Ae^{-jk_B x+j\omega t} \tag{6.27}$$

where

$$k_B=\frac{\omega}{c_B} \tag{6.28}$$

is substituted in Equation 6.25. The result is:

$$\alpha^4 k_B{}^4=\omega^2+\beta k_B{}^2\omega^2-\delta\omega^4 \tag{6.29}$$

The terms with β and δ represent the correction for shear and the rotary inertia.

The above equation would be expected to be invalid whenever these corrections are large. We may, therefore, replace $k_B{}^2$ on the right-hand side by its zero-order approximation ω/α^2 ($\delta\doteq\beta\doteq 0$). The above equation then simplifies to:

$$c_B{}^2=\frac{\omega^2}{k_B{}^2}=\frac{\alpha^2\omega}{\left(1+\beta\dfrac{\omega}{\alpha^2}-\delta\omega^2\right)^{\frac{1}{2}}}$$

[1] See pp. 480–81.
[2] *Ibid.*

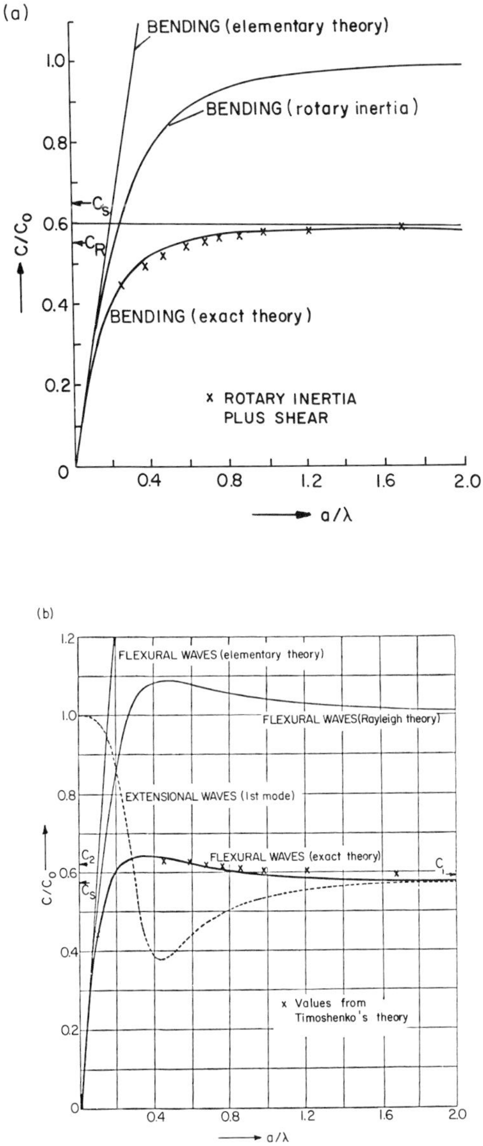

Fig. 6.3 Velocity of bending waves as a function of frequency; *a*, phase velocity; *b*, group velocity.

$$c_B = \alpha \sqrt{\omega}\left(1 - \frac{1}{4}\beta\frac{\omega}{\alpha^2} + \frac{1}{4}\delta\omega^2 + \ldots\right) \tag{6.30}$$

In the lower-frequency range, rotary inertia and the shear deflection can be neglected. Equation 6.25 then simplifies to the classical beam equation:

$$\alpha^4 \frac{\partial^4 \xi}{\partial x^4} + \frac{\partial^2 \xi}{\partial t^2} = 0 \tag{6.31}$$

where

$$\alpha^4 = \frac{\lambda_E J}{m} \tag{6.32}$$

The velocity c_B is, then, given by:

$$c_B = \alpha \sqrt{\omega} \tag{6.33}$$

Figure 6.3 shows the phase velocity c_B of bending waves as a function of frequency. If rotary inertia and shear are neglected, the curve is a straight line of slope $\sqrt{\omega}$. Rotary inertia and shear reduce the velocity considerably at the higher frequencies. Figure 6.3 also shows the accurate curve, which will be derived in Chapter XV. Agreement between the Timoshenko-Rayleigh beam equation and the results of the exact theory is seen to be excellent.

Shear Correction

Figure 6.4 shows two cross sections of a beam separated by a distance δx along the neutral surface. Let the variable width of the beam at a height y be z, and let the bending moment at the left section be M and at the right section, $M + \delta M$. Then, at any height y, the longitudinal stress is:

$$\sigma_x = \lambda_E \frac{y}{R} \tag{6.34}$$

where R is the radius of curvature, which is defined by:

$$R d\theta_1 = dx \quad \text{and} \quad R = \frac{1}{\dfrac{\partial \theta_1}{\partial x}} = \frac{1}{\dfrac{\partial^2 \xi}{\partial x^2}} \tag{6.35}$$

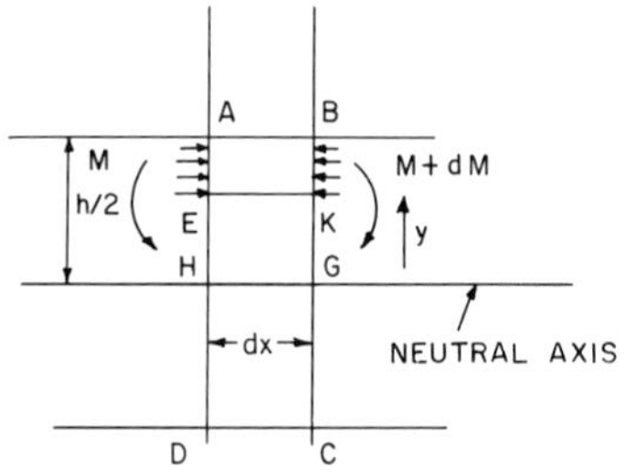

Fig. 6.4 Distribution of shear forces over the cross section of a beam.

The bending moment is:

$$M=\int \sigma_x y d\sigma=\lambda_E\frac{\partial^2\xi}{\partial x^2}\int y^2 d\sigma=\lambda_E\frac{\partial^2\xi}{\partial x^2}J \tag{6.36}$$

where $J=\int y^2 d\sigma$ is the second moment of area of the cross section. Hence, because of Equations 6.34 to 6.36,

$$\frac{\sigma_x}{y}=\frac{\lambda_E}{R}=\lambda_E\frac{\partial^2\xi}{\partial x^2}=\frac{M}{J} \tag{6.37}$$

The infinitesimal longitudinal thrust on an element of cross-sectional area zdy of the left-hand face of the elementary volume becomes:

$$\sigma_x zdy=\frac{My}{J}zdy \tag{6.38}$$

Similarly, the infinitesimal horizontal thrust on the corresponding element of the right-hand face is:

$$\frac{(M+\partial M)y}{J}zdy \tag{6.39}$$

The resultant of the two horizontal forces is obtained by forming the difference of their integrals:

$$\int_y^{h/2}\frac{(M+\partial M)}{J}yzdy-\int_y^{h/2}\frac{M}{J}yzdy=\int_y^{h/2}\frac{\partial M}{J}yzdy=\frac{\partial M}{J}\int_y^{h/2}yzdy \tag{6.40}$$

where y is the integration variable in the y-direction.

Since the net horizontal force on the portion $ABKE$ is zero, the excess thrust at BK must be balanced by the horizontal shearing force on the surface EK. Hence, if τ represents a mean shear stress at height y for a section of width z, the shearing force on EK is $\tau z\cdot\partial x$, and

$$\tau z\cdot\partial x=\frac{\partial M}{J}\int_y^{h/2}\eta z d\eta \tag{6.41}$$

or

$$\tau=\frac{\partial M}{\partial x}\frac{1}{Jz}\int_y^{h/2}\eta z d\eta=\frac{F_{sh}}{Jz}\int_y^{h/2}\eta z d\eta \tag{6.42}$$

since the shear force $F_{sh}=\partial M/\partial x$ (Eq. 6.8), if rotary inertia is neglected. The above computation for the shear stress is only an approximation, since the shear stress also varies considerably along the width z of the element. For greater accuracy, exact solutions must be derived by solving the differential equations and adapting the solution to the boundary conditions.

Next we have to compute the deflection that is produced by the shear stress. A shear force uniformly distributed over the cross section σ of the beam would change the angle that the cross section enclosed with the normal to the neutral axis by the amount:

$$\theta_2 = \frac{\tau}{\lambda_{sh}} = \frac{F_{sh}}{\sigma \lambda_{sh}} \tag{6.43}$$

And plane sections spaced a distance dx from each other would be displaced by the distance:

$$d\eta_2 = \theta_2 dx = \frac{F_{sh}}{\sigma \lambda_{sh}} dx \tag{6.44}$$

However, because of the nonuniform distribution of the shear stress, the true displacement differs from this value. It is standard practice to write:

$$d\xi_2 = \gamma \frac{F_{sh}}{\sigma \lambda_{sh}} dx \tag{6.45}$$

where γ is a number that depends on the shape of the cross section.

An approximate computation of the magnitude of γ can be made by equating the shear energy to the work performed by the shear force. The shear energy per length dx of the beam is given by:

$$dx \int \frac{\tau^2}{2\lambda_{sh}} d\sigma \tag{6.46}$$

whereas the work performed by the shear force is:

$$W = \frac{1}{2} F_{sh} d\xi_2 = \frac{1}{2} \gamma \frac{F_{sh}^2}{\sigma \lambda_{sh}} dx \tag{6.47}$$

Hence, because of Equation 6.45,

$$dx \int \frac{\tau^2}{2\lambda_{sh}} d\sigma = \frac{1}{2} \gamma \frac{F_{sh}^2}{\sigma \lambda_{sh}} dx \tag{6.48}$$

or

$$\gamma = \frac{\sigma}{F_{sh}^2} \int \tau^2 d\sigma \tag{6.49}$$

This integral is evaluated by substituting Eq. 6.42 for τ or by using one of the more complex solutions derived in the literature. A value of γ then is obtained that is equal to 1.20 for a rectangular cross section, 1.11 for a circular cross section, and 2.00 to 2.40 for I-sections.

Progressive Wave Solution for an Infinite Beam and the End Distortion

The classical differential equation for the beam (Eq. 6.31) is of the fourth order, and the complex solution is:

$$\tilde{\xi} = (\bar{A} e^{-jkx} + \bar{B} e^{+jkx} + \bar{C} e^{-kx} + \bar{D} e^{+kx}) e^{j\omega t} \tag{6.50}$$

where

$$k=\frac{\omega}{c_B}=\frac{\sqrt{\omega}}{\alpha} \tag{6.51}$$

as can be proved by substituting the solution into the differential equation. The magnitude c_B represents the velocity of bending waves in the beam:

$$c_B=\alpha\sqrt{\omega} \tag{6.52}$$

Damping can be taken into account by assuming a complex elastic constant $\bar{\lambda}_E=\lambda_E\,(1+j\eta)$. The friction losses then modify the factor α^4 in the differential equation of the beam (Eq. 6.31) to $\alpha^4\,(1+j\eta)=\alpha^4\,(1+j\eta/4+\ldots)^4$. Wave number and bending-wave velocity then become:

$$\bar{k}=\frac{\sqrt{\omega}}{\alpha\left(1+\frac{j\eta}{4}+\ldots\right)}=\frac{\sqrt{\omega}}{\alpha}\left(1-\frac{j\eta}{4}+\ldots\right)$$

$$=k_0\left(1-\frac{j\eta}{4}+\ldots\right) \tag{6.53}$$

$$\bar{c}_B=\alpha\left(1+\frac{j\eta}{4}+\ldots\right)\sqrt{\omega} \tag{6.54}$$

$$\bar{c}_B=c_B\left(1+\frac{j\eta}{4}+\ldots\right) \tag{6.55}$$

The term $\bar{C}e^{-kx}$ represents the distortion field that decreases exponentially with the distance x from the end of the beam at $x=0$. The term

$$\bar{D}e^{kx}=(\bar{D}e^{+kl})e^{-kl+kx}=\bar{D}'e^{-k(l-x)} \tag{6.56}$$

where

$$\bar{D}'=\bar{D}e^{kl} \tag{6.57}$$

represents a distortion field that decreases exponentially with the distance from the right-hand end of the beam. Both terms decrease 2π Nepers (that is, by a factor 1/520) per wave length. Because of their rapid decrease with the distance from the ends of the beam, the distortion fields are of importance only in the immediate vicinity of the ends of the beam. The term $\bar{B}e^{jkx}$ represents a wave that is incident at the end $x=0$; the term $\bar{A}e^{-jkx}$, a wave that is reflected there. If the ends of the beam are not damped by friction, $|\bar{A}|=|\bar{B}|$ because of the conservation of energy during perfect reflection.

Wave Reflection at End of Beam

If a beam is infinitely long, because the solution must be finite everywhere,

$$\bar{D}=0 \tag{6.58}$$

If the beam is of finite length, $\bar{D}$ represents the magnitude of the exponential distortion term at the beam end at $x=l$. Since this distortion decreases rapidly with distance, it does not affect the motion of the beam end at $x=0$. Equation 6.58 may, therefore, be assumed always to apply, if we are interested only in the conditions at the end of the beam at $x=0$, provided that the length of the beam is greater than about $\lambda/4$.

End of Beam Freely Suspended

If the end of the beam is free at $x=0$, the bending moment is zero, because no force acts to the left of $x=0$; hence,

$$\frac{\partial^2 \xi}{\partial x^2}=0 \tag{6.59}$$

This condition leads to the equation:

$$\bar{C}-\bar{B}-\bar{A}=0 \tag{6.60}$$

If no force acts on the end of the beam, and if rotary inertia is neglected, the shear force must vanish at $x=0$:

$$\frac{\partial M}{\partial x}=0 \quad \text{or} \quad \frac{\partial^3 \xi}{\partial x^3}=0 \tag{6.61}$$

because of Equation 6.9. Hence, we also have:

$$\bar{C}+j\bar{B}-j\bar{A}=0 \tag{6.62}$$

If Equation 6.60 is subtracted from Equation 6.62,

$$\bar{B}(1+j)+\bar{A}(1-j)=0 \tag{6.63}$$

or

$$\bar{B}=-\bar{A}\frac{1-j}{1+j}=-\bar{A}\frac{(1-j)^2}{2}=j\bar{A} \tag{6.64}$$

The reflected wave $\bar{A}$ and the incident wave $\bar{B}$ have the same amplitude, but, in contrast to the reflection of a longitudinal wave, the reflected wave and the incident wave are 90° out of phase. This is a consequence of the distortion term $\bar{C}e^{-kx}$.

If $\bar{A}$ from Equation 6.64 is substituted in Equation 6.60,

$$\bar{C}=\bar{A}+\bar{B}=\bar{B}(1-j) \tag{6.65}$$

or

$$C=\sqrt{2}\,B \tag{6.66}$$

and the solution becomes:

$$\begin{aligned}\xi&=-j\bar{B}[e^{-jkx}+je^{jkx}+(1-j)e^{-kx}]\\&=\bar{B}e^{-j\pi/4}[e^{-j(kx+\pi/4)}+e^{j(kx+\pi/4)}+\sqrt{2}\,e^{-kx}]\\&=2\bar{B}e^{-j\pi/4}\left[\cos\left(kx+\frac{\pi}{4}\right)+\frac{e^{-kx}}{\sqrt{2}}\right]\end{aligned} \tag{6.67}$$

The term $\bar{C}e^{-kx}$ represents a distortion of the sinusoidal vibration pattern that decreases exponentially (i.e., very rapidly) with increasing distance from the end of the beam. Thus, for a bending-wave reflection at the free end of a beam, the amplitude C of the end distortion is equal to the resultant of the incident and the reflected wave; and the end distortion increases the velocity amplitude of the ends of the beam by a factor of two.

Beam Supported at End

If the end of the beam is rigidly supported, and because of the condition in Equation 6.58,

$$(\hat{\xi})_{x=0}=0=\bar{A}+\bar{B}+\bar{C}+\bar{D}=\bar{A}+\bar{B}+\bar{C} \tag{6.68}$$

Because the bending moment vanishes, also at $x=0$,

$$\frac{\partial^2\hat{\xi}}{\partial x^2}=\bar{A}+\bar{B}-\bar{C}=0 \tag{6.69}$$

If the last two equations are subtracted,

$$\bar{C}=0 \tag{6.70}$$

Hence,

$$\bar{B}=-\bar{A} \tag{6.71}$$

and

$$\hat{\xi}=-\bar{B}(e^{jkx}-e^{-jkx})=-2j\bar{B}\sin kx \tag{6.72}$$

The end distortion is now zero.

Beam Clamped Rigidly at End

If the beam is rigidly clamped at one end,

$$(\hat{\xi})_{x=0}=\left(\frac{\partial\hat{\xi}}{\partial x}\right)_{x=0}=0 \tag{6.73}$$

or

$$\bar{A}+\bar{B}+\bar{C}=0 \tag{6.74}$$

and

$$-j\bar{A}+j\bar{B}-\bar{C}=0 \tag{6.75}$$

Hence,

$$\bar{B}(1+j)+\bar{A}(1-j)=0 \tag{6.76}$$

or

$$\bar{A}=-\bar{B}\frac{1+j}{1-j}=-j\bar{B} \tag{6.77}$$

and

$$\bar{C}=-(\bar{A}+\bar{B})=-\bar{B}(1-j) \tag{6.78}$$

Hence,

$$\begin{aligned}\hat{\xi}&=-j\bar{B}[e^{-jkx}+je^{jkx}-(1+j)e^{-kx}]\\&=\bar{B}e^{-j\pi/4}[e^{-j(kx+\pi/4)}+e^{j(kx+\pi/4)}-\sqrt{2}\,e^{-kx}]\\&=2\bar{B}e^{-j\pi/4}\left[\cos\left(kx+\frac{\pi}{4}\right)-\frac{e^{-kx}}{\sqrt{2}}\right]\end{aligned} \tag{6.79}$$

The solution is similar to that of the freely suspended beam (Eq. 6.67), except for the sign of the distortion term.

Beam Driven at Its End by a Point Force

If a point force is applied to the free end of the beam $x=0$, this force exerts no bending moment at $x=0$, and Equations 6.58 and 6.60 are valid. Since there is no reflection from the end at infinity, $\bar{B}=0$, and

$$\bar{C}=\bar{A} \quad \text{or} \quad \hat{\xi}=\bar{A}(e^{-kx}+e^{-jkx}) \tag{6.80}$$

If rotary inertia and shear are neglected,

$$\bar{F}=\frac{\partial \bar{M}}{\partial x}=\lambda_E J\frac{\partial^3\hat{\xi}}{\partial x^3}=\lambda_E Jk^3(-1+j)\cdot\bar{A} \tag{6.81}$$

Thus, for a beam driven at its end, the end distortion near $x=0$ is the same as the amplitude of the bending wave and hence doubles the vibration amplitude. The right-hand side of the above equation appears here with a plus sign, because the force acts on the left-hand face of the elementary volume near $x=0$. Therefore, the force tends to rotate this volume in a clockwise direction and generates a negative bending moment. (Hence, $-Fdx+(\partial M/\partial x)dx=0$.) The velocity is then given by:

$$\begin{aligned}\bar{V}=j\omega\hat{\xi}&=\frac{j\omega\bar{F}}{\lambda_E Jk^3(j-1)}(e^{-kx}+e^{-jkx})\\ &=\frac{\bar{F}(e^{-kx}+e^{-jkx})}{(1+j)\,mc_B}\\ &=\frac{\bar{F}(e^{-kx}+e^{-jkx})}{2\bar{Z}_c}\end{aligned} \tag{6.82}$$

The last form on the right is obtained with the aid of the following substitutions:

$$k=\frac{\omega}{c_B} \qquad \lambda_E J=m\alpha^4=m\frac{c_B{}^4}{\omega^2} \qquad \text{and} \qquad \bar{Z}_c=\frac{1+j}{2}mc_B \tag{6.83}$$

The magnitude $\bar{Z}_c$ represents the impedance of the beam for the progressive wave that is generated at the driven end and propagates to infinity.

Because of the end distortion (the term $\bar{C}e^{-kx}$, Eq. 6.50), the amplitude of the free end (Eq. 6.80) is twice as large as that of the wave that propagates along the beam (the term $\bar{A}e^{-jkx}$ in Eq. 6.80). The driving-point impedance thus is smaller. However, the end distortion does not lead to a propagating wave, but to a wattless near field; and the driving-point impedance consists of two terms of equal magnitude, one real, the other imaginary.

The impedance $\bar{Z}_c=(1+j)mc_B/2$ has properties similar to those of the characteristic impedance of a telephone line, and it will be called the characteristic impedance of the beam. In contrast to the characteristic impedance of a telephone line or of a longitudinally vibrating rod—because of the end distortion near field—the characteristic impedance of the beam is complex. It consists of a frequency-dependent resistance in series with a frequency-dependent mass; the loss factor of this combination is one. If a beam is driven by a compliant spindle, a resonance is generated because of the mass component of the characteristic impedance. This resonance appears as a broad peak in the smoothed-out frequency curve of the system. Because of the square-root dependence of the resistance and the mass impedance, the frequency curve differs from that of a simple point-mass spring system, and the peak is narrow, as shown in Figure 6.5.

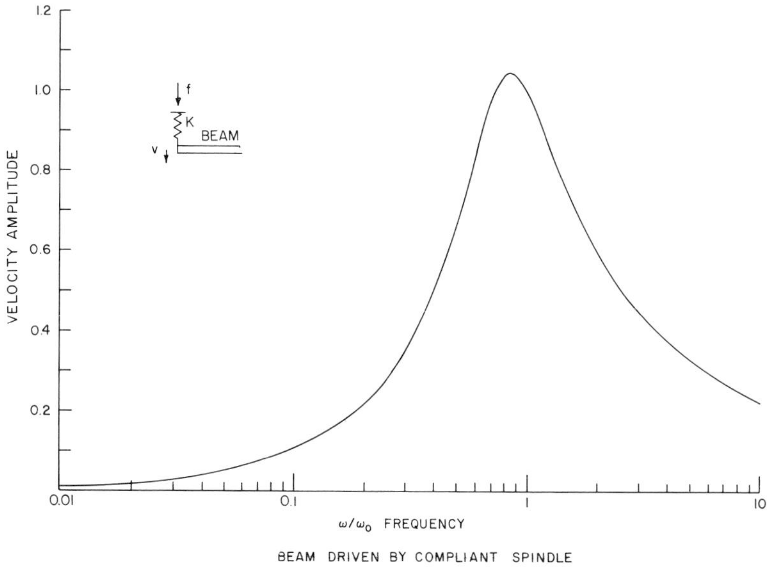

Fig. 6.5 Frequency curve of a beam driven by a compliant spindle. Because of the frequency dependence of the characteristic impedances, in the frequency curve of the impedance an antiresonant peak is generated that is steeper than that of a simple tuned circuit.

The transfer impedance is defined as the ratio of the driving force to the velocity at a point different from the driving point. If this second point is farther than about $\lambda/4$ from the driving point, the distortion term is negligible, and the transfer impedance becomes:

$$\bar{Z}_t = \frac{\bar{F}}{\bar{V}} = (1+j)\, mc_B e^{jkx} \tag{6.84}$$

This impedance characterizes the wave that propagates along the beam.

Beam Driven at Its Center by a Point Force

A beam driven at its center can be regarded as consisting of two identical halves, each of which is driven by half the force. But the boundary conditions are here slightly different. The condition $\partial^2\xi/\partial x^2 = 0$ for zero bending moment at the driving point has to be replaced by the condition $\partial\xi/\partial x=0$ (the shear deflection being neglected), which implies horizontal slope at the driving point. For the right-hand half, the following equations apply:

$$\hat{\xi}=\bar{A}e^{-jkx}+\bar{C}e^{-kx} \tag{6.85}$$

$$\left(\frac{\partial\hat{\xi}}{\partial x}\right)_{x=0}=0=k(j\bar{A}+\bar{C}) \tag{6.86}$$

Hence,

$$\hat{\xi}=\bar{A}(e^{-jkx}-je^{-kx}) \tag{6.87}$$

and

$$\frac{\bar{F}}{2}=\frac{\lambda_E Jm}{m}\left(\frac{\partial^3\hat{\xi}}{\partial x^3}\right)_{x=0}=2j\alpha^4mk^3\bar{A}=2j\omega\sqrt{\omega}\,\alpha m\bar{A} \tag{6.88}$$

The ratio of the driving force to the velocity of a point x is:

$$\bar{Z}=\frac{\bar{F}}{j\omega\hat{\xi}}=\frac{4j\omega\sqrt{\omega}\,\alpha m}{j\omega(e^{-jkx}-je^{-kx})}=\frac{4mc_B}{e^{-jkx}-je^{-kx}} \tag{6.89}$$

The driving-point impedance of a beam driven at its center is given by:

$$\bar{Z}_d=\frac{F}{j\omega(\xi)_{x=0}}=\frac{4mc_B}{1-j}=2(1+j)mc_B \tag{6.90}$$

and its transfer impedance when $x>\lambda/4$ is given by:

$$\bar{Z}_t=4mc_Be^{jkx} \tag{6.91}$$

Both these impedances are greater by a factor of 4 than those for a beam driven at one end. The condition of zero slope doubles the driving-point impedance. The second factor of two is a consequence of the excitation of waves in both the left- and the right-hand sections of the beam.

Beam of Finite Length

Natural Functions and Natural Frequencies

The beam equation (6.31) can also be solved by circular and hyperbolic functions:

$$\xi=A\cosh kx+B\sinh kx+C\cos kx+D\sin kx \tag{6.92}$$

If the beam is free at the end $x=0$, bending moment and shear force vanish at this end:

$$\frac{\partial^2\xi}{\partial x^2}=0 \quad \text{and} \quad \frac{\partial^3\xi}{\partial x^3}=0 \tag{6.93}$$

The condition leads to the relation:

$$B=D \quad \text{and} \quad A=C \tag{6.94}$$

Thus, as always, the end distortion doubles the vibration amplitude. If these values are substituted,

$$\xi = A(\cosh kx + \cos kx) + B(\sinh kx + \sin kx) \tag{6.95}$$

If the rod is also free at the end $x=l$, the boundary condition $\partial^2\xi/\partial x^2 = 0$ furnishes the relation:

$$B = -A\frac{\cosh kl - \cos kl}{\sinh kl - \sin kl} \tag{6.96}$$

and the solution becomes:

$$\xi = \left[A\cosh kx + \cos kx - \frac{\cosh kl - \cos kl}{\sinh kl - \sin kl}\cdot(\sinh kx + \sin kx\right] \tag{6.97}$$

This solution represents the natural functions of a beam with both ends free, if the values $k = k_\nu$ are chosen to satisfy the boundary condition $\partial^3\xi/\partial x^3 = 0$ at the end $x = l$.

Figure 6.6 shows the shapes of beams at the various natural modes for six different boundary conditions; the mode constant C determines the natural frequency for the mode shown.

Beam Free at End $x = 0$ and Driven by a Point Force at End $x = l$

The vibration of a beam that is free at the end $x=0$ and driven at the end $x=l$ is given by Equation 6.96, if the constant A is determined so that the boundary condition

$$F = -\lambda_E J\frac{\partial^3\xi}{\partial x^3} \tag{6.98}$$

is fulfilled at the end $x=l$. The solution then becomes:

$$\frac{1}{\bar{Z}} = \frac{\bar{V}}{\bar{F}_0} = \frac{\gamma}{2(1-\cosh \bar{k}l\cos \bar{k}l)}[(\sinh \bar{k}x + \sin \bar{k}x)\cdot(\cosh \bar{k}l - \cos \bar{k}l) - (\sinh \bar{k}l - \sin \bar{k}l)\cdot(\cosh \bar{k}x + \cos \bar{k}x)] \tag{6.99}$$

where γ is an abbreviation for:

$$\gamma = \frac{-j\omega}{\bar{k}^3\lambda_E J} = \frac{-j\omega}{m\alpha^4\bar{k}^3} = \frac{-j}{m\bar{c}_B} \tag{6.100}$$

Damping has been included by assuming that k is complex:

$$\bar{k} = k\left(1 - \frac{j\eta}{4} + \ldots\right) \tag{6.101}$$

the magnitude η being the loss factor of Young's modulus λ_E.

If the observation point coincides with the driving point, $x=l$, and

$$\frac{1}{\bar{Z}} = \frac{\bar{V}}{\bar{F}_0} = \frac{\gamma}{(1-\cosh \bar{k}l\cos \bar{k}l)}(\sin \bar{k}l\cosh \bar{k}l - \cos \bar{k}l\sinh \bar{k}l) \tag{6.102}$$

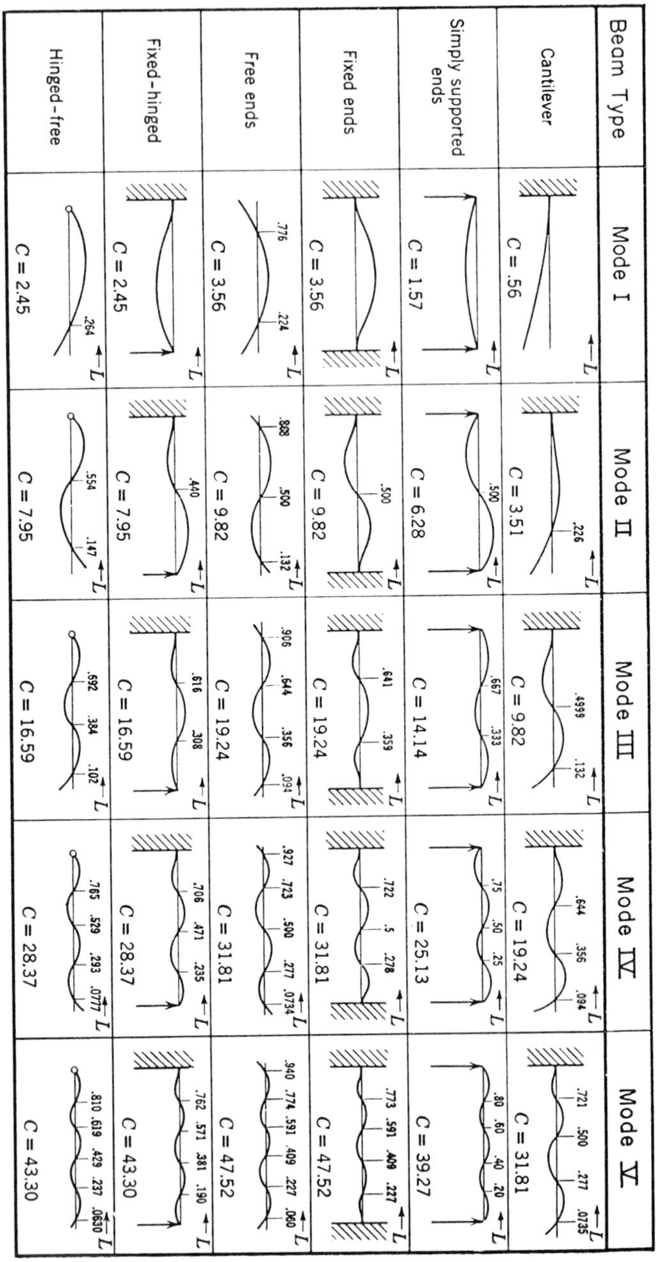

$$f_n = C[EIg/(wL^4)]^{\frac{1}{2}}$$

Fig. 6.6 The shapes of six different types of beams at their bending resonances; E, Young's modulus, ψ; I, sectional moments of inertia; g, acceleration due to gravity, inches per second; w, weight of unit length, pounds per inch; L, length, inches.

The roots of the denominator represent the natural frequencies of the beam. For very low frequencies, $\cos kl = 1 - k^2l^2/2! + k^4l^4/4!$, $\cosh kl = 1 + k^2l^2/2! + k^4l^4/4!$, $\sin kl \doteq kl - k^3l^3/3!$, and $\sinh kl \doteq kl + k^3l^3/3!$; and Equation 6.102 reduces to $4F/j\omega M$ and becomes iden tical to the term $1/\bar{Z}_0$ of the natural mode solution. This term represents the motion of and around the center of gravity, as if the beam were perfectly rigid. If the point of observation is at the end opposite the driving point, the solution reduces to $-2/j\omega M$.

The characteristic impedance, which is the driving-point impedance for an infinitely long beam, can be derived from the above result by assuming that $k\eta l/4 \gg 1$ and that $kl \gg 1$. The quantities $\cos kl$ and $\sin kl$ then reduce to $\frac{1}{2}\, e^{jkl + k\eta l/4}$ and · $-\frac{1}{2} j e^{jkl + k\eta l/4}$. Equation 6.102 then simplifies to:

$$\frac{1}{\bar{Z}_d} = -\gamma\left(\frac{1}{j} - 1\right) = \frac{2}{(1+j)\, m\bar{c}_B} = \frac{1}{\bar{Z}_c} \tag{6.103}$$

The maxima are given with sufficient accuracy by the minima of the denominator of Equation 6.102. Since the imaginary parts vary only slowly with frequency, the maxima are given by the zeros of the denominator:

$$\cosh kl \cos kl = 1 \qquad \text{or} \qquad \cos kl = \frac{1}{\cosh kl} \tag{6.104}$$

But $\cosh kl \gg 1$ at frequencies above the fundamental frequency; therefore,

$$\cos kl \to 0 \qquad \text{and} \qquad \sin kl \to \pm 1 \tag{6.105}$$

and $kl = (2\nu + 1)\, \pi/2$. Also, $\cosh kl = \sinh kl$, and Equation 6.102 reduces to:

$$\frac{1}{\bar{Z}} = \frac{\gamma \cosh kl}{Im(\cosh \bar{k}l \cos \bar{k}l)} = \frac{\gamma}{-j\eta k\dfrac{l}{4}} = \frac{1}{\eta\omega M\dfrac{1}{4}} = \frac{1}{R_\nu} \tag{6.106}$$

where $M = ml$ is the total mass of the rod.[3] For the minima, the real part of the numerator vanishes ($\sin \bar{k}l \doteq \cos \bar{k}l$), and Equation 6.102 reduces to:

$$\frac{1}{\bar{Z}} = \frac{1}{R_{\max}} = \gamma\frac{2\eta kl}{4} = \frac{\eta\omega ml}{2m^2c_B{}^2} = \frac{\eta\omega M}{2m^2c_B{}^2} = \frac{4R_{\min}}{Z_c{}^2} = \frac{\dfrac{\eta\omega M}{4}}{\dfrac{m^2c_B{}^2}{2}}$$

$$= \frac{R_\nu}{\dfrac{m^2c_B{}^2}{2}} = \frac{R_\nu}{|Z_C|^2} \tag{6.107}$$

where $\bar{Z}_c = (1+j)\, mc_B/2$ is the characteristic impedance of a beam driven at its end.[4] If the receiver and the driver are at opposite ends, $x = 0$, and the maxima are the same as above; the minima, then, are shallow troughs. To compute them, damping may be neglected, $kl \doteq \nu\pi$, and kl may be assumed to be large enough so that the one in the denominator can be neglected. The minima are then given by:

[3] This result has been derived with the aid of Eqs. 69–73, p. XLI, and the imaginary part of the numerator has been neglected.

[4] Again, Eqs. 69–73, p. XLI, have been used to decompose the circular and hyperbolic functions into real and imaginary parts.

$$\frac{1}{\bar{Z}} = \frac{\pm\gamma \sinh kl}{\cosh kl} = \pm\gamma = \frac{\pm j}{mc_B} = \frac{\pm(1-j)}{\bar{Z}_t} \tag{6.108}$$

and

$$\frac{1}{|\bar{Z}|} = \frac{\sqrt{2}}{|\bar{Z}_t|} \tag{6.109}$$

since $\cosh kl = \sinh kl \gg \sin kl$, if $kl \gg 1$.

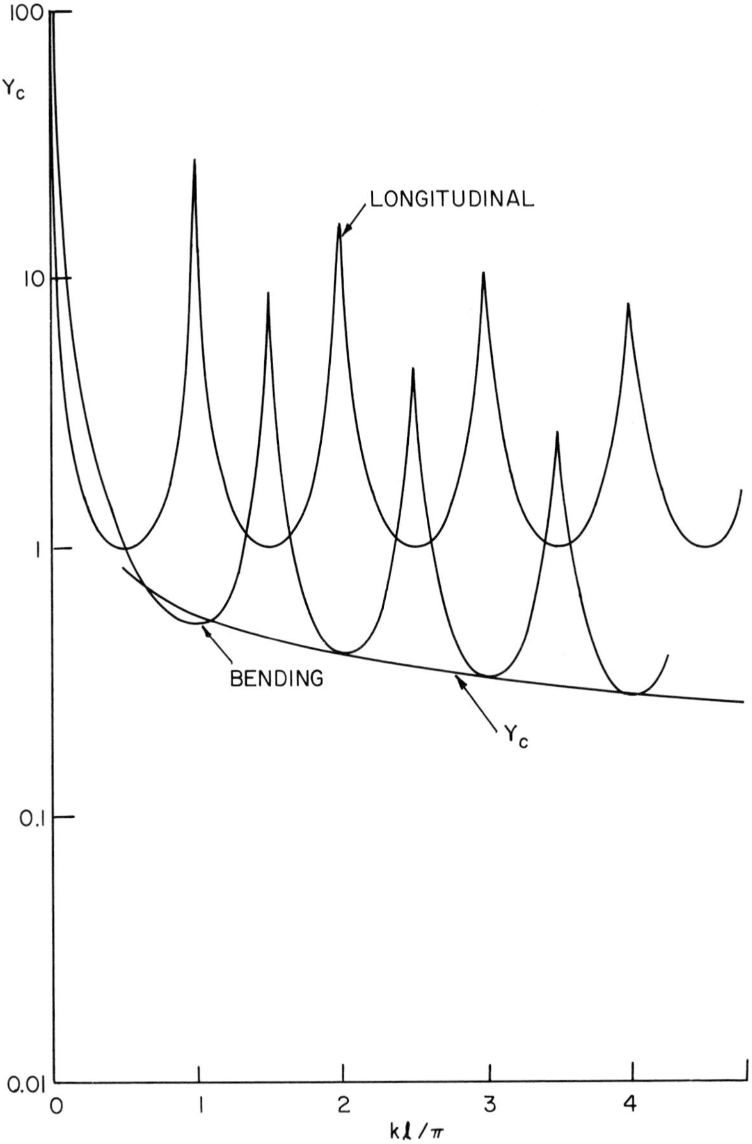

Fig. 6.7 Computed response curve for a beam performing bending vibrations. A curve for the longitudinal vibrations of the same beam is plotted for comparison.

Figure 6.7 shows the theoretical results; it also shows, for comparison, the velocity amplitude for longitudinal vibrations. The shape of the curve when multiplied by $\sqrt{kl}$ is practically the same as that for longitudinal vibrations, except for the part below the first resonances and the difference in the natural frequencies. This similarity justifies the standard procedure of replacing the complicated natural functions for bending vibrations by those for longitudinal vibrations.

We note that it is the real part of the characteristic admittance—not its absolute value—that determines the line through the troughs of the frequency curve of the velocity amplitude of the free end of the beam, and that its absolute value—not its real part—determines the geometric mean through the frequency curve of the velocity amplitude of the driven end.

If the driver generated a progressive wave $\bar{f}/\bar{Z}_t$ of the same amplitude as if the rod were infinitely long, this wave would be reflected with a phase $-j$ (see Eq. 6.64) at the end of the beam. The end distortion then would double the resultant amplitude (see Eq. 6.65), and the amplitude at the free end of the beam would be $\hat{\xi}=[\bar{F}(1-j)\cdot 2]/\bar{Z}_t$. However, the amplitude of the shallow troughs is half as large. A similar result is obtained for a longitudinally vibrating rod and for plates, and it seems to apply to all other vibrators. The reflected wave travels back into the driver (where it is absorbed) and opposes the generation of the outgoing wave, so that the driver has to work against twice the resistance.

Since the reflected wave opposes the outgoing wave at the driver, the velocity amplitude at the driver is particularly small, and an antiresonance is generated. In contrast, at a resonance, the phase of the reflected wave is such that it does not impede the driver; thus, the reflected wave trains are not affected by the driver, and a reverberant vibration field is generated in the vibrator. The amplitude thereby builds up to great values.

The vibration amplitude can be computed in the same manner as that for the rod in Equation 5.129 by replacing the series by $2(1-j)\ (R+R^2+\ldots)$, because reflection at the driver increases the amplitude by $(1-j)$ and the end distortion increases it by another factor of two. The quantity $R=e^{-kl\eta/2}=1-kl\eta/2+\ldots$ is the decrease in amplitude for a wave that travels from the driver to the end of the rod and back to the driver; Equation 6.106 is thus reobtained.

The vibration may also be excited by a bending moment on the end $x=l$ of the rod. An external couple L then takes the place of the external force. The boundary conditions for $x=0$ are:

$$\frac{\partial^2\xi}{\partial x^2}=0 \quad \text{and} \quad \frac{\partial^3\xi}{\partial x^3}=0 \tag{6.110}$$

and the solution is of the form of Equation 6.95. The boundary conditions for $x=l$ are:

$$\frac{\partial^3\hat{\xi}}{\partial x^3}=0 \qquad \text{or} \qquad \bar{B}=-\frac{\bar{A}\,(\sinh kl+\sin kl)}{\cosh kl-\cos kl} \tag{6.111}$$

and

$$\frac{j\omega}{k^2}\frac{\partial^2\hat{\xi}}{\partial x^2}=\frac{j\omega\bar{L}}{\alpha^4k^2m} \tag{6.112}$$

If the constant A is eliminated in Equation 6.95 with the aid of the last equation (6.112), the velocity amplitude of the free end at $x=0$ becomes:

$$\frac{\tilde{v}}{\bar{L}}=j\frac{\gamma^*(\cosh \bar{k}l-\cos \bar{k}l)}{1-\cosh \bar{k}l\cos \bar{k}l} \tag{6.113}$$

where

$$\gamma^*=\frac{1}{\alpha^2m}=\frac{1}{\sqrt{\lambda_E Jm}}=\frac{\omega}{mc_B{}^2} \tag{6.114}$$

For further computations, Equation 6.53 applies:

$$\bar{k}l=kl\left(1-\frac{j\eta}{4}+\ldots\right) \tag{6.115}$$

and $\cos \bar{k}l$ and $\cosh \bar{k}l$ are then decomposed into real and imaginary parts.[5] If damping is small, $\cosh \eta k_0l/4$ and $\cos \eta k_0l/4$ may be replaced by 1, and $\sin \eta k_0l/4$ and $\sinh \eta k_0l/4$ may be replaced by $\eta k_0l/4$, and the squares and higher powers of η may be neglected. If, furthermore, $kl\gg 1$ (this excludes the frequency range up to about the second resonance peak):

$$\cosh k_0l\doteq\sinh k_0l \tag{6.116}$$

For the computation of the maxima, the real part of the denominator $1-\cos k_0l\cosh k_0l=0$, and $k_0l\approx(2\nu+1)\pi/2$, since $\cosh kl\gg 1$. The maxima are then given by:

$$\frac{\tilde{v}}{\bar{L}}=\frac{1}{\frac{M}{2}\eta c_B} \tag{6.117}$$

where M is the total mass of the beam and $c_B=\alpha\sqrt{\omega}$ is the bending-wave velocity. Since c_B increases with the square root of the frequency, the maxima decrease in inverse proportion to the square root of the frequency. The minima are found for $kl\doteq\nu$; since kl may be considered large in comparison to 1, $\cosh k_0l=\sinh k_0l\doteq e^{kl}$ is large and the 1 in the denominator can be neglected; the minima are given by:

$$\frac{\tilde{v}}{\bar{L}}=\gamma^*=\frac{1}{\sqrt{\lambda_E Jm}} \tag{6.118}$$

[5] See Eqs. 69–73, p. XLI.

Thus, if the vibration is excited by a bending moment, the line drawn through the troughs does not decrease with frequency, but remains horizontal. This shows that bending moments are particularly effective in exciting high-frequency vibrations.

Figure 6.8 shows a comparison of the frequency curves for longitudinal, bending, and torsional vibrations. Because successive troughs have opposite phase,[6] electric cross talk alternately increases and decreases the height of successive troughs (Fig. 6.8*d*).

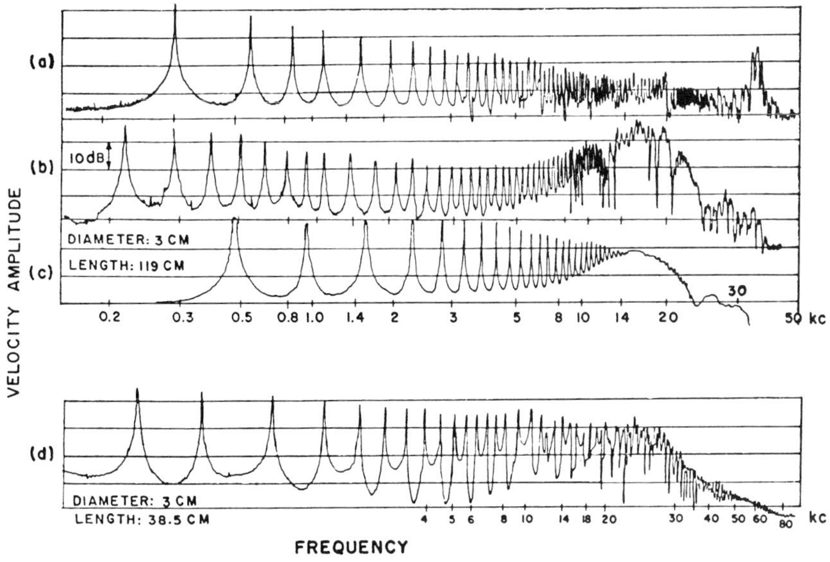

Fig. 6.8 Velocity response of two polystyrene beams for three types of vibration, with receiver at the free end; *a*, *b*, and *c*, a polystyrene beam, diameter 3 cm., length 119 cm.; *d*, a polystyrene beam, diameter 3 cm., length 38.5 cm.; *a*, torsional vibration; *b*, bending vibration; *c*, longitudinal vibration; *d*, bending vibration, with cross talk added.

If the frequency curve for bending vibrations is recorded for actual samples, the peaks are almost always split into double peaks or are broader than normally expected. Beams are never strictly homogeneous or isotropic, and they always have a slightly different stiffness for vibrations in two planes perpendicular to one another. This phenomenon is illustrated by the frequency curves shown in Figure 6.9. Because of the damping, some of the resonances may appear single; but when the test piece is cooled, so that damping becomes smaller, the two peaks are clearly visible (Fig. 6.10).

[6] See pp. 36, 137.

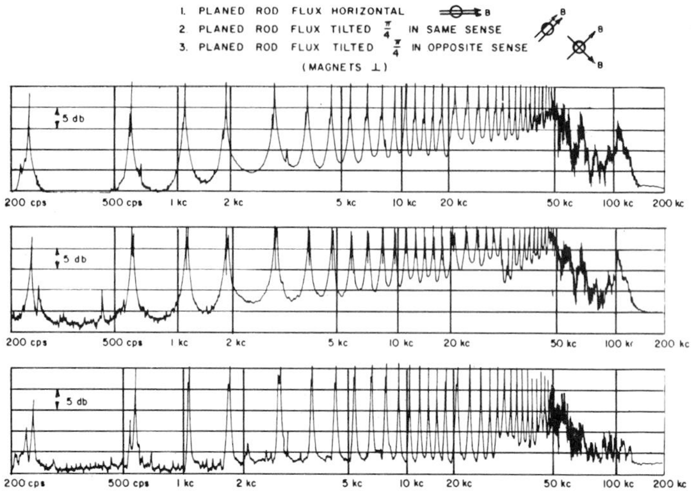

Fig. 6.9 Frequency curves for a polystyrene beam excited to bending vibrations in two planes perpendicular to one another (at 45°, with the receiver polarized in the same plane and perpendicular to it); *a*, flux horizontal; *b*, flux tilted $\pi/4$ in same sense; *c*, flux tilted $\pi/4$ in opposite sense.

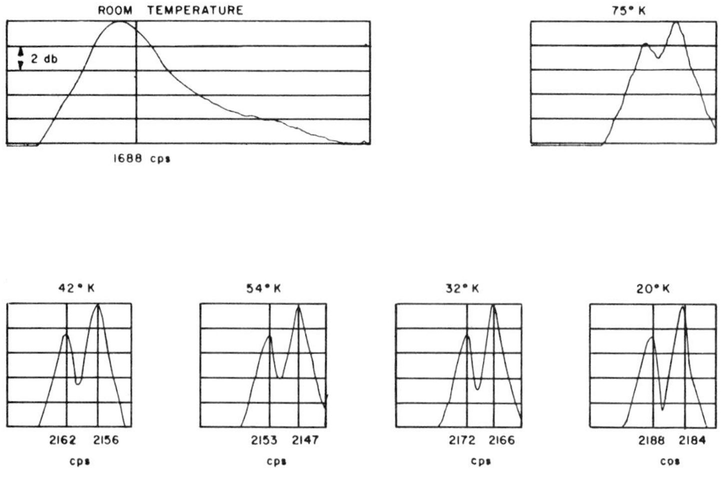

Fig. 6.10 Frequency curves of polymethyl methacrylate beam at various temperatures. Cooling decreases damping, and the two peaks become clearly visible.

Transmission of a Mass-Loaded Joint

The transmission of longitudinal vibrations in a beam from one end to the other can be suppressed considerably at higher frequencies by attaching a mass to the beam, or, still better, by cutting the beam into two parts and connecting the two parts by a heavy mass, as described in Chapter V. The mass, because of its inertia, represents a strong discontinuity, and the incident wave is partially reflected to the driven end. The situation is completely different if the beam is excited to bending vibrations. If the mass loading is not very extended, so that its moment of inertia is not very large, bending vibrations are transmitted through the mass regardless of its weight. The mass loading, then, seems to have the same effect as clamping the vibrator by a knife edge that is held rigidly in space. The velocity is zero at the clamp, but slope and bending moment are the same on both sides.

Such a mass-loaded beam represents the one-dimensional analogue of a plate with a stiffening rib or of two plates connected at one edge by a heavy (i.e., welded) joint. The joint or the stiffening rib, then, because of the increased mass of the vibrator, acts like a mass loading.

Let us first study the effect of a mass-loaded joint, two beams connected rigidly through a mass. Because the solution must be finite at $x=\infty$ and $x=-\infty$ at the driven end, it is given by:

$$\hat{\xi}_1=\bar{A}e^{-jkx}+\bar{R}e^{jkx}+\bar{B}e^{kx} \qquad (x\leq 0) \tag{6.119}$$

and the solution for the second part of the beam is given by:

$$\hat{\xi}_2=\bar{T}e^{-jkx}+\bar{D}e^{-kx} \qquad (x\geqq 0) \tag{6.120}$$

The boundary conditions lead to the equations:

$$(\hat{\xi})_{x=0}=\bar{A}+\bar{B}+\bar{R}=\bar{T}+\bar{D}=0 \tag{6.121}$$

$$\frac{1}{k}\left(\frac{\partial\hat{\xi}}{\partial x}\right)_{x=0}=-j\bar{A}+\bar{B}+j\bar{R}=-j\bar{T}-\bar{D} \tag{6.122}$$

$$\frac{1}{k^2}\left(\frac{\partial^2\hat{\xi}}{\partial x^2}\right)_{x=0}=-\bar{A}+\bar{B}-\bar{R}=-\bar{T}+\bar{D} \tag{6.123}$$

$\bar{D}$ can be eliminated in the first of the last three equations. If $\bar{R}$ is eliminated by subtracting the last from the first, the result obtained is:

$$\bar{T}=\frac{1}{1+j}\bar{A} \qquad \text{or} \qquad T=\frac{\bar{A}}{\sqrt{2}} \tag{6.124}$$

Thus, $1/\sqrt{2}$, or 0.707, of the incident amplitude is transmitted through the joint, regardless of the frequency. However, we have assumed that the mass loading is large enough to clamp the beam effectively in the frequency range of interest. The mass loading is large enough if its mass reactance ωM is large as compared to the characteristic impedance of the beam.

Recommended Reading

BICKLEY, W. G., AND A. TALBOT, *An Introduction to the Theory of Vibrating Systems,* Oxford University Press, Inc., New York, 1961.

BISHOP, R. E. D., AND D. C. JOHNSON, *The Mechanics of Vibration,* Cambridge University Press, New York, 1960.

MCLACHLAN, N. W., *Theory of Vibrations,* Dover Publications, Inc., New York, 1951.

RAYLEIGH, LORD, *The Theory of Sound,* Macmillan and Co., Ltd., London, 1894, vol. I.

SNOWDON, J. C., "Transverse vibration of free-free beams," *J.A.S.A.*, **35** (1963), 47.

———, "Transverse vibrations of simply clamped beams," *J.A.S.A.,* **35** (1963), 115.

———, "Mechanical impedance of simply supported beams," *J.A.S.A.,* **35** (1963), 228.

———, "Response of a simply clamped beam to vibratory forces and moments," *J.A.S.A.*, **36** (1964), 495.

TIMOSHENKO, S., *Theory of Elasticity*, McGraw-Hill, Inc., New York, 1934.

VII / GENERAL THEORY OF HOMOGENEOUS COMPLEX VIBRATORY SYSTEMS

The two preceding chapters demonstrated the theoretical treatment of simple systems with distributed mass and compliance, such as vibrating strings, rods, and beams. In this chapter, the preceding derivations will be generalized for more complex homogeneous systems and for three-dimensional vibrators, but they must be restricted to vibrators that are described by a scalar point function. The solution will be written in a form that makes it directly applicable to numerical evaluations. The solution will then be used in a subsequent chapter for the study of rectangular plates excited at the center by a point force and for some other important examples.

Differential Equation for a System with Continuously Distributed Mass and Compliance

Because of internal creep, elastic lags, and similar phenomena, the elastic properties and the dissipation of a mechanical system depend on the history of the motion. The details of the history of the system are contained implicitly in the Fourier coefficients of the motion. The history of each harmonic component is well known, and the dispersion and dissipation can be accounted for by introducing a complex elastic constant:

$$\bar{\lambda}=\lambda_0(1+j\eta) \tag{7.1}$$

in much the same manner as a complex dielectric constant is introduced to account for the dielectric losses in the electrical theory. In the above expression, λ_0 is the stiffness of the system, and η is the loss factor (or the logarithmic decrement divided by π) for the motion that is described by $\bar{\lambda}$. The complex modulus of elasticity may be considered to be given with the substance. (The stiffness constant λ_0 can be deduced from the resonant frequency; the loss factor η can be deduced from the band width of the resonance curve of a tuned system whose compliant element is made of the given substance.)

The vibration of a point-mass compliant element system is described by a set of network equations. In contrast, the vibration of a continuous system is described by a differential equation of the type

$$m\ddot{\xi}+\bar{\lambda}\cdot L\left(\frac{\partial}{\partial x},\frac{\partial}{\partial y},\frac{\partial}{\partial z}\right)\xi=\tilde{f}=Fe^{j\omega t} \tag{7.2}$$

where m is the mass per unit area or volume; ω, the angular frequency; $\xi(x, y, z)$, the displacement; $\bar{\lambda}$, the complex stiffness; $\tilde{f}$, the external force per unit area or volume; and L, a linear self-adjoint[1] differential operator that describes the elastic strain of the material. The first term represents the inertia of the system; the second, the elastic restoring force. For a longitudinally vibrating rod,

$$\lambda\cdot L\left(\frac{\partial}{\partial x},\frac{\partial}{\partial y},\frac{\partial}{\partial z}\right)=\lambda_E\frac{\partial^2}{\partial x^2} \tag{7.3}$$

and for a transversely vibrating plate,

$$\lambda\cdot L\left(\frac{\partial}{\partial x},\frac{\partial}{\partial y},\frac{\partial}{\partial z}\right)=\frac{\lambda_E h^2}{12\rho(1-\nu^2)}\left(\frac{\partial^2}{\partial x^2}+\frac{\partial^2}{\partial y^2}\right)^2 \tag{7.4}$$

where λ_E is Young's modulus; h, the thickness of the plate; ρ, its density; and ν, Poisson's contraction.

The solution for the lumped parameter system was obtained by partial-fraction development. The solution for the continuous system can be obtained by developing the displacement into the natural functions $\xi_\nu = \xi_\nu(x, y, z)$ of the differential equation of the homogeneous dissipationless system:

$$\tilde{\xi}=\sum_\nu \hat{\xi}_\nu(x, y, z)e^{j\omega t} \tag{7.5}$$

where ω is the frequency of the force. The natural functions $\hat{\xi}_\nu(x, y, z)$ are not normalized and may contain any constant multiplier; they represent the amplitude distributions for the nontrivial periodic solutions, $\tilde{\xi}_\nu = \hat{\xi}_\nu(x, y, z)\, e^{j\omega_\nu t}$, of the homogeneous differential equation of the dissipationless system ($\lambda=\lambda_0$, $\eta=0$), since they are supposed to be periodic solutions, $\partial^2\tilde{\xi}_\nu/\partial t^2=(j\omega_\nu)^2\tilde{\xi}_\nu$; and the homogeneous differential equation of the dissipationless system

$$m\ddot{\xi}_\nu+\lambda_0 L\left(\frac{\partial}{\partial x},\frac{\partial}{\partial y},\frac{\partial}{\partial z}\right)\cdot\xi_\nu=0 \tag{7.6}$$

reduces to:

$$\lambda_0 L\left(\frac{\partial}{\partial x},\frac{\partial}{\partial y},\frac{\partial}{\partial z}\right)\cdot\tilde{\xi}_\nu=m\omega_\nu^2\tilde{\xi}_\nu \tag{7.7}$$

The time factor and any real or imaginary constant multiplier that may still be contained in $\hat{\xi}_\nu$ can be canceled out, left and right, and the last equation becomes a differential equation for the amplitude $\hat{\xi}_\nu$ or the instantaneous

[1] E.g., see Courant-Hilbert, *Methods of Mathematical Physics* (New York, 1953), vol. I.

displacement ξ_ν of the νth mode:

$$\lambda_0 L \cdot \xi_\nu = m\omega_\nu{}^2 \cdot \xi_\nu \tag{7.8}$$

This is the form in which this equation is usually given in the textbooks of mathematics. The magnitudes $\omega_\nu{}^2$ are the so-called *eigen* values, i.e., the squares of the natural frequencies of the system that is described by this equation. Thus, the homogeneous equation shows that the application of the operator $\lambda_0 L\ (\partial/\partial x, \partial/\partial y, \partial/\partial z)$ to a natural function ξ_ν is equivalent to multiplying this function by $m\omega_\nu{}^2$. The result will make it possible later to eliminate the operator L from the equations.

If the above series (Eq. 7.5) is entered, the differential equation becomes:

$$-m\omega^2 \sum_\nu \tilde{\xi}_\nu + \sum_\nu \lambda_0(1+j\eta)\, L\left(\frac{\partial}{\partial x}, \frac{\partial}{\partial y}, \frac{\partial}{\partial z}\right) \cdot \tilde{\xi}_\nu = \tilde{f} \tag{7.9}$$

Since the frequencies of the variations of the left- and the right-hand sides must be the same, the natural modes ξ_ν are excited to forced vibrations of a frequency equal to that of the force.

The natural functions ξ_ν obey orthogonality relations:

$$\int \xi_\nu \xi_\mu d\sigma = 0 \qquad \text{if } \nu \neq \mu$$

$$\int \xi_\nu{}^2 d\sigma = \langle \xi_\nu{}^2 \rangle \sigma \neq 0 \qquad \text{if } \mu = \nu \tag{7.10}$$

where $\langle \xi_\nu{}^2 \rangle$ is the space-average square of ξ_ν over the system and σ is the size of the system ($d\sigma = dx \cdot dy \cdot dz$). The natural functions, which are not normalized here, represent the true deformations of the system. To prove the orthogonality condition, the homogeneous equation is written out for the νth and the μth natural modes:

$$\begin{aligned} \lambda_0 L \cdot \xi_\nu &= m\omega_\nu{}^2 \xi_\nu \\ \lambda_0 L \cdot \xi_\mu &= m\omega_\mu{}^2 \xi_\mu \end{aligned} \tag{7.11}$$

If the first equation is multiplied by ξ_μ, the second, by ξ_ν, and the resultant equations subtracted and integrated over the system, the following equation is obtained:

$$\int \lambda_0(\xi_\mu L\xi_\nu - \xi_\nu L\xi_\mu) d\sigma = m(\omega_\nu{}^2 - \omega_\mu{}^2) \int \xi_\nu \xi_\mu d\sigma \tag{7.12}$$

The left-hand side can be evaluated by partial integration. In physical problems, if the system is isolated, L is a self-adjoint operator, and the left-hand side is zero. Since $\omega_\nu{}^2$ and $\omega_\mu{}^2$ are assumed to be different, the integral on the right-hand side must vanish whenever $\nu \neq \mu$.

The series can then be reduced to a single term by canceling out the time factors $e^{j\omega t}$, left and right, by multiplying by $\tilde{\xi}_\mu$, and by integrating over the system. All the mixed terms that contain the product $\xi_\nu \xi_\mu$ vanish, and

Equation 7.9 reduces to:

$$m[-\omega^2+(1+j\eta)\omega_\nu^2]\int \hat{\xi}_\nu^2 d\sigma=\int F\hat{\xi}_\nu d\sigma \tag{7.13}$$

This equation determines the amplitude with which the natural functions are excited; it can be brought into a considerably more convenient form by dividing by $\hat{\xi}_\nu(A)$, where $\hat{\xi}_\nu(A)$ is the value of the natural function at the point of observation x_A, y_A, z_A. The equation then takes the following form:

$$[-\omega^2+(1+j\eta)\omega_\nu^2]\frac{m\sigma\langle\hat{\xi}_\nu^2\rangle}{\hat{\xi}_\nu^2(A)}\cdot\hat{\xi}_\nu(A)=\int\frac{F\hat{\xi}_\nu(x,y,z)d\sigma}{\hat{\xi}_\nu(A)} \tag{7.14}$$

The left side contains the dimensionless factor $\langle\hat{\xi}_\nu^2\rangle/\hat{\xi}_\nu^2(A)=\langle\xi_\nu^2\rangle/\xi_\nu^2(A)$, and the right-hand side, the factor $\hat{\xi}_\nu(x,y,z)/\hat{\xi}_\nu(A)=\xi_\nu(x,y,z)/\xi_\nu(A)$; these factors[2] depend only on the co-ordinates of the point of observation and on the natural functions of the system. The first factor will be abbreviated by the letter q_ν:

$$q_\nu=\frac{\langle\xi_\nu^2\rangle}{\xi_\nu^2(A)} \tag{7.15}$$

The magnitude $M=\sigma m$ represents the total mass of the system. The following abbreviations are useful:

$$M_\nu(A)=q_\nu M=M\frac{\langle\xi_\nu^2\rangle}{\xi_\nu^2(A)} \tag{7.16}$$

$$F_0=\int F(x,y,z)d\sigma \tag{7.17}$$

$$\kappa_\nu(A)F_0=\int\frac{F(x,y,z)\,\xi_\nu(x,y,z)}{\xi_\nu(A)}d\sigma \tag{7.18}$$

With these abbreviations, Equation 7.14 becomes:

$$[-\omega^2+(1+j)\omega_\nu^2]M_\nu(A)\hat{\xi}_\nu(A)=\kappa_\nu(A)F_0 \tag{7.19}$$

The constant $\kappa_\nu(A)$ can again be interpreted as the fraction of the total force F_0 that is available for exciting the νth mode of the system; it will, therefore, be called the excitation constant. The introduction of the constant $\kappa_\nu(A)$ is the most important step in the derivation; the constant $\kappa_\nu(A)$ can be absorbed by the mode parameters of the system by dividing Equation 7.19 by $\kappa_\nu(A)$ and by replacing M_ν by $M_\nu^*=M_\nu/\kappa_\nu(A)$,as follows:

$$M_\nu^*[-\omega^2+(1+j\eta)\omega_\nu^2]\hat{\xi}_\nu(A)=F_0 \tag{7.20}$$

The solution may finally be written in the following condensed form, which is very convenient for further computations:

$$\hat{\xi}(A)=\sum_{\nu=0}^{\infty}\hat{\xi}_\nu(A)=F_0\sum_{\nu=0}^{\infty}\frac{1}{M_\nu^*[-\omega^2+\omega_\nu^2(1+j\eta)]}$$

[2] Any phase factor or other constant multiplier cancels out when these ratios are formed.

$$= F_0 \sum_{\nu=0}^{\infty} \frac{1}{M_\nu^*(-\omega^2+\bar{\omega}_\nu^2)} \tag{7.21}$$

where $\bar{\omega}_\nu^2 = \omega_\nu^2 (1+j\eta)$. From the physical point of view, the following form of the solution is important:

$$\bar{V} = j\omega \sum_{\nu=0}^{\infty} \hat{\xi}_\nu = F_0 \sum_{\nu=0}^{\infty} \frac{\omega}{M_\nu^*[j(\omega^2-\omega_\nu^2)+\omega_\nu^2\eta]}$$

$$= F_0 \sum_{\nu=0}^{\infty} \frac{1}{R_\nu^* + j\omega M_\nu^* + \dfrac{1}{j\omega K_\nu^*}} = F_0 \sum_{\nu=0}^{\infty} \frac{1}{\bar{Z}_\nu} = \frac{F_0}{\bar{Z}} \tag{7.22}$$

where

$$M_\nu(A) = q_\nu M = \frac{\langle \xi_\nu^2 \rangle}{\xi_\nu^2(A)} M \tag{7.23}$$

$$M_\nu^*(A) = \frac{M_\nu(A)}{\kappa_\nu(A)} \tag{7.24}$$

$$R_\nu^*(A) = \frac{\omega_\nu^2}{\omega} \eta M_\nu^*(A) \tag{7.25}$$

$$K_\nu^*(A) = \frac{1}{\omega_\nu^2 M_\nu^*(A)} \tag{7.26}$$

$$\bar{Z}_\nu = R_\nu^* + j\omega M_\nu^* + \frac{1}{j\omega K_\nu^*} \quad \text{and} \quad \frac{1}{\bar{Z}} = \sum_{\nu=0}^{\infty} \frac{1}{\bar{Z}_\nu} \tag{7.27}$$

M is the total mass, and $M_\nu^*(A)$, $R_\nu^*(A)$, and $K_\nu^*(A)$ represent the effective mass, the effective resistance, and the effective compliance of the system for the νth mode of vibration, referred to the motion of an arbitrary point A and to the total driving force F_0. If the vibrator is freely suspended, the solution contains a term of zero order:

$$\frac{1}{\bar{Z}_0(A)} = \frac{1}{j\omega M} + \frac{y_A L_x}{I_x} - \frac{x_A L_y}{I_y} \tag{7.28}$$

which represents the motion of the center of gravity and the rotation around it, as if the system were perfectly rigid. In this term, L_x and L_y represent the x and y components of the moments of the external forces with respect to the center of gravity; x_A and y_A are the co-ordinates of the point of observation with respect to the center of gravity; and I_x, and I_y are the moments of inertia around the x- and y-axes, the displacements ξ_ν being assumed to occur in the z-direction.

The artifice of writing the Fourier coefficient of the force as the product of the total force and an excitation constant made it possible to include the excitation constants in the mode parameters of the system and to express the solution as the product of the total force and a function of the frequency and of the co-ordinates of the reference point. This function may be called the mechanical admittance; its reciprocal, the mechanical impedance of the system, relative to the selected reference point A and relative to the total force F_0 applied to the system. The form of each term of the solution is similar to the solution for the velocity of a simple series-resonant circuit, and every term can be represented by a tuned circuit. Thus, the mechanical impedance of a vibratory system can be represented by a sum of such solutions, that is, by a canonical circuit with an infinite number of branches in parallel (Fig. 1.11). Each branch represents the contribution of a natural mode of the system. For weakly excited modes, the excitation constant κ_ν is small, and the corresponding mode impedances are very large. Such branches, then, contribute only at frequencies close to their resonant frequencies.

The Mode Parameters

The mode parameters κ_ν, q_ν, $M_\nu{}^*$, $R_\nu{}^*$, and $K_\nu{}^*$ depend on the nature of the driving force and its point of attack, on the natural functions of the system, and on the co-ordinates of the point of observation. The practical value of the preceding theory is that the mode parameters usually can be computed in a very simple manner; in more complicated cases (e.g., a circular plate excited at its center), they can be computed rigorously and tabulated or estimated with a high degree of accuracy by using asymptotic formulas.

The driving force is usually a point force (like the force excited by the moving coil of a loud-speaker on its membrane) or a continuously distributed force of constant amplitude (like a sound wave that impinges on a microphone). A point force can be defined as the limiting case of a continuous force distribution that is very large in the immediate vicinity of the driving point and zero everywhere else. Such a point force can be represented in the following form:

$$F_0(x_F, y_F, z_F) = \int F_0 \delta(x_F - x)\, \delta(y_F - y)\, \delta(z_F - z)\, dx dy dz \qquad (7.29)$$

where $\delta(x)$ is Dirac's function, defined by:

$$\delta(x) = 0 \quad x \neq 0 \quad \text{and} \quad \int_{-\infty}^{\infty} \delta(x)\, dx = 1 \qquad (7.30)$$

For such a point force, the excitation constant is given by:

$$\kappa_\nu = \frac{1}{F_0} \int \frac{F_0 \delta(x_F - x)\, \delta(y_F - y)\, \delta(z_F - z)}{\xi_\nu(A)} \xi_\nu(x, y, z) dx dy dz$$

$$=\frac{\xi_\nu(x_F, y_F, z_F)}{\xi_\nu(x_A, y_A, z_A)}=\frac{\xi_\nu(F)}{\xi_\nu(A)} \tag{7.31}$$

where F and A represent abbreviations for the co-ordinates x_F, y_F, z_F, x_A, y_A, and z_A. Thus, the excitation constant is equal to the ratio of the mode amplitude at the force point to that at the point of observation. If the force point coincides with the point of observation,

$$\kappa_\nu=\frac{\xi_\nu(F)}{\xi_\nu(A)}=1 \tag{7.32}$$

regardless of the complexity of the system.

For a continuous force distribution of constant amplitude,

$$F(x, y, z)=F=\text{const} \quad \text{and} \quad F_0=\int_\sigma F d\sigma=F\sigma \tag{7.33}$$

and

$$\kappa_\nu(A)=\int_\sigma \frac{F\xi_\nu(x, y, z)}{F\sigma\xi_\nu(A)} d\sigma=\frac{\langle\xi_\nu\rangle}{\xi_\nu(A)} \tag{7.34}$$

becomes equal to the space-average amplitude divided by the amplitude of the reference point.

The mode constant q_ν is defined as the average square of the velocity of the system divided by the square of the velocity at the point of observation. If the system is one-dimensional (e.g., a rod) or two-dimensional and rectangular (e.g., a rectangular plate), then the mode amplitude ξ_ν usually varies sinusoidally over the system; for instance,

$$\xi_\nu(x)=\xi_{0\nu} \sin(\kappa_x l_x+\varphi_x) \tag{7.35}$$

for a one-dimensional vibration, and

$$\xi_\nu(x, y)=\xi_{0\nu} \sin(\kappa_x l_x+\varphi_x) \sin(\kappa_y l_y+\varphi_y) \tag{7.36}$$

for a two-dimensional vibration. The average square of a sinusoidal function over an integral multiple of the period (as in the solution for the longitudinally vibrating rod) is $\frac{1}{2}$; it is approximately $\frac{1}{2}$, if this intrval is different from an integal multiple of half the period, but is at least as great as one or two periods (e.g., if the solution for the freely suspended beam is integrated over the length of the beam, because of the end distortion). However, above the first or second mode, the end distortion that occurs in freely suspended plates has very little effect on this mean square and can be neglected.

The mode parameters are functions of the point of observation and of the driving point. If the vibrator is driven at its center or at its free endor edge (at a crest of a sine or cosine that represents, or approximates, the amplitude distribution), the mode parameter q_ν is usually $\frac{1}{2}$ for one-dimensional vibrations and $\frac{1}{4}$ for two-dimensional vibrations:

$$q_\nu = \begin{cases} \dfrac{1}{2} & \text{one-dimensional vibration} \\ \dfrac{1}{4} & \text{two-dimensional vibration} \end{cases} \qquad (7.37)$$

The mode masses M_ν, then, are either $\frac{1}{2}$ or $\frac{1}{4}$ the total mass of the system:

$$M_\nu = \begin{cases} \dfrac{M}{2} & \text{one-dimensional vibration} \\ \dfrac{M}{4} & \text{two-dimensional vibration} \end{cases} \qquad (7.38)$$

The masses $M_\nu{}^*$ are also $M/2$ or $M/4$, respectively, if the driving point coincides with the point of observation.

Frequency Response Curve for the Velocity Amplitude

Every term in the series solution is of the same structure as the solution for a tuned circuit. If the applied force is a point force, and the point of observation coincides with the driving point, all the constants κ_ν are positive and equal to one, and the tuned circuits consist only of positive elements. Foster's circuit theorem then applies, and resonances and antiresonances alternate in the frequency response curve of the system. But if the point of observation is not the driving point, or if the driving force is not a single point force or is continuously distributed over the system, some of the constants κ_ν are negative, and the corresponding terms in the series solution have negative signs; Foster's theorem then no longer applies, and resonances may be followed by shallow troughs in the frequency response curve of the system. The theory of the continuous system shows how such negative terms may be generated. If κ_ν is negative (since all the mode parameters contain κ_ν as a factor or a divisor), the corresponding mode masses, mode resistances, and mode compliances become negative. Negative elements indicate that the velocity is in antiphase with the force. For instance, at a resonance when a particular nodal line is crossed, the velocity may be in phase with the driving force in one nodal area and in antiphase in the adjacent nodal areas. The energy principle has no effect on this result, since the work performed by the driving force is not related to the velocity at some point other than the driving point.

Locus of the Mechanical Impedance of a System with Continuously Distributed Mass and Compliance in the Complex Plane

When the frequency is varied, the end point of the complex admittance vector describes a curve in the complex plane that gives valuable information about the mechanical design of the system and about the manner in which the vibrations are excited. The locus in the complex plane of the admittance that is represented by each term of the solution is a circle;[3] if the term occurs in a driving-point impedance, M_ν is positive and $\kappa_\nu = 1$. The end point of the admittance vector moves in a clockwise sense as the frequency is increased. The locus of a sum of such terms—and, consequently, the locus of the driving-point impedance of the whole system (except for a few degenerated cases)—is always represented by a series of right-hand loops, as seen in Figure 7.1*a*. The measured value of the mechanical driving-point impedance of an early magnetic loud-speaker is shown in Figue 7.1*a*. If the driving force is continuously distributed, the driving-point impedance becomes similar to a transfer impedance; some of the constants κ_ν (that is, all the elements in particular branches) then become negative. Right-hand spirals may then be followed by left-hand spirals. Also, because of the drastic decrease of the excitation constant κ_ν with the order of the mode for a continuously distributed force, the diameter of successive spirals decreases at a considerably faster rate than for a point force. Figure 7.1*b* illustrates this phenomenon for a condenser microphone that is excited by a sound wave.

Figure 7.1*c* represents the response for a water column in a steel tube, closed at the bottom by an electromagnetically excited membrane. All the natural frequencies, the internal friction of the membrane, and the internal friction of the water column were taken into account. The smaller spiral in Figure 7.1*c* represents the mechanical impedance of the membrane and is plotted with reversed sign; the large spiral represents the impedance of the water column (see Fig. 5.10). The vector that connects two points of corresponding frequency on both spirals is equal in magnitude and phase to the driving-point impedance of the tube filled with the water. The agreement between the computation and the experimental result is excellent if the computation is based on the measured natural frequencies and the measured value of the damping of the membrane.

Figure 7.1*d* shows the curve for the input impedance of the human ear. This curve was considered the standard for many years; however, right- and left-hand loops can never occur at frequencies below the fundamental resonance of the eardrum. These curves have been replaced recently by more accurate ones, which follow the theoretically predicted form.

[3] See Eq. 2.48, p. 74.

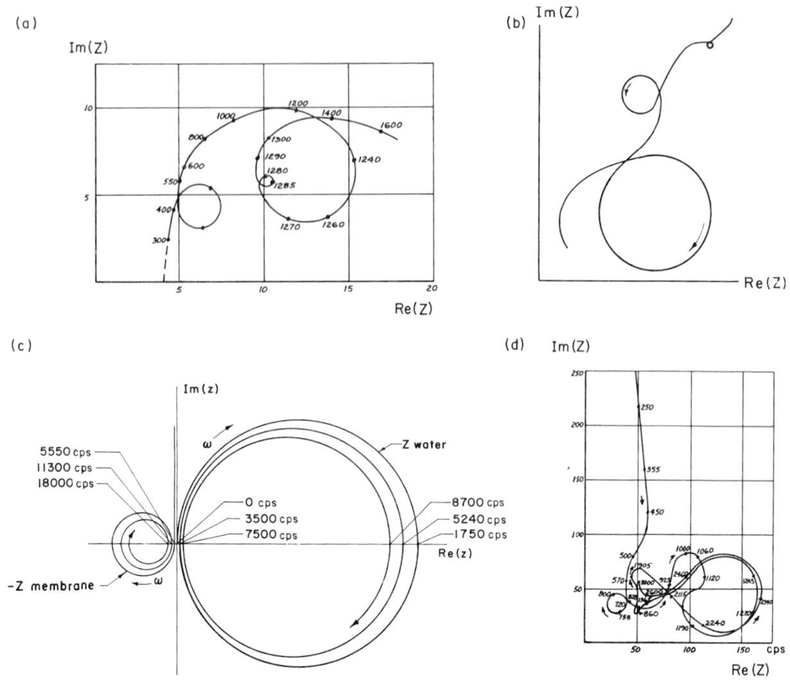

Fig. 7.1 Loci of the mechanical impedances of four systems; *a*, an early magnetic loudspeaker; *b*, a condenser microphone excited by a sound wave; *c*, a water column in a steel tube, closed at the bottom by an electromagnetically excited steel membrane (*large spiral*, impedance of water column; *small spiral*, impedance of membrane, plotted with opposite sign); *d*, human ear (recent more accurate measurements have replaced this erroneous curve).

The locus of the impedance of a tuned circuit is a straight vertical line to the right of the origin. This line can be interpreted as a circle of very large radius; the frequency curve and the locus of the impedance in the complex plane, therefore, obey the same general laws as the admittance.

Driving-Point and Transfer Impedances at High Frequencies

The preceding derivations led to an exact solution for the vibrating system at any frequency and for any kind of internal dissipation. This solution is very useful for the study of mechanical systems at very low frequencies, where the individual resonances are clearly distinguishable and where only a few terms in the series usually need to be taken into account. At the higher frequencies, the fluctuations of the frequency interval between successive resonances can be neglected, and damping is large enough to cause the contributions of the individual modes to overlap into a continuous curve. In this frequency range, the behavior of shells, membranes, plates, and similar vibrators is described by simple asymptotic high-frequency laws, and the results become independent of the shape of the vibrator and of the boundary conditions. Individual resonances become unnoticeable if the frequency difference $\epsilon_\nu = \omega_\nu - \omega_{\nu-1}$ between successive resonances is smaller than the band width $\omega_\nu/Q = \omega_\nu\eta$ of the resonance curves of the individual modes, that is, if

$$\epsilon_\nu \leq \frac{\omega_\nu}{Q} = \omega_\nu\eta \qquad \text{or} \qquad \omega \geq \epsilon_\nu Q \tag{7.39}$$

This condition is also equivalent to the assumption that reflections from the boundary are negligibly small and do not contribute noticeably to the amplitude of the point of observation. To prove this statement, the last inequality may be rewritten as follows:

$$\omega_\nu\eta = \frac{\omega_\nu\eta\lambda_\nu c}{c\lambda_\nu} \approx 2\beta \cdot f_\nu \geq \epsilon_\nu \qquad \text{or} \qquad 2n\beta \geq 1 \tag{7.40}$$

where

$$\beta = \frac{\omega_\nu\eta\lambda_\nu}{2c} \qquad f_\nu \approx \frac{c}{\lambda_\nu} \qquad \text{and} \qquad n = \frac{f_\nu}{\epsilon_\nu} \tag{7.41}$$

and where c is the propagation velocity, λ_ν is the wave length, $\omega_\nu\eta/2$ is the damping per unit time in Nepers, $\omega_\nu\eta/2c$ is the damping per unit distance (since the wave travels the distance c in unit time), and β is the damping per unit wave length. The magnitude $n/2$ is equal to the number of wave lengths to the boundary of the system, if the system is a longitudinally vibrating rod, and it is of the same order of magnitude as this number in more complex cases. The last equation, then, demands that the attenuation of a progressive wave that travels from the receiver to the boundary of the system be greater than about 1 Neper.

In the frequency range where the contributions of the various modes overlap to a continuous curve, the series solution can be transformed into an integral. To derive this integral, each term is multiplied by $\Delta\nu = 1$, and the denominators and numerators are multiplied by the frequency difference $\Delta\omega_\nu$ between successive resonances, as follows:

$$\bar{Y}_c = \frac{1}{\bar{Z}_c(A)} = \sum_{\nu=1}^{\infty} \frac{j\omega\,\Delta\omega_\nu}{M_\nu^*(-\omega^2 + \bar{\omega}_\nu^2)}\left(\frac{\Delta\nu}{\Delta\omega_\nu}\right)$$

$$= \sum_{\nu=1}^{\infty} \frac{j\omega\,\Delta\omega_\nu}{\epsilon_\nu M_\nu^*(\bar{\omega}_\nu^2 - \omega^2)} \tag{7.42}$$

where

$$\epsilon_\nu = \frac{\Delta\omega_\nu}{\Delta\nu} = \frac{\partial\omega_\nu}{\partial\nu} \qquad \text{and} \qquad \bar{\omega}_\nu^2 = \omega_\nu^2(1 + j\eta) \tag{7.43}$$

We imagine now that each term, exclusive of the factor $\Delta\omega_\nu$, is plotted above the ω_ν axis (that the terms are complex need not concern us here), so that every term represents the contribution of a natural mode. The product of each term with the corresponding $\Delta\omega_\nu$ then gives one of the elementary areas shown in Figure 7.2, the sum of which is equal to the total area under the step curve. If the number of terms is large enough, the step curve may be replaced by a continuous mean curve. Thus, replacing the step curve by a continuous curve is equivalent to replacing the sum by the integral:

$$\frac{1}{\bar{Z}_c}=\bar{Y}_c=\int_{\omega_1}^{\omega_2}\frac{1}{\epsilon_\nu M_\nu^*}\frac{j\omega}{\bar{\omega}_\nu^2-\omega^2}d\omega_\nu=\int_{\omega_1}^{\omega_2}\frac{1}{\epsilon_\nu M_\nu^*}\frac{j\bar{\omega}\left(1+\frac{j\eta}{2}\right)}{(1+j\eta)\,[\omega_\nu^2-\bar{\omega}^2]}d\omega_\nu$$

$$=\frac{j}{1+\frac{j\eta}{2}}\int_{z_1}^{z_2}\frac{1}{\epsilon_\nu M_\nu^*}\frac{dz}{z^2-1} \tag{7.44}$$

where

$$\bar{\omega}^2=\frac{\omega^2}{1+j\eta}\doteq(1-j\eta)\omega^2 \qquad z=\frac{\omega_\nu}{\bar{\omega}} \qquad \text{and} \qquad \bar{\omega}_\nu^2=(1+j\eta)\omega_\nu^2 \tag{7.45}$$

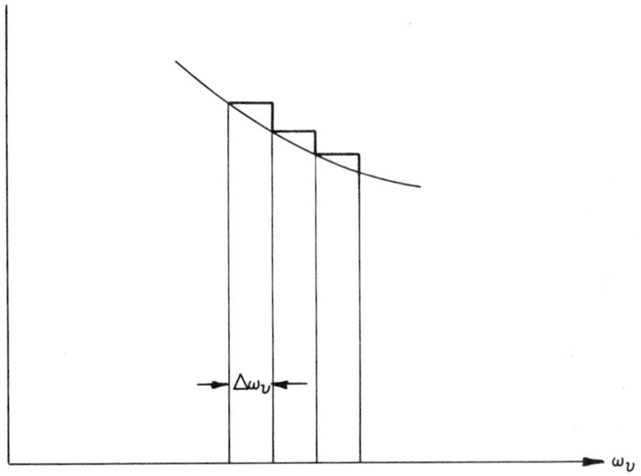

Fig. 7.2 Transformation of the series solution into an integral.

Squares and higher powers of η have been neglected. The transition to the integral is permissible only if the contribution of each term is small as compared to the contributions of all others terms, so that $\epsilon_\nu=\Delta\omega_\nu/\Delta\nu=\partial\omega_\nu/\partial\nu$ can be replaced by average asymptotic values that vary only slowly with the frequency ω_ν.

Replacing the step curve by a continuous curve is equivalent to considering $M_\nu^*\ \partial\omega_\nu/\partial\nu$ a continuous function of ω_ν and assuming ω_ν to be a continuous variable. The result of the computation then is the same as if we had assumed that the system is infinitely large, so that its resonances are infinitely close, because $M_\nu^* \, \partial\omega_\nu/\partial\nu$ is asymptotically independent of the size of the system; the density of the resonances is always proportional to its area or volume, and hence also to its mode masses. The result thus turns out to represent the driving-point admittance of a system that is infinitely large, or damped so that the reflection from the boundaries are negligible. Because this asymptotic value of the impedance will turn out to be identical to the characteristic impedance of the system, the symbol $\bar{Z}_c(A)$ has been used to represent it. (The characteristic impedance has been defined previously as the impedance of the system if reflections from the boundary are suppressed or the system is made infinitely large.) The product $\epsilon_\nu M_\nu^*(A)/M$ is called the high-frequency parameter of the system. In the cases of practical interest, this high-frequency parameter seems always to be proportional to a particular power of the frequency. Thus,

$$\frac{\epsilon_\nu M_\nu^*(A)}{M} = \text{const } \omega_\nu^{\,n} \tag{7.46}$$

The mode masses contain the factor $1/\kappa_\nu$. If the driving point does not coincide with the point of observation and if the vibration pattern is two-dimensional, κ_ν may vary drastically with mode number; in such instances, κ_ν should be retained in the integrand.

Let us now distinguish the following cases:

(*a*) *Two-or three-dimensional point sources:*

The examples in which $n=1$ ior $n=2$ turn out to describe the sound generation by point forces in two- or three-dimensional spaces. Since the velocity that is generated by a point force is infinite at the source, the integral for the admittance then becomes infinite and the driving-point impedance zero, which is the correct result.

(*b*) *Longitudinal vibrations of rods, transverse vibrations of plates:*

If the mode masses M_ν^* and the frequency differences $\omega_\nu - \omega_{\nu-1} = \epsilon_\nu$ between successive modes are constant, or asymptotically constant, as for longitudinal vibrations of rods or two-dimensional transverse vibrations of plates,

$$\frac{1}{\omega M_\nu^*}\frac{\partial \nu}{\partial z} = \text{const} = \alpha = \frac{1}{\epsilon_\nu M_\nu^*} \tag{7.47}$$

The integral then becomes:

$$\bar{Y}_c = \frac{j\alpha}{1+\dfrac{j\eta}{2}} \int_{z_1}^{z_2} \frac{dz}{z^2-1} = \frac{j\alpha}{2\left(1+\dfrac{j\eta}{2}\right)} \left(\ln \frac{z-1}{z+1}\right)_{z_1}^{z_2} \tag{7.48}$$

or

$$\bar{Y}_c\left(1+\frac{j\eta}{2}\right) = j\,\frac{\alpha}{2}\, ln\left[\frac{(z_2-1)(z_1+1)}{(z_1-1)(z_2+1)}\right] \tag{7.49}$$

In performing the above and the following integrations, damping must be included or the integral would not exist. If damping is included, the integrand is an analytic function of $z=|z|\sqrt{1+j\eta}$ and integrations can be performed in the standard manner. The sign of η then determines the sign of the contribution of the integrand near $|z|=1$ (and resolves the ambiguity of a term $\pm j\pi$ that results in the integration), whereas the value of η, as long as $\eta^2 \ll 1$ has no effect on the result.

The term $j\eta/2$ in the denominator represents the effect of the losses on the wave impedance of the system. It can be neglected in most applications. The admittance $\bar{Y}_c$ then represents a reactive admittance, unless either z_1 or z_2 is smaller than 1. The frequency ω then must be between the limits ω_1 and ω_2, and

$$\begin{aligned}\bar{Y}_c &= j\frac{\alpha}{2} ln\left[\frac{(z_2-1)(z_1+1)}{(z_1-1)(z_2+1)}\right] = j\frac{\alpha}{2}\left[(\pm)j\pi + ln\frac{(1-z_2)(z_1+1)}{(z_1-1)(z_2+1)}\right] \\ &= j\frac{\alpha}{2}\left[(\pm)j\pi + ln\frac{(1-z_2)(z_1+1)}{(z_1-1)(z_2+1)}\right] \\ &= \frac{\alpha\pi}{2} + j\frac{\alpha}{2} ln\left[\frac{(1-z_2)(z_1+1)}{(z_1-1)(z_2+1)}\right] \\ &= \frac{\pi}{2\varepsilon_\nu M_\nu^*} + jB \end{aligned} \tag{7.50}$$

where jB has been written for the imaginary part.

The minus sign had to be selected for $ln\,(-1) = -j\pi$, because the real part of the admittance must be a positive conductance. That the minus sign has to be selected can also be deduced mathematically by substituting the limit $z_1=0$ into the expression $ln\,(z-1)/(z+1)$ and taking the limiting value $(-j\pi)$ and subtracting from it the corresponding limiting value $(+j\pi)$ for $z=z_2\to\infty$, or by substituting $z_1\to 0$, $z_2\to\infty$ in the last formula and determining the sign $\pm j\pi$ from the condition that $\bar{Y}_c=0$ for $z_1=0$, $z_2=0$.

(*c*) *Constant mode density within narrow frequency band:*

Sometimes resonant frequencies crowd in a finite frequency interval, as for a cylinder near its ring resonance frequency, and $\triangle n$ resonances then have nearly the same resonant frequency.

$$\begin{aligned}\bar{Y}_c &= \frac{\triangle n j\omega}{M_\nu^*(-\omega^2+\bar{\omega}_\nu^2)} \\ &= \frac{j\triangle n}{M_\nu^*}\,\frac{\omega}{\omega^2\left[-1+\dfrac{\omega_\nu^2(1+j\eta)}{\omega^2}\right]} = \frac{j\triangle n}{\omega M_\nu^*(z^2-1)}\end{aligned} \tag{7.51}$$

If the frequency is within the range of the natural frequencies of the modes in the band $\triangle n$, greater accuracy may be desired, and it becomes expedient to use the formula derived previously for $\epsilon_\nu M_\nu^* = \text{const.}$

(*d*) *Curved shell membrane modes:*

For cylindrical shells at low frequencies up to the ring resonance frequency, membrane forces predominate, and the frequency difference between successive modes is inversely proportional to the square root of the resonant frequency; thus,

$$\frac{1}{\bar{\omega}M_\nu}\frac{\partial\nu}{\partial z}=\beta\sqrt{\frac{\omega_\nu}{\omega}}=\frac{1}{M_\nu{}^*\epsilon_\nu}$$

$$\beta=\frac{1}{M_\nu{}^*\epsilon_\nu\sqrt{\dfrac{\omega_\nu}{\omega}}} \tag{7.52}$$

and

$$\bar{Y}_c=\frac{j\beta}{1+\dfrac{3j\eta}{4}}\int_{z_1}^{z_2}\frac{\sqrt{z}\,dz}{z^2-1}=\frac{j\beta}{1+\dfrac{3j\eta}{4}}\left(\frac{1}{2}\,ln\,\frac{\sqrt{z}-1}{\sqrt{z}+1}+\text{arc tan}\sqrt{z}\right)_{z_1}^{z_2} \tag{7.53}$$

or

$$\left(1+\frac{3j\eta}{4}\right)\bar{Y}_c=\frac{j\beta}{2}\left[ln\left[\frac{\sqrt{z_2}-1}{\sqrt{z_1}-1}\,\frac{\sqrt{z_1}+1}{\sqrt{z_2}+1}\right]-2\text{ arc tan}\frac{\sqrt{z_1}-\sqrt{z_2}}{1+\sqrt{z_1z_2}}\right] \tag{7.54}$$

These modes generate a real component in the characteristic admittance, only if either z_1 or z_2 is smaller than one, that is, if the frequency of the force is between the limits ω_1 and ω_2. If this is the case, the above formula takes the form:

$$\left(1+\frac{3j\eta}{4}\right)\bar{Y}_c=\frac{\beta}{2}\left[\pi+j\ \ln\frac{\sqrt{z_2}-1}{1-\sqrt{z_1}}\,\frac{\sqrt{z_1}+1}{\sqrt{z_2}+1}-j2\text{ arc tan}\frac{\sqrt{z_1}-\sqrt{z_2}}{1+\sqrt{z_1z_2}}\right] \tag{7.55}$$

Again, the reactive component is greater than the resistive component only near the frequency limits of the mode band that has been considered, and the resistive component is

$$\bar{Y}_c=\frac{\beta}{2}\pi=\frac{\pi}{2\epsilon_\nu M_\nu{}^*\sqrt{\dfrac{\omega_\nu}{\omega}}}\approx\frac{\pi}{2\epsilon_\nu M_\nu{}^*} \tag{7.56}$$

because only the modes $\omega_\nu\approx\omega$ generate a resistive component.

(*e*) *Bending of beams and one=dimensional plate modes:*

For one dimensional bending vibrations, such as those of a beam, the frequency difference between successive modes is proportional to the square root of the frequency, and:

$$\frac{1}{\bar{\omega}M_\nu{}^*}\frac{\partial\nu}{\partial z}=\frac{1}{\epsilon_\nu M_\nu{}^*}=\frac{\gamma}{\sqrt{\dfrac{\omega_\nu}{\omega}}}\quad\text{or}\quad\gamma=\frac{\sqrt{\dfrac{\omega_\nu}{\omega}}}{\epsilon_\nu M_\nu{}^*}=\text{const}=(\gamma)_{\omega\nu=\omega} \tag{7.57}$$

The driving-point admittance thus becomes:

$$\bar{Y}_c=\frac{j\gamma}{1+\dfrac{j\eta}{4}}\int_{z_1}^{z_2}\frac{dz}{\sqrt{z}(z^2-1)} \tag{7.58}$$

To solve this integral, let $z=u^2$,

$$\int_{u_1}^{u_2}\frac{2udu}{u(u^4-1)}=\int_{u_1}^{u_2}du\left(\frac{1}{u^2-1}-\frac{1}{u^2+1}\right)$$

$$=\left(\frac{1}{2}\,ln\frac{u-1}{u+1}-\tan^{-1}u\right)_{u_1}^{u_2}$$

$$=\left(\frac{1}{2}\,ln\frac{\sqrt{z}-1}{\sqrt{z}+1}-\tan^{-1}\sqrt{z}\right)_{z_1}^{z_2} \tag{7.59}$$

The result can thus be written as follows:

$$\bar{Y}_c\left(1+\frac{j\eta}{4}\right)=j\frac{\gamma}{2}\left[\ln\left(\frac{\sqrt{z_2}-1}{\sqrt{z_2}+1}\,\frac{\sqrt{z_1}+1}{\sqrt{z_1}-1}\right)-2\text{ arc tan}\frac{\sqrt{z_2}-\sqrt{z_1}}{1+\sqrt{z_1z_2}}\right] \tag{7.60}$$

and if the frequency is within the band limits of the modes:

$$\bar{Y}_c\left(1+\frac{j\eta}{2}\right)=\frac{\gamma}{2}\left(\pi+j\left[ln\left(\frac{\sqrt{z_2}-1}{1-\sqrt{z_1}}\,\frac{\sqrt{z_1}+1}{\sqrt{z_2}+1}\right)-2\text{ arc tan}\frac{\sqrt{z_2}-\sqrt{z_1}}{1+\sqrt{z_1z_2}}\right]\right) \tag{7.61}$$

If the band limits are $z_1=0$ and $z_2=\infty$, and $j\eta/4$ is neglected,

$$\bar{Y}_c=\frac{\gamma}{2}\pi(1-j)=\frac{\pi(1-j)}{2\epsilon_\nu M_\nu{}^*} \tag{7.62}$$

The term with j accounts for the end distortion of the beam, or the exponential deformation near the driving point. In this special case, the wattless (or reactive) part of the driving-point admittance is of the same magnitude as its real part. The real part is as always:

$$Re(\bar{Y}_c)=\frac{\pi}{2\epsilon_\nu M_\nu{}^*} \tag{7.63}$$

The results are surprising. The real part of the characteristic admittance does not depend on the band width of the mode spectrum, except that the mode density has to be great enough so that the summation can be replaced by integration in the series solution for the system. The modes whose resonant frequency is different from the frequency of the force ($z_1>1$, $z_2<1$) generate only a reactive component. This reactive component is significant only if the frequency is close to one of the two limits ω_1 or ω_2 (when $z_1=1$, or $z_2\cong 1$). Except for the one-dimensional bending modes it is zero in all cases if the limits of the frequency band over which the mode frequencies are distributed are zero and infinity. Thus, if $\omega_1=0$, $\omega_2=\infty$,

$$\bar{Y}_c=Y_c=\frac{\pi}{2\epsilon_\nu M_\nu{}^*}\qquad\text{and}\qquad \bar{Z}_c=\frac{2}{\pi}\epsilon_\nu M_\nu{}^* \tag{7.64}$$

But for one-dimensional beam modes

$$\bar{Y}_c = \frac{\pi}{2\epsilon_\nu M_\nu^*}(1-j) \tag{7.65}$$

$$\bar{Z}_c = \frac{1}{\bar{Y}_c} = \frac{(1+j)}{\pi}\epsilon_\nu M_\nu^* \tag{7.66}$$

The distortion term that occurs in the beam equation then leads to a (watt-less) vibration near field. For beam modes, ϵ_ν and consequently also the driving-point impedance increase proportionally to the square root of the frequency. This frequency dependence must be taken into account if the force is a noise force.

The preceding computations show that the real part of the driving-point admittance is generated by modes whose resonant frequencies are not very different from the frequency of the force, that is, for which $|z|=1$. Integration through $z=|z|(1+j\eta/2)$ then yields the terms with $j\pi$ that represent this real part. Thus, only modes that have a natural frequency not very different from that of the force consume driving power, propagate energy through the system to the boundaries of the system where it is absorbed, and generate the real part of the characteristic driving-point admittance, which, therefore, is essentially a radiation conductance. Because the loss of energy due to energy transportation is very much greater than that due to internal friction, internal friction has only a second-order effect on the result.

For an infinitely large system (since the characteristic driving-point admittance also represents the properties of a similar infinitely large system) the above conclusions are almost trivial. They are equivalent to the statement that energy can only propagate to the boundaries with wave numbers that correspond to progressive waves excited by the force.

If κ_ν varies drastically with ω_ν, i.e., if the driving point and the point of observation are different and if the vibration pattern is two-dimensional, the average value of κ_ν for the modes within the frequency band $\Delta\omega_\nu$ has to be used. This average value will be found to decrease considerably with the distance from the driver. The use of the average value is permissible because κ_ν, M_ν, and ω_ν are statistically independent, so long as damping is not excessively large.

That the real part of the characteristic admittance (the acoustic conductance) is always given by Equation 7.63 can be deduced from the integral in Equation 7.44. Its integrand contributes to the real part of the solution only near its pole $z=1$. In computing the real part of Y_c, the frequency-dependent factors can therefore be replaced by their value at the pole frequency $\omega_\nu=\omega$: contour integration then leads to the stated result. The imaginary part depends on the detailed variation of the factor $\epsilon_\nu M_\nu$ in the integrand. A study of practical instances shows, that the imaginary part is either zero or small in comparison to the imaginary part that is normally generated by the resonances and antiresonances, and hence can be neglected in most applications.

As will be illustrated in Chapter X by many examples, the characteristic admittance represents the mean line through the frequency curve for the velocity of the system when resonance peaks and antiresonance minima are averaged out. Reflections from the boundaries increase the velocity at certain frequencies and reduce at others, so that their contribution to the geometric mean is zero. The real part of the characteristic admittance then describes the energy that propagates from the driven point to the boundaries of the system.

The same formulas can be used to compute the transfer impedances. An example of such a computation will be given in a later chapter.

Mean Square of Velocity and the Effective Impedance at High Frequencies

The computation of the characteristic admittance is equivalent to computation of the energy that propagates from the driving point to the boundary of the system. It was assumed that the system was damped so that the mode response curves added to a continuous curve. The computation neglected reflections from the boundaries and consequently also neglected the reverberant vibrational energy stored by the system. Sometimes we are interested in the mean square of the amplitude averaged over the system, that is, in the total vibrational energy of the system. Since in computing the mean square, resonances and the reverberant sound field are not averaged out, we shall expect that the mean square amplitude will be a function of the damping of the system. The energy is made up of the sum of the squares of the mode contributions. Because of the orthogonality of the natural functions, the square of the velocity integrated over the system equals the sum of the integrals of the squares of the mode amplitudes. But this sum can be written as:

$$\langle\dot{\xi}^2\rangle = \sum_\nu \langle\dot{\xi}_\nu^2\rangle = \sum_\nu \dot{\xi}_\nu^2(A)\cdot\frac{\langle\xi_\nu^2\rangle}{\xi_\nu^2(A)} = \sum_\nu q_\nu(A)\dot{\xi}_\nu^2(A) \tag{7.67}$$

and can be expressed as an integral by taking the square of the absolute value of the integral in Equation 7.42, multiplying it by $q_\nu(A)$, and applying a procedure similar to that which led to Equation 7.50:

$$\langle \dot{\xi}^2 \rangle = \int_{\omega_1}^{\infty} \frac{\omega^2 q_\nu F_0^2}{M_\nu^{*2} \epsilon_\nu} \frac{d\omega_\nu}{\omega_\nu^4 \eta^2 + (\omega^2 - \omega_\nu^2)^2}$$

$$= \int_{\omega_1}^{\infty} \frac{\omega^2 q_\nu F_0^2}{(1+\eta^2) M_\nu^{*2} \epsilon_\nu} \frac{d\omega_\nu}{\omega_\nu^4 - \dfrac{2\omega^2 \omega_\nu^2}{1+\eta^2} + \dfrac{\omega^4}{1+\eta^2}} \tag{7.68}$$

Many of the modes that contribute to the amplitude of the driving point yield only negligible contributions to the vibrational energy, since the square of their amplitude is so much smaller than the square of the amplitude of modes in the resonant range. The above integral, consisting mainly of the contributions of the resonating modes, depends on the damping. A weak frequency dependence of the first factor of the integral does not affect its value if the damping is small. This rule can be demonstrated on the basis of special examples. The first factor may, therefore, be considered constant during the integration and equal to its value at the frequency of the force. In evaluating the integral, η^2 can again be neglected. The integral can be transformed into a known form:

$$\langle \dot{\xi}^2 \rangle = \frac{\omega^2 q_\nu(A) F_0^2}{(1+\eta^2)\epsilon_\nu M_\nu^{*2}(A)} \int_0^{\infty} \frac{d\omega_\nu}{\omega_\nu^4 + 2[-\omega^2(1-\eta^2)]\omega_\nu^2 + \omega^4 \left(1 - \dfrac{\eta^2}{2}\right)^2}$$

$$= \frac{q_\nu(A) \pi F_0^2}{M_\nu^{*2}(A) 2 \epsilon_\nu \omega \eta} \tag{7.69}$$

The lower limit ω_1 has been replaced by 0.

On the right-hand side, only the lowest power of η, which is the first power, has been retained. The ratio of the force to the root-mean-square velocity in then given by:

$$\left[\frac{F_0^2}{\langle \dot{\xi}^2 \rangle}\right]^{\frac{1}{2}} = \left[\frac{2}{\pi} \frac{\omega\eta}{\kappa_\nu(A)} \frac{\epsilon_\nu M_\nu^*(A)}{M}\right]^{\frac{1}{2}} \cdot M = \sqrt{\frac{R_\nu^*}{q_\nu} \frac{2\epsilon_\nu M_\nu^*}{\pi}} \tag{7.70}$$

where

$$R_\nu^* = \omega\eta M_\nu^* = \omega\eta q_\nu \frac{M}{\kappa_\nu} \tag{7.71}$$

On the right-hand side, A represents any randomly selected reference point; this form is convenient for numerical computations. The result is, of course, independent of A, as is proved by the second form of the right-hand side of Equation 7.54.

It can further be shown by decomposing the integration range into several subranges, that the contributions of modes to the mean square is negligible if their resonant frequencies differ by more than their band width from the frequency of the force, provided that their Q is greater than 20.

In averaging over the energies, the squares of the mode masses appear in the result. The signs of the κ_ν^2, therefore, are all positive. The mode masses, and the characteristic conductance for a two-dimensional vibratro decrease as $1/\sqrt{r}$ with the distance r, as is easily proved by direct integration or by mode methods (see Chapter VIII). The amplitude of the square root of the contribution of a mode band should therefore decrease in proportion to $r^{-\frac{1}{4}}$.

Sometimes a system is excited by a band of white noise. The frequency components then are uncorrelated, and the amplitude of the system is proportional to the square root of the mean squares of the contributions of the various modes. The mean square of the vibration amplitude at a point A is obtained by setting $q_\nu(A)=1$ in Equations 7.67 to 7.69. For a noise force whose power spectrum is $F_0^2(\omega)$,

$$F_0^2 = \int_0^\infty F_0^2(\omega)d\omega \tag{7.72}$$

the contribution of the νth mode becomes:

$$\langle \dot{\xi}_\nu^2 \rangle = \int_0^\infty q_\nu \dot{\xi}_\nu^2(\omega)d\omega = \int_0^\infty q_\nu \frac{F_0^2(\omega)}{M_\nu^{*2}(A)} \cdot \frac{\omega^2 d\omega}{\omega^4 - 2\omega^2\omega_\nu^2 + \omega_\nu^4(1+\eta^2)}$$

$$= \frac{\pi q_\nu(A)}{2\omega_\nu \eta} \frac{F_0^2(\omega)}{M_\nu^{*2}(A)} \tag{7.73}$$

During the integration, $F_0^2(\omega)$ has been assumed to change slowly with the frequency. If the frequency difference between successive modes is ϵ_ν, there are $1/\epsilon_\nu$ modes per cycle, and the energy per cycle is $1/\epsilon_\nu$ times the energy, as given by Equation 7.54. The ratio $F_0(\omega)/\langle \xi_\nu^2(\omega)\rangle^{\frac{1}{2}}$ turns out to be given by Equation 7.55. This result could have been expected. Since the integral depends wholly on the contributions in the resonance range, whether integration is performed with respect to ω or ω_ν does not make any difference.

Dissipation Resistance Referred to Space-Average Square of Velocity

The work performed by the external force in exciting the system, computed with the aid of the driving-point impedance, is given by:

$$W = \frac{F_0^2}{|Z_c(A)|^2} \cdot \text{real part}\,[Z_c(A)] = \frac{F_0^2}{\frac{2}{\pi}\epsilon_\nu M_\nu^*(A)} \tag{7.74}$$

whether $\epsilon_\nu M_\nu^*$ is constant or proportional to $(\omega_\nu)^{\frac{1}{2}}$. This work may be expressed as the product of the space-average square of the velocity with the aid of Equation 7.69 and an effective dissipation resistance R_{eff} of the system:

$$W=\langle\dot{\xi}^2\rangle R_{\text{eff}}=\left[\frac{F_0{}^2\pi\kappa_\nu(A)}{\epsilon_\nu M_\nu{}^*(A)2\omega\eta M}\right]R_{\text{eff}} \tag{7.75}$$

Equating the last two expressions leads to the result:

$$R_{\text{eff}}=\frac{\eta\omega M}{\kappa_\nu(A)}=\frac{\omega\eta M_\nu{}^*(A)}{q_\nu(A)}=\frac{R_\nu{}^*}{q_\nu} \tag{7.76}$$

Thus, the effective dissipation resistance is usually two to four times greater than the resistance of a mode resonating at the frequency of the force. This result illustrates once more that the energy of the system is predominantly determined by the energy of the resonating modes; therefore, the dissipation resistance for these modes also determines the dissipation of the system. In contrast, the amplitude of the system at the driving point is predominantly determined by the contributions of all the modes of the system that are excited to forced vibrations at the frequency of the external force. The contributions of an individual mode become predominant, showing up as a resonance peak in the frequency curve of the system, only if the frequency of the force is close to the resonant frequency of a mode, and if damping is not very large.

Inhomogeneous Vibratory Systems

Most of the inhomogeneous systems that are of practical interest can be derived by mass loading a homogeneous system. For instance, a shell with joints may be made up of homogeneous parts connected through rigid stiffening rings. The mass-loaded system can be treated in a manner very similar to that for the homogeneous system. It is expedient to represent the mass distribution m by the total mass M of the system and a distribution function φ (x, y, z), as follows:

$$m=M\varphi(x,y,z) \tag{7.77}$$

where

$$\int\varphi(x,y,z)d\sigma=1 \tag{7.78}$$

It is proved in the theory of differential equations that the natural function ξ_ν, which represents the vibration amplitudes of the homogeneous system, have to be replaced by the functions:

$$\varphi(x,y,z)^{\frac{1}{2}}\ \xi_\nu(x,y,z) \tag{7.79}$$

which are proportional to the square root of the local kinetic energy density of the system[4]; all the relations obtained in the derivation of the series solution apply for the new functions ξ_ν; correspondingly, $\langle \xi_\nu^2 \rangle$ has to be replaced by $\langle \varphi \xi_\nu^2 \rangle$, q_ν by $\langle \varphi \xi_\nu^2 \rangle / \xi_\nu^2\ (A)$, and κ_ν by $_\sigma\int \varphi_\nu^{\frac{1}{2}} \xi_\nu F d\sigma / F_0 \varphi_\nu(A)^{\frac{1}{2}} \xi_\nu(A)$ in succeeding formulas. In particular, expressions for the characteristic impedance also maintain their validity. If the system is inhomogeneous, the product of the mode mass M_ν and the average frequency difference ϵ_ν between successive resonances will usually vary in a more complex manner than in a homogeneous system, but this variation can be taken into account if high accuracy is desired. Normally, this variation does not seem to have a great effect on the value of the characteristic point impedance, and the equation

$$Z_c \cong \text{const}\ \epsilon_\nu(\omega)\ M_\nu(\omega) \approx \epsilon_\nu(\omega)\ M_\nu(\omega) \tag{7.80}$$

seems to apply with sufficient accuracy. In computing the mode masses, the inhomogeneity of the system can frequently be neglected; the mass-loaded parts of the system usually have smaller amplitudes than the nonloaded parts, and their kinetic energies do not contribute significantly. The theory of inhomogeneous systems can now be derived on lines similar to those in the theory of homogeneous systems. This theory will be discussed in Chapter X.

Recommended Reading

CRANDALL, S. H., (ed.), *Random Vibration,* Technology Press of The Massachusetts Institute of Technology, Cambridge, and John Wiley & Sons, Inc., New York, 1958.

MORSE, P. M., *Vibration and Sound,* McGraw-Hill, Inc., New York, 1948.

POWELL, A., "On the approximation to the infinite solution by the methods of normal modes for random vibrations," *J.A.S.A.*, **30** (1958), 1136–39.

SKUDRZYK, E. J., "Vibrations of a system with a finite or infinite number of resonances," *J.A.S.A.*, **30** (1958), 1140–52.

[4] A similar result has been derived in Chapter IV, Eq. 4.50, for lumped parameter systems.

Addition During Printing

Reflections do not contribute to the geometric mean of the resonance maxima and the antiresonance minima. The geometric mean line through the frequency wave of driving point velocity, therefore, is given by the absolute value of the characteristic admittance. The wattless distortion field generated by the driver decreases rapidly with the distance, and the transfer admittance for points farther from the driver than about half a bending wavelength is real. For one-dimensional modes at the end of the vibrator opposite to that of the driver, the antiresonances become replaced by shallow troughs. The amplitude of the incident wave then is equal to the amplitude of the troughs in the frequency curve.

This phenomenon can be understood by considering a rod or beam. The reflected wave then generates a similar series of reflections as the outgoing wave at the driver. For a rod, this wave is given by an equation similar to Eq. 5.124, except that the first term on the right is two instead of one, and that the whole right hand side is multiplied by e^{-jkl}. Thus, the wave incident at the boundary of the vibrator is equivalent to a force distribution that acts at the boundary of the vibrator, and excites it as if it were an externally applied force. The amplitude of the trough, therefore, is given by the sum of the characteristic conductance and a term that is proportional to and not very different from the antiresonance admittance for the driving point if the vibration is a one-dimensional one, and for that for a force distribution at the boundaries if the vibration is a two-dimensional one. Unless damping is very great, this antiresonance term is negligible. This result can be deduced rigorously from Eq. 5.129 for the rod or from its generalization for a beam with the aid of Eq. 6.67.

For two-dimensional vibrators, cancellation of the reflections at the antiresonant frequencies is imperfect, and the minima vary in depth (see p. 244). However, this imperfection in the means of nature becomes apparent only at the antiresonances, where large contributions counteract, and the shape of the remaining part of the frequency curve is hardly different from that for a one-dimensional vibrator. The characteristic admittance can, therefore, be determined from the points of inflection of the frequency curve (when plotted to a logarithmic amplitude scale for unit driving force) which in the one-dimensional case have exactly the same ordinate as the characteristic admittance and hence have very nearly the same ordinate also in the two-dimensional case. That this conclusion is correct is borne out by all the experimental results.

Equation 7.86 also gives the mean square of the amplitude at a given point A, if the factor $q_\nu(A)$ is dropped, provided that the point of observation A is sufficiently far from the driver, so that the sum of the products $\xi_\nu(A)\,\xi_\mu(A)$ is zero. Equation 7.69 (the $q_\nu(A)$ being left out), therefore, applies only for such distances. Because of the narrow band of modes that are excited—most of the contributions arise from modes whose resonant frequencies are within a mode bandwidth from the driving frequency—the mixed products, as can be readily shown, cancel only if the distance from the driving point is greater than about $Q\lambda_B/2$. The square of the amplitude at the driven point can be considerably greater than would be computed on the basis of this equation.

VIII / THE PLATE

The derivation of the plate equations is difficult, and only recently have satisfactory theories been developed. Even the derivation of the classical plate equation is a problem that is left to advanced treatises on elasticity. The assumptions of the classical plate theory are basically those of Bernoulli's theory of bending, and rotary inertia and shear force are neglected. To derive the plate equation, a knowledge of the fundamental elastic equations and of the various waves that propagate in solids is essential. To avoid interrupting the discussion of the vibrations of homogeneous systems, the plate theory will be derived in a later chapter.[1]

Classical Plate Equation

The classical plate equation for bending vibrations is reasonably accurate when the bending wave length is greater than five times the plate thickness; it is given by:[2]

$$\alpha^4 \nabla^4 \xi + \frac{\partial^2 \xi}{\partial t^2} = p \tag{8.1}$$

where

$$\nabla^2 = \frac{\partial^2}{\partial x^2} + \frac{\partial^2}{\partial y^2} \quad \text{and} \quad \alpha^4 = \frac{\lambda_E h^2}{12(1-\nu^2)\rho} \tag{8.2}$$

The magnitude m is the mass of the plate per unit area; h, the thickness; ν, Poisson's contraction; λ_E, Young's modulus; and p, the driving force per unit area. This equation applies so long as the distance from the edge of the plate to the point whose vibration is being considered is larger than the thickness of the plate.

If the plate is clamped, so that its perimeter lies in the x-y-plane, the boundary conditions are:

$$\xi = 0 \qquad \frac{\partial \xi}{\partial r} = 0 \qquad \text{or} \qquad \frac{\partial \xi}{\partial x} = \frac{\partial \xi}{\partial y} = 0 \tag{8.3}$$

where r is the normal to the tangent line. In these last equations, bending moment and shear force have to be expressed in terms of the displacement

[1] See pp. 488–503.

[2] *Ibid.*

and its derivations. The boundary conditions then contain both elastic constants and are relatively complex. If the plate is supported only at its edges, the boundary conditions are:

$$\xi=0 \qquad \frac{\partial^2\xi}{\partial r^2}+\nu\frac{\partial^2\xi}{\partial s^2}=0 \tag{8.4}$$

where s is the co-ordinate along the boundary of the plate; M_s, the bending moment about the tangent to the boundary line; and r, the co-ordinate normal to it. If the boundary is subject to a shearing force N_0 per unit length and to couples G_0 and H_0 about ds and dr, respectively, then

$$G_s=G_0 \qquad \text{and} \qquad N-\frac{\partial H}{\partial s}=N_0-\frac{\partial H_0}{\partial s} \tag{8.5}$$

Rectangular Plate Excited at Its Center to Transverse Vibrations by a Point Force

A solution in closed form and in rectangular co-ordinates for a freely suspended plate is still out of reach, because solutions of the plate equations that have a logarithmic singularity at the driving point and satisfy the boundary conditions of a rectangle are not yet known. But the natural functions for the simply supported rectangular or circular plate are known, and a series solution can be derived by developing the displacement into a series of the natural functions. These natural functions for a simply supported rectangular plate are:

$$v=V_{mn}\sin\frac{m\pi x}{l_1}\sin\frac{n\pi y}{l_2}\cos\omega_{mn}t \qquad \text{where} \qquad m, n=1, 2, 3, \ldots \tag{8.6}$$

and where l_1 is the length and l_2 is the width of the plate and the natural frequencies ω_{mn} are:

$$\omega_{mn}=\omega_{ap}m^2+\omega_{bp}n^2 \tag{8.7}$$

where

$$\omega_{ap}=\frac{\alpha^2\pi^2}{l_1^2} \qquad \omega_{bp}=\frac{\alpha^2\pi^2}{l_2^2} \qquad \text{and} \qquad \alpha^4=\frac{\lambda_E h^2}{12(1-\nu^2)\rho}=\frac{c_p{}^2h^2}{12(1-\nu^2)} \tag{8.8}$$

where h is the thickness of the plate and ν its Poisson's contraction. The constant α is given by Equation 8.2, and $c_p=(\lambda_E/\rho)^{\frac{1}{2}}$ is the velocity of sound in a rod of the same material as the plate.

To simplify the derivations, let the plate be excited by a point force at its center, and let the velocity pickup be located at the same point. Each of the excitation constants κ_{mn} is unity, and the mode masses and mode resistances are:

$$M_{mn}{}^*=\frac{q_{mn}M}{\kappa_{mn}}=q_{mn}M \qquad \text{and} \qquad R_{mn}{}^*=\eta\frac{\omega_{mn}{}^2}{\omega}M_{mn}{}^* \tag{8.9}$$

The complete solution (as represented by the sum of the contributions of all the natural modes) can be written as follows:

$$\frac{\tilde{v}}{\tilde{f}_0}=\frac{1}{\bar{Z}}=\frac{1}{\bar{Z}_0}+\sum\frac{1}{R_{mn}{}^*+j\omega M_{mn}{}^*+\dfrac{1}{j\omega K_{mn}{}^*}} \tag{8.10}$$

where f_0 is the driving force. The magnitude $\bar{Z}_0$ represents the contribution of the motion at the center of gravity of the plate, and the sum represents the contributions of the natural modes of the plate; η is the loss factor of the material, and $q_{mn}=\frac{1}{4}$ if $m\neq 0$ or $n\neq 0$, or $q_{mn}=\frac{1}{2}$ if either $m=0$ or $n=0$. In the first term of the denominator of the sum, $\eta(\omega_{mn}{}^2/\omega^2)$ is practically equal to η, since this term contributes only near the resonant frequency. The boundary conditions are contained in the natural frequencies ω_{mn} and in the values of the mode constants q_{mn}.

To simplify the computation, let the plate be supported at its edges, so that Equation 8.7 applies; $\bar{Z}_0$ then is zero (because the plate would not move if it were rigid). If the values of the mode parameters are substituted, the result becomes:

$$\frac{\tilde{v}}{\tilde{f}_0}=-\frac{1}{j\omega M}\sum\frac{\dfrac{1}{q_{mn}}}{\dfrac{j\eta\omega^2{}_{mn}}{\omega^2}+\dfrac{(\omega_{ap}m^2+\omega_{bp}n^2)^2}{\omega^2}-1} \tag{8.11}$$

However, the supported plate is of little interest, since the experimental results usually show poor agreement with the theoretical predictions because of the unknown friction at the edges and because of the finite mass of the supports that have to be used for such measurements.

Similar computations can be performed for a freely suspended plate, but the natural frequencies and the mode constants must be calculated by tedious processes.

A great deal of information can be obtained by neglecting the distortion at the edges of the freely suspended plate (corresponding to the exponential near field at the ends of a freely suspended beam) and by replacing the sines with cosines, so that the velocity is a maximum at the edges of the plate. The motion at the center of gravity of the freely suspended plate is accounted for by including a term $1/\bar{Z}_0=1/j\omega M$ in the series solution. This solution may be expected to be very accurate at the highei frequencies and for points at least half a bending wave length away from the edges of the plate.

The computed results are valuable, since they show all the significant characteristics that are formed in the frequency curves of more complex vibrators. The heights of the resonance peaks in the frequency curve are very nearly equal to the maxima of the terms in the solution:

$$\frac{\tilde{v}}{\tilde{f}_0}=\frac{1}{R_\nu{}^*}=\frac{1}{\eta\omega_{mn}\cdot Mq_{mn}} \tag{8.12}$$

The contributions of the remaining modes (since they are excited at a frequency greatly different from their resonant frequencies) are 90° out of phase, and only their squares add to that of the resonating mode. The reader can easily convince himself that the error in computing the height of a peak is less than 7 per cent (0.6 dB.), if the valley between successive peaks is 10 dB. (i.e., a factor of 3.3) lower than the height of the peak.

At the antiresonances, the admittance becomes real (the imaginary parts of the terms can be dropped), and the solution simplifies to:

$$\left(\frac{1}{Z}\right)_{\text{ant}} = \frac{1}{\omega M}\sum \frac{\dfrac{1}{q_{mn}}\,\eta\,\dfrac{\omega_{mn}{}^2}{\omega^2}}{\left(1-\dfrac{\omega_{mn}{}^2}{\omega^2}\right)^2+\eta^2\left(\dfrac{\omega^2}{\omega_{mn}{}^2}\right)^2}$$

$$\approx \sum \frac{\eta}{\omega q_{mn} M}\,\frac{1}{\left(\dfrac{\omega}{\omega_{mn}}-\dfrac{\omega_{mn}}{\omega}\right)^2} \tag{8.13}$$

In this expression, ω represents the frequency of the antiresonance ($\omega \neq \omega_{mn}$). Since the terms no longer add at right angles, and since they are of similar magnitude, many terms usually have to be added in order to get a reasonably good approximation for the antiresonance minima. At lower frequencies, the resonant frequencies are irregularly spaced, and the difference between successive resonant frequencies is often considerably larger than the average value. The antiresonances (Eq. 8.13) may then be considerably farther below the line $v_0 = F/Z_c$ than the maxima are above it. The wider the spacing between resonant frequencies, the deeper the antiresonances. The detailed computation shows that the two terms whose resonant frequencies are closest to the frequency of the antiresonance give the correct magnitude of the velocity at the antiresonance. But, to compute the velocity accurately, ten or more terms must be taken into account. The depth of the antiresonances is thus a function of the regularity of the spacing of the resonant frequencies as well as of the Q of the system. If the plate is driven at the center, and if the center is also the point of observation, $\kappa_{mn}=1$, $q_{mn}=\frac{1}{4}$ for the two-dimensional modes, and $q_\nu=\frac{1}{2}$ for the one-dimensional modes. The solution (Eq. 8.10) can then easily be evaluated numerically. Figure 8.1*a* shows this solution for a plate of a length twice the width ($\omega_a=1$, $M=1$, and $\eta=\frac{1}{25}$). The characteristic impedance for the above plate is $16/\pi^2$, as will be shown later. The line $Y=1/Z_c$ is drawn through the computed curves of Figure 8.1.

A closer study then reveals that the lower resonant frequencies for a freely supported plate of the dimensions $l_1/l_2=3$ are distributed similarly to those for a supported plate of the dimensions $l_1/l_2=2$, and the curves measured for such a plate (Fig. 8.2*a*) are practically coincident with those computed for $l_1/l_2=2$.

Figure 8.1*b* shows a similar curve calculated for a plate with the receiver at the mid-point of the shorter edge. In these computations, the effect of the

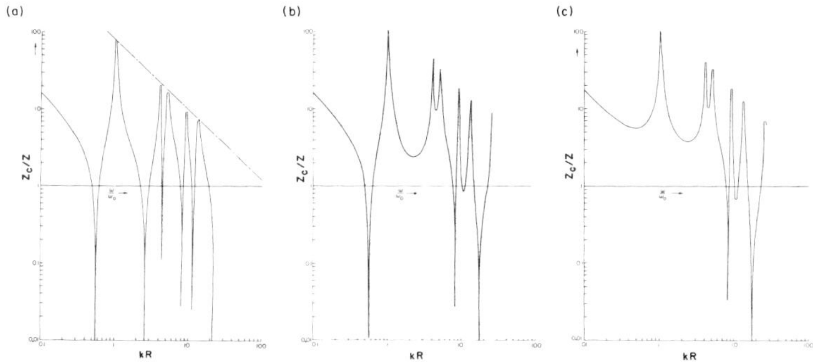

Fig. 8.1 Theoretical velocity amplitudes at three positions on a rectangular plate (length-width ratio, 2 : 1 ; $\eta = \frac{1}{25}$); *a*, at the mid-point; *b*, at the mid-point of the shorter edge; *c*, at one corner. (See Fig. -.2.)

edge distortion on the factor $q_\nu = \langle \xi_\nu^2 \rangle / \xi_\nu^2(A)$ has been neglected. Figure 8.2*b* represents the measured curve for the same case. The values κ_{mn} are now given by:

$$\kappa_{mn} = (-1)^{(m+1)/2} \tag{8.14}$$

The general character of the curve is similar to the previous one, except for the greater number of antiresonances.

If the plate is driven at its center and the receiver is mounted at a corner of the plate, the values κ_{mn} become alternately positive and negative:

$$\kappa_{mn} = (-1)^{(m+1)/2} \cdot (-1)^{(n+1)/2} \quad \text{where} \quad m, n = 1, 3, 5, \ldots \tag{8.15}$$

And since the values κ_{mn} enter as factors, the signs of the terms of the series solution alternate, and many of the antiresonances become flat minima (Fig. 8.1*c*). The average height of the minima approaches the value $1/Z_c$; but if resonances are more closely spaced than the average, the minima may have a larger amplitude. Figure 8.2*c* shows the experimental result. In contrast to the minima for the one-dimensional rod that is driven at one end and has the receiver attached to its other end, some of the minina here are antiresonances and not just flat troughs.

The preceding computations illustrate the power of the mode-parameter method. The only information about the plate that is needed is its natural frequencies, the relative position of the point of observation with respect to the nodal line pattern, and the relative kinetic energy of the various modes (q_{mn}). Small variations in the thickness or the elastic properties of the plate lead to slight changes in the resonant frequencies, but have practically no effect on the other mode parameters. Therefore, the resonant frequencies represent the prime parameters of the problem.

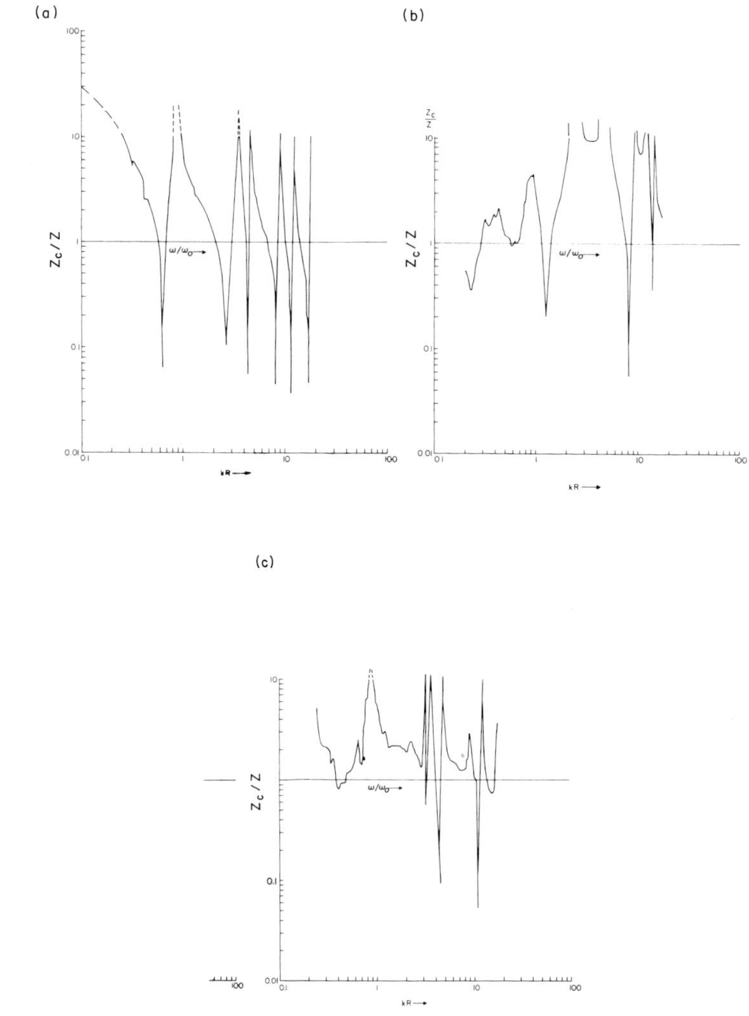

Fig. 8.2 Measured velocity amplitudes at three positions on a rectangular plate (length-width ration, 3 : 1; $\frac{1}{25}$); *a*, at the mid-point; *b*, at the mid-point of the shorter edge; *c*, at one corner. (See Fig. 8.1.)

Centrally Symmetrical Vibrations of a Circular Plate

A circular plate that performs natural vibrations or that is excited by a point force at its center can be analyzed rigorously. The solutions that we shall obtain will form the transition between a one-dimensional vibration, such as that of a rod, and a more general two-dimensional vibration. For the sake of simplicity, we shall not consider vibrations with radial nodal lines.

Plate Equation in Radial Co-ordinates

The expressions of interest in plate theory take the following form in radial co-ordinates:[3]

$$\nabla^2\xi=\frac{\partial^2\xi}{\partial x^2}+\frac{\partial^2\xi}{\partial y^2}=\frac{1}{r}\frac{d}{dr}\left(r\frac{d}{dr}\xi\right) \tag{8.16}$$

$$M_{zs}=D\left(\frac{d^2\xi}{dr^2}+\frac{\nu}{r}\frac{d\xi}{dr}\right) \tag{8.17}$$

$$M_{zr}=D\left(\frac{1}{r}\frac{d\xi}{dr}+\nu\frac{d^2\xi}{dr^2}\right) \tag{8.18}$$

where

$$D=\frac{\lambda_E h^3}{12(1-\nu^2)} \tag{8.19}$$

The magnitude M_{zs} is the bending moment on a section perpendicular to r, and M_{zr} is the bending moment on a section perpendicular to the direction s of the tangent. The shear forces obey the relations:

$$N_s=-D\frac{d}{dr}\left[\frac{1}{r}\frac{d}{dr}\left(r\frac{d\xi}{dr}\right)\right]-=D\frac{d}{dr}\nabla^2\xi \quad \text{and} \quad N_r=0 \tag{8.20}$$

(because of the symmetry around the central axis), and the torsion obeys the relation

$$H=0 \tag{8.21}$$

The resultant shear force on a ring of width dr per unit of its area is:

$$\frac{2\pi(r+dr)\,N_s(r+dr)-2\pi rN_s(r)}{2\pi r}=-\frac{1}{r}\frac{\partial}{\partial r}\left(r\frac{d}{dr}\nabla^2 D\xi\right)$$
$$=-D\nabla^2(\nabla^2\xi) \tag{8.22}$$

and the differential equation then becomes:

$$D\nabla^2(\nabla^2\xi)=p-m\frac{\partial^2\xi}{\partial t^2} \tag{8.23}$$

where p is the driving force per unit area of the plate.

Natural Modes of a Circular Disk

For periodic vibrations, the classical plate equation takes the form:

$$\alpha^4\nabla^2\nabla^2\xi+\frac{\partial^2\xi}{\partial t^2}=0 \tag{8.24}$$

or

$$\left(\nabla^2+\frac{\omega}{\alpha^2}\right)\left(\nabla^2-\frac{\omega}{\alpha^2}\right)\xi=0 \tag{8.25}$$

[3] See pp. 475, 492–499.

where, as before,

$$\alpha^4 = \frac{\lambda_E h^2}{12(1-\nu^2)\rho} = \frac{D}{\rho} \tag{8.26}$$

This equation is solved by functions that satisfy either the differential equation

$$\left(\nabla^2 - \frac{\omega}{\alpha^2}\right)\xi = 0 \tag{8.27}$$

or the differential equation

$$\left(\nabla^2 + \frac{\omega}{\alpha^2}\right)\xi = 0 \tag{8.28}$$

The solutions of the former equation are the Bessel's functions $J_0\ (kr)$ and $N_0\ (kr)$, where

$$k = \frac{\sqrt{\omega}}{\alpha} \tag{8.29}$$

Those of the latter equation are the Bessel's functions $I_0\ (kr)$ and $K_0\ (kr)$. The complete solution is:

$$\xi = AJ_0(kr) + BN_0(kr) + CI_0(kr) + DK_0(kr) \tag{8.30}$$

To understand the significance of the various terms, let the plate be a circular disk that performs free vibrations. Since no external force acts at the center, the solution must be finite for $r=0$, and B and D must be zero. The solution will then be given by:

$$\xi = AJ_0(kr) + CI_0(kr) \tag{8.31}$$

The first term represents the essential part of the vibrations, whereas the second is generated by the boundary condition at the edge of the plate; this term is similar to the term that describes the end distortion of the vibration of a beam. At the higher frequencies,

$$\begin{aligned} I_0(kr) &\approx \sqrt{\frac{2}{\pi kr}}\, e^{kr} \\ &= \frac{e^{kR}}{\sqrt{\frac{\pi kr}{2}}}\, e^{-k(R-r)} \end{aligned} \tag{8.32}$$

and the $I_0\ (kr)$ term decreases approximately exponentially with the distance $R-r$ from the edge. If the plate is freely supported or clamped rigidly at its circumference, $\xi=0$ at $r=R$:

$$0 = AJ_0(kR) + CI_0(kR) \tag{8.33}$$

and the solution becomes:

$$\xi = A\frac{J_0(kr)I_0(kR) - J_0(kR)I_0(kr)}{I_0(kR)} \tag{8.34}$$

This solution still has to satisfy a second boundary condition. If the plate is clamped rigidly, $\partial\xi/\partial r=0$ at $r=R$; if it is freely supported, M_{zs} (Eq. 8.17) is zero at $r=R$. The second boundary condition determines the *eigen* values kR and the natural frequencies.

For most purposes, approximate solutions of the plate equation are satisfactory. If the edge distortion of the vibration is neglected (because of its exponential decrease with the distance from the edge), the solution becomes identical to that for a membrane, except that the propagation velocity is the bending-wave velocity:

$$c=c_B=\alpha\sqrt{\omega} \quad \text{and} \quad k=\frac{\sqrt{\omega}}{\alpha} \tag{8.35}$$

where

$$\alpha^4=\frac{h^2\lambda_E}{12(1-\nu^2)\rho} \tag{8.36}$$

This is proved by entering the high-frequency (asymptotic) approximation to the Bessel's function

$$\xi=\xi_0(kr)\cong\xi_0\sqrt{\frac{2}{\pi kr}}\cos\left(kr-\frac{\pi}{4}\right) \tag{8.37}$$

in the plate equation. Since the edge distortion has been neglected, Equation 8.37 leads to only approximate values for the first few natural frequencies, but its accuracy increases at the higher frequencies. If the plate is free at its edges,

$$kR=\left(\mu+\frac{1}{4}\right)\pi\approx\mu\pi \quad \text{where} \quad \mu=1,2,3,\ldots \tag{8.38}$$

If it is rigidly supported,

$$kR\doteq\left(\mu+\frac{3}{4}\right)\pi\approx\mu\pi \tag{8.39}$$

and

$$\omega=\omega_\nu\doteq\frac{\mu^2\pi^2\alpha^2}{R^2} \tag{8.40}$$

Circular Plate Excited by a Point Force at Its Center

For a circular plate that is excited by a point force at its center, a solution can be derived in closed form. The derivation of this solution is relatively laborious, but it is worth the effort.

The standard differential equation for the plate is derived under the assumption that the plate is thin, so that the force distribution does not change appreciably over distances equal to the thickness of the plate. At the point of attack of a point force, the shear stress becomes infinite, and the standard method of deriving the solution breaks down. The solution can then be obtained by a limiting process, in which it is assumed that the external force is uniformly distributed over a disk whose radius is negligibly small as compared to the bending wave length in the plate. Wave propagation can be neglected over this disk, and the solution becomes identical with the quasi-static solution for the same force distribution. This quasi-static solution must be matched to the solution for the plate outside this disk with the aid of the usual conditions of continuity for the deflection, the slope, and the bending moment. This solution gives the correct value of the deflection and the slope of the plate at the singularity $r=0$, but the second derivative (the curvature) of the deflection becomes logarithmically infinite, and the third derivative becomes infinite, like $1/r$. This physically unrealistic behavior of the solution at the origin makes it necessary to proceed to the limit only after all steps have been carried through.

Static Solution for a Circular Plate under Uniform Pressure

For the computation, the point force has to be replaced by a pressure p distributed over a circular plate of radius b. Since b is to be very small, propagation effects can be neglected; and the solution for this small circular area is obtained by integrating the plate equation for static deflections.

To obtain this solution, let

$$\psi=\nabla^2\xi \tag{8.41}$$

Equation 8.23 then becomes:

$$D\frac{1}{r}\frac{d}{dr}\left(r\frac{\partial\psi}{\partial r}\right)=p \tag{8.42}$$

and integrated:

$$Dr\frac{d(\psi)}{dr}=\frac{1}{2}pr^2+A \tag{8.43}$$

that is,

$$-hN_s=\frac{1}{2}pr+\frac{A}{r} \tag{8.44}$$

Because, the shear force N_s must be finite for $r=0$, $A=0$.

Integrating again, we get:

$$D\psi=\frac{1}{4}pr^2+B \tag{8.45}$$

that is,

$$D\frac{1}{r}\left(\frac{d}{dr}r\frac{d\xi}{dr}\right)=\frac{1}{4}pr^2+B \tag{8.46}$$

Further integrations then lead to:

$$Dr\frac{d\xi}{dr}=\frac{1}{16}pr^4+\frac{1}{2}Br^2+C \tag{8.47}$$

and

$$D\xi = \frac{1}{64} pr^4 + \frac{1}{4} Br^2 + C \ln r + D \tag{8.48}$$

If the plate has no central hole, $C=0$; otherwise, ξ would be infinite at the center. Hence,

$$D\xi = \frac{1}{64} pr^4 + \frac{1}{4} Br^2 + \text{const} \tag{8.49}$$

Matching the Static Solution for the Center of the Plate and the Wave Solution by Conditions of Continuity

The static solution (Eq. 8.49) can be written in the following form:

$$D(\xi - \xi_0) = \frac{1}{64} pr^4 + B_0 r^2 \tag{8.50}$$

where ξ_0 is the deflection at $r=0$. The solution outside the small disk is given by Equation 8.30:

$$\xi D = AJ_0(kr) + BI_0(kr) + CY_0(kr) + EK_0(kr) \tag{8.51}$$

where J_0, I_0, Y_0, and K_0 are the Bessel's functions.[4] The function $Y_0 = (1/\pi)N_0$, rather than N_0, is used for convenience. At $r=b$, the two solutions meet, and deflection, slope, bending moment, and shear force must be continuous. This continuity is established if ξ, $\partial\xi/\partial r$, $\partial^2\xi/\partial r^2$, and $\partial^3\xi/\partial r^3$ are continuous at $r=b$, where $b \rightarrow 0$. It is expedient to develop the foregoing Bessel's functions into series and to retain only the lowest powers. Thus,

$$\begin{aligned} J_0(kr) &= 1 - x^2 + \ldots \\ I_0(kr) &= 1 + x^2 + \ldots \\ Y_0(kr) &= 2[\gamma + (1-\gamma)x^2 + (1-x^2)\ln x + \ldots] \\ K_0(kr) &= -\gamma + (1-\gamma)x^2 - (1+x^2)\ln x \end{aligned} \tag{8.52}$$

where

$$x = \frac{kr}{2} \tag{8.53}$$

and γ is the Euler's constant. In the subsequent differentiations,

$$\frac{\partial}{\partial r} = \frac{\partial}{\partial x}\frac{\partial x}{\partial r} = \frac{k}{2}\frac{\partial}{\partial x} \tag{8.54}$$

[4] As defined by G. N. Watson, *A Treatise on the Theory of Bessel Functions* (New York, 1945), Eq. 2, p. 60, and Eq. 14, p. 80.

For $r=b$, the following equations must be fulfilled:

$$\frac{1}{64}pr^4+B_0r^2=A(1-x^2)+B(1+x^2)+C[2\gamma+(2-2\gamma)x^2+(2-2x^2)\ln x]$$
$$+E[-\gamma+(1-\gamma)x^2-(1+x^2)\ln x+D\xi_0] \quad (8.55)$$

$$\frac{p}{16}r^3+2B_0r=kx(-A+B)+C\left[(1-2\gamma)kx+\frac{k}{x}-2kx\ln x\right]$$
$$\cdot E\left[\left(\frac{1}{2}-\gamma\right)kx-\frac{k}{2x}-kx\ln x\right] \quad (8.56)$$

$$\frac{3}{16}pr^2+2B_0=\frac{k^2}{2}(-A+B)+C\left[-(1+2\gamma)\frac{k^2}{2}-\frac{k^2}{2x^2}-k^2\ln x\right]$$
$$\cdot E\left[-\left(\frac{1}{2}+\gamma\right)\frac{k^2}{2}+\frac{k^2}{4x^2}-\frac{k^2}{2}\ln x\right] \quad (8.57)$$

$$\frac{3}{8}pr=C\left(\frac{k^3}{2x^3}-\frac{k^3}{2x}\right)+E\left(\frac{-k^3}{4x^3}-\frac{k^3}{4x}\right) \quad (8.58)$$

It is expedient to multiply Equation 8.58 by $r^3/2$, Equation 8.57 by r^2, and Equation 8.56 by r, and to replace kr by $2x$:

$$\frac{3}{16}pr^4=2C(1-x^2)-E(1+x^2) \quad (8.59)$$

$$\frac{3}{16}pr^4+2B_0r^2=2x^2(-A+B)+C[-(1+2\gamma)2x^2-2-4x^2\ln x]$$
$$+E\left[-\left(\frac{1}{2}+\gamma\right)2x^2+1-2x^2\ln x\right] \quad (8.60)$$

$$\frac{1}{16}pr^4+2B_0r^2=2x^2(-A+B)+C[(1-2\gamma)2x^2+2-4x^2\ln x]$$
$$+E\left[\left(\frac{1}{2}-\gamma\right)2x^2-1-2x^2\ln x\right] \quad (8.61)$$

If Equation 8.61 is subtracted from Equation 8.60,

$$\frac{1}{8}pr^4=-4C(1+x^2)+2E(1-x^2) \quad (8.62)$$

and if this result is multiplied by $(1+x^2)/2$ and added to Equation 8.59 after it has been multiplied by $(1-x^2)/2$,

$$\frac{1}{4}pr^4\left(1-\frac{x^2}{2}\right)=-8Cx^2 \quad (8.63)$$

On the left-hand side, $x^2/2$ may be neglected, and

$$C=\frac{-1}{32}\frac{pr^4}{x^2}=-\frac{1}{8}\frac{pr^2\pi}{k^2\pi}=-\frac{1}{8}\frac{F_0}{k^2} \quad (8.64)$$

where F_0 is the force at the center of the plate. If this value is substituted in Equation 8.59,

$$\frac{1}{8}pr^4=\frac{1}{8}\frac{pr^4}{x^2}(1+x^2)+2E(1-x^2) \quad (8.65)$$

The right-hand side is two orders of magnitude larger than the left-hand side. If we neglect x^2 because it is small as compared with one,

$$E = \frac{-1}{16}\frac{pr^4}{x^2} \tag{8.66}$$

If the values of C and D are introduced into Equation 8.61, this equation reduces to:

$$\frac{1}{16}pr^4 + 2B_0r^2 = 2x^2(-A+B) \tag{8.67}$$

and

$$2B_0r^2 = 2x^2(-A+B) - \frac{1}{16}pr^4 \tag{8.68}$$

With this value, and with C and E substituted, Equation 8.55 becomes:

$$-\frac{3}{64}pr^4 + 2x^2(-A+B) = A(1-x^2) + B(1+x^2) - \frac{1}{8}pr^4[(1-\gamma) - ln x] - D\xi_0 \tag{8.69}$$

If r approaches zero,

$$A + B = D\xi_0 + \ldots \quad \text{and} \quad A = D\xi_0 - B \tag{8.70}$$

and the solution can be written as follows:

$$v = (v_0 - B')J_0(kr) + B'I_0(kr) - j\frac{F_0}{\pi Z_c}[Y_0(kr) + 2K_0(kr)] \tag{8.71}$$

where

$$Z_c = \frac{8Dk^2}{\omega} = \frac{8}{\omega}\left(\frac{D}{\rho h}\right)m\frac{\omega}{h^2} = 8\alpha^2 m = Z_c \tag{8.72}$$

and

$$B' = \frac{j\omega B}{D} \tag{8.73}$$

The magnitude Z_c will turn out to be the characteristic impedance of the plate (that is, the driving-point impedance of a similar plate of infinite size). The constants B' and v_0 are determined by the boundary conditions at $r = R$. The simplest form of the boundary condition is that for a clamped plate. If v denotes the velocity amplitude of the plate,

$$v = 0 \quad \text{and} \quad \frac{\partial v}{\partial r} = 0 \quad \text{at} \quad r = R \tag{8.74}$$

Thus,

$$0 = \frac{1}{k}\left(\frac{\partial v}{\partial r}\right)_{r=R} = (v_0 - B')J_0 + B'I_0' - j\frac{F_0}{\pi Z_c}(Y_0' + 2K_0') \tag{8.75}$$

Hence,

$$B' = \frac{\left[j\frac{F_0}{\pi Z_c}(Y_0' + 2K_0')\right] - v_0J_0'}{I_0' - J_0'} \tag{8.76}$$

If this value is substituted into the first boundary conditions,

$$(v)_{r=R}=v_0J_0+\frac{j\dfrac{F_0}{\pi Z_c}(Y_0'+2K_0')-v_0J_0'}{I_0'-J_0'}(I_0-J_0)-j\frac{F_0}{\pi Z_c}(Y_0+2K_0) \tag{8.77}$$

or

$$\frac{v_0}{F_0}=\frac{j}{\pi Z_c}\frac{(Y_0'+2K_0')(I_0-J_0)-(Y_0+2K_0)(I_0'-J_0')}{J_0'I_0-J_0I_0'} \tag{8.78}$$

where the primes note derivatives with respect to the argument of the Bessel's functions, which, if not written, is always kR.

Properties of the Solution

Asymptotic Solution

The ratio Z_c/Z, which is proportional to the velocity V_0 at the center of a circular plate that is excited at its center by a point force, is plotted in Figure 8.3 for $\eta=\frac{1}{25}$. For frequencies above the first series resonance ($kR>1$), the Bessel's functions may be replaced with sufficient accuracy by their asymptotic representations:

$$J_0(z)=\left(\frac{2}{\pi z}\right)^{\frac{1}{2}}\cos\left(z-\frac{\pi}{4}\right) \qquad I_0(z)=\frac{e^z}{(2\pi z)^{\frac{1}{2}}} \tag{8.79}$$

$$Y_0(z)=\left(\frac{2\pi}{z}\right)^{\frac{1}{2}}\sin\left(z-\frac{\pi}{4}\right) \quad \text{and} \quad K_0(z)=\left(\frac{\pi}{2z}\right)^{\frac{1}{2}}e^{-z}\approx 0 \tag{8.80}$$

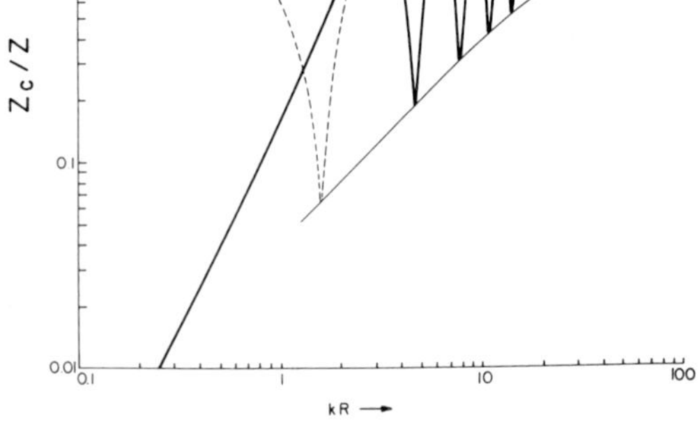

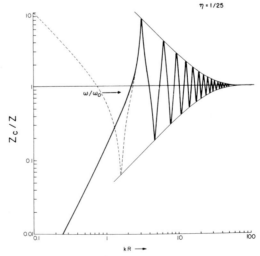

Fig. 8.3 Velocity amplitude of a circular plate excited at its center by a point force ($\eta=\frac{1}{25}$).

The solution then simplifies to:

$$\frac{\bar{V}_0}{\bar{F}}=\frac{-j}{Z_C}j\frac{1-\tan\left(kR-\frac{\pi}{4}\right)}{1+\tan\left(kR-\frac{\pi}{4}\right)}=\frac{-j}{Z_c}\cot(kR) \tag{8.81}$$

To the same degree of approximation,

$$B'=j\frac{2^{\frac{1}{2}}F_0}{Z_c}\frac{e^{-kR}}{\sin kR}=-\frac{V_0 2e^{-kR}}{\cos kR} \tag{8.82}$$

The constant B' is very small, and it can be neglected in the first term on the right-hand side of Equation 8.75. In the second term, I_0 (kr) increases exponentially with kr. This term describes an exponential distortion of the motion near the boundary that is limited to a very small region of the plate. The K_0 and Y_0 terms describe a similar distortion at the center of the plate. For frequencies above the fundamental and for distances greater than half a bending wave length from the center of the plate, the asymptotic representation is sufficiently accurate. The solution then simplifies to:

$$\bar{V}=\frac{-jF_0\sqrt{2}\cos\left[k(R-r)+\frac{\pi}{4}\right]}{\sqrt{\pi kr}\,Z_c\sin kR} \tag{8.83}$$

The solution is invalid for $k\,(R-r)<1$ and for $kr<1$. For the center, $V=V_0$; and for the boundary, $r=R$ and $v=0$. The solution now is very similar to that for the rod, and the effect of damping, the fluctuation in amplitude with the distance from the driven point, and all other phenomena may be expected to be very similar to those of the rod. The physical significance of the solution can be easily demonstrated. Because of the focusing effect of the circular boundary, the amplitude of the reflected wave is the same at all points as that of the outgoing wave, and, except for a phase change of $\pi/2$ (the edge of the plate being assumed to be clamped), the various wave trains add:

$$\begin{aligned}\bar{V}&\approx\frac{F}{Z_c}[1+2(je^{-j2kR}+j^2e^{-j4kR}-\ldots)]\\&=\frac{-jF}{Z_c}\cot\left(kR-\frac{\pi}{4}\right)\end{aligned} \tag{8.84}$$

The factor 2 on the right-hand side shows that the wave is reflected at the center and that the reflected wave doubles the velocity.

For the one-dimensional rod and for the circular plate, the maxima are as high above the characteristic level F/Z_c as the minima are below (Fig. 8.3). For a two-dimensional system with a rectangular or irregular boundary, the envelopes of the maxima and the minima may be expected to rise and fall with the density of the resonant frequencies in frequency space, but, as a whole, may not be expected to deviate much from those with a circular boundary. Figure 8.4 shows the accurately computed velocity distribution

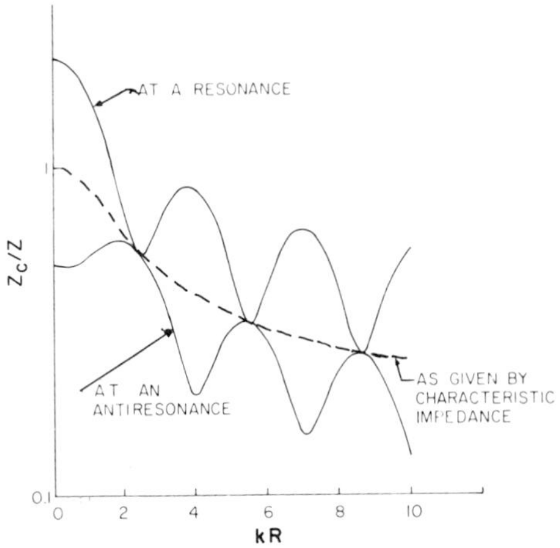

Fig. 8.4 Amplitude distribution over a circular plate driven at its center; *solid line*, at a resonance ($kR=4\pi$); *dotted line*, at an antiresonance ($kR=4\frac{1}{2}\pi$); *broken line*, curve that would be excited in a similar plate of infinite radius.

over the surface of a plate driven at a resonance ($kR=4\pi$) and at an antiresonance ($kR=4\frac{1}{2}\pi$) for $\eta=\frac{1}{25}$. The broken line represents the level that would be excited in a similar plate of infinite radius.

Wave Impedance for Bending Waves in an Infinite Plate

Let us consider the solution for a very large circular plate driven at its center. If the plate is large and damped, so that the reflections from the boundary $r=R$ do not contribute, the shape of the plate is immaterial, and we may use the solution for the circular plate to describe the motion of points far from the boundary. If $kr>1$, the solution for the circular plate reduces to a progressive wave that diverges from the center of the plate:

$$\bar{V}=\left[J_0(kr)-j\frac{1}{\pi}Y_0(kr)\right]=V_0H_0^{(2)}(kr)$$

$$\approx V_0\left(\frac{2}{\pi kr}\right)^{\frac{1}{2}}e^{-j(kr-\pi/4)} \tag{8.85}$$

where $H_0^{(2)}$ is the Hankel's function of the second kind and where $V_0=F_0/Z_c$. In conjunction with the corresponding fraction of the J_0 term, the Y_0 term represents the outgoing wave at the center of the plate. The remaining fraction of the J_0 term in Equation 8.77 represents the contributions of the resonating modes. The K_0 term, which has been omitted in Equation 8.85, compensates the pole at $r=0$, but otherwise decreases rapidly (exponentially) with the distance from the center. Figure 8.5 shows a comparison between the accurately computed solution and the foregoing asymptotic solution. The solutions are practically identical for $kr>4$. For

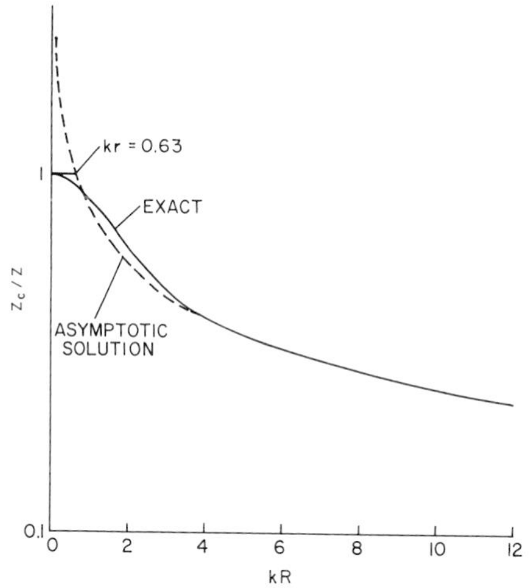

Fig. 8.5 Comparison of the exact and the asymptotic solutions; *solid line*, exact solution; *broken line*, asymptotic solution.

practical purposes it seems sufficient to approximate the exact solution by:

$$V = V_0 = \frac{F}{Z_c} \qquad \text{where} \qquad kr \le 0.63$$

$$V = V_0 \sqrt{\frac{2}{\pi kr}}\, e^{-j(kr-\pi/4)} \qquad \text{where} \qquad kr \ge 0.63 \tag{8.86}$$

The velocity at the center of the plate is determined by the characteristic impedance Z_c. It is independent of the frequency and of the bending wave number k. A circular disk of radius $r = 0.63/k = 0.1\lambda$ moves with almost the same velocity as the center point. The power $\frac{1}{2}F^2/Z_c = \frac{1}{2}V_0^2 Z_c$ that is supplied by the force spreads out in the form of circular wave fronts. Since the wave travels a distance c_B per second, the energy per unit area of the plate is:

$$\frac{\frac{1}{2}V_0^2 Z_c}{2\pi r c_B} = \frac{1}{2}\frac{V_0^2 8\alpha^2 m}{2\pi r\alpha\sqrt{\omega}} = \frac{2V_0^2 m}{\pi kr} \tag{8.87}$$

And the amplitude, which is proportional to the square root of the energy density, decreases in inverse proportion to $\sqrt{kr}$. At low frequencies, when the bending-wave velocity $c_B = \alpha\sqrt{\omega}$ is small, the energy leaks slowly away from the driving point, and the amplitude decreases at a small rate with distance; in contrast, at high frequencies, when c_B is large, the amplitude decreases greatly with distance. The driving force generates the power:

$$\frac{1}{2}V_0 F = \frac{V_0^2 Z_c}{2} \tag{8.88}$$

which spreads over circles of radius r. This power can also be expressed in terms of the two-dimensional radiation resistance per unit length of the circular wave front:

$$V_0^2 Z_c = V^2 r_{\text{rad}} \cdot 2\pi r = \frac{V_0^2 2}{\pi k r} \cdot 2\pi r \cdot r_{\text{rad}} = V_0^2 \cdot \frac{4}{k} r_{\text{rad}} \tag{8.89}$$

where V has been expressed by Equation 8.86. Hence,

$$r_{\text{rad}} = \frac{k}{4} Z_c = 2\alpha m \sqrt{\omega} = 2mc_B \tag{8.90}$$

The energy density

$$\frac{1}{2} V^2 \frac{r_{\text{rad}}}{c_{ph}} = V^2 m \tag{8.91}$$

is twice as large as the kinetic energy density, just as in three-dimensional sound propagation.

Velocity Distribution over a Rectangular Plate or a Plate with Asymmetric Boundaries

In a circular plate that is excited at its center, focusing takes place, and the reflected amplitude increases as the wave propagates to the center of the plate. Except for maxima and minima, the intensity obeys a $1/kr$ law, as is illustrated in Figure 8.4.

If the geometric mean between the maxima and minima is plotted, the reflections from the boundaries do not contribute, and the shape of the boundary has no effect on the distribution of the vibration. The results obtained for a circular plate may then be expected to apply to plates of any shape. In contrast, averaging arithmetically over a finite frequency band (for instance, by driving the plate with white noise so that the phases are incoherent, and using a third-octave filter) is equivalent to determining the root-mean-square amplitude over the given frequency band, that is, the vibrational energy. The result of such a measurement, therefore, is not directly related to the characteristic admittance, as has been shown in Chapter VIII.

If damping is not very large, a rectangular plate or a plate with irregular boundaries represents the two-dimensional analogue of a reverberation chamber.[5] It can be shown that a point force excites a two-dimensional wave field, in contrast to three-dimensional fields, and is very poorly diffused. As a consequence, the reflected energy density tends to con-

[5] A reverberation chamber is a chamber whose walls are highly reflective. Because of the many reflections at the walls, the sound waves travel in all directions (diffuse sound field) with approximately the same probability.

centrate near the driver (see Eq. 7.70), and the reverberant energy density decreases with distance. As a crude approximation, we can assume that intensity decreases (see Eq. 8.85) with the distance from the driver until this decrease becomes masked by the reverberant background. The ration of the intensity at the driver to the reverberant background can be computed by methods standard in reverberation theory, the only difference being that the computation is now two-dimensional and that the amplitude remains finite at the driver.

If l is the average distance, the wave front travels between successive reflections; l_0 is the average distance to the boundary of the plate, and $2\delta = \omega\eta/c_{ph} = k/Q$ is the attenuation per unit length. The reverberant intensity in the plate is given by:

$$\begin{aligned} V^2{}_{\text{rev}} &\doteq V_0{}^2 \frac{2}{\pi k l_0}(1 + e^{-2\delta l} + e^{-4\delta l} + \ldots) \\ &= V_0{}^2 \frac{2}{\pi k l_0} \frac{1}{1 - e^{-2\delta l}} \doteq \frac{V_0{}^2}{\pi k l_0{}^2 l \delta} = \frac{2 V_0{}^2 Q}{\pi k^2 l_0 l} \end{aligned} \tag{8.92}$$

Hence,

$$\frac{V_{\text{rev}}}{V_0} = \left(\frac{2Q}{\pi k_B{}^2 l_0 l}\right)^{\frac{1}{2}} \tag{8.93}$$

and

$$\frac{V^2{}_{\text{rev}}}{V^2} = \frac{V^2{}_{\text{rev}}}{V_0{}^2 \dfrac{2}{\pi k r}} = \frac{Qr}{k l_0 l} = \frac{Qr\lambda}{2\pi l_0 l} \tag{8.94}$$

This ratio is one if:

$$\frac{r}{\dfrac{l_0}{\lambda_B}} = 2\pi l \eta \tag{8.95}$$

or

$$r = \frac{\eta l l_0 \sqrt{\omega}}{\alpha} \tag{8.96}$$

These computations can easily be improved in a manner similar to that for three-dimensional spaces.

Figure 8.6 shows the square root of the energy density, averaged over a third-octave band, as a function of the distance from the driver for an aluminum plate (dimensions, 3 ft. by 7 ft. by $\frac{1}{3}$ in.). When damping is small, the amplitude of the vibration hardly decreases with the distance from the driver because of the high reverberant level; but if the damping is increased by applying an automobile undercoating, the amplitude decreases continuously with the distance from the driver. For very high damping, the curve is seen to approach the theoretical curve for a heavily damped circular plate, as would be expected.

Figure 8.7 shows similar measurements for a glass plate (Pittsburgh plate glass, 200 by 300 cm., 0.95 cm. thick, the constant $\alpha = 290$), which was

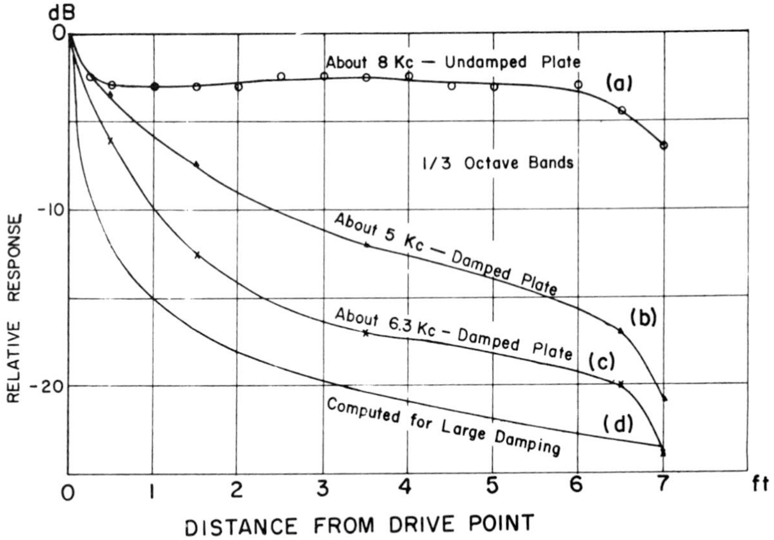

Fig. 8.6 Measured velocity distribution over a damped and an undamped rectangular aluminum plate, as a function of the distance from the driven point ($\frac{1}{3}$ octave bands); *a*, about 8 kc., undamped plate; *b*, about 5 kc., damped plate; *c*, about 6.3 kc., damped plate; *d*, computed for large damping (according to D. C. Green, l. c.)

mounted in a frame between foam rubber. Measurements were not performed at distances less than 20 cm. from the driver, but it was possible to extrapolate the curves for distances nearer the driver by plotting them on a log-log scale with the slope $-\frac{1}{2}$ and computing the abscissa r for $kr=0.63$ (see Fig. 8.5 and Eq. 8.86).

Damping can be determined by plotting the points on a log-log scale $[y=\log(e^{-\delta r}/kr)=\text{const}-\delta r-\frac{1}{2}\ln r]$; it affects the result only at frequencies above 20 kc. at the greater distances, and it makes the curves bend downward as r becomes greater. The broken line separates the region where the reverberant intensity is significant from the region where the incident vibration predominates. Equation 8.96 gives the correct order of magnitude for the radius r in this region and its correct frequency dependence.

The more accurate computations in Chapter VII (Eq. 7.70) show that so long as damping is not excessively large, the amplitude excited by noise bands should decrease as $1/\sqrt{r}$ and that for very high damping the curve should become identical with that for the characteristic admittance.

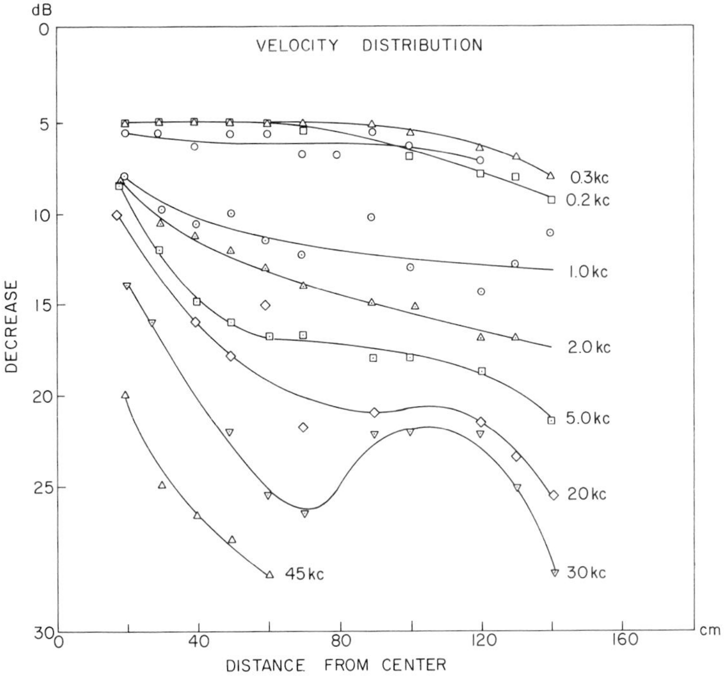

Fig. 8.7 Measured velocity distribution over a rectangular glass plate, as a function of the distance from the driven point (according to J. N. Lange).

Distortion Field near the Edge of the Plate

If the plate is freely suspended, or rigidly clamped, the vibration field differs from the field that is described by the asymptotic or approximate solution, because of the edge distortion. This edge distortion can be computed accurately for the circular plate. Asymptotically, the function $I_0\,(kr)$ that describes this distortion (see Eq. 8.51) is an exponential function, like that for the beam, that decreases by a factor of about $\frac{1}{520}$ per bending wave length distance from the circumference of the plate. Because of this rapid decrease with distance, the curvature of the edge of the plate can have only little effect on this term, provided that the radius of the plate is greater than the wave length, and we may assume that the edge of the plate behaves very nearly the same as the end of a beam. The expressions for the end distortion of a beam may, therefore, be expected to apply approximately for the edge distortion of the plate if λ_E in the beam equation is replaced by the elastic constant $\lambda_E/(1-\nu^2)$ of the plate equation.

Recommended Reading

GREENE, D. C., "Vibration and sound radiation of damped and undamped flat plates," *J.A.S.A.*, **33** (1961), 1315.

LANGE J. N., "Bending wave propagation in rods and plates," *J.A.S.A.*, **35** (1963), 378.

LOVE, A. E. H., *The Mathematical Theory of Elasticity,* Dover Publications, Inc., New York, 1944.

MORSE, P. M., *Vibration and Sound,* McGraw-Hill, Inc., New York, 1948.

PRESCOTT, J., *Applied Elasticity,* Longmans, Green and Co., Ltd., London, 1924.

RAYLEIGH, LORD, *The Theory of Sound,* Macmillan and Co., Ltd., London, 1894, vol. I.

SKUDRZYK, E. J., KAUTZ, BARBARA R., AND D. C. GREENE, "Vibration of and bending wave propagation in plates," *J.A.S.A.*, **33** (1961), 36.

IX / MODE PARAMETERS AND CHARACTERISTIC IMPEDANCE

The present chapter shows how the mode parameters are computed in some of the instances of practical interest. The solution is then obtained by substituting these parameters into Equation 7.22.

Longitudinally Vibrating Rod

The natural functions of a longitudinally vibrating rod are:

$$\xi_\nu = \xi_{0\nu} \cos \frac{\nu \pi x}{l} \qquad \text{[ends free]} \tag{9.1}$$

or

$$\xi_\nu = \xi_{0\nu} \sin \frac{\nu \pi x}{l} \qquad \text{[ends rigidly supported]} \tag{9.2}$$

The constants

$$q_\nu = \frac{\langle \xi_\nu^2 \rangle}{\xi_\nu^2(A)} \tag{9.3}$$

become

$$q_\nu = \frac{\langle \xi_\nu^2 \rangle}{\xi_\nu^2(A)} = \frac{\xi_{0\nu}^2}{2\xi_\nu^2(A)} \tag{9.4}$$

If the driving force is a point force that acts at the point $x = x_F$, and if the ends are free, the excitation constant becomes:

$$\kappa_\nu = \frac{\xi_\nu(x_F)}{\xi_\nu(x_A)} = \frac{\cos \dfrac{\nu \pi x_F}{l}}{\cos \dfrac{\nu \pi x}{l}} \tag{9.5}$$

If the ends are rigidly supported,

$$\kappa_\nu = \frac{\sin \dfrac{\nu \pi x_F}{l}}{\sin \dfrac{\nu \pi x}{l}} \tag{9.6}$$

The mode masses are:

$$M_\nu^* = q_\nu \frac{M}{\kappa_\nu} = \frac{\xi_{0\nu}^2 M \xi_\nu(A)}{2\xi_\nu^2(A)\xi_\nu(F)} = \frac{\xi_{0\nu}^2 M}{2\xi_\nu(A)\, \xi_\nu(F)} \tag{9.7}$$

If the reference point is a point of maximum motion, $q_\nu = \frac{1}{2}$; and if the driving point coincides with the point of observation, $\kappa_\nu = 1$. The mode masses M_ν are then equal to $M/2$. If the rod is driven at the end opposite the reference point, $\kappa_\nu = \pm 1$ and $M_\nu = \pm M/2$, depending on whether ν is odd or even. The remaining mode parameters are computed with the aid of Equations 7.23 to 7.27. The mode admittances are given by:

$$\frac{1}{\bar{Z}_\nu} = \frac{j\omega}{M_\nu^*(\bar{\omega}_\nu^2 - \omega^2)} = \frac{2\xi_\nu(A)\dfrac{\xi_\nu(F)}{\xi_{0\nu}^2}}{j\omega_\nu M\left(\dfrac{\omega}{\omega_\nu} - \dfrac{\omega_\nu}{\omega}\right) + \eta\dfrac{\omega_\nu^2}{\omega}M} \tag{9.8}$$

and by:

$$\frac{1}{\bar{Z}_0} = \frac{1}{j\omega M} \tag{9.9}$$

The natural frequencies are proportional to the fundamental frequency ω_1:

$$\omega_\nu = \nu\omega_1 \tag{9.10}$$

Hence,

$$\omega_\nu - \omega_{\nu-1} = \epsilon_\nu = \frac{\partial\omega_\nu}{\partial\nu} = \omega_1 = \frac{\pi c}{l} \tag{9.11}$$

The characteristic impedance is:

$$Z_c = \frac{2}{\pi}\epsilon_\nu M_\nu^* = \frac{2}{\pi}\omega_1\frac{M}{2} = \frac{c}{l}M = cm \tag{9.12}$$

where m is the mass per unit length of the rod.

The mechanical transfer impedance can be computed by the same method. If the driving point is a point of maximum velocity, and if the natural functions are sinusoidal, the integrand in the integrals for the velocity of the driving point (Eq. 7.44) must be multiplied by $\cos k_\nu x$ (the force being assumed at $x=0$; the point of observation, at x). The integral can then be transformed into the form:

$$\int_0^\infty \cos px \frac{dx}{q^2 + x^2} = \frac{\pi}{2q}e^{-pq} \tag{9.13}$$

and the transfer impedance becomes:

$$\bar{Z}_t = Z_c e^{jkx} \tag{9.14}$$

The same results can be obtained by integration of the differential equation for a point force.[1] The transfer impedance for a point of observation a distance x from the driven end turns out to be given by:[2]

$$\bar{Z}_t = \frac{\tilde{f}}{j\omega\tilde{\xi}} = \frac{\lambda_E \sigma}{\bar{c}} e^{jkx} = \sigma\rho\bar{c}e^{jkx} = m\bar{c}e^{jkx} \tag{9.15}$$

If $x=0$, $\bar{Z}_t$ becomes identical to the characteristic impedance.

[1] See pp. 162–64.
[2] See Eqs. 5.126–28, p. 164.

Transversely Vibrating Beam

If the distortion of the sinusoidal distribution of the vibrations near the free ends of a beam is neglected, the natural functions are given by:

$$\xi_\nu \doteq A \cos k_B x \qquad \text{[both ends free]} \tag{9.16}$$

$$\xi_\nu = A \sin k_B x \qquad \text{[both ends rigidly supported]} \tag{9.17}$$

$$\xi_\nu \doteq B \sin k_B x \qquad \text{[end at } x=0 \text{ rigidly supported, other end free]} \tag{9.18}$$

If the reference point coincides with a maximum of the vibration (because of the sinusoidal space distribution of the vibrations),

$$\frac{\langle \xi_\nu{}^2 \rangle}{\xi^2{}_{\max}} = q_\nu = \frac{1}{2} \tag{9.19}$$

Also, if the driving point and the point of observation are coincident, $\kappa_\nu = 1$, and

$$M_\nu \doteq \frac{1}{2} M \tag{9.20}$$

The error in this last formula is very small for the higher modes.

The end distortion is important if the point of observation is at the end of a freely suspended beam. The velocity distribution then is given by Equation 6.67. In computing the mean-square amplitude, the second term can be neglected, and

$$\langle \xi^2 \rangle \doteq 4B^2 \left\langle \cos^2\left(kx + \frac{\pi}{4}\right)\right\rangle = 2B^2 \tag{9.21}$$

The amplitude at the end of the beam is:

$$|\xi(0)| = 2\sqrt{2}\,B \tag{9.22}$$

and

$$\xi^2(0) = 8B^2 \tag{9.23}$$

Thus, the square of the amplitude of the end of the beam is equal to four times the mean square of the amplitude over the beam, and

$$q_\nu = \frac{\langle \xi_\nu{}^2 \rangle}{\xi_\nu{}^2(0)} = \frac{1}{4} \tag{9.24}$$

The mode masses are now equal to one fourth the total mass of the beam.

The contribution of the motion of and around the center of gravity is of interest. For a free beam excited to bending vibrations, Equation 7.28 becomes:

$$\frac{1}{\bar{Z}_0} = \frac{1}{j\omega M}\left[1 - 3\left(\frac{2x_A}{l} - 1\right)\left(1 - \frac{2x_F}{l}\right)\right] \tag{9.25}$$

where x_A is the distance of the point of observation and x_F, the distance of the driving point from the end of the beam. The last expression reduces to $4/j\omega M$ for $x_F=0$ and $x_A=0$ and to $-2/j\omega M$ for $x_F=0$ and $x_A=l$.

Approximate values of the natural frequencies if both ends are free or both ends are clamped are given by:

$$k_B l \doteq \frac{\omega_\nu}{c_B} l \doteq \nu\pi \tag{9.26}$$

where $c_B=\alpha\sqrt{\omega}$ is the velocity of propagation of the bending waves and $\alpha=(\lambda_E J/m)^{\frac{1}{4}}$, J being the second moment of area of cross section of the beam about an axis perpendicular to the plane of the vibration through the axis of the beam. If the above value of c_B is substituted into the frequency equation,

$$\omega_\nu \doteq \frac{\nu^2\pi^2\alpha^2}{l^2} \doteq \nu^2\omega_0 \tag{9.27}$$

and

$$\omega_0 = \frac{\pi^2\alpha^2}{l^2} \tag{9.28}$$

is a parameter that has the dimension of a frequency (but is not a resonant frequency). The accurate values of the resonant frequencies for a beam free at both ends are:

$$\omega_\nu = \omega_0(1.5056^2,\ 2.5^2,\ 3.5^2,\ 4.5^2,\ \ldots) \tag{9.29}$$

These frequencies can be approximated very satisfactorily by the series:

$$\omega_\nu = \omega_0\left(\nu+\frac{1}{2}\right)^2 \quad \text{where} \quad \nu=1,\ 2,\ \ldots \tag{9.30}$$

If the beam is clamped at the end $x=0$ and free at the end $x=l$,

$$k_B l = \frac{\omega_\nu}{c_B} l \doteq (2\nu-1)\frac{\pi}{2} \tag{9.31}$$

and

$$\omega_\nu \doteq (2\nu-1)^2 \frac{\pi^2}{4}\frac{\alpha^2}{l^2} \tag{9.32}$$

or

$$\omega_\nu \doteq \omega_0\left(\nu-\frac{1}{2}\right)^2 \tag{9.33}$$

where ω_0 is the same constant as above and $\nu=1,\ 2,\ 3\ \ldots$. The accurate computation leads to the values:

$$\omega_\nu = \omega_0(0.597^2,\ 1.494^2,\ 2.5^2,\ 3.5^2,\ \ldots) \tag{9.34}$$

At the higher frequencies, the resonant frequencies and the frequency difference between successive resonances are given with sufficient accuracy by:

$$\omega_\nu \doteq \omega_0\nu^2 \tag{9.35}$$

and

$$\epsilon_\nu = \frac{\partial\omega_\nu}{\partial\nu} = 2\nu\omega_0 = 2\sqrt{\frac{\omega_\nu}{\omega_0}}\ \omega_0 = 2\sqrt{\omega_\nu\omega_0} \tag{9.36}$$

irrespective of the boundary conditions. The characteristic (driving-point) impedance of the beam driven at its free end then becomes (see Eq. 7.62):

$$\bar{Z}_c=\left(\frac{1+j}{\pi}\right)\epsilon_\nu M_\nu{}^*=\frac{(1+j)\,2\pi\alpha\,\sqrt{\omega}\,\frac{M}{4}}{\pi l}=\frac{(1+j)}{2}mc_B \tag{9.37}$$

where ω_ν has been replaced by ω. The direct computation leads to the same value of the characteristic impedance and to the transfer impedance (see Eq. 6.84):

$$\bar{Z}_t=\frac{mc_B(1+j)}{e^{-kx}+e^{-jkx}} \tag{9.38}$$

Rectangular Plate

The natural vibrations for a rectangular plate of length l_1, width l_2, whose edge is supported, are described by:

$$V=v_{mn}\sin\frac{m\pi x}{l_1}\sin\frac{n\pi y}{l_2}\quad\cos\omega_{mn}t\qquad\text{where } m,n=1,2,3,\ldots \tag{9.39}$$

and where

$$\omega_{mn}=\omega_{ap}m^2+\omega_{bp}n^2\qquad\omega_{ap}=\frac{\alpha^2\pi^2}{l_1{}^2}\quad\text{and}\quad\omega_{bp}=\frac{\alpha^2\pi^2}{l_2{}^2} \tag{9.40}$$

where α is the constant defined by Equation 8.1, λ_E is Young's modulus, h is the thickness of plate, ρ is the density, ν is Poisson's contraction, and $c_0=(\lambda_E/\rho)^{\frac{1}{2}}$ is the velocity of sound in the plate material. If the square of the velocity amplitude (Eq. 9.39) is integrated over the system,

$$\begin{aligned}q_\nu&=\frac{1}{V_{mn}{}^2(A)}\int\int V_{mn}{}^2\sin^2\frac{m\pi x}{l_1}\sin^2\frac{n\pi y}{l_2}dxdy\\&=\frac{1}{4}\frac{V_{mn}{}^2}{V_{mn}{}^2(A)}\qquad\text{if } m\neq 0\text{ and } n\neq 0\\&=\frac{1}{2}\frac{V_{mn}{}^2}{V_{mn}{}^2(A)}\qquad\text{if either } m \text{ or } n \text{ is zero}\end{aligned} \tag{9.41}$$

where

$$V_{mn}(A)=V_{mn}\sin\frac{m\pi x_A}{l_1}\sin\frac{n\pi y_A}{l_2} \tag{9.42}$$

If the point of observation is a point of maximum velocity, $V_{mn}(A)=V_{mn}$, and

$$q_\nu=\frac{1}{4}\quad\text{or}\quad\frac{1}{2} \tag{9.43}$$

according to whether the velocity distribution is two-dimensional (if $m\neq 0$ and $n\neq 0$) or one-dimensional (if either m or n is equal to zero).

If the plate is large as compared to the bending wave length, the boundary conditions may be expected to have very little effect on its vibration. We may assume perfect symmetry for the driving point, and only the odd *eigen* functions are excited; if the point of observation coincides with the driving point, $\kappa_\nu = 1$ and $M_\nu = \frac{1}{4}M$ ($\nu = 1, 3, 5, \ldots$).

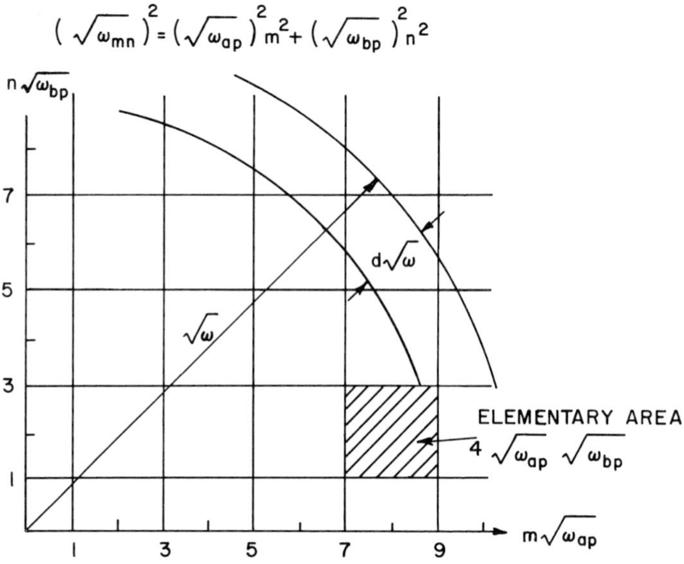

Fig. 9.1 Representation of the natural frequencies of a rectangular plate by a grating in the frequency plane.

The roots of the resonant frequencies are given by the diagonals of a square grid pattern (Fig. 9.1) that is obtained by drawing parallel lines through the points $m(\omega_{ap})^{\frac{1}{2}}$ on the x-axis and through the points $n(\omega_{bp})^{\frac{1}{2}}$ on the y-axis ($m, n = 1, 3, 5, \ldots$). The square of the distance of a grid point from the origin then is $m^2\omega_{ap} + n^2\omega_{bp}$ by the law of Pythagoras, and this distance is the same as ω_{mn}. The number $d\nu$ of resonances in the frequency range between ω and $\omega + \Delta\omega$ is represented by the ratio of the area of a circular ring of radius $(\omega)^{\frac{1}{2}}$ and of width $d(\omega)^{\frac{1}{2}}$ in the positive quadrant to the area $2(\omega_{ap})^{\frac{1}{2}} \cdot 2(\omega_{bp})^{\frac{1}{2}}$ of one of the rectangles (every resonant frequency can be considered as a corner of such a rectangle):

$$d\nu = \frac{2\pi\omega^{\frac{1}{2}} d(\omega^{\frac{1}{2}})}{16(\omega_{ap}\omega_{bp})^{\frac{1}{2}}} = \frac{\pi}{16} \frac{d\omega}{(\omega_{ap}\omega_{bp})^{\frac{1}{2}}} \tag{9.44}$$

because each of the rectangles contains the representative point of the resonant frequency of an excited mode. The characteristic impedance parameter becomes:

$$Z_c = \frac{2}{\pi} \epsilon_\nu M_\nu = \frac{1}{2\pi} \frac{\partial\omega}{\partial\nu} M = \frac{8}{\pi^2} \sqrt{\omega_{ap} \cdot \omega_{bp}}\, M$$

$$= \frac{8}{\pi^2} \frac{\alpha\pi}{l_1} \frac{\alpha\pi}{l_2} M = 8\alpha^2 m \tag{9.45}$$

where $l_1 l_2 = \sigma$ is the area of the plate and m is its mass per unit area. Figure 9.2 shows the characteristic impedance Z_c of an aluminum and an iron plate as a function of their thickness.

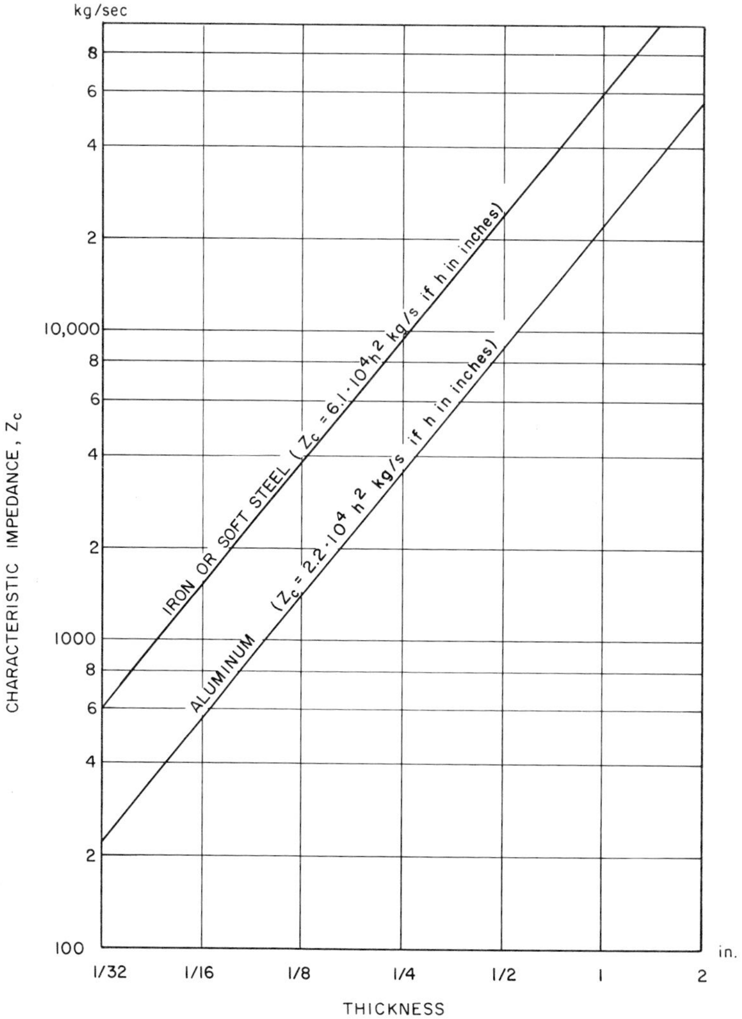

Fig. 9.2 Characteristic impedance of an iron plate and an aluminum plate, as a function of their thickness h; for an iron (or soft steel) plate, $Z_c = 6.1 \cdot 10^4 \cdot h^2$ kg. per second (if h is measured in inches), $c = 5{,}000$ m. per second, $\nu = 0.29$, $\rho = 7.8$ gm. per cubic centimeter; for an aluminum plate, $Z_c = 2.2 \cdot 10^4 h^2$ kg. per second (if h is measured in inches), $c = 5{,}100$ m. per second, $\nu = 0.34$, $\rho = 2.72$ gm. per cubic centimeter.

If the force is not a point force, but is distributed with constant intensity over a line such as the y-axis, the vibration pattern becomes one-dimensional, and only modes corresponding to $n=0$ and $m=2\nu+1$ ($\nu=1, 2, 3, \ldots$) are excited. The number of resonances below a frequency ω_ν then is given by:

$$\omega_m = \omega_{ap} m^2 \tag{9.46}$$

and, because m is odd only,

$$\epsilon_\nu = 2\frac{\partial \omega_m}{\partial m} = 4m\omega_{ap} = 4(\omega_m \omega_{ap})^{\frac{1}{2}} \doteq 4(\omega\omega_{ap})^{\frac{1}{2}} \tag{9.47}$$

For a one-dimensional sinusoidal vibration, $q_\nu = \frac{1}{2}$, $M_\nu = M/2$, $\omega_\nu = \nu^2 \omega_{ap}$, and the characteristic impedance becomes:

$$\left(\frac{1+j}{\pi}\right)\epsilon_\nu M_\nu = \left(\frac{1+j}{2\pi}\right) 4\sqrt{\omega_\nu \omega_{ap}}\, M \doteq 2\left(\frac{1+j}{\pi}\right)\sqrt{\omega\omega_{ap}}\, M$$

$$= 2(1+j)\,\alpha\sqrt{\omega}\frac{M}{l_1} = 2(1+j)c_B\frac{M}{l_1} \tag{9.48}$$

just as for a beam of mass M/l_1 per unit length that is driven at its center.

Centrally Symmetrical Vibrations of a Circular Plate

The centrally symmetrical natural functions for a circular plate are of the form:

$$\xi_\nu = AJ_0\left(\frac{\gamma_\nu r}{a}\right) + BI_0\left(\frac{\gamma_\nu r}{a}\right) \tag{9.49}$$

where J_0 and I_0 are Bessel's functions[3] and a is the radius of the plate. The second term represents the distortion of the vibration that is due to the complex boundary conditions at the circumference of the plate. This term decreases exponentially with the distance from the boundary at high frequencies and is very similar to the exponential term in the solution for a beam. It is relatively insignificant and can be neglected at the high frequencies. The solution then reduces to

$$\xi = \xi_0 J_0\left(\frac{\gamma_\nu r}{a}\right) \tag{9.50}$$

where

$$\frac{\gamma_\nu}{a} = \frac{\omega_\nu}{c_B} = k_B \tag{9.51}$$

is determined by the boundary conditions of the plate. This simplified solution is identical with that for a circular membrane, the propagation velocity being the velocity of the bending waves c_B in the plate. If the

[3] See pp. 251.

plate is freely supported, γ_ν is the root of the equation $J_0(\gamma_\nu)=0$. The bending-wave velocity c_B is obtained by substituting Equation 9.50 into the differential equation of the plate or, still simpler, by substituting the solution for a plane progressive wave $\xi = Ae^{-jk_B x+j\omega t}$ into this equation. The result is:

$$c_B=\alpha\sqrt{\omega} \tag{9.52}$$

where the stiffness constant α of the plate is given by Equation 8.1. The natural frequencies of the plate are given by:

$$\omega_\nu=\frac{\gamma_\nu c_B}{a}=\gamma_\nu \alpha\frac{\sqrt{\omega_\nu}}{a} \tag{9.53}$$

or

$$\omega_\nu=\frac{\gamma_\nu^2\alpha^2}{a^2}=\frac{\omega_1\gamma_\nu^2}{\gamma_1^2} \tag{9.54}$$

and

$$\omega_1=\frac{\gamma_1^2\alpha^2}{a^2} \tag{9.55}$$

is the fundamental resonant frequency of the plate or membrane. If the reference point is assumed at the center $x=0$ of the membrane,

$$q_\nu=\frac{1}{\pi a^2}\int_0^a J_0^2\left(\frac{\gamma_\nu r}{a}\right)2\pi r dr=J_0^2(\gamma_\nu)+J_1^2(\gamma_\nu)=J_1^2(\gamma_\nu) \tag{9.56}$$

If the force is a point force acting at the center of the membrane, $\kappa_\nu=1$; if the force is a constant pressure p over the membrane,

$$\kappa_\nu=\frac{1}{\pi a^2 p}\int_0^a pJ_0\frac{\gamma_\nu r}{a}2\pi r dr=\frac{2J_1(\gamma_\nu)}{\gamma_\nu}=\frac{\langle\xi_\nu\rangle}{\xi_{0\nu}} \tag{9.57}$$

where $\langle\xi_\nu\rangle/\xi_{0\nu}$ is the mean value of the amplitude distribution over the membrane referred to the amplitude at the center.

In problems of sound radiation, the mean value of the amplitude is of interest. If the force is a point force at the center of the membrane, the parameters referred to the mean amplitude are:

$$\kappa_\nu(m)=\frac{1}{\dfrac{\langle\xi_\nu\rangle}{\xi_{0\nu}}} \tag{9.58}$$

$$q_\nu(m)=\frac{q_\nu}{\dfrac{\langle\xi_\nu\rangle}{\xi_{0\nu}}}=\frac{\gamma_\nu^2}{4} \tag{9.59}$$

Table 9.1 gives the values of γ_ν, q_ν, $\langle\xi_\nu\rangle$, and R_ν, q_ν/q_1, $(\gamma_\nu/\gamma_1)^2$, $\langle\xi_\nu\rangle/\xi_{0\nu}$, and the ratio of the mode resistances R_ν/R_1 for constant η for the first five modes, referred to the amplitude at the center, referred to the mean values

Table 9.1 *The significant parameters for a circular membrane for the first five modes.*

Membrane	ν	1	2	3	4	5
General data	γ_ν	2.405	5.520	8.654	11.792	14.931
	$\langle\xi_\nu\rangle/\xi_{0\nu}$	0.432	−0.123	0.0627	−0.0394	0.0277
	$\langle\xi_\nu\rangle/\langle\xi_1\rangle$	1.0	−0.285	0.145	−0.091	0.064
	$(\gamma_\nu/\gamma_1)^2$	1.0	5.268	12.948	24.040	38.543
Point force at center, constants referred to center	q_ν	0.269	0.116	0.0737	0.0541	0.0426
	q_ν/q_1	1.0	0.431	0.274	0.201	0.158
	R_ν/R_1	1.0	11.961	45.936	116.162	234.719
Point force at center, constants referred to mean amplitude	κ_ν	2.3165	−8.1105	15.9374	−25.3591	36.1350
	q_ν	1.4434	7.6304	18.7199	34.7901	55.6262
	q_ν/q_1	1.0	5.2864	12.9693	24.1029	38.5383
	M_ν/M	0.6231	−0.9408	1.1746	−1.3719	1.5394
	M_ν/M_1	1.0	−1.5099	1.8851	−2.2017	2.4706
	R_ν/R_1	1.0	−41.9024	316.035	−1272.41	3670.23
Constant pressure, constants referred to amplitude at center	q_ν	0.269	0.116	0.0737	0.0541	0.0426
	q_ν/q_1	1.0	0.431	0.274	0.201	0.158
	κ_ν	0.4317	−0.1233	0.06275	0.03943	0.02767
	M_ν/M	0.6231	0.9408	1.1746	−1.3719	1.5394
	M_ν/M_1	1.0	−1.5099	1.8851	−2.2017	2.4706
	R_ν/R_1	1.0	−41.9024	316.035	−1272.41	3670.23
Constant pressure distribution, referred to mean amplitude	$\kappa_\nu(m)$	1.0	1.0	1.0	1.0	1.0
	$q_\nu(m)$	0.6231	−0.9408	1.1746	−1.3719	1.5394
	$q_\nu(m)/q_1(m)$	1.0	−1.5099	1.8851	−2.2017	2.4706
	$R_v(m)/R_1(m)$	1.0	−41.9024	316.035	−1272.41	3670.23

of the amplitude of the membrane for a point force at the center, and for a uniform pressure distribution.

At high frequencies, $J_0(\gamma_\nu)$ and $J_1(\gamma_\nu)$ in Equation 9.56 may be replaced by their asymptotic values, and

$$q_\nu = J_0^2(\gamma_\nu) + J_1^2(\gamma_\nu) = \frac{2}{\pi k_B a}\left[\cos^2\left(k_B a - \frac{\pi}{4}\right) + \sin^2\left(k_B a - \frac{\pi}{4}\right)\right]$$
$$= \frac{2}{\pi k_B a} = \frac{2\alpha}{a\pi\sqrt{\omega}} \tag{9.60}$$

The frequency difference between successive radial resonances is asymptotically given by (see Eq. 9.52):

$$k_B a = \frac{\omega_\nu}{c_B} a = \sqrt{\omega_\nu}\frac{a}{\alpha} = \nu\pi \quad \text{and} \quad \epsilon_\nu = \frac{\partial\omega_\nu}{\partial\nu} = \frac{2\sqrt{\omega}\,\alpha\pi}{a} \tag{9.61}$$

The mode mass follows from Equation 9.60, and the characteristic impedance of the circular plate becomes:

$$Z_c = \frac{2}{\pi}\epsilon_\nu M_\nu = \frac{2\sqrt{\omega}\,\alpha\pi}{\pi a}\cdot\frac{4\alpha M}{\pi^2 a\sqrt{\omega}} = \frac{8\alpha^2 M}{a^2\pi} = \frac{8\alpha^2 M}{\sigma} = 8\alpha^2 m \tag{9.62}$$

which, as would have been expected, is the same as that of a rectangular plate.

The plate equation may also be directly integrated. For a transversely vibrating plate, the differential equation is:

$$m\alpha^4(\nabla^4 - k_B{}^4)\tilde{v}(r) = j\omega\tilde{p}_A(r) \tag{9.63}$$

The magnitude $\tilde{v}$ represents the velocity of the plate, and $\tilde{p}_A(r)$ is the driving pressure. For ease of computation, the driving force must be considered to be generated by a continuous pressure distribution $\tilde{p}_A(r)$ that is very large within a small circle of radius b and negligibly small beyond this radius. The velocity distribution $v(r)$ and the driving pressure $p_A(r)$ can be expressed by their spectra (Hankel's transforms):

$$V(r) = \int_0^\infty S_v(\kappa_r)J_0(\kappa_r r)\kappa_r d\kappa_r \tag{9.64}$$

$$P_A(r) = \int_0^\infty S_p(\kappa_r)J_0(\kappa_r r)\kappa_r d\kappa_r \tag{9.65}$$

and

$$S_p(\kappa_r) = \lim_{b=0}\int_0^b P_A(r)\cdot J_0(\kappa_r r) r dr$$

$$= \int_0^b P_A r dr = \frac{F}{2\pi} \tag{9.66}$$

The Bessel's function $J_0(\kappa_r r)$ is a solution of the wave equation in cylindrical co-ordinates:

$$\nabla^2 J_0(\kappa_r r) + \kappa_r{}^2 J_0(\kappa_r r) = 0 \tag{9.67}$$

Application of the operator ∇^2 is equivalent to multiplication by $-\kappa_r{}^2$, and application or ∇^4 is equivalent to multiplication by $\kappa_r{}^4$. Equation 9.63 is, therefore, equivalent to the relation:

$$\alpha^4(\kappa_r{}^4 - k_B{}^4)S_v(\kappa_r) = \frac{j\omega F}{2\pi m} \tag{9.68}$$

which is obtained by introducing Equation 9.64 to 9.66 into Equation 9.63

and dropping the integral signs. Fourier integration then yields:

$$\frac{V(0)}{F}=\frac{1}{F}\int_0^\infty S_v(\kappa_r)\,J_0(0)\,\kappa_r d\kappa_r$$

$$=\int_0^\infty \frac{j\omega}{m\alpha^4 4\pi(\kappa_r{}^4-k_B{}^4)}2\kappa_r d\kappa_r=\frac{\omega}{8k_B{}^2\alpha^4 m}=\frac{1}{8\alpha^2 m} \quad (9.69)$$

or

$$Z_c=\frac{F}{V(0)}=8\alpha^2 m \quad (9.70)$$

as above (Eq. 9.62).

Characteristic Driving-Point Admittance of Cylindrical Shell Excited by a Transverse Point Force

Direct integration of the three differential equations that describe the vibration of a cylinder is practically impossible. Since the kinetic energy of the longitudinal component of the vibration is almost negligible, the mode masses may be assumed equal to $M/4$ with sufficient accuracy. Heckl[4] has computed the density of the resonances on the basis of a simplified equation for the natural frequencies. A more accurate computation is possible on the basis of the following frequency equation, which is also given in Heckl's paper:

$$\Omega'^2=\frac{\sigma^4}{(n^2+\sigma^2)^2}+\gamma^2(n+\sigma^2)^2 \quad (9.71)$$

This equation can be simplified by introducing the polar co-ordinates:

$$r^2=n^2+\sigma^2 \quad \text{and} \quad \frac{\sigma^2}{r^2}=\cos^2\phi \quad (9.72)$$

where $\sigma/R=m\pi R/l$ is the axial wave number, n the number of modes along the circumference, where $\gamma^2=\beta^2/12$, $\beta=h/R$, $\Omega'=\omega/\omega_c$, and where $\omega_c=2\pi R/c_{pl}$ is the radial, resonant frequency. It then becomes:

$$\Omega'^2=\cos^4\theta+\gamma^2 r^4 \quad (9.73)$$

or

$$r^4=\frac{\Omega'^2-\cos^4\phi}{\gamma^2} \quad (9.74)$$

If the frequency Ω' is changed by $\Delta\Omega'$, r will change by Δr. If we asume

[4] See M. Heckl, "Schallabstrahlung von punktfoermig angeregten Hohlzylindern," *Acustica*, **9** (1959), 86.

that ϕ is maintained constant, $\Delta\Omega'$ and Δr are connected by the relation

$$(\Delta r)_{\phi=\text{const}}=\frac{\Omega'\Delta\Omega'}{2\gamma^2 r^3} \tag{9.75}$$

The area between the curves $\Omega'=$const and $(\Omega'+\Delta\Omega')=$const is given by

$$A=\int r\Delta\phi\Delta r=\frac{\Delta\Omega'}{2\gamma}\int_{\phi_1}^{\pi/2}\frac{d\phi}{\sqrt{1-\frac{1}{\Omega'^2}\cos^4\phi}} \tag{9.76}$$

The area in the r, ϕ plane that corresponds to one natural frequency is $\Delta n=1$, $\Delta\sigma=\pi R/l$, $\Delta n\Delta\sigma=\pi R/l$, and the number of natural frequencies per unit frequency interval is given by:

$$\frac{\Delta n}{\Delta\Omega'}=\frac{A}{\frac{\pi R}{l}\Delta\Omega'}=\frac{l}{2\gamma\pi R}\int_{\phi_1}^{\pi/2}\frac{d\phi}{\sqrt{1-\frac{1}{\Omega'^2}\cos^4\phi}} \tag{9.77}$$

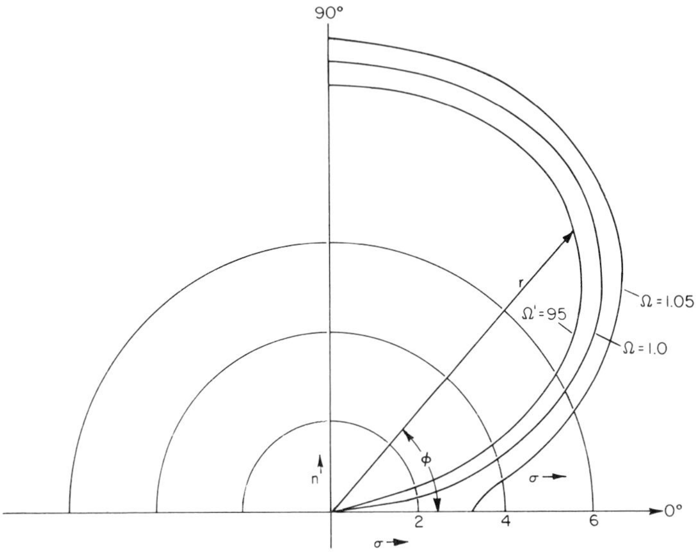

Fig. 9.3 Calculation of density of resonances of cylindrical shell.

Figure 9.3 shows a graphic representation of the curves $\Omega'=$const, $(\Omega'+\Delta\Omega')=$const, with n and σ as rectangular, r and ϕ as polar co-ordinates. The upper limit of integration in Equation 9.77 is always $\phi=\pi/2$, unless the cylinder is very thick or very short. But such cases will be excluded here. For $n=0$, Equation 9.71 leads to the expression

$$\Omega'^2=1+\gamma^2\sigma^4 \tag{9.78}$$

and the lowest possible frequency is $\Omega'=1$, corresponding to $\sigma=0$; this is true when the cylinder is infinitely long. Hence, the value $n=0$ occurs only if $\Omega'>1$, i.e., if the frequency is above the circumferential resonant frequency of the cylinder. In this case, the lower limit of φ in the preceding integral is zero, and

$$\frac{\Delta n}{\Delta\Omega'}=\frac{\Delta n}{\Delta\omega}\cdot\omega_0=\frac{l\sqrt{3}}{\pi h}I(\Omega') \quad \text{and} \quad I(\Omega')=\int_0^{\pi/2}\frac{d\phi}{\sqrt{1-\frac{1}{\Omega'^2}\cos^4\phi}} \tag{9.79}$$

where $I(\Omega')$ is the value of the above integral. When $\Omega'<1$, only modes $n=1$, 2, 3 . . . are possible, and the lower limit of integration has to be replaced by the value of ϕ that corresponds to $n=1$. This value is very nearly the same as the φ value given by

$$\cos\phi_1=\sqrt{\Omega'} \quad \text{or} \quad \phi_1=\cos^{-1}\sqrt{\Omega'}=\sin^{-1}\left(\frac{\pi}{2}-\sqrt{\Omega'}\right) \tag{9.80}$$

for which the integrand becomes imaginary. This is easily proved by solving the frequency equation for $n=1$. Using ϕ_1 as given by Equation 9.80 is equivalent to neglecting the discontinuity in the n values in the range where n is small. The error is negligible so long as $\Omega'^2\ll 1$, but it becomes larger near $\Omega'^2=1$, particularly if the shell is thick, so that the number of resonances is relatively small.

At low frequencies, Ω' is small, and φ_1 is nearly $\pi/2$. We can then write:

$$\phi=\frac{\pi}{2}-\epsilon \tag{9.81}$$

and

$$\int_{\phi_1}^{\pi/2}\frac{d\varphi}{\sqrt{1-\frac{1}{\Omega'^2}\cos^4\phi}}=\int_0^{\sin^{-1}\sqrt{\Omega'}}\frac{d\epsilon}{\sqrt{1-\frac{1}{\Omega'^2}\sin^4\epsilon}}=\int_0^{\sqrt{\Omega'}}\frac{d\epsilon}{\sqrt{1-\frac{\epsilon^4}{\Omega'^2}}}$$

$$=\sqrt{\Omega'}\int_0^1\frac{dz}{\sqrt{1-z^4}}=\sqrt{\Omega'}\frac{\pi}{2\sqrt{2}} \tag{9.82}$$

At low frequencies ($\Omega^2\ll 1$), the density of the resonances is thus given by:

$$\frac{\Delta n}{\Delta\Omega'}=\frac{l\sqrt{3}}{\pi h}\sqrt{\Omega'}\frac{\pi}{2\sqrt{2}} \tag{9.83}$$

or

$$\frac{1}{\epsilon_\nu}=\frac{\Delta n}{\Delta\omega}=\sqrt{3}\frac{\frac{l}{h}\sqrt{\omega}}{2\sqrt{2}\,\omega_0^{3/2}}=\frac{0.612\frac{l}{h}\sqrt{\omega}}{\omega_0^{3/2}} \tag{9.84}$$

Heckl, using a simple approximation to the frequency equation; and a less direct procedure, obtained practically the same result. His numerical factor is $9\sqrt{3}/8$ or $=1.94$.

For $\Omega'=1$, the integral has a pole and becomes infinite, as is easily seen by replacing the cosine by the first two terms of its Taylor series. This pole is generated by the series $n=0$ of the natural modes. As a consequence of the approximations introduced during the computation, these resonant frequencies of the $n=0$ modes are represented by:

$$\Omega'^2=1+\gamma^2\sigma^4 \tag{9.85}$$

and

$$\left(\frac{\partial\Omega'}{\partial\kappa}\right)_{\Omega'=1}=4\gamma^2\sigma^3\frac{\partial\sigma}{\partial\kappa}=4\gamma^2\sigma^2\cdot R \tag{9.86}$$

is zero for $m=0$ ($\sigma\to 0$), where $\kappa=m\pi/l$. Therefore, the value $m=0$ must be excluded in dealing with the $n=0$ modes. It expedient to suppress the whole series $n=0$ in the frequency equation by considering only modes for which $n\geq 1$. If greater accuracy is required, the few $n=0$ resonances can easily be considered separately. The lower limit of integration then is given by $\Omega'=1$, $n=1$:

$$\Omega'^2=1=\frac{(r^2-n^2)^2}{r^4}+\gamma^2r^4 \tag{9.87}$$

or

$$1-2r^2+\gamma^2r^8=0 \tag{9.88}$$

The solution $r\approx\frac{1}{2}$ corresponds to imaginary σ and must be excluded; r must at least be one. We may thus write:

$$\gamma^2r^8=2r^2-1\approx 2r^2 \qquad \text{or} \qquad r=\frac{1.08}{\sqrt[3]{\gamma}} \tag{9.89}$$

This is a sufficiently good approximation so long as β is small. Hence,

$$\sin\theta=\frac{1}{r}=\frac{\sqrt[3]{\gamma}}{1.08}\approx\sqrt[3]{\gamma} \tag{9.90}$$

represents the lower limit of integration in the case $\Omega'=1$, if the resonances $n=0$ are suppressed, and

$$I(1)=\int_{\sqrt[3]{\gamma}}^{\pi/2}\frac{d\phi}{\sqrt{1-\frac{1}{\Omega'^2}\cos^4\phi}} \tag{9.91}$$

This integral must be evaluated graphically or by approximations. Also, in the range near $\Omega'=1$, the integral $f(\Omega')$ has to be evaluated graphically. It is expedient to divide the integration range into two parts, from an arbitrarily selected point $\theta=\frac{1}{2}$, to $\pi/2$ and from $\alpha=\sqrt[3]{\gamma}$ to $\frac{1}{2}$. Thus, for $\Omega'=1$:

$$\int_{\alpha}^{\pi/2} \frac{d\phi}{\sqrt{1-\cos^4\phi}} \doteq \int_{\alpha}^{1/2} \frac{d\phi}{\sqrt{1-\left(1-\frac{\phi^2}{2!}+\frac{\phi^4}{4!}\right)^4}} + \int_{1/2}^{\pi/2} d\phi$$

$$= \int_{\alpha}^{1/2} \frac{d\phi}{\sqrt{2\phi}} + \left(\frac{\pi}{2}-\frac{1}{2}\right)$$

$$= \frac{1}{\sqrt{2}}\left[ln\frac{1}{2\alpha} + ln\,4.54\right] = \frac{1}{3\sqrt{2}} ln\left(\frac{40}{\beta}\right) = \frac{1}{4.25} ln\frac{K'}{\beta} \quad (9.92)$$

By computing the value of the integral numerically, we may find a better value of K' to match the exact value approximately over a fairly wide range. If the match is made at $\beta=0.01$, $K'=80$.

No difficulties arise when $\Omega'^2 \gg 1$. The integral then becomes very nearly equal to $\pi/2$, and the density of the resonances becomes:

$$\frac{\Delta n}{\Delta\omega} = \frac{l\sqrt{3}}{\pi h\omega_0}\frac{\pi}{2} = \frac{l\sqrt{3}}{2h\omega_0} \quad (9.93)$$

Comparison with the corresponding result for a plate shows that the number of resonances of the cylinder in the plate range is twice as great as that of a plate of the same surface area and the same thickness. This obviously is a consequence of the degeneracy of the circumferential amplitude distribution, which only has to satisfy the condition of strict periodicity of a period equal to the circumference of the cylinder. Comparison of Equation 9.93 with Equation 9.92 shows that the maximum (for $\Omega'=1$) is by a factor $(\sqrt{2}/3\pi)\ ln\ (80/\beta)=0.15\ ln\ (80/\beta)$ greater than the density $\Delta n/\Delta\omega$ of the resonances in the plate range. Figure 9.4 shows the density function $I(\Omega')$ as a function of the frequency and for various values of β. We notice an increase in the density function toward $\Omega'=1$, which is the greater; the smaller is $\beta=\gamma\cdot\sqrt{12}$.

The driving-point admittance then is given by:

$$Re(\bar{Y}_c) = \frac{\pi}{2\epsilon_\nu M_\nu} = \frac{l\sqrt{12}}{M\beta\, c_{pl}} I(\Omega') \frac{\sqrt{3}}{2mc_{pl}}\left(\frac{I}{\frac{\pi}{2}}\right) = \frac{0.55\, I(\Omega')}{mc_{pl}h} \quad (9.94)$$

Figure 9.5 shows a measurement of the frequency curve of a shell. The three ranges, the $\sqrt{\omega}$ range, the maximum, and the plate range are cleaerly discernible, and the mean line through the measurements turns out to be identical with the theoretical curve. Thus, a cylinder behaves very differently from a plate. At low frequencies, the characteristic driving-point admittance increases proportionally to the square root of the frequency and attains approximately the value of a plate of the same area at the frequency ω_c. It then increases by a factor crudely equal to $0.15\ ln(80R/h)$ over a narrow frequency band $\Delta\omega$, and then stays constant at twice the value for a plate of the same area. (Because of the degeneracy of the natural functions in the circumferential direction, odd and even circumferential distributions are excited, and the number of resonances is twice that of a plate of the same area.)

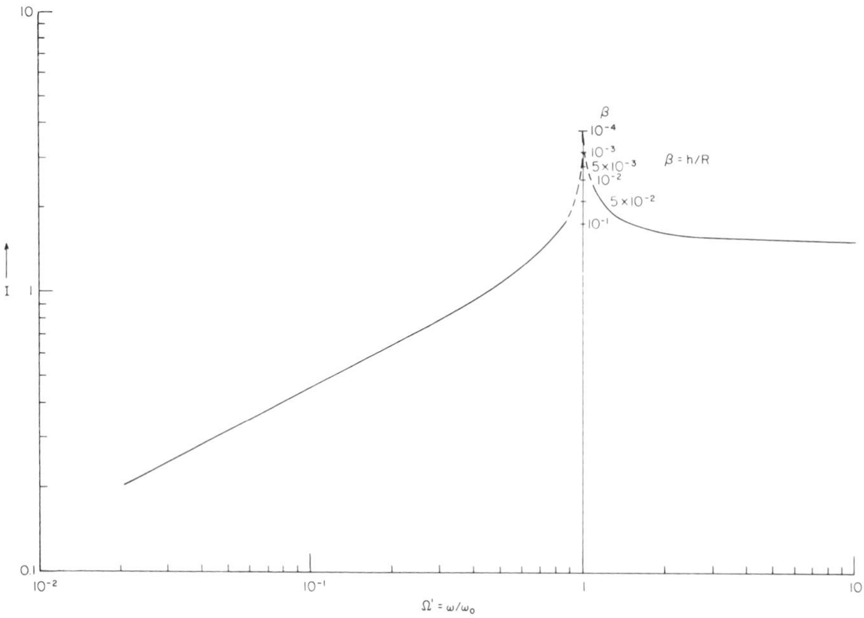

Fig. 9.4 Density of resonances of cylindrical shell.

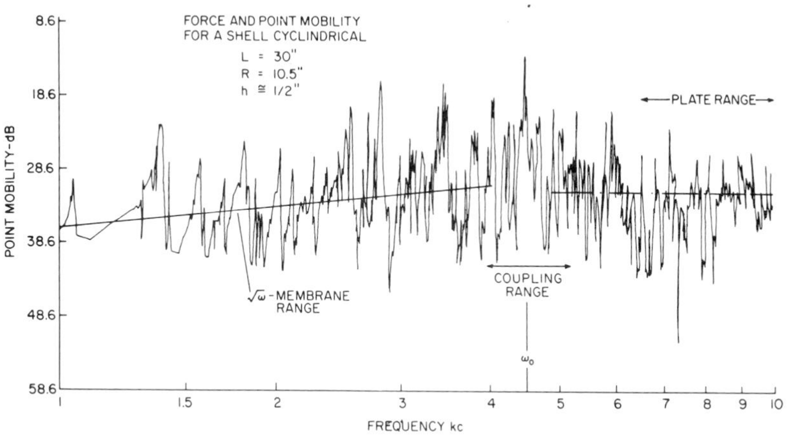

Fig. 9.5 Frequency curve of the driving point velocity of a cylindrical shell.

Recommended Reading

HECKL, M., "Schallabstrahlung von Platten bei punktfoermiger Anregung," *Acustica* **9**(1959), 371, 801/N

HECKL, M., "Schallabstrahlung von punktfoermig angeregten Hohlzylindern," *Acustica*, **9** (1959), 86.

SKUDRZYK, E. J., *Grundlagen der Akustik*, Springer Verlag, Vienna, 1954, Chap. XV.

X / SUMMARY OF THEORY OF COMPLEX VIBRATORY SYSTEMS

Vibration studies today are predominantly concerned with the determination of the frequency curve of the vibration amplitude, with the sound radiation of vibrators of high degrees of complexity, and with the reduction of the vibration and noise level in prescribed frequency ranges by the introduction of small changes in the mechanical structure of the vibrator and by changes in the size and shape of its components.

Homogeneous Systems

The classical theory of vibrations is based on the integration of differential equations and on the matching of the solutions for the various parts of the vibrator with the aid of conditions of continuity. Any slight change in the shape of the vibrator necessitates a complete repetition of the computation. But, regardless of the laborious computation, the supposedly high accuracy of the classical theory is an illusion. The materials are never completely homogeneous or isotropic, and the natural frequencies and nodal line patterns usually differ considerably from those predicted, particularly at the higher frequencies.

In contrast to the classical theory, some of the recent theories are not so much concerned with numerical evaluations, but are concerned with the general properties of the functions that describe the vibrations. Fundamental to the method used in this book is the proof that any lumped or homogeneous system, or a system consisting of homogeneous parts and mass loadings, can be rigorously represented by a canonical circuit, that is, by a paralled connection of an infinite number of series-resonant circuits, one for each mode of the system, as shown in Figure 1.11. Let the conclusions derived in connection with this figure be summarized here.

For the driving-point admittance, all the circuit elements are positive, and the shunt branches represent simple tuned circuits. Since the admittance or impedance must have a positive slope. Because of the condition of positive slope (Foster's theorem), resonances and antiresonances alternate. At very low and very high frequencies, the system behaves like either a capacitance or an inductance, depending on whether none, one, or two shunt circuits are degenerate.

It is expedient to draw a line through the geometric mean between the resonance peaks and the antiresonance minima. This is best done by recording the frequency curve to a logarithmic scale and drawing a line through the points of inflection (see Fig. 5.5). The maxima, then, are usually just as high above this line as the minima are below it.[1] If the resonances follow one another with constant frequency differences, then the maxima are a factor Q above, and the minima, a factor Q below this line. It is expedient to call the velocity represented by this line the characteristic velocity and to define the ratio of the characteristic driving-point velocity to the driving force as the characteristic driving-point admittance of the system. This characteristic driving-point conductance turns out to be identical to the driving-point conductance when the system is heavily absorbent or terminated by its wave impedance or to be identical to that of a similar system that is infinitely large or so heavily damped that no energy is reflected back to the driving point. The concept of a characteristic condutance is very similar to that of the characteristic admittance in the theory of lines and filters, except that the mechanical vibrator usually is two- or three-dimensional. The characteristic admittance can be computed directly by solving the differential equation of the system for a point force or on the basis of the general mode solution, if large damping is assumed. Or, it can be computed by the method derived in Chapter VIII; the characteristic impedance is equal to the product of three factors: the average frequency difference between successive modes, the mode mass (usually one half or one fourth of the total mass of the system), and a constant that usually is equal to $2/\pi$. Again, the characteristic conductance turns out to be represented by the line that passes approximately through the points of inflection of the measured frequency curves (see Fig. 8.1). The peaks are a factor Q above this line, but the antiresonance minima are a factor below this line that depends predominantly on the relative spacing between the resonant frequencies and, to a lesser extent, on the Q of the system. At the higher frequencies, the characteristic conductance seems to be very nearly equal to the geometric mean between the peaks and the antiresonance minima, as illustrated in the curves of Figure 10.1 Similar results are obtained for

[1] If the vibrator is a rod that is excited at one end, there are always frequencies for which the reflected wave is in phase or is in antiphase with the outgoing wave. In the first case, the reflected wave increases the amplitude of the outgoing wave; in the second, it decreases it. Since the increase is the same as the decrease, reflection does not, on the average, affect the geometric mean value of the amplitude. However, we do not have a single reflection alone, but an infinite series of reflections. The reflected waves then add up to a geometric series and increase the amplitude at the driving point by a factor that is exactly equal to Q (for the fundamental amplitude) or decrease it by a factor of $1/Q$. Thus, the geometric mean between the peaks and the minima is equal to the amplitude of the outgoing wave. If the system is of more dimensions, the reflected waves, regardless of where they come from, are very nearly in phase with the outgoing wave at the resonant frequencies of the system, and the amplitude is increased by a factor that is very nearly equal to Q. But the minima are produced by the canceling of large magnitudes. Apparently, not all the waves return exactly in phase or antiphase, but the accuracy that is required for canceling is considerably greater; so the canceling is somewhat deficient, causing the minima to vary considerably, particularly at the lower frequencies.

more complex systems, such as plates with mass loadings and joints and shells with joints. Thus, the knowledge of the characteristic admittance is equivalent to the knowledge of the approximate frequency curve of the system.

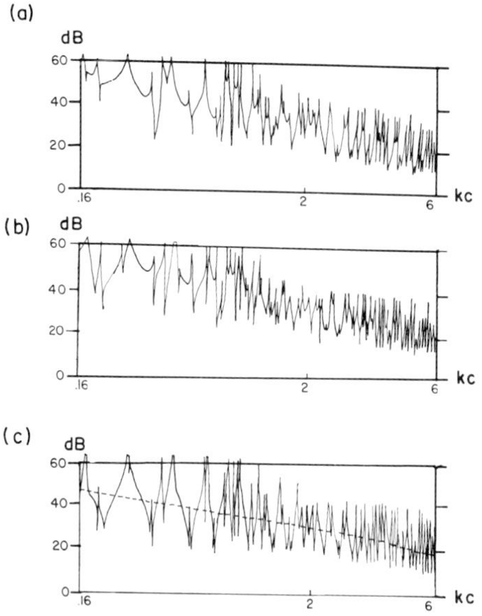

Fig. 10.1 Displacement amplitude of a rectangular plate (displacement amplitude= velocity amplitude/ω; dimensions, 2 ft. wide, 6 ft. long, and $\frac{3}{8}$ in. thick); *a*, edge displacement; *b*, corner displacement; *c*, driving-point displacement.

The driving-point admittance is a function of limited variation, regardless of the complexity of the mechanical system. The frequency curve of the driving-point admittance must satisfy Foster's theorem, which imposes strong limitations on its variations. If a driving-point admittance were used as a filter, all the band-pass ranges would be of the nature of simple resonance peaks; therefore, it would not be possible to generate broad transmission ranges and sharp cutoff ranges. The reason for the restricted variation of a driving-point admittance is that the elements of the equivalent canonical circuit must all be positive.

For the transfer admittance, the equivalent circuit elements must no longer all be positive. Negative elements in the canonical circuit indicate that the circuit is excited, as if the exciting force had a phase opposite to that of the driving force. If, for instance, the velocity is in phase with the driving force in one nodal area, it must be in antiphase with the driving force in the adjacent nodal areas; thus, the velocity changes sign every time the nodal line is crossed. The energy principle has no effect on this result, since the work performed by the driving force is not related to the velocity at some point other than the driving point. Some of the shunt circuits in the canonical circuit for the transfer admittance will be made up of negative elements, and canceling effects are possible that cannot occur in the driving-point admittance.

In the driving-point admittance, all the modes are excited with the same phase as the force. The contributions of successive modes, therefore, add at low and high frequencies; but in the frequency range between the two resonances one circuit is driven above its resonance and acts like an inductance, and the other is driven below it and acts like a capacitance; and their contributions have opposite signs and compensate one another at a frequency between the two resonant frequencies. Thus, an antiresonance is generated between the two resonances (Fig. 1.16*a*). In the transfer impedance, the elements of two circuits may have opposite signs; their contributions then add in the frequency range between their resonant frequencies and generate a shallow trough (Fig. 1.16*b*), similar to the trough in the transmission curve of a band-pass filter. Outside the frequency range between the two resonant frequencies, the two contributions counteract one another and generate a steeply decreasing peak. Figure 1.17 shows typical frequency curves for a driving-point and a transfer impedance to a linear and a logarithmic scale.

It is expedient to generalize the concepts of characteristic driving-point admittance and characteristic driving-point velocity for points other than the driving point. The characteristic admittance (or transfer admittance) then is the admittance (transfer admittance) of a similar system, which is either infinitely large or highly absorbent, so that no energy is reflected back to the driving point; and the characteristic velocity is the velocity amplitude at that point. The characteristic transfer admittance and the characteristic velocity can be computed by formulas similar to those for the corresponding driving-point magnitudes, either by integrating the differential equation of the system for a point force or by using the transformation of the series solution into an integral. The characteristic admittance and the characteristic velocity then play the same role for any arbitrary point of the system as the corresponding magnitudes play for the driving point.

Figure 4.12 illustrates the generation of shallow troughs in the transfer impedance of a system consisting of four masses coupled by springs. At the driving point, all minima are antiresonances, but every time the receiver is moved away from the driving point by one mass, another antiresonance is replaced by a shallow trough. Successive modes then contribute with the opposite sign. The thick curve in Figure 5.5*a* shows the transfer impedance of a rod driven at one end, with the receiver placed at the other end. All the antiresonances that are observed in the frequency curve for the driven end are replaced by shallow troughs. The characteristic velocity for the end of the rod is now identical to the line through the bottom of the troughs. The resonant peaks are all separated and are above the level of the characteristic velocity by a factor Q. Damping affects the height and the width of the resonance peaks and reduces the characteristic velocity in the same manner as it reduces the amplitude of a progressive wave that travels from the driver to the receiver. The decrease of the characteristic velocity at the higher frequencies in Figure 5.5*a* is due to the damping. Figure 6.7 shows similar results for a transversely vibrating beam. Because of the $1/\sqrt{\omega}$ decrease of the transfer admittance of the beam, the line through the trough of the frequency curve decreases proportionately to $\sqrt{\omega}$.

The curve for the velocity distribution over a plate at an antiresonant frequency (Fig. 8.4, *lower curve*) gives additional information about the generation of a shallow trough; it shows the velocity distribution over a circular plate that is excited at its center at an antiresonant frequency. The curve through the peaks of the antiresonant velocity distribution is identical to the characteristic velocity. Thus, a shallow trough of a height equal to the characteristic velocity is generated if, at the antiresonant frequency, the receiver is at a velocity maximum. The probability that this happens is very small, unless the receiver is at a point where the velocity always is a maximum, as for a point at the end of a freely vibrating rod or at the edge of a circular plate that is excited at its center. The edge of a rectangular plate is a line of maximum velocity only for the one-dimensional modes whose nodal lines are parallel to it. When the receiver is in the middle of an edge, practically all the shallow troughs are generated by the one-dimensional modes of the plate with nodal lines parallel to this edge. A few of the troughs may be generated by modes that, at the antiresonant frequency, happen to generate a velocity maximum at the position of the receiver, but this happens very rarely. For the one-dimensional bending modes of the rectangular plate, the characteristic impedance increases proportionately to the square root of the frequency, as for a transversely vibrating beam. The height of the troughs in the curves (Fig. 8.1), therefore, decreases as $1/\sqrt{\omega}$ because of the $\sqrt{\omega}$ increase of the characteristic impedance for one-dimensional modes. At higher frequencies, the one-dimensional modes are completely masked by the two-dimensional modes whose characteristic impedance is constant, as has already been shown in Figure 8.1*c*. The only troughs that still remain are those for which the receiver position coincides with velocity loops at antiresonant frequencies. At a corner of the plate, the two sets of one-dimensional modes whose nodal lines are parallel to the two edges generate shallow troughs. Again, these two series of troughs are masked at the higher frequencies by the many two-dimensional modes, as illustrated in Figure 8.1*c*.

Also, the resonance peaks themselves are very interesting. The second and third resonances in Figure 8.1*a* are relatively close together and separated by an antiresonance. The circuits that represent the two modes in the transfer impedance with respect to the mid-point of the edge have elements of opposite signs. Therefore, the contributions of the two modes do not cancel

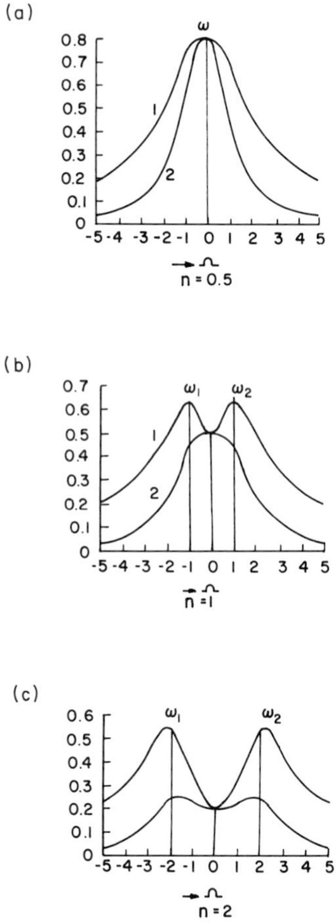

Fig. 10.2 Frequency curves of the primary and secondary velocities as a function of the normalized frequencies for various degrees of coupling (*n*- degree of coupling).

any more in the range between their two resonant frequencies, but add to a shallow trough or to a band-filterlike curve (Fig. 8.1*b*). Outside the frequency band, between the two resonant frequencies, the two modes cancel one another and reduce the transmission. This canceling effect is not very great in Figure 8.1*b* because the two peaks are relatively far apart, but it may sometimes be considerable, as it is for coupled circuits that are tuned to the same frequency. Homogeneous systems may exhibit double peaks in the driving-point admittance, if damping is large and the frequency difference between the two resonances is small; so the contributions of the two modes are essentially real in the frequency range between the two resonances, and they consequently cannot cancel one another. However, in

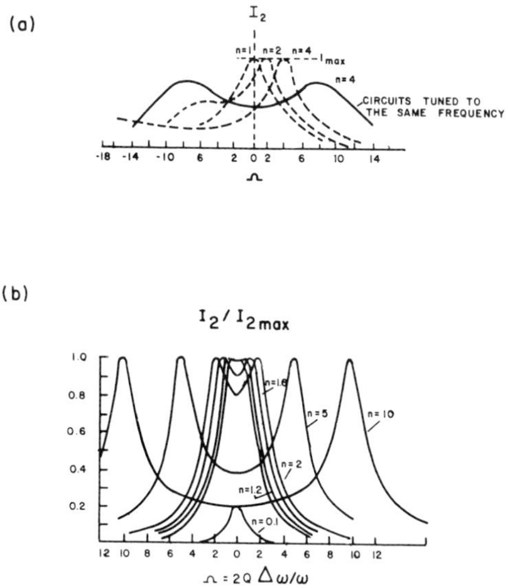

Fig. 10.3 Frequency curves of a coupled system for slightly detuned circuits and for various degrees of coupling; *a*, the secondary response of two differently damped coupled circuits ($Q_1/Q_2=5$) for optimum tuning of the two circuits for $n=1$, 2, and 4 (*solid curve*, computed for the two circuits when tuned to the same frequency for $n=4$); *b*, response for two identical circuits tuned to the same frequency.

spite of the splitting up or broadening of the resultant peak, the fundamental shape of the curve is similar to that of a simple resonance curve. But the transfer impedance of homogeneous systems may exhibit coupled circuit behavior near some of their resonances, if two resonant frequencies are close to one another and if the two sets of mode parameters have opposite signs. The frequency curve, then, is similar to the frequency curve of a band filter (see, for instance, Figs. 10.2 and 10.3). The peak of the curve may be much steeper than that of a single resonance curve. However, there is still a considerable difference between the band-filterlike peaks that occur in the transfer impedance of a homogeneous system and the transmission curve of truly coupled systems. The ratio of the amplitude of a band-filterlike peak in the transfer admittance of a homogeneous system to the characteristic velocity is usually somewhat greater than Q, but never greater than $2Q$, because the result is due to the simple addition of two contributions. But for truly coupled circuits, this ratio approaches Q^2, Q^3, or a higher power of Q, depending on the number of circuits that are coupled. Thus, the zero that occurs in the driving-point admittance is replaced by a shallow trough, and zeros are no longer separated by infinities. Basically, the same result is obtained if more than two circuits are considered, since their contributions are relatively small at frequencies different from their resonance range.

Coupled Circuits and Inhomogeneous Systems

A truly coupled system is obtained only if a strong discontinuity that reduces the characteristic velocity is introduced, that is, if the two systems are not connected tightly, but are loosely coupled. The discontinuity usually is a heavy mass, a compliant element, or the impedance of another homogeneous system. To say that coupling is loose is another way of saying that the discontinuity is effective in reducing the transmitted characteristic velocity. At the resonant frequency of the coupled system, the impedance of the discontinuity is compensated by the impedance of the tuning elements of the coupled systems, and the amplitude increases by a factor of Q because of the resonance and by another factor of Q, or of the order of magnitude of Q, because of the elimination of the impedance of the discontinuity.

Coupled circuit behavior can be impressively demonstrated by mass loading a rod that is excited to longitudinal vibrations. This system may be conceived as a one-dimensional model for a mass-loaded (longitudinal) joint. At low frequencies, as long as the mass impedance of the mass loading is small in comparison to the characteristic impedance of the rod, the solution is nearly the same as if the mass were absent. The maxima are slightly smaller because of the increased total mass of the system, but the average level is the same as that for an unloaded rod, since the mass loading has no effect on the amplitude of the outgoing wave that is generated at the driver. The same result can be deduced from the above formula for the characteristic impedance. The mass loading becomes effective when its impedance attains or exceeds the characteristic impedance of the driven part of the rod. The transfer impedance for troughs in the frequency curve for the vibration of the free end of the rod can be easily derived by computing the amplitude of the wave that would be propagated through the mass loading if the second part of the rod were infinitely long. The transmitted amplitude then decreases proportionally to the transmission factor T, where

$$T=\frac{2}{\dfrac{j\omega M}{\sigma\rho c}+2} \tag{10.1}$$

σ being the cross section of the rod, ρc its wave resistance, and M the mass body. Because of the mass loading, the characteristic velocity decreases as $1/\omega M$ from one side of the mass loading to the other. Figure 5.6 shows five frequency curves of the same rod, with and without mass loading at different points and recorded to a logarithmic scale. The uppermost curve applies to the unloaded rod. The height of the troughs is constant, as predicted for the rod. In the second curve, the rod is mass-loaded at a point, so that every second resonance is a coupled circuit resonance. Because of the mass loading, the troughs now decrease at a rate inversely proportional to the frequency. Every second peak is a double peak. The single peaks should be higher by a factor of Q; the double peaks, higher by a factor of Q^2. This conclusion is borne out by detailed computations and by measurements. In the second curve of Figure 5.6, the troughs decrease as predicted, and the double peaks in the logarithmic recording are twice as high above the characteristic velocity as in the uppermost recording, taken without mass loading. In the third curve, all the peaks are double peaks. The last curve in Figure 5.6 shows the frequency curve of a rod mass-loaded at one end. The peaks in the last curve are all single and, therefore, by a factor of Q higher than the characteristic level, which again decreases proportionally to $1/\omega$. Because of the principle of reciprocity, the amplitude of the free end is the same, whether the end with mass or the unloaded end is driven. The mean amplitude of the free end and the resonance peaks decrease proportionally to:

$$\left(\frac{Z_c + j\omega M}{Z_c}\right)^{-1} \tag{10.2}$$

which is the amplitude that would be propagated into the rod if the mass were driven and the rod were infinitely long. A computation of the characteristic impedance on the basis of the integral solution (Eq. 7.44) is inaccurate in this case, because the mode masses decrease considerably as the mode number is decreased, and the contribution of the zero-order mode dominates the result. The series solution, then, cannot be approximated accurately by an integral. In designing experiments with mass loading,s the connection obtained by squeezing the masses over the rod or cementing them to the rod is not sufficient (Fig. 5.7), as has already been pointed out in Chapter V.

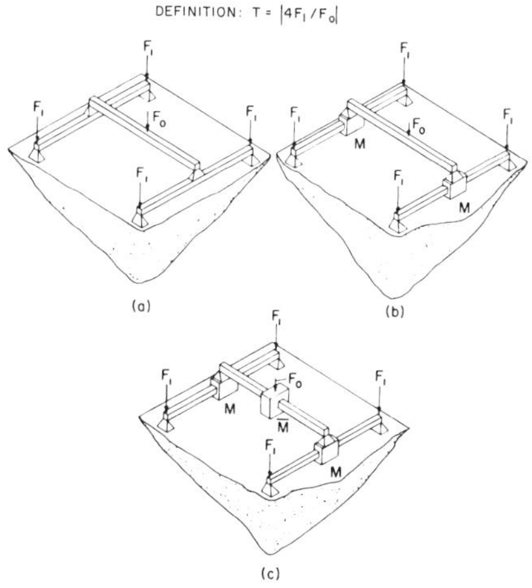

Fig. 10.4 Simply supported beams driven at the center, with and without mass loading (definition, $T = |4\,F_1/F_0|$); *a*, with no mass loading; *b*, with the lower beams loaded by a central mass; *c*, with all beams loaded by a central mass.

(a)

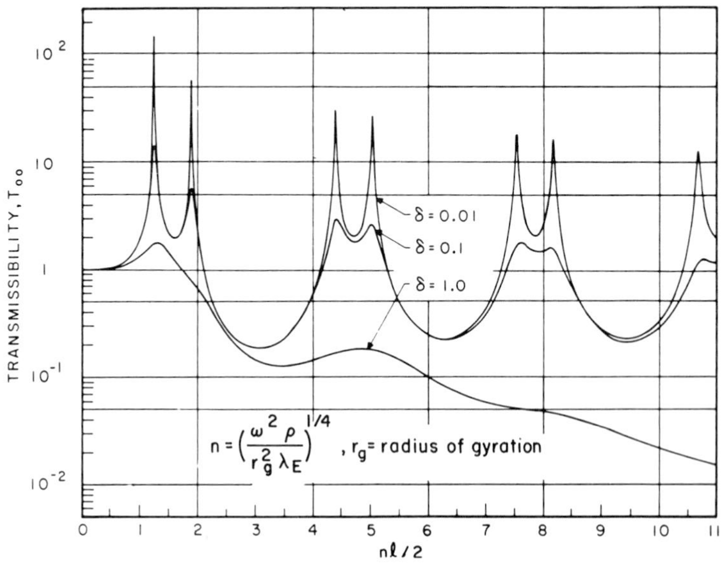
TRANSMISSIBILITY, T_{oo}
10^2
10
1
10^{-1}
10^{-2}
δ = 0.01
δ = 0.1
δ = 1.0
$n = \left(\frac{\omega^2 \rho}{r_g^2 \lambda_E}\right)^{1/4}$, r_g = radius of gyration
0 1 2 3 4 5 6 7 8 9 10 11
$n\ell/2$

(b)

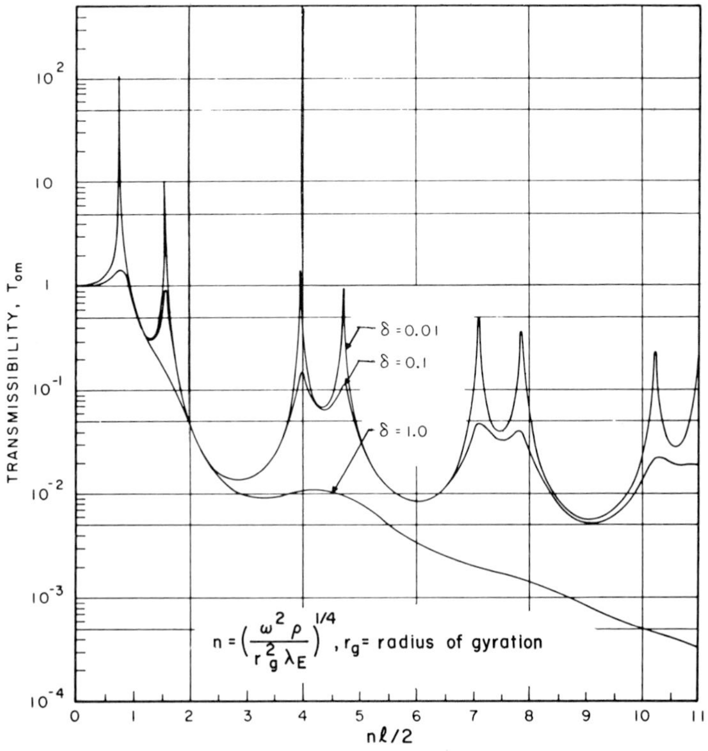
TRANSMISSIBILITY, T_{om}
10^2
10
1
10^{-1}
10^{-2}
10^{-3}
10^{-4}
δ = 0.01
δ = 0.1
δ = 1.0
$n = \left(\frac{\omega^2 \rho}{r_g^2 \lambda_E}\right)^{1/4}$, r_g = radius of gyration
0 1 2 3 4 5 6 7 8 9 10 11
$n\ell/2$

(c)

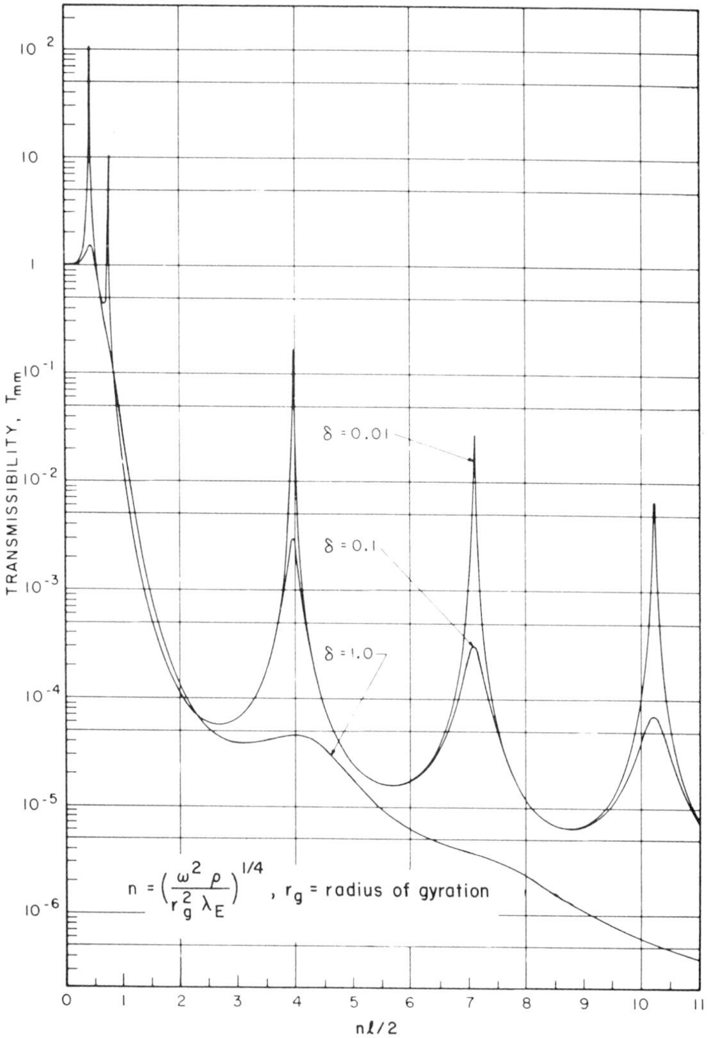

Fig. 10.5 Transmission curves of the beams shown in Fig. 10.4 (definition, $T=|4\,F_1/F_0|$; $n=(\omega^2\rho/r_g{}^2\lambda_E)^{\frac{1}{4}}$, where r_g=radius of gyration); *a*, transmission curve of the beam shown in Fig. 10.4*a*; *b*, of the beam shown in Fig. 10.4*b* (mass ratio, $\gamma=8.0$); *c*, of the beam shown in Fig. 10.4*c* (mass ratios, $\gamma=16.0$ and 64.0). From J. C. Snowdon, "Mechanical impedance and uansmissibility of simply supported beams," *J.A.S.A.*, **35** (1963), 228–33.

Figure 5.8*a* shows a model for two one-dimensional systems joined by a mass-loaded joint, but isolated from one another by a compliant layer between them. Again, the computation reduces to the computation of the amplitude transmitted by the joint, which now acts like a low-pass filter. The frequency curve (Fig. 5.8*b*) can easily be estimated.

Figure 10.4*a* shows a beam that rests on two other beams. This system is equivalent to a beam that drives two other beams that are supported at one end. The discontinuity in the system is still very weak, and the height of the peaks of the transmission curve (Fig. 10.5*a*) is proportional to Q rather than to Q^2. The systems shown in Figures 10.4*b* and 10.4*c* have additional masses attached to the two center points. It represents a coupled system, and the slope of the characteristic impedance is steeper by a factor of $\sqrt{\omega}$ and ω at the lower frequencies (Fig. 10.5*b*, c). True coupled circuit behavior is therefore possible. If the transfer velocity had been plotted in Figure 10.5*b*, instead of the ratio of the output force to the driving force, the valleys would have been deeper by approximately a factor of Q, and the height of the peaks would have been proportional to Q^2 rather than to Q.

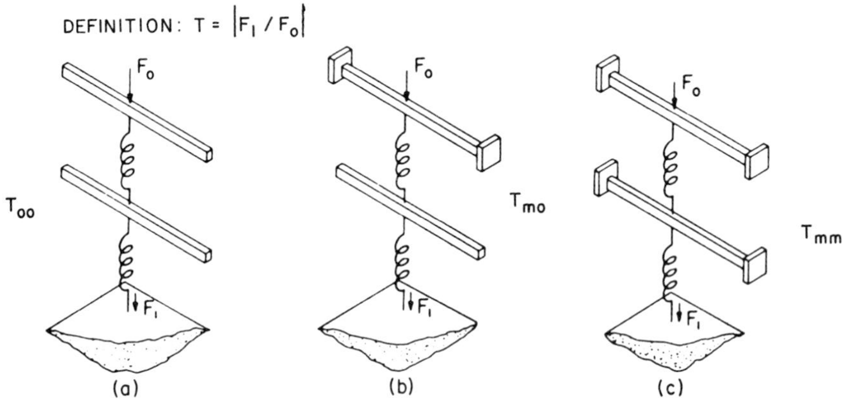

Fig. 10.6 "Free-free" beams driven and spring-mounted at their mid-points in two-stage systems, with and without mass loading (definition, $T = |F_1/F_0|$); *a*, with no mass loading; *b*, with the ends of the upper beams mass-loaded; *c*, with the ends of both beams mass-loaded. From J. C. Snowdon, "Mechanical impedance of free-free beams," *J.A.S.A.*, **37** (1965), 240–49.

Figure 10.6 shows a still more complex system, made up of beams and compliances. Coupled circuit behavior now is very apparent. The characteristic velocity (Fig. 10.7) has the theoretically predicted slope, and the peaks have exactly the height predicted by asymptotic theory.

Frequently, plates and shells are screwed together, and the joints are strengthened by stiffening rings or ribs that act like mass loadings. Longitudinal waves are transmitted through such joints in a manner similar to that in a mass-loaded longitudinal rod, and at the higher frequencies the joint considerably reduces the amplitude of the transmitted wave. However, for transverse vibrations the situation is entirely different. If a shell or

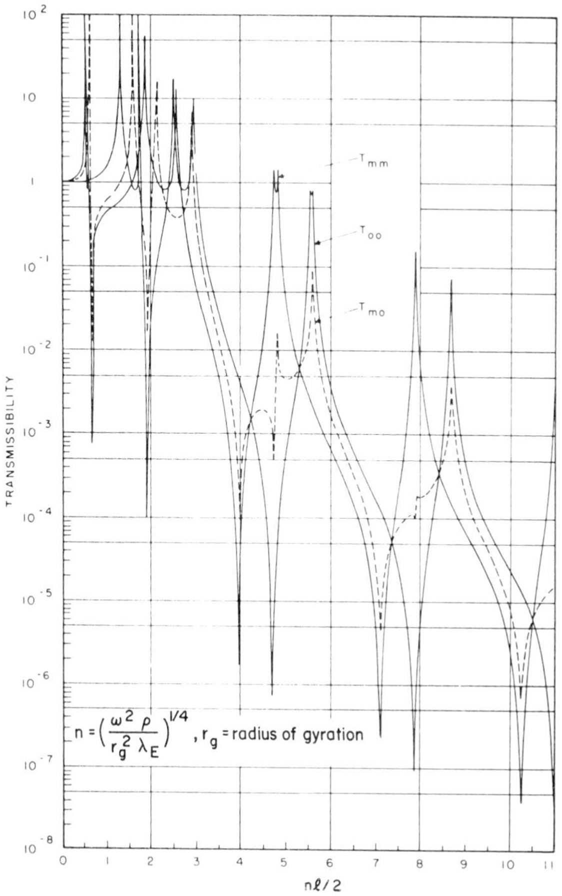

Fig. 10.7 Transmission curves of the "free-free" beams shown in Fig. 10.6 (mass ratio, $\gamma=6.0$, compliance ratio, $\xi=0.125$, damping factor, $\delta=0.01$; $n=(\omega^2\rho/r_g^2\lambda_E)^{\frac{1}{4}}$, where r_g=radius of gyration); T_{oo}, transmission curve of the beam shown in Fig. 10.6*a*; T_{mo} of the beam shown in Fig. 10.6*b*; T_{mm}, of the curve shown in Fig. 10.6*c*. From J. C. Snowdon, "Transverse Vibrations of free-free beams," *J.A.S.A.*, **37** (1965), 47–53).

plate is excited to transverse vibrations, its characteristic impedance is much smaller than it is for longitudinal vibrations, and, therefore, it is usually very small in comparison to the mass impedance of the joint. The joint then acts as if the plate were clamped whenever the mass impedance of the joint exceeds the characteristic impedance of the plate (which happens even at very low frequencies) and reduces the vibration amplitude to zero. However, the bending moment that the plate exerts on the joint is considerable as compared to the reaction of the joint because of its moment of inertia (as can be verified by a simple numerical computation), and the joint fully

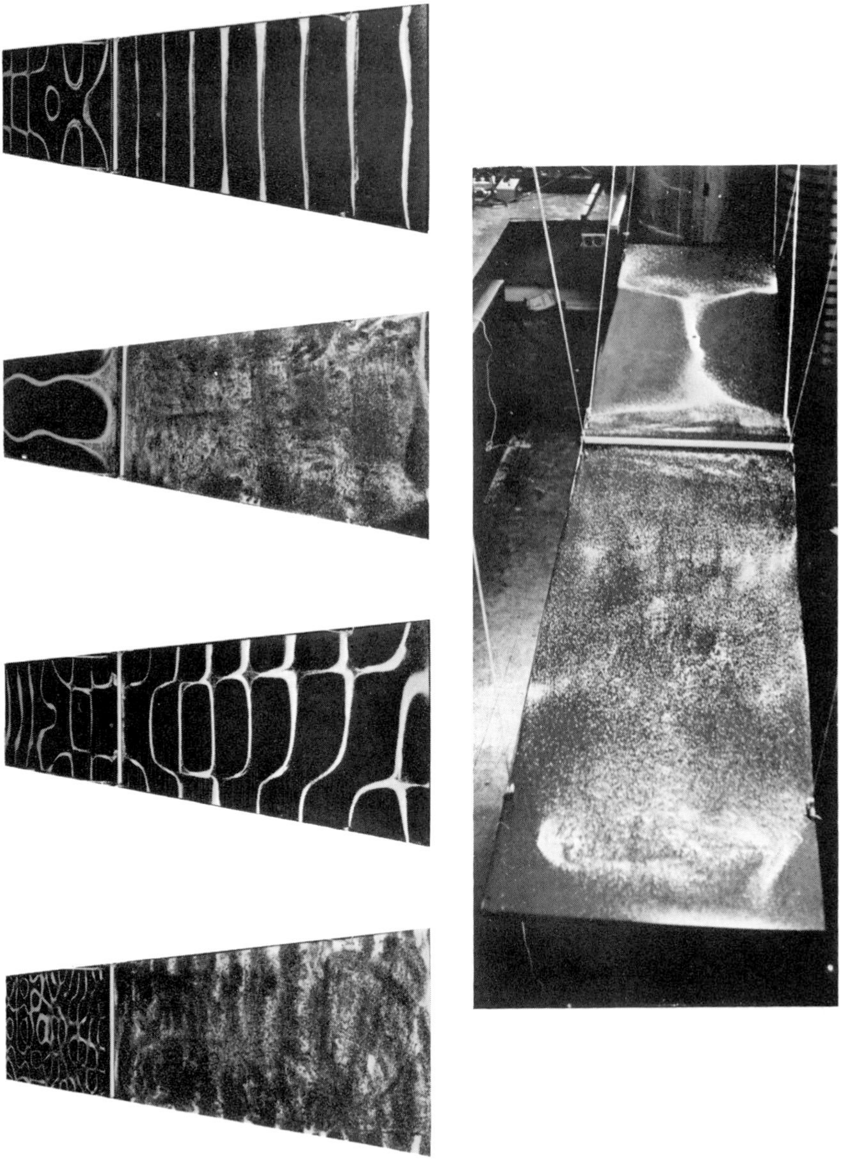

Fig. 10.8 Nodal line pattern in front of and behind a mass-loaded joint; *a*, two-dimensional vibrations (the transmitted waves have nodal lines parallel to the joint); *b*, one-dimensional vibrations (with the nodal lines normal to the joint, waves are not transmitted); *c*, nodal line pattern at a bending resonance of the joint (oblique incident waves now are transmitted; if the joint is stiff, such a transmission can be observed only at a few frequencies); *d*, nodal line pattern at higher frequencies. From J. R. McCormick, Master's thesis (1963), The Pennsylvania State University.

transmits the slope and the bending moment. The rotary inertia reduces the transmission only at very high frequencies or when the plate is very thin.[2] For a transversely vibrating rod, the amplitude of the transmitted wave is $1/\sqrt{2}$ times that of the incident amplitude, and the joint attenuates the vibration by 3 dB., as can be shown by a simple computation.

The situation is very similar for a transversely vibrating plate. Provided that the joint is sufficiently stiff in its longitudinal direction, it acts like a knife-edge and transmits a wave whose nodal lines are parallel to it. This behavior is seen very clearly in the nodal line patterns shown in Figure 10.8.

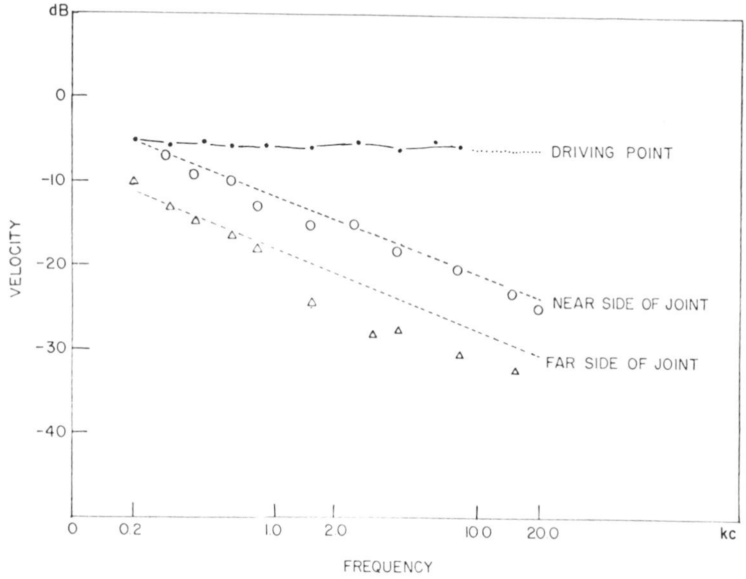

Fig. 10.9 Frequency curve of the velocity amplitude transmitted by a mass-loaded joint. From J. R. McCormick, Master's thesis (1963), The Pennsylvania State University.

Figure 10.9 shows the measured value (averaged over a frequency band that contains a few resonances) of the transmission curve of a joint when the plate at the near side of the joint is excited by a point force. All the experimental results are in good agreement with the theory. Figure 10.10 shows the transmission factor of the joint as a function of the angle of incidence. The transmission factor is $1/\sqrt{2}$ for normal incidence, as for a one-dimensional rod, and is zero for grazing incidence. It can be shown that the wave pattern that is excited by a point force is made up of many different waves that propagate in all directions. The effective transmission factor of the

[2] As in the case investigated by M. Heckl, "Wave propagation on beam plate systems," in Bolt, Beranek, and Newman Report No. 773, Job No. 110022 (September, 1960).

joint, then, is equal to the mean value of the transmission factor, which is 0.45, or about 7 dB. Since grazing and oblique incidence is eliminated by the first joint, further joints generally reduce the transmitted wave by only 3 dB. (as in the case of normal incidence). This result has been verified experimentally for a plate with a joint and for shells with as many as eight stiffening rings. The effects produced by ribs are very similar to those produced by joints. Because of the small characteristic impedance for bending waves, the ribs can be quite light in weight and still have a high acoustic efficiency.

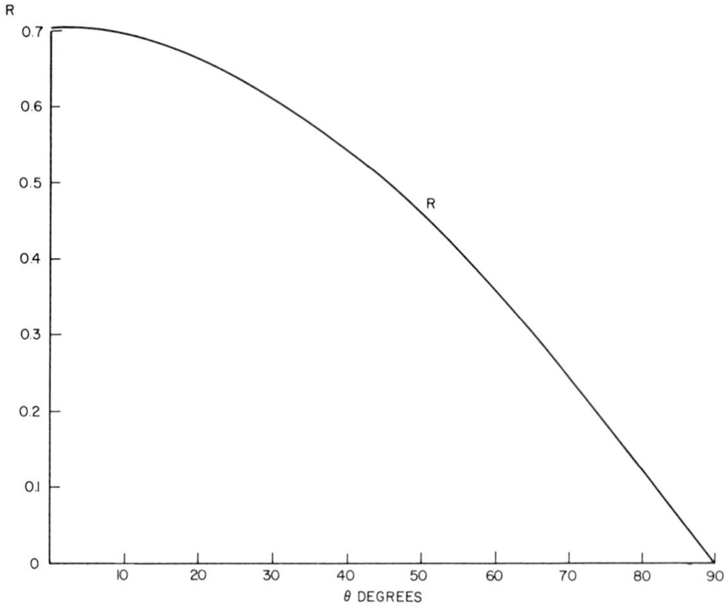

Fig. 10.10 Ratio of the transmitted to the incident amplitude for a mass-loaded joint, as a function of the angle of incidence.

Systems with ribs and joints exhibit coupled resonances at the bending resonant frequencies of the ribs or mass loadings. Figure 10.11*a* shows the frequency curve of the amplitude transmitted by a joint. Its decrease starts when $\omega M = Z_c$, and the coupling resonances occur at the bending resonant frequencies of the joint (Fig. 10.11*b*). However, the effect of the bending resonances of the ribs and the joints on the over-all transmission (Fig. 10.11*c*) of the system is very small. In fact, bending resonances of the stiffening ribs could affect the transmission only very rarely, either when the bending wave length corresponds to the distance between the nodal lines of the

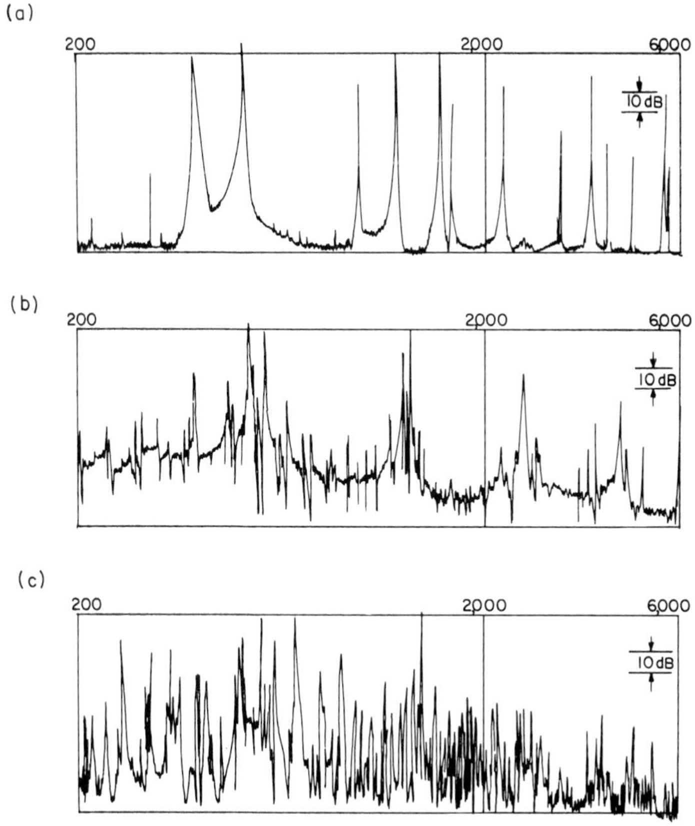

Fig. 10.11 Frequency curves of the joint; *a*, frequency curve for bending vibrations of the bar that represents the mass loading of the joint; *b*, frequency curve of the plate with mass-loaded joint when it is driven at the joint (the bending resonances of the joint generate maxima); *c*, transmission of the joint when the plate is driven at its center (the bending resonances of the joint hardly show). From J. R. McCormick, Master's thesis (1963), The Pennsylvania State University.

plate as measured along the stiffening rib (coincidence effect) or when the plate is very thin.[3]

Joints are, therefore, not very efficient in reducing bending vibrations. To eliminate such transmissions, joints would have to be built in such a manner that bending moments are not transmitted. Also, since the waves transmitted by a joint have their fronts parallel to it, ribs mounted normal to the joint might be expected to reduce considerably the transmission of the joint. A closer study, however, shows that ribs that are normal to the joint act

[3] The behavior of ribs and joints has been investigated by James R. McCormick and David S. Pallet in their Master's theses, Physics Department, The Pennsylvania State University.

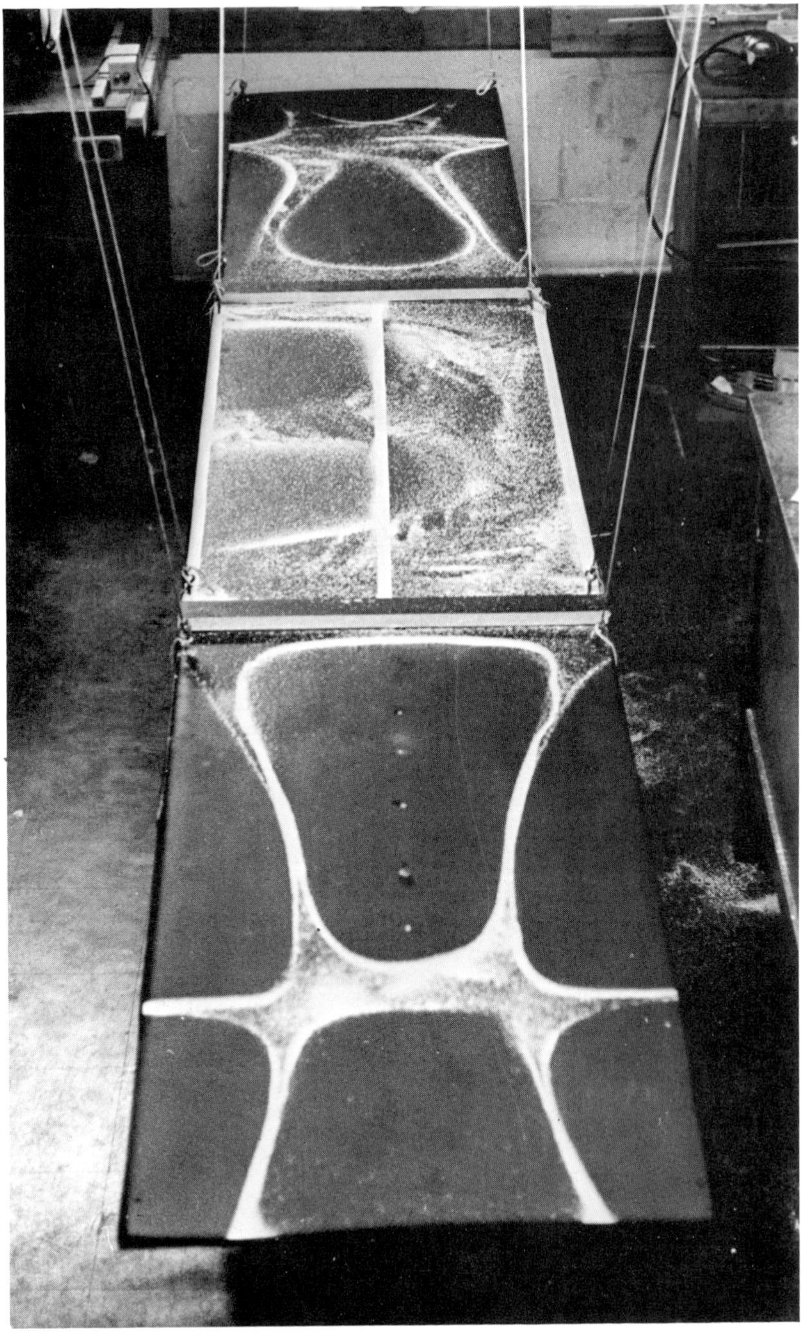

Fig. 10.12 Rib systems; when stiffened by ribs normal to them, they act like a single rib or in transmitting the vibration like an ideal lever. From D. S. Pallet, Master's thesis (1964), The Pennsylvania State University.

like perfect levers and transmit the vibration to the adjacent part of the plate almost without loss (Fig. 10.12). It is true that the moment of inertia of the longitudinally mounted ribs around their central axis is very great, but so is the lever arm of the bending force at the edge of the plate rib system, and the two effects compensate each other. The best way to reduce the transmission of a joint or a rib is to make the rib very narrow, so that the lever arm of the bending force exerted by the plate around the center of the rib or joint is small and the dimensions of the rib or joint normal to the plate are as great as possible in order to ensure a great moment of inertia.

Joined sections are frequently isolated from one another by compliant rings or compliant layers. Such layers would effectively reduce the transmission of vibrations if the connecting screws were also isolated. Screws will always transmit vibrations if their compliance impedance is greater than the characteristic impedance of the two systems they are joining (which usually is the case). Mass-loading the joints may be expected to reduce the transmission of the screws, particularly at the higher frequencies.

Recommended Reading

CREMER, L., "The propagation of structure-borne sound," Department of Scientific and Industrial Research, Sponsored Research (Germany), Report No. 1, British Government, 1948.

———, "Calculation of sound propagation in structures," *Acustica*, **3** (1953), 317–35.

HECKL, M., "Wave propagation on beam plate systems," in Bolt, Beranek and Newman Report No. 773, Job. No. 110022 (September, 1960).

———, "Wave propagation on beam plate systems," *J.A.S.A.*, **33** (1961), 640–51.

———, LYON, R. H., MAIDANIK, G., AND E. E. UNGAR, "New methods for understanding and controlling vibrations of complex structures," Aeronautical Systems Division, Dir/Aeromechanics, Flight Dynamics Laboratory, Wright-Patterson AFB, Ohio, Report No. ASD-TN-61-122, June, 1962.

MÜLLER, H. L., "Biegewellen-Dämmung an symmetrischen und exzentrischen Sperrmassen," *Frequenz*, **11** (1960), 342–50.

SKUDRZYK, E. J., "Vibrations of a system with a finite or an infinite number of resonances," *J.A.S.A.*, **30** (1958), 1140–52.

———, KAUTZ, B. R., AND D. C. GREENE, "Vibration of and bending-wave propagation in plates," *J.A.S.A.*, **33** (1961), 36–45.

SNOWDON, J. C., "Transverse vibration of free-free beams," *J.A.S.A.*, **35** (1963), 47–52.

———, "Mechanical impedance and transmissibility of simply supported beams," *J.A.S.A.*, **35** (1963), 228–33.

———, "Transverse vibration of simply clamped beams," *J.A.S.A.*, **35** (1963), 1152–61.

———, "Approximate expressions for the mechanical impedance and transmissibility of beams vibrating in their transverse modes," *J.A.S.A.*, **36** (1964), 366–75.

———, "Response of simply clamped beam to vibratory forces and moments," *J.A.S.A.*, **36** (1964), 495–501.

———, "Mechanical impedance of free-free beams," *J.A.S.A.*, **37** (1965), 240–49.

———, "Response of internally damped cantilever beams to sinusoidal vibrations," *J.A.S.A.*, **38** (1965), 271–81.

———, "Vibration of cantilever beams to which dynamic absorbers are attached," *J.A.S.A.*, **39** (1966).

UNGAR, E. E., "Transmission of plate flexural waves through reinforcing beams: dynamic stress concentrations," *J.A.S.A.*, **33** (1961), 633–39.

XI / STATISTICAL FORCE FIELDS

In the preceding chapters, a mechanical vibrator was described by its response to sinusoidal excitation, i.e., by its mechanical impedance or admittance. The computations were performed for sinusoidally varying force distributions and for particular points of observation. By basing the computations on the true mode amplitudes ξ_ν, rather than on the normalized mode amplitudes, a lumped parameter solution was obtained in which every term was of the same form as the solution for a simple point-mass compliant element system. The lumped parameter solution (and only this solution) could be represented by a canonical circuit, and the theory of electrical networks became applicable to mechanical vibrators. The lumped parameter solution was particularly suited for numerical computations. But it did have one serious disadvantage. The lumped parameters depended on the co-ordinates of the point of observation through the factor

$$\frac{\langle \xi_\nu^2 \rangle}{\kappa_\nu(A)\xi_\nu^2(A)} \tag{11.1}$$

and it was difficult to see how the solution varied with the point of observation.

Solution of a Continuous System in Terms of Normalized Natural Functions for Harmonically Varying Forces

If we are interested in the variation of the mode amplitude over the system and in functions or integrals of the mode amplitude, it becomes expedient again to separate out the above factor and to introduce the normalized natural functions $\varphi_\nu(x, y)$. The normalized natural functions $\varphi_\nu(x, y)$, like the functions $\xi_\nu(x, y)$, are solutions of the homogeneous differential equation that obey the normalizing conditions:

$$\int_\sigma \varphi_\nu(x, y)\varphi_\mu(x, y)dxdy = 0 \qquad \text{for } \mu \neq \nu \tag{11.2}$$

$$\int_\sigma \varphi_\nu^2(x, y)dxdy = \langle \varphi_\nu^2 \rangle \sigma = 1 \tag{11.3}$$

Thus, "normalizing to one" means that the product of the mean square of the normalized natural function and the area (or volume) of the system is one or that the mean square of the normalized function is equal to one over the area (or volume) of the system. This property of the normalized natural function is mathematically convenient, but it makes the physical interpretation of the results more difficult.

The mode amplitude ξ_ν is proportional to the normalized natural function φ_ν:

$$\xi_\nu(x, y) = C_\nu \varphi_\nu(x, y) \tag{11.4}$$

where C_ν is a factor of proportionality. The factor C_ν can be expressed in terms of ξ_ν, as follows:

$$\int \xi_\nu^2(x, y) d\sigma = \langle \xi_\nu^2 \rangle \sigma = C_\nu^2 \int \varphi_\nu^2(x, y) d\sigma = C_\nu^2 \tag{11.5}$$

Hence,

$$C_\nu = [\langle \xi_\nu^2 \rangle \sigma]^{\frac{1}{2}} \tag{11.6}$$

and

$$\xi_\nu(x, y) = \langle \xi_\nu^2 \sigma \rangle^{\frac{1}{2}} \varphi_\nu(x, y) \tag{11.7}$$

Thus, the true amplitude is obtained by multiplying the normalized natural function by the root-mean-square value of the amplitude and by the square root of the area (or volume) of the system.

In this chapter we shall be primarily concerned with the more complex force distributions, which need not vary sinusoidally with time. The natural functions, then, are only tools for deriving the results, and it is convenient to use them in a form that is normalized to one. The solutions given in Chapter VII can also be readily derived directly in terms of the normalized natural functions. The vibrator is described, as always, by its differential equation:

$$-m\omega^2 \tilde{\xi} + rj\omega\tilde{\xi} + \lambda_0(1 + j\eta) L \cdot \tilde{\xi} = \tilde{p}(x, y) \tag{11.8}$$

In this equation, external (sliding) friction has been taken into account by the term $rj\omega\tilde{\xi}$; the friction force is proportional to the velocity of the masses.

The third term describes the elastic restoring force. By limiting the computation to strictly harmonic or decaying harmonic vibrations, elastic losses are taken rigorously into account by introducing a complex elastic constant. Since we are predominantly interested in continuously distributed forces here, the symbol $p(x, y)$ is used to denote the force (pressure) per unit area. The natural functions ξ_ν are the *eigen* functions of the operator L; they satisfy the homogeneous equation:

$$\lambda_0 L \cdot \tilde{\xi}_\nu = m\omega_\nu^2 \tilde{\xi}_\nu \tag{11.9}$$

If the displacement ξ is expressed as a series of the natural functions ξ_ν, the differential equation becomes:

$$\sum m\left(-\omega^2 + \frac{rj\omega}{m} + \bar{\omega}_\nu^2\right)\tilde{\xi}_\nu = \tilde{p}(x, y) \tag{11.10}$$

The losses because of external friction can be lumped with the inertia term by replacing $-\omega^2$ by $-\bar{\omega}^2 = -\omega^2(1+r/j\omega m)$, and the last equation reduces to the same simple form as that for a nondissipative vibrator:

$$\sum_\nu m(-\bar{\omega}^2+\bar{\omega}_\nu{}^2)\xi_\nu = \tilde{p} \tag{11.11}$$

Multiplication by a normalized natural function $\varphi_\nu = \xi_\nu/C_\nu$ and integration over the system then lead to:

$$m(\bar{\omega}_\nu{}^2-\bar{\omega}^2)C_\nu\sigma\langle\varphi_\nu{}^2\rangle = \int p(x_F, y_F)\varphi_\nu(x_F, y_F)d\sigma_F \tag{11.12}$$

or

$$C_\nu = \int \frac{p(x_F, y_F)\varphi_\nu(x_F, y_F)dx_F dy_F}{m(\bar{\omega}_\nu{}^2-\bar{\omega}^2)} \tag{11.13}$$

In the latter integral, x_F and y_F represent the integration variables. The mode amplitude at a point x, y is given by:

$$\hat{\xi}_\nu(x, y) = C_\nu\varphi_\nu(x, y) = \frac{\varphi_\nu(x, y)}{m(\bar{\omega}_\nu{}^2-\bar{\omega}^2)}\int \hat{p}(x_F, y_F)\varphi_\nu(x_F, y_F)dx_F dy_F \tag{11.14}$$

Solution in Terms of the Green Function

If the force is a periodic point force of magnitude

$$F_0 = \int p(x, y)dxdy \tag{11.15}$$

and acts at the point x_F, y_F, the mode amplitude $\hat{\xi}_\nu$ becomes (see Eq. 11.13):

$$\hat{\xi}_\nu(x, y; \omega) = C_\nu\varphi_\nu(x, y) = \frac{\varphi_\nu(x, y)F_0\varphi_\nu(x_F, y_F)}{m(\bar{\omega}_\nu{}^2-\bar{\omega}^2)} \tag{11.16}$$

The displacement amplitude that is generated by unit force of frequency ω at x_F, y_F, at the point x, y, is obtained by summing over the contributions of all modes:

$$G(x, y; x_F, y_F; \omega) = \sum_\nu \frac{\varphi_\nu(x, y)\varphi_\nu(x_F, y_F)}{m(\bar{\omega}_\nu{}^2-\bar{\omega}^2)}F_0 \tag{11.17}$$

The last expression is identical with the lumped parameter solution derived in Chapter VII, except for a difference in notation. The solution $G(x, y; x_F, y_F; \omega)$ for a periodic point force of unit amplitude ($F_0 = 1$) is called the Green function; it is symmetrical in the co-ordinates of the force point and those of the point of observation.

If the force is not a point force of unit amplitude, but is distributed with a density $p(x_F, y_F)$, the solution can be obtained by interpreting the forces on each elementary area dx_F, dy_F as point forces, and by summing over all the elementary areas, as follows:

$$\xi(x, y; \omega) = \int p(x_F, y_F) G(x, y; x_F, y_F; \omega) dx_F dy_F \tag{11.18}$$

where F_0 has been replaced by the force on an elementary area:

$$F_0 = p(x_F, y_F) dx_F dy_F \tag{11.19}$$

The solution now is represented with the aid of the Green function of the system.[1] Again, the solution is identical with the solution in Equation 7.22, except for a change in the notation. This is easily seen by substituting Equation 11.17 into the integrand and writing the integral over x_F, y_F as $\kappa_\nu F_0$. The Green function as given by Equation 11.17 is hardly more than an abbreviation or a name for the series of the contributions of the natural modes. In many instances, the series can be summed and replaced by an expression in closed form. In other instances, the Green function can be derived directly by integrating the differential equation for a point force and matching this solution to the boundary conditions.

Solution for Nonperiodic Forces in the Form of a Fourier Integral

If the exciting force is not periodic, force and displacement can be resolved into their Fourier transforms. To arrive at a simple notation, functions that describe a Fourier spectrum are denoted by the capital letter $S(\omega; x, y)$, and a subscript denotes the variable of which S is the Fourier transform. Thus,

$$S_p(\omega; x_F, y_F) = \lim_{T \to \infty} \int_{-T}^{+T} p(t; x_F, y_F) e^{-j\omega t} dt \tag{11.20}$$

is the Fourier transform of the pressure $p(t; x_F, y_F)$, and

$$p(t; x_F, y_F) = \int_{-\infty}^{\infty} S_p(\omega; x_F, y_F) e^{j\omega t} \frac{d\omega}{2\pi} \tag{11.21}$$

is the reverse transformation. In the reverse transformation, the integration variable is the frequency $\omega/2\pi$ and not the radial frequency ω, and the frequency range extends from $-\infty$ to $+\infty$. No factors 2 or $\sqrt{2\pi}$, then, ap-

[1] That Eq. 11.17 is the solution is plausible. To be strictly correct, this solution would have to be substituted in the differential equation (11.8), and it would have to be proved that it satisfies this equation. This is done in textbooks on differential equations and need not be repeated here.

pear in front of the integrals, which will be derived later. Similarly,

$$\xi(x, t)=\int_{-\infty}^{\infty} S_\xi(\omega, x)e^{j\omega t}\frac{d\omega}{2\pi} \tag{11.22}$$

or

$$S_\xi(\omega, x)=\int_{-\infty}^{\infty} \xi(x, t)e^{-j\omega t}dt \tag{11.23}$$

In general, it is not permissible to replace $\xi\,(x,t)$ by its Fourier integral in Equation 11.8, because this equation applies only to a harmonic or a decaying harmonic vibration, but not to vibrations $\xi\,(x, t)$ of arbitrary time variations. However, it can be shown that this procedure is permissible if η either is constant or is the loss factor of an elastic substance, provided that effects due to heat conduction are excluded.[2]

If the pressure and displacement are expressed by their Fourier integrals, the differential equation of the system becomes:

$$\begin{aligned}\int\Big[&-m\omega^2 S_\xi(\omega; x, y)+rj\omega S_\xi(\omega; x, y)\\ &+\lambda_0(1+j\eta)L\Big(\frac{\partial}{\partial x}\frac{\partial}{\partial y}\Big)S_\xi(\omega; x, y)\Big]e^{j\omega t}\frac{d\omega}{2\pi}\\ &=\int S_p(\omega; x, y)e^{j\omega t}\frac{d\omega}{2\pi}\end{aligned} \tag{11.24}$$

[2] If the motion is not harmonic, and if the displacements are small, losses due to the dissipation in the elastic material can be taken into account by time derivatives in the differential operator $L\ (\partial/\partial x,\ \partial^2/\partial x\ \partial t,\ \ldots)$, which describes the elastic restoring force (see pp. 98–99). The time derivatives represent elastic aftereffects; the space derivatives represent a coupling and an interaction (distance effects) of the various parts of the body; and the mixed derivatives represent such phenomena as the effects of heat conduction. (The regions that are compressed by the vibration have a higher temperature than those that are extended; heat currents are set up, and, because of their time lag, mechanical energy is transformed into heat in an irreversible manner.) The resulting differential equation then becomes very complex and can no longer be solved by a series of natural functions of the nondissipative system. If, however, distance effects and internal dissipation by heat conduction are neglected, the operator L splits up into the product of two operators, $L\ (\partial/\partial x,\ \partial/\partial t)=L\ (\partial/\partial x)\ L\ (\partial/\partial t)$, one containing space derivatives and representing the elastic restoring forces, the other containing only time derivatives and representing the elastic aftereffects. This statement cannot be proved, but it seems to be borne out in all known cases.

If we assume, then, that the sequence of integration and differentiation is interchangeable (as is always the case in computations applying to physical phenomena), the part of the operator representing the time derivatives when it is applied to the integrand of a Fourier integral becomes equivalent to a complex elastic constant, and the methods used in the previous chapters become applicable.

The solution for frequency dependent $\eta(\omega)$ can be derived by transforming Equation 11.8 into an integral equation in the same manner, as this has been done at the end of chapter II for the point mass, compliant element vibrator (see Eq. 2.145), by solving 11.24, finding the time function and verifying it as solution by substitution into the integral equation.

Since the above equation must be fulfilled at all times, and consequently for all values of ω, the integration signs can be omitted, and

$$[-m\omega^2+rj\omega+\lambda_0(1+j\eta)L]S_\xi(\omega;\,x,y)=S_p(\omega;\,x,y) \tag{11.25}$$

Thus, the Fourier spectra $S_\xi(\omega;x,y)$ satisfy the same differential equation as the harmonic time functions $\xi(x,y;t)$ and $p(x,y;t)$. Hence,

$$S_\xi(\omega;\,x,y)=\sum_\nu S_{\xi\nu}(\omega;\,x,y)$$
$$=\sum_\nu \frac{\varphi_\nu(x,y)}{m(\bar{\omega}_\nu^{\,2}-\bar{\omega}^2)}\int S_p(\omega;\,x_F,y_F)\varphi_\nu(x_F,y_F)dx_Fdy_F \tag{11.26}$$

Thus there is no need to distinguish between Fourier components and harmonically changing variables. Both obey the same relations.

The response of the system is obtained by integrating with respect to the frequency $\omega/2\pi$,

$$\xi(x,t)=\sum\int S_{\xi\nu}(\omega;\,x,y)e^{j\omega t}\frac{d\omega}{2\pi}$$
$$=\sum\varphi_\nu(x,y)\int_{-\infty}^{\infty}\frac{e^{j\omega t}\dfrac{d\omega}{2\pi}}{m(\bar{\omega}_\nu^{\,2}-\bar{\omega}^2)}\int S_p(\omega;\,x_F,y_F)\varphi_\nu(x_F,y_F)dx_Fdy_F \tag{11.27}$$

The Fourier method of solving the vibration equation is very powerful and mathematically simple. The integrals can usually be solved by contour integration, from $\omega=-\infty$ to $\omega=0$ and to $\omega=+\infty$. The frequencies $\omega=0$ and $\omega=\pm\infty$ are very special frequencies, and their inclusion in the integration range can lead to strange phenomena, unless the parameters involved (loss factor and elastic constant) are given in their exact form. If approximations are used, they must be represented by expressions that assume reasonable values, not only in the frequency range we are interested in, but also at the frequencies $\omega\to 0$ and $\omega\to\pm\infty$. For example, to compute the impulse response of a vibrator with the aid of the Fourier solution, let the exciting force be a very short pulse that acts at the point x_F, y_F at the time t_F; this pulse can be represented analytically in the following form:

$$f(t;\,x_F,y_F)=U(x_F,y_F)\delta(t-t_F) \tag{11.28}$$

where $\delta(t-t_F)$ is the Dirac's function

$$\int_{-\infty}^{\infty}\delta(t-t_F)dt=1 \qquad \text{and} \qquad \delta(t-t_F)=0 \qquad \text{for } t\neq t_F \tag{11.29}$$

The magnitude $U(x_F,y_F)$ is the time integral or the so-called impulse of the force. Fourier transformation leads to:

$$S_F(\omega; x_F, y_F) = \int_{-\infty}^{\infty} f(t; x_F, y_F) e^{-j\omega t} dt = U(x_F, y_F) \int_{-\infty}^{\infty} \delta(t - t_F) e^{-j\omega t} dt$$

$$= U(x_F, y_F) e^{-j\omega t_F} \qquad (11.30)$$

The spectral amplitude at zero frequency is always equal to the time integral of the function $f(t)$ as is proved by putting $\omega = 0$ in the first form of the right-hand side of the last equation. The last form of the right-hand side shows that the spectral amplitude of a short pulse is constant (is the same at zero frequency as it is at all frequencies). Hence, it is equal to the time integral of the pulse. It is worth while to memorize this result. The phase angle of the spectral amplitude is negative and proportional to t_F and ω; it is zero if $t_F = 0$. (It is shown in the theory of Fourier integration that a factor $e^{-j\omega t_F}$ in the Fourier amplitudes corresponds to a displacement of the origin of time from $t = 0$ to $t = t_F$.) If the impulse of the force is unity, $U(x_F, y_F) = 1$.

The Fourier components of the pulse that are contained within a narrow frequency band $d\omega$ excite each mode of the system as if the driving force were $Ue^{-j\omega t_F} d\omega$, and the resultant mode amplitude $\xi_\nu(x, y; t)$ is given by:

$$[\xi_\nu(x, y; t)]_{\text{pulse}} = g_\nu(x, y; x_F, y_F; t_F)$$

$$= \int_{-\infty}^{\infty} \frac{Ue^{-j\omega t_F}}{m(\bar{\omega}_\nu^2 - \bar{\omega}^2)} \cdot \varphi_\nu(x, y) \varphi_\nu(x_F, y_F) e^{j\omega t} \frac{d\omega}{2\pi}$$

$$= U \frac{\varphi_\nu(x, y) \varphi_\nu(x_F, y_F)}{m} \int_{-\infty}^{\infty} \frac{-e^{j\omega(t - t_F)}}{(\bar{\omega}^2 - \bar{\omega}_\nu^2)} \frac{d\omega}{2\pi} \qquad (11.31)$$

The function $g_\nu(x, y; x_F, y_F; t_F)$ is called the modal pulse response of the system.

If the vibrator is not heavily damped, the loss factor is a small quantity that affects the vibration only in its resonance range. We may, therefore, feel tempted to neglect the frequency variation of $\eta_R = -r/\omega m$ by replacing ω by ω_ν if ω is positive and by $-\omega_\nu$ if ω is negative:

$$\mp j \frac{r}{\omega m} \cong \mp j \frac{r}{\omega_\nu m} = \mp j \eta_R \qquad (11.32)$$

The loss factor η_R represents the angle of lag of the velocity with respect to the phase of the force. If the generator (or the phasor or complex vector) rotates in the opposite direction, ω changes sign, and η must also change sign; otherwise, the angle of lag would turn into an angle of lead, and resistances would turn into power generators. The integral then simplifies to:

$$I=\int_{-\infty}^{\infty}\frac{1}{2\pi}\frac{d\omega e^{j\omega(t-t_F)}}{-\omega^2(1\mp j\eta_R)+\omega_\nu^2}=\int_{-\infty}^{\infty}\frac{1}{2\pi}\frac{-d\omega e^{j\omega(t-t_F)}}{(1\mp j\eta_R)\left(\omega^2-\dfrac{\omega_\nu^2}{1\mp j\eta_R}\right)} \tag{11.33}$$

The integral can be evaluated by contour integration. For positive values of $t-t_F$, the path of integration can be closed by a semicircle of infinite radius above the real axis ($\omega=\omega+j\delta$). The exponent then has a negative real part, and the integrand converges to zero over this semicircle because of the denominator.

The poles are the roots of the denominator. They are given by:

$$\omega=+\omega_1=\frac{\omega_\nu}{\sqrt{1-j\eta_R}}=\omega_\nu\left(1+\frac{j\eta_R}{2}+\ldots\right) \tag{11.34}$$

$$\omega=\omega_2=\frac{-\omega_\nu}{\sqrt{1+j\eta_R}}=-\omega_\nu\left(1-\frac{j\eta_R}{2}+\ldots\right) \tag{11.35}$$

Figure 11.1 shows the path of integration and the position of the poles. The integral thus becomes:

$$I=\int\frac{-d\omega e^{j\omega(t-t_F)}}{2\pi(1\mp j\eta_R)(\omega-\omega_1)(\omega-\omega_2)}=2\pi j(a_1+a_2) \tag{11.36}$$

where a_1 and a_2 are the residues at the poles ω_1 and ω_2, respectively, and η_R takes the negative sign for positive frequencies and the positive sign for negative frequencies. The residue at pole ω_1 is obtained by excluding the factor $(\omega-\omega_1)$ and substituting $\omega=\omega_1$ in all the other terms of the integrand.

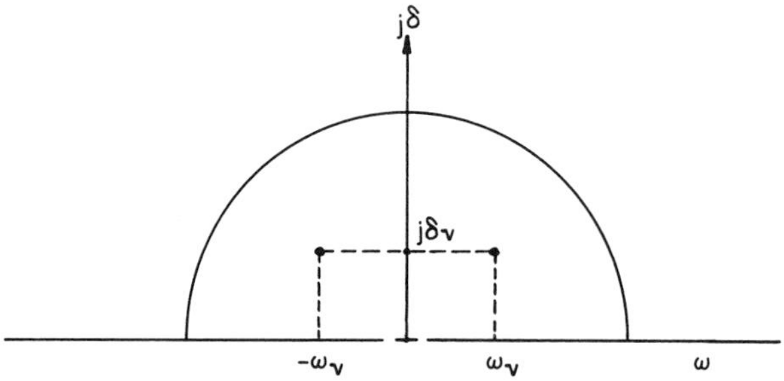

Fig. 11.1 The path of integration and the poles of the integrand for evaluating the integral equation (11.33) for the impulse response of a vibrator.

Thus, for the pole $\omega=+\omega_1$,

$$a_1=\frac{-e^{j\omega_1(t-t_F)}}{2\pi(1-j\eta_R)(\omega_1-\omega_2)}=\frac{-e^{j\omega_\nu(1+j\eta_R/2)(t-t_F)}}{2\pi 2\omega_\nu(1-j\eta_R)} \tag{11.37}$$

and, similarly, for the pole $\omega = -\omega_2$, η being negative,

$$a_2 = \frac{-1}{2\pi} \frac{e^{j\omega_2(t-t_F)}}{(1+j\eta_R)(\omega_2-\omega_1)} = \frac{e^{-j\omega_\nu(1-j\eta_R/2)(t-t_F)}}{2\pi 2\omega_\nu(1+j\eta_R)} \tag{11.38}$$

The integral therefore becomes:

$$\frac{j}{2\omega_\nu}\left[\frac{e^{j\omega_\nu(1+j\eta_R/2)(t-t_F)}}{1+j\eta_R} - \frac{e^{j\omega_\nu(1-j\eta_R/2)(t-t_F)}}{1-j\eta_R}\right]$$

$$= \frac{e^{-\omega_\nu\eta_R(t-t_F)/2}}{\omega_\nu}\left[\sin\omega_\nu(t-t_F) + \eta_R\cos\omega_\nu(t-t_F)\right]$$

$$= \frac{e^{-\omega_\nu\eta_R(t-t_F)2}}{\omega_\nu}\sin\left[\omega_\nu(t-t_F)+\eta_R\right] \tag{11.39}$$

Squares and higher powers of η_R have been neglected. Because of the phase η_R, the displacement is finite at $t=0$. The system is deflected before the impulse even has a chance to act on it. This strange result is a consequence of having neglected the frequency variation of the loss factor. A similar phenomenon is well known in communications theory. A signal may arrive at the terminals of a series of cascaded filters or of a telephone line before it has been generated. In communications theory, this phenomenon is a consequence of the standard practice of approximating the frequency variation of the phase retardation of the Fourier components by a linear relationship or of neglecting the phase retardation entirely.

If η is small, the error in the computations is negligible even in this extreme case, where the true loss factor is infinite at zero frequency. The computations can be easily generalized to include an elastic loss factor η by replacing ω_ν^2 by $\omega_\nu^2(1+j\eta)$ and correspondingly $\omega_\nu^2/(1\mp j\eta_R)$ in Eq. 11.33 by $\omega_\nu^2/(1\mp j\eta_t)$ where $\eta_t = \eta_R + \eta$. The result is very similar, the initial phase being η_R again, but the decay constant is η_t.

The impulse response of the system is proportional to the integral I, and the complete solution is

$$[\xi_\nu(x,t)]_{\text{pulse}} = g_\nu(x, y; t; x_F, y_F; t_F)$$
$$= U\frac{\varphi_\nu(x,y)\varphi_\nu(x_F,y_F)}{\omega_\nu m}\cdot e^{-\eta_t\omega_\nu(t-t_F)/2}\sin\omega_\nu(t-t_F) \tag{11.40}$$

where terms with squares and higher powers of η and the initial phase η_R of the sine term have been neglected and where $\eta_t = \eta_R + \eta$ is the sum of the resistive and elastic loss factors.

The general solution for the pulse response of the system is given by the sum of the modal responses; it can be written in the following form:

$$g(x, y; t; x_F, y_F; t_F) = \sum_\nu g_\nu(x, y; t; x_F, y_F; t_F)$$

$$= \sum_\nu \frac{U(t-t_F)\varphi_\nu(x,y)\varphi_\nu(x_F,y_F)}{\omega_\nu m} e^{-\delta_\nu(t-t_F)}\sin\omega_\nu(t-t_F) \tag{11.41}$$

where $U(t-t_F)$ is the unit step function:

$$U(t-t_F)=0 \qquad t<t_F$$
$$U(t-t_F)=1 \qquad t>t_F \tag{11.42}$$

Solution Based on the Impulse Response of the Vibrator

In the preceding sections, a sinusoidally varying force distribution has been assumed as a starting point, and the general solution has been built up by a series of resonance terms. Every one of these terms had the same form as the expression for the velocity of a simple point-mass compliant element system. By decomposing the force into its Fourier spectrum and considering the Fourier components individually, an accurate solution could be derived for nonperiodic forces.

Fourier integration over an infinite time interval represents a mathematical formalism that, strictly speaking, requires a knowledge of the elastic constant and of the loss factor in the whole frequency range $-\infty<\omega<\infty$. A truly resonant vibration can be excited only if the force is periodic and lasts long enough so that the vibration can build up to its steady-state value, and from a physical point of view it is frequently more appropriate to interpret the force distribution as a series of short pulses. Because of the assumed linearity of the fundamental equations, every one of the pulses excites the system as if it were at rest at the instant of the pulse, and the solution is obtained by adding all the decaying vibrations that are excited by the pulses.

Impulse Response by Direct Integration of the Differential Equation

The impulse response of a vibrator has been investigated in the preceding sections on the basis of the Fourier solution. In this section, the impulse response will be derived by direct integration of the differential equation of the vibrator. For this purpose the solution is written in the form:

$$\xi(x,t)=\sum_\nu \xi_\nu(x,t)=\sum_\nu \varphi_\nu(x)g_\nu(t) \tag{11.43}$$

where $\varphi_\nu(x)$ represents the modal amplitude distribution, and $g_\nu(t)$, its variation with time; for harmonic vibrations, $g_\nu(t)$ is proportional to $e^{-j\omega t}$. The solution will be represented by a sum of decaying vibrations, so that the assumption of a complex elastic constant is no longer strictly correct, but it is a good approximation, unless the loss factor varies drastically with frequency. If the above series is substituted in the differential equation, we obtain:

$$m\sum_\nu \frac{\partial^2\xi_\nu}{\partial t^2}+\sum_\nu r\frac{\partial \xi_\nu}{\partial t}+m(1+j\eta)\sum_\nu \omega_\nu{}^2\xi_\nu=p(x, y; t) \tag{11.44}$$

Again, we have to multiply, left and right, by $\varphi_\nu(x,y)$ and to integrate over the system, because of the orthogonality of the $\varphi_\nu(x, y)$

$$m\frac{\partial^2 g_\nu}{\partial t^2}+r\frac{\partial g_\nu}{\partial t}+m(1+j\eta)\omega_\nu{}^2 g_\nu=\int p(x, y; t)\varphi_\nu(x)d\sigma \tag{11.45}$$

For a point force,

$$\int p(x, y; t)d\sigma=F(t) \tag{11.46}$$

and Equation 11.45 simplifies to:

$$m\left(\frac{d^2g_\nu}{dt^2}+\frac{r}{m}\frac{dg_\nu}{dt}+\bar{\omega}_\nu{}^2 g_\nu\right)=F(t)\varphi_\nu(x_F, y_F) \tag{11.47}$$

If the system is energized and then left on its own, the right-hand side becomes zero, and the solution is a decaying vibration of the form:

$$g_\nu(t)=Re[C_\nu e^{-(r/2m)t+j\bar{\omega}_\nu{}^*t}] \tag{11.48}$$

where

$$\bar{\omega}_\nu{}^*=\sqrt{\bar{\omega}_\nu{}^2-\frac{r^2}{m^2}}=\sqrt{\omega_\nu{}^2(1+j\eta)-\frac{r^2}{4m^2}}=\omega_\nu\left(1+\frac{j\eta}{2}\right)-\frac{8r^2}{2m^2\omega_\nu{}^2} \tag{11.49}$$

$=\omega_\nu+j\omega_\nu\,\eta/2+$terms of second and higher order in η, $r/\omega_\nu m$. If this value is substituted, and if the deflection is assumed zero at $t-t_F$, the solution simplifies to:

$$g_\nu(t-t_F)=C_\nu e^{-\delta_\nu(t-t_F)}\sin\omega_\nu(t-t_F) \tag{11.50}$$

where $\delta_\nu=r/2m+\omega_\nu\eta/2+$higher-order terms and $\omega_\nu{}^*\doteq\omega_\nu$. The constant C_ν is determined by the velocity that has been imparted to the system at $t=t_F$.

If the system has been excited by an infinitely short pulse,

$$\int F(t)dt=U \tag{11.51}$$

Integration over the interval of the pulse leads to:

$$\left(\frac{dg_\nu}{dt}\right)_{t_2}-\left(\frac{dg_\nu}{dt}\right)_{t_1}+\frac{r}{m}\Big[(g_\nu)_{t_2}-(g_\nu)_{t_1}\Big]+\int_{t_1}^{t_2}\omega_\nu{}^2 g_\nu dt$$

$$=\frac{U}{m}\varphi_\nu(x_F, y_F) \tag{11.52}$$

Since the displacement during the short interval of the pulse is infinitely small, and since the system was at rest at $t=0$, only the first term on the left is significant. Hence,

$$m\frac{dg_\nu}{dt}=C_\nu\left\{[(\omega_\nu \cos \omega_\nu(t-t_F)-\delta_\nu \sin \omega_\nu(t-t_F)]e^{-\delta_\nu(t-t_F)}\right\}_{t=t_F}$$
$$=C_\nu\omega_\nu=U\varphi_\nu(x_F, y_F)$$

or

$$C_\nu=\frac{U}{\omega_\nu}\varphi_\nu(x_F, y_F) \tag{11.53}$$

and

$$\xi_\nu(t)=\varphi_\nu(x, y)g_\nu(t-t_F)=\frac{U}{m\omega_\nu}\varphi_\nu(x, y)\varphi_\nu(x_F, y_F)e^{-\delta_\nu(t-t_F)} \sin \omega_\nu(t-t_F) \tag{11.54}$$

as before. The Fourier solution was based on hypothetical knowledge of the frequency variation of all the parameters that were involved in the computation from $\omega=-\infty$ to $\omega=+\infty$. The above computation is based on the assumption that the parameters of the vibrator do not vary drastically with frequency and that $\eta^2 \ll 1$, so that the loss factor for decaying vibration is the same as that for steady-state vibrations.

Vibration of a System for Nonperiodic Forces in Terms of Its Impulse Response

If the force distribution is a function of the time, it can be resolved into elementary impulses that act on areas $dx_F dy_F$ at the time t_F, as follows:

$$p(x_F, y_F; t_F)dx_F dy_F dt_F=p(x_F, y_F)\delta(x-x_F)\delta(y-y_F)\delta(t-t_F)dx_F dy_F dt_F \tag{11.55}$$

(See Fig. 11.2.) The solution for a force distribution that varies in space and time is obtained by summing over all the elementary areas and integrating over the time from $-\infty$ to t, as follows:

$$\xi(x, y; t)=\int_{-\infty}^{t}\int_x\int_y g(x, y; t \mid x_F, y_F; t_F)p(x_F, y_F; t_F)dx_F dy_F dt_F$$

$$=\sum_\nu \frac{\varphi_\nu(x, y)}{\omega_\nu m}\int_{-\infty}^{t}\int_x\int_y p(x_F, y_F; t_F)e^{-\delta_\nu(t-t_F)}\varphi_\nu(x_F, y_F)$$
$$\sin \omega_\nu(t-t_F)dx_F dy_F dt_F \tag{11.56}$$

Since each pulse acts on the system as if the system were at rest, the restoring force at the instant of the pulse is zero, and the resonance denominator that occurs in the Fourier solution is replaced by a denominator that is proportional to the mass impedance of the vibrator. Equation 11.56

represents the convolution integral to the Fourier solution (Eq. 11.27).[3]

From the physical point of view, this solution is almost obvious. The exciting force is represented as a series of elementary pulses. Since the system is linear, the responses to all the elementary pulses add. For each pulse, the system acts as if it were initially at rest and underformed—as if the elastic forces were initially zero—and the system starts its motion as if it consisted only of mass. The deformation is proportional to the force per unit area and inversely proportional to the mass impedance $\omega_\nu m\sigma$.

The time-dependent exponential in the integrand represents the memory of the system, and the time integration takes care of what has happened to the system in the past. Because the decay time is inversely proportional to the damping, the memory of the system improves as the amount of damping becomes smaller.

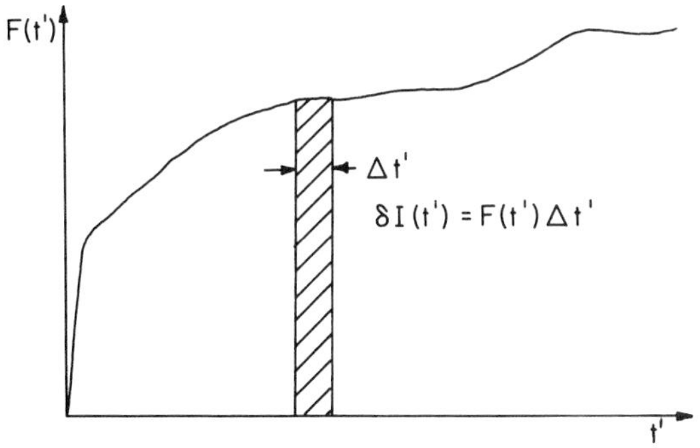

Fig. 11.2 A continuously varying force, which may be interpreted as a series of infinitely short pulses.

Statistically Varying Force Distributions

Power Spectrum and Correlation Function

Frequently, the force distribution is of a statistical nature, such as the force produced by the wind or the force on the walls of a moving vehicle

[3] The factor σ is implicitly contained in the integral as a consequence of the normalization of the φ_ν; $<\varphi_\nu^2> = 1/\sigma$. It is a well-known theorem that the function whose spectrum is given by the product of two spectra can be expressed as the convolution integral of the time functions that correspond to the spectra. The sinusoidally decaying impulse represents the time function whose spectrum is given by the resonance denominator $m\,(\bar{\omega}_\nu^2 - \bar{\omega}^2)$ (i.e., by the spectrum that is transmitted by the system if it is excited by the constant spectrum of an infinitely short pulse), and $p(x_F, y_F; t_F)$ is the time function that corresponds to the exciting force spectrum.

that is caused by the boundary layer turbulence. The exact time pattern of such forces is never fully known—nor would we care to know it. We are usually satisfied with the knowledge of certain average properties of statistically distributed forces, such as the mean values, the maxima and minima, and the mean-square value. To compute these averages, standard Fourier analysis would be unnecessarily cumbersome, because it includes an analysis of the phases of the harmonic constituents, which are of practically no significance in such studies.

Primarily, we are seeking the magnitude of the harmonic amplitudes. If the time function is $f(t)$, its Fourier amplitude[4] is given by:

$$S_f(\omega) = \int_{-\infty}^{\infty} f(t) e^{-j\omega t} dt \tag{11.57}$$

The integral for the Fourier amplitude exists if $f(t)$ converges rapidly enough toward the limits, but this does not normally happen if the function is a statistically varying force. To eliminate convergence problems, the function $f(t)$ is set equal to zero (truncated) for $|t| > T$. The Fourier amplitude of such a function depends on the limits $-T$ and $+T$; in fact, it usually increases proportionally to the square root of the integration interval $2T$. In statistical phenomena the energies usually add, and the amplitude is proportional to the square root of the mean energy. The Fourier coefficient, therefore, turns out to be proportional to the square root of the average square of the function $f(t)$ and to the integration time $2T$. To counteract the increase of the integral with the integration time, the integrand is divided by $1/\sqrt{2T}$. For turbulence or for forces exerted by the wind and for all other cases in which the function $f(t)$ does not change its predominant characteristics (its statistical properties) with time, the function $S_f(\omega)/\sqrt{2T}$ approaches a limiting value as T approaches infinity. Therefore, the integral

$$\frac{S_f(\omega)}{\sqrt{2T}} = \lim_{T=\infty} \frac{1}{\sqrt{2T}} \int_{-T}^{T} f(t) e^{-j\omega t} dt \tag{11.58}$$

exists and is uniquely determined. Conversely, we may conclude that if this integral exists and if it is independent of T for large values of T, the function $f(t)$ has essentially the same properties at all times. Such functions then are defined as statistically homogeneous. If $f(t)$ dies out with time, $S_f(\omega)/\sqrt{2T}$ decreases with T because of the factor $1/\sqrt{2T}$ on the right-hand side of the equation, and $f(t)$ is not statistically homogeneous. To eliminate

[4] It is most convenient to define the Fourier amplitude without the usual factor $1/\sqrt{2\pi}$ and over the frequency range $-\infty$ to $+\infty$. If in the reverse transformation the frequency $\omega/2\pi$ or the wave number $k/2\pi$ is considered the integration variable, no numerical factors, 2, 2π, or 4, occur in any of the formulas. Why this procedure is not strictly followed in the literature is not understandable.

the phases, $S_f(\omega)$ is multiplied by its conjugate complex value; to enforce convergence, it is divided by the length of the integration interval $2T$:

$$W_f(\omega)=\frac{S_f(\omega)S_f^*(\omega)}{2T} \tag{11.59}$$

The new quantity $W_f(\omega)$ is called the power or energy spectrum, because it satisfies the relation

$$\int_{-\infty}^{\infty} W_f(\omega)\frac{d\omega}{2\pi}=\lim_{T=\infty}\frac{1}{2T}\int_{-\infty}^{\infty} S_f(\omega)S_f^*(\omega)\frac{d\omega}{2\pi}=\langle f(t)^2\rangle \tag{11.60}$$

This is proved as follows: If $S_f^*(\omega)$ is expressed by its Fourier integral, the right-hand side[5] becomes:

$$\lim_{T=\infty}\frac{1}{2T}\int_{-\infty}^{\infty} S_f(\omega)\frac{d\omega}{2\pi}\int_{-T}^{T} f(t)e^{j\omega t}dt=\lim_{T=\infty}\frac{1}{2T}\int_{-T}^{T} f(t)^2 dt=\langle f(t)^2\rangle \tag{11.61}$$

because of the inverse relation

$$f(t)=\int_{-\infty}^{\infty} S_f(\omega)e^{j\omega t}\frac{d\omega}{2\pi} \tag{11.62}$$

Thus, the integral over the energy spectrum yields the energy, that is, the mean square of the function.

Let it be pointed out once more that all the spectra are defined over the frequency interval $-\infty$ to $+\infty$ and that $2T$ is the interval for the time integration. Therefore, the energy spectrum is derived by dividing the square of the absolute value of the Fourier amplitude by the integration interval $2T$.

If the function $f(t)$ were periodic with a period of $2T$, Equation 11.57 would—except for a factor $1/T$—represent the Fourier coefficient. The energy would then be given by the sum of the squares of the Fourier amplitudes, and the spectral energy density would be given by the product of the average square of the amplitude of a spectral line, multiplied by the number $n=1/(1/2T)=2T$ of spectral lines per unit frequency interval. The factor $1/T$ in front of the Fourier integral to be squared times the number of lines $2T$ per unit frequency interval, then, leads to the factor $1/T$ in the power spectrum, and Equation 11.59 is obtained again.

The energy or power spectrum is usually deduced from the correlation function $W_f(\rho)$. This very important function[6] is defined by the following integral:

[5] Broken brackets are used to denote space or time averages.

[6] It is convenient to use the same letter W for the correlation function and to differentiate the correlation function from the power spectrum by denoting the variable in its argument by ρ, τ, or ξ.

$$W_f(\rho)=\lim_{T=\infty}\frac{1}{2T}\int_{-T}^{T} f(t)f(t+\rho)dt \tag{11.63}$$

where it is assumed that the mean value of $f(t)$ is zero. If this is not true, this mean value must be substracted from $f(t)$ in the above integral. The function $W_f(\rho)$ is a measure of how drastically $f(t)$ changes with t. In the range in which $f(t)$ and $f(t+\rho)$ depend on each other, $W_f(\rho)$ is not zero, and the correlation is said to be finite. If the values of $f(t)$ and $f(t+\rho)$ are not related to each other, their mean product and, consequently, also the correlation $W_f(\rho)$ are zero.

The correlation function is the Fourier transform of the power spectrum, and the power spectrum is the Fourier transform of the correlation function. The first statement is proved as follows:

$$W_f(\rho)=\lim_{T=\infty}\frac{1}{2T}\int_{-T}^{T} dtf(t+\rho)\int_{-\infty}^{\infty} S_f(\omega)e^{j\omega t}\frac{d\omega}{2\pi}$$

$$=\lim_{T=\infty}\frac{1}{2T}\int_{-\infty}^{\infty}\frac{d\omega S_f(\omega)}{2\pi}\int_{-T}^{T} f(t+\rho)e^{j\omega(t+\rho)}\cdot e^{-j\omega\rho}dt$$

$$=\int_{-\infty}^{\infty}\frac{S_f(\omega)S_f(-\omega)e^{-j\omega\rho}}{2T}\frac{d\omega}{2\pi}=\int_{-\infty}^{\infty} W_f(\omega)e^{-j\omega\rho}\frac{d\omega}{2\pi} \tag{11.64}$$

since $S_f(-\omega)=S_f{}^*(\omega)$, because $f(t)$ is real. This follows directly from the integral relation of Equation 11.58. The power spectrum $W(\omega)$ (Eq. 11.59) is an even function of ω, and $W(-\omega)=W(\omega)$. If the integration variable ω is replaced by $-\omega$,

$$W_f(\rho)=\int_{-\infty}^{\infty} W_f(\omega)e^{j\omega\rho}\frac{d\omega}{2\pi} \tag{11.65}$$

The second statement is the reverse relation,

$$W_f(\omega)=\int_{-\infty}^{\infty} W_f(\rho)e^{-j\omega\rho}d\rho \tag{11.66}$$

and it is proved in a similar manner.

For $\rho=0$, the correlation function reduces to the mean-square value of the time function:

$$W_f(\rho)=\frac{1}{2T}\int_{-T}^{T} f(t)^2dt=\langle f^2\rangle \tag{11.67}$$

This conclusion follows directly from Equation 11.63.

For practical application, the "normalized" correlation function $W_f(\rho)$ is usually preferred; it will be denoted by a lower case $w(\rho)$. This function is defined as:

$$W_f(\rho)=\langle f^2\rangle w_f(\rho) \tag{11.68}$$

so that $w_f(0)=1$. The integral

$$d_c=\int_{-\infty}^{\infty} w_f(\rho)d\rho \tag{11.69}$$

is a measure of the correlation. It is called the correlation interval.[7]

In a similar manner, a normalized power spectrum is defined by:

$$W_f(\omega)=\langle f\rangle^2 w_f(\omega) \tag{11.70}$$

The correlation interval then becomes equal to the normalized power spectrum at zero frequency. For if $w_f(\rho)$ in Equation 11.69 is expressed by its normalized power spectrum,

$$d_c=\lim_{T=\infty}\int_{-T}^{T}\int_{-\infty}^{\infty}\frac{d\omega}{2\pi}w_f(\omega)e^{j\omega\rho}d\rho$$

$$=\lim_{T=\infty}\int_{-T}^{T} d(\omega T)w_f(\omega)\frac{\sin\omega T}{\pi\omega T}=w_f(0) \tag{11.71}$$

since $\lim_{T=\infty}(\sin\omega T/\pi\omega T)$ acts like the delta function $\delta(\omega T)$ in integrals.

The correlation function usually is a simple exponentially or oscillatory decaying function that decreases rapidly to zero. It can easily be determined experimentally. The power spectrum is the Fourier transform of the correlation function. Because of the rapid decrease of the correlation function, integration can be limited to a very short interval, and the mathematical procedure becomes simple.

At first sight it seems very strange that such statistical phenomena as turbulence, flow noise, and noise produced by wind can be described by such a simple function as the power spectrum or the correlation function. The reason that this is possible lies in the averaging over a very long interval. Because of this averaging, any irregularities found in the short time variations of the time functions are smoothed out, and we are left with functions that vary smoothly and slowly with their arguments. However, in dropping the phases, we also have lost a considerable amount of information, and it is not possible to reconstruct the original time functions

[7] In the literature, this integral is usually identified with twice the correlation time or correlation length. But the above definition has considerable advantages.

from their power spectra. For an exponential correlation function,

$$w(\rho)=e^{-|\rho|/L} \tag{11.72}$$

The magnitude L is half the correlation length or correlation time, because

$$d_c=\int_{-\infty}^{\infty} w(\rho)d\rho=2\int_{0}^{\infty} w(\rho)d\rho=2\left(\frac{e^{-\rho L}}{-\frac{1}{L}}\right)_0^{\infty}=2L \tag{11.73}$$

If the correlation interval is very small as compared to the other significant intervals, the correlation function acts similarly to a delta function. The particular form of the correlation function, then, is immaterial, and integrals over the correlation function become very simple. For instance,

$$\int_{-\infty}^{\infty} w_f(\rho)\varphi(\rho)d\rho=\varphi(0)\int_{-\infty}^{\infty} w_f(\rho)d\rho=\varphi(0)d_c \tag{11.74}$$

The correlation function may then be replaced by:

$$w(\rho)=d_c\delta(\rho) \tag{11.75}$$

and

$$W_f(\rho)=d_c\langle f\rangle^2\delta(\rho) \tag{11.76}$$

where $\delta(\rho)$ is the delta or Dirac's function. This simplification will be used below.

Cross-Spectral Density and Cross-Correlation Function

In computing the power spectrum, the spectral amplitude is multiplied by its conjugate complex value and divided by the integration interval. Instead of multiplying the spectral amplitude by its complex conjugate, we can multiply the spectral amplitude at a given point by the complex conjugate of the spectral amplitude at some other point. The function that results is very important in evaluating some of the vibration integrals; it is called the cross-spectral density. Since it is a power spectrum, we shall denote it by the letter W. Thus,

$$W_\xi(\omega;\,x,x')=\lim_{T=\infty}\frac{S_\xi(\omega,x)S_\xi^*(\omega,x')}{2T} \tag{11.77}$$

where x and x' are the co-ordinates of different points. By replacing $S_\xi(\omega, x)$ by its Fourier transform, the following relation can be derived:

$$W_\xi(\omega;\,x,x')=\lim_{T=\infty}\frac{1}{2T}\int_{-T}^{T}\xi(x,t)e^{-j\omega t}dt\int_{-T}^{T}\xi(x',t')e^{j\omega t'}dt'$$

$$=\lim_{T=\infty}\frac{1}{2T}\int_{-T}^{T}\int_{-T}^{T}\xi(x,\tau+t')\xi(x',t')e^{-j\omega\tau}d\tau\,dt' \tag{11.78}$$

where

$$\tau = t - t' \tag{11.79}$$

Thus, the cross-spectral density is the Fourier transform of the cross-correlation function. The function $\xi(x, t)$ is defined only in the interval $-T \leqq t \leqq T$; to obtain a simple result, the values of τ for which the integrand contributes noticeably to the integral must be very small as compared to T; this is always true for statistically varying functions whose average value is zero, provided that T is sufficiently great. The t' integration, then, corresponds to averaging the product $\xi(x, \tau + t')\xi(x', t')$ over the interval $-T \leqq t' \leqq T$. This average, which is called the cross-correlation function, is denoted by $W_\xi(x, x'; \tau)$. Thus,

$$W_\xi(x, x'; \tau) = \langle \xi(x, \tau + t')\xi(x', t') \rangle$$

$$= \lim_{T=\infty} \frac{1}{2T} \int_{-T}^{T} \xi(x, t' + \tau)\xi(x', t')dt' \tag{11.80}$$

Using this result, we obtain:

$$W_\xi(\omega; x, x') = \lim_{T=\infty} \int_{-T}^{T} W_\xi(x, x'; \tau)e^{-j\omega\tau}d\tau \tag{11.81}$$

Correspondingly,

$$W_p(\omega; x_F, x_F') = \frac{S_p(\omega, x_F)S_p^*(\omega, x_F')}{2T} \tag{11.82}$$

represents the cross-spectral density of the pressure distribution. The notation is very convenient: W is the energy or power, and the subscript indicates the variable to which W refers; the magnitude ω indicates that we are concerned with the spectral density at the frequency ω; and x and x' show that W represents a cross-spectral density. If the argument does not contain ω, but contains the parameter τ, we infer that $W_\xi(x, x'; \tau)$ represents the correlation function whose cross-spectral density is $W_\xi(\omega; x, x')$. The reverse relation

$$W_\xi(x, x'; \tau) = \int_{-\infty}^{\infty} W_\xi(\omega; x, x')e^{j\omega\tau}\frac{d\omega}{2\pi} \tag{11.83}$$

shows that $W_\xi(\omega; x, x')\ e^{j\omega t}$ can be interpreted as the narrow-band cross-correlation function; therefore, it is represented by the symbol $W_\xi(\omega; x, x'; \tau)$. Also, $W_\xi(\omega, x)$ represents the power spectrum.[8]

[8] If the function ξ is defined only over an interval $-T$ to T, it may be assumed to be periodic and of the period $2T$: thus, $\xi(t) = a_r \cos \omega_r t + b_r \sin \omega_r t$, and $\xi_r^2(t) = (a_r^2/2) + (b_r^2/2)$, where $\omega_r - \omega_{r-1} = \Delta\omega = 2\pi\Delta f = \pi/T$. The energy $W_r(\omega, x)\Delta f$ contained in the frequency band Δf must, then, on the average, be equal to the average energy of a spectral line of the equivalent periodic phenomenon. Hence, $W_\xi(\omega, x)\Delta f = W_\xi(\omega, x)(1/T) = (a_r^2 + b_r^2)/2$ or $W_\xi(\omega, x) = T(a_r^2 + b_r^2)/2$.

Thus far we have considered only the time variance of the functions p and ξ. If the variable p is of a statistical nature, the average value of a function of x, x' is a function of the distance $\zeta = x - x'$ only between the two points, and

$$W_\xi(\omega; x, x'; \tau) = W_\xi(\omega, x - x', \tau) = W_\xi(\omega, \zeta, \tau) \tag{11.84}$$

If the time is not varied, $\tau = 0$, and

$$W_\xi(\omega, \zeta, 0) = W_\xi(\omega, \zeta) \tag{11.85}$$

can be interpreted as the narrow-band space correlation function. Thus, for $\tau = 0$, the cross-spectral density becomes identical with the narrow-band space correlation function.

Vibration Excited by Statistically Varying Forces[9]

Fourier Methods

In the study of statistically varying forces, the mean square of the vibration amplitude and the power spectrum of the vibrations are of primary concern; the detailed motion is of no practical interest. The mean square of the vibration amplitude at a point x is connected with the power spectrum for the motion of that point by the following relation:

$$\xi^2(x) = \int_{-\infty}^{\infty} W_\xi(\omega, x)\frac{d\omega}{2\pi} = \lim_{T=\infty}\frac{1}{2T}\int_{-\infty}^{\infty} S_\xi(\omega, x)S_\xi^*(\omega, x)\frac{d\omega}{2\pi} \tag{11.86}$$

On the right-hand side, the Fourier amplitudes $S_\xi(\omega, x)$ and $S_\xi^*(\omega, x)$ can be replaced by the solution (Eq. 11.26) of the differential equation of the system:

$$\xi^2(x) = \int_{-\infty}^{\infty} W_\xi(\omega, x)\frac{d\omega}{2\pi} = \lim_{T=\infty}\frac{1}{2T}\int_{-\infty}^{\infty}\frac{d\omega}{2\pi}$$

$$\cdot \left[\sum_\nu \frac{\varphi_\nu(x)}{m(\bar{\omega}_\nu^2 - \bar{\omega}^2)}\int_\sigma S_p(\omega, x_F)\varphi_\nu(x_F)dx_F\right.$$

$$\left.\cdot \sum_\mu \frac{\varphi_\mu(x)}{m(\bar{\omega}_\mu^{2*} - \bar{\omega}^{2*})}\int_\sigma S_p^*(\omega, x_F')\varphi_\mu(x'_F)dx_F'\right]$$

$$= \lim_{T=\infty}\int_{-\infty}^{\infty}\frac{d\omega}{2\pi}\sum_\nu\sum_\mu\frac{\varphi_\nu(x)\varphi_\mu(x)\sigma^2}{\bar{X}_\nu\bar{X}_\mu^*}\int_\sigma\int_\sigma\frac{S_p(\omega, x_F)S_p^*(\omega, x_F')}{2T}$$

$$\cdot\ \varphi_\nu(x_F)\varphi_\mu(x_F')dx_F dx_F' \tag{11.87}$$

[9] See A. Powell, "Response of structures to jet noise," in *Random Vibrations*, ed. by S. H. Crandall (Cambridge, Mass., 1958).

where the asterisk denotes conjugate complex and

$$\bar{X}_\nu = \sigma m(\bar{\omega}_\nu^2 - \bar{\omega}^2) = M(\bar{\omega}_\nu^2 - \bar{\omega}^2) \tag{11.88}$$

The x-dependence is eliminated by averaging over the system. Because of the orthogonality conditions $\langle \varphi_\nu \varphi_\mu \rangle = 0$ and $\sigma \langle \varphi_\nu^2 \rangle = 1$, Equation 11.87, after the integration signs on the left and right are dropped, reduces to:

$$\langle W_\xi(\omega, x) \rangle = W_\xi(\omega) = \sum_\nu \frac{\sigma}{|X_\nu^2|} \int\int W_p(\omega; x_F, x_F') \varphi_\nu(x_F) \varphi_\nu(x_F') dx_F dx_F' \tag{11.89}$$

where $W_\xi(\omega)$ has been written for the mean value of the power spectrum $W_\xi(\omega, x)$ over the vibrator; $W_p(\omega; x_F, x_F')$ in the integrand is the narrow-band correlation function. For statistical phenomena, $W(\omega; x_F, x_F') = W(\omega; x_F - x_F')$, since the correlation then depends only on the distance $x_F - x_F'$ between the two points x_F and x_F'. It is expedient to express $W_p(\omega, \zeta)$ by its Fourier transform:

$$W_p(\omega, \zeta) = \int_{-\infty}^{\infty} \langle p^2 \rangle w_p(\omega, \kappa) e^{j\kappa\zeta} \frac{d\kappa}{2\pi} \tag{11.90}$$

where $\zeta = x_F - x_F'$, so that $w_p(\omega, \kappa)$ is the normalized narrow-band space-power spectrum. Equations 11.86 and 11.87, then, are equivalent to:

$$W_\xi(\omega) = \sum_\nu \frac{\sigma \langle p^2 \rangle}{|X_\nu|^2} \int\int\int \frac{d\kappa}{2\pi} w_p(\omega, \kappa) e^{j\kappa(x_F - x_F')} \varphi_\nu(x_F) \varphi_\nu(x_F') dx_F \, dx_F'$$

$$= \sum_\nu \frac{\sigma \langle p^2 \rangle}{|X_\nu|^2} \int_{-\infty}^{\infty} \frac{d\kappa}{2\pi} w_p(\omega, \kappa) \left[\frac{S_{\varphi\nu}(\kappa) S_{\varphi\nu}^*(\kappa)}{\sigma} \right] \sigma$$

$$= \sum_\nu \frac{\sigma^2 \langle p^2 \rangle}{|X_\nu|^2} \int_{-\infty}^{\infty} w_p(\omega, \kappa) W_{\varphi\nu}(\kappa) \frac{d\kappa}{2\pi} = \sum_\nu \frac{\langle p^2 \rangle \sigma^2}{|X_\nu|^2} \kappa_\nu^2(\omega) \tag{11.91}$$

where, in the subscripts, φ_ν has been written as φ_ν. The second form of the right-hand side was obtained with the aid of the relation:

$$S_{\varphi\nu}(\kappa) = \int \varphi_\nu(x_F) e^{-j\kappa x_F} \, dx_F \tag{11.92}$$

In the third form of the right-hand side,

$$\frac{S_{\varphi\nu}(\kappa) S_{\varphi\nu}^*(\kappa)}{\sigma} = W_{\varphi\nu}(\kappa) \tag{11.93}$$

where σ (which takes the place of the $2T$ in the time integration) represents the integration interval. In the last form of the right-hand side of Equation 11.91, the symbol $\kappa_\nu^2(\omega)$ is used to abbreviate the integral; it represents the effect of the variation of the mode amplitude and of the nodal line pattern on the vibration amplitude. Because it depends on the force spectrum and on the natural functions, it is frequently called the joint admittance; however, we shall refer to it as the excitation constant for statistical force distributions:

$$\kappa_\nu^2(\omega)=\int_{-\infty}^{\infty} w_p(\omega,\kappa)W_{\varphi\nu}(\kappa)\frac{d\kappa}{2\pi} \tag{11.94}$$

For a statistically distributed force pattern, the mean square of the force $F^2{}_{\mathrm{eff}}$ is equal to the square of the force on one correlation area σ_{cor} multiplied by the number of correlation areas $n=\sigma/\sigma_{\mathrm{cor}}$; thus,

$$F^2{}_{\mathrm{eff}}=\langle p^2\rangle\sigma^2{}_{\mathrm{cor}}\frac{\sigma}{\sigma_{\mathrm{cor}}}=\langle p^2\sigma^2\rangle\frac{\sigma_{\mathrm{cor}}}{\sigma} \tag{11.95}$$

Comparison with Equation 11.91 shows that in the absence of nodal lines,

$$\kappa_\nu^2(\omega)=\frac{\sigma_{\mathrm{cor}}}{\sigma} \tag{11.96}$$

which is a result that can easily be remembered. Equation 11.91 also shows that the nodal line pattern of the natural functions has a filtering effect on the force distribution; it acts like a filter whose frequency curve is equal to the space-power spectrum of the natural function. If $w_p(\omega,\kappa)$ is the normalized power spectrum of the force distribution and $W_{\varphi\nu}$ (κ) is the power spectrum of the natural function $\varphi_\nu(x)$, the effective spectrum that acts on the vibrator becomes:

$$\langle p^2\rangle\kappa_\nu^2(\omega)=\int_{-\infty}^{\infty}\langle p^2\rangle w_p(\omega,\kappa)W_{\varphi\nu}(\kappa)\frac{d\kappa}{2\pi} \tag{11.97}$$

where $W_{\varphi\nu}(\kappa)$ is the space-power spectrum of the natural function φ_ν. The power spectrum reaches a maximum when the space wave length equals twice the distance between the nodal lines of the vibrator.

If the vibrator contains many nodal areas, the boundary conditions have very little effect on the mean-square amplitude, and they may be assumed to be of the simplest possible form. For instance, we may assume that at $x=0$ and at $x=l$, $\varphi_\nu(x)=0$. In most cases of practical interest, $\varphi_\nu(x)$ is a sinusoidal function of the type

$$\varphi_\nu(x)=\sqrt{\frac{2}{l}}\sin\kappa_\nu x \tag{11.98}$$

where

$$\sin\kappa_\nu l=0 \tag{11.99}$$

or

$$\kappa_\nu=\frac{\nu\pi}{l} \tag{11.100}$$

$W_{\varphi\nu}(\kappa)$, then, is of the same mathematical form as the power spectrum of a burst of sinusoidal oscillations:

$$S_{\varphi\nu}(\kappa)=\int_0^l \sqrt{\frac{2}{l}}\sin\kappa_\nu x\, e^{-j\kappa x}dx \tag{11.101}$$

This integral is given in the standard tables. It simplifies to:

$$\begin{aligned}S_{\varphi\nu}(\kappa)&=\sqrt{\frac{2}{l}}\frac{e^{-j\kappa l}(-j\kappa\sin\kappa_\nu l-\kappa_\nu\cos\kappa_\nu l)+\kappa_\nu}{\kappa_\nu{}^2-\kappa^2}\\&=\sqrt{\frac{2}{l}}e^{-j(\kappa-\kappa_\nu)l/2}\frac{2j\kappa_\nu\sin\dfrac{(\kappa-\kappa_\nu)l}{2}}{\kappa_\nu{}^2-\kappa^2}\end{aligned} \tag{11.102}$$

because of the boundary conditions, and because $\cos\nu\pi=e^{j\pi\nu}$. The power spectrum is given by the square of the absolute value $S_{\varphi\nu}$ divided by the range of integration σ. Hence,

$$W_{\varphi\nu}(\kappa)=\frac{8}{l^2}\frac{\kappa_\nu{}^2\sin^2\dfrac{(\kappa-\kappa_\nu)l}{2}}{(\kappa_\nu{}^2-\kappa^2)^2} \tag{11.103}$$

The statistical excitation constant then becomes:

$$\begin{aligned}\kappa_\nu{}^2(\omega)&=l\int_{-\infty}^{\infty}\frac{w_p(\omega,\kappa)\kappa_\nu{}^2\sin^2\dfrac{(\kappa-\kappa_\nu)l}{2}}{(\kappa_\nu{}^2-\kappa^2)^2\dfrac{l^4}{16}}\frac{\dfrac{d\kappa l}{2}}{2\pi}\\&=\frac{1}{2l}\int_{-\infty}^{\infty}w_p(\omega,\kappa)\left[\frac{4u_\nu{}^2\sin^2(u-u_\nu)}{\pi(u_\nu{}^2-u^2)^2}\right]du\end{aligned} \tag{11.104}$$

If the problem is two-dimensional, a similar factor $W_{\varphi\nu}(\kappa_y)$ is generated by the variation of the natural functions in the y-direction, where κ_y is the space wave number in the y-direction. If $u=\kappa l/2$ is large enough, $4u_\nu{}^2\sin^2(u-u_\nu)/[\pi(u_\nu{}^2-u^2)^2]$ acts like the delta function $\delta(u_\nu{}^2-u^2)$, replacing $\kappa l/2$ by $-\kappa_\nu l/2$ and by $+\kappa_\nu l/2$ in succession.[10] Because of the δ-function effect of the integrand, the result can also be written as follows:

$$\begin{aligned}\kappa_\nu{}^2(\omega)&=w_p(\omega,\kappa_\nu)\int_0^{\infty}W_{\varphi\nu}(\kappa)\frac{d\kappa}{2\pi}+w_p(\omega,-\kappa_\nu)\int_{-\infty}^{0}W_{\varphi\nu}(\kappa)\frac{d\kappa}{2\pi}\\&=w_p(\omega,\kappa_\nu)\int_{-\infty}^{\infty}W_{\varphi\nu}(\kappa)\frac{d\kappa}{2\pi}=w_p(\omega,\kappa_\nu)\langle\varphi_\nu{}^2\rangle=\frac{w_p(\omega,\kappa_\nu)}{\sigma}\end{aligned} \tag{11.105}$$

[10] To prove this statement, let $u_\nu=\nu\pi$ and $u=u_\nu+y$. The integrand then contains the factor $(4u_\nu{}^2\sin^2 y)/[\pi(2u_\nu y+y^2)^2]$. Since the integrand contributes only near $y=0$, u_ν being very large, the term y^2 can be neglected, and the y-integral reduces to one.

where σ is the integration length, area, or volume, because the integral over the power spectrum is equal to the mean square of the function $\langle \varphi_\nu^2 \rangle = 1/\sigma$, and $w_p(\omega, \kappa_\nu) = w_p(\omega, -\kappa_\nu)$. The last result applies, if the vibrator exhibits a nodal line pattern.

If the vibrator is a narrow, but long, piston membrane, $\varphi(x) = \text{const} = 1/\sqrt{\sigma} = 1/\sqrt{l}$ (because of the normality condition), and

$$S_\varphi(\kappa) = \int_{-l/2}^{l/2} \frac{1}{\sqrt{\sigma}} e^{-j\kappa x} dx = \frac{\sqrt{l}}{2} \frac{\sin \frac{\kappa l}{2}}{\frac{\kappa l}{2}}$$

$$W_\varphi(\kappa) = \pi \left[\frac{1}{\pi} \left(\frac{\sin \frac{\kappa l}{2}}{\frac{\kappa l}{2}} \right)^2 \right] \tag{11.106}$$

If κl is large, the function in the bracket acts like a $\delta(\kappa l/2)$ function, and the statistical excitation constant becomes:

$$\kappa_\nu^2(\omega) = \frac{w_p(\omega, 0)}{l} \tag{11.107}$$

When the noise generated by hydrodynamic flow is measured, the pressure fluctuations are generated by the transportation of the flow pattern over the sensitive area of the hydrophone. If the flow pattern (turbulence) were frozen, the received frequency would be:

$$\frac{\omega_r}{2\pi} = \frac{u_0}{\lambda_{\text{space}}} = \frac{u_0}{2\pi} \cdot \frac{2\pi}{\lambda_{\text{space}}} = \frac{u_0}{2\pi} \kappa \quad \text{and} \quad d\omega_r = u_0 d\kappa \tag{11.108}$$

where u_0 is the velocity of the flow and λ_{space} is the space wave length of the pressure component in the flow pattern that generates the frequency $\omega_r/2\pi$. Thus, the received frequency is a function only of the space wave number κ. Because the flow pattern is not frozen, the ω component in the power spectrum is related to the lifetime of the flow pattern (see below) and determines the amplitude of the space components κ, regardless of what the receiver is. If κ is expressed by ω_r, the integral for the statistical excitation constant becomes

$$\kappa_\nu^2(\omega) = \frac{1}{4} \int w_p\left(\omega, \frac{\omega_r}{u_0}\right) \left(\frac{\sin \frac{\omega_r l}{2u_0}}{\frac{\omega_r l}{2u_0}} \right)^2 \frac{d\omega_r}{2\pi u_0} \tag{11.109}$$

For a very long receiver, Equation 4.107 applies, and the excitation constant becomes zero. A long receiver is insensitive to pressure fluctuations. The maxima and minima cancel, and the resultant output is zero. The above integral shows that the receiver sees the power spectrum as if it were weighted by the factor $\sin^2 (\omega_r l/2u_0)^2/(\omega_r l/2u_0)$. A receiver of finite length l is fully sensitive to the pressure fluctuations up to $\omega_r l/u_0 = \pi$, but for higher frequencies, its output decreases proportionally to $1/\omega_r^2$.

Equation 11.105 shows that the main problem in the computation is the determination of the time-space-power spectrum $w_p(\omega, \kappa)$ of the force distribution. Fortunately, the power spectrum is easily deduced from the correlation function. In most practical cases, the normalized correlation function is of the form

$$w_p(\rho)=e^{-|\tau|/\theta}e^{-|\zeta|/L} \tag{11.110}$$

where 2θ is the correlation time and $2L$ is the correlation distance of the force distribution. The magnitudes θ and L then also determine the power spectrum. Because τ and ζ are separated in the exponents of the correlation function,

$$w(\omega, \kappa)=w_p(\omega)\cdot w_p(\kappa) \tag{11.111}$$

where

$$w_p(\omega)=\int_{-\infty}^{\infty} e^{-|\tau|/\theta}e^{-j\omega\tau}d\tau=\int_0^{\infty} e^{-(1/\theta+j\omega)\tau}d\tau+\int_{-\infty}^{0} e^{(1/\theta-j\omega)\tau}d\tau$$

$$=\int_0^{\infty}[e^{-(1/\theta+j\omega)\tau}+e^{-(1/\theta-j\omega)\tau}]d\tau$$

$$=\frac{1}{\frac{1}{\theta}+j\omega}+\frac{1}{\frac{1}{\theta}-j\omega}=\frac{\frac{2}{\theta}}{\omega^2+\frac{1}{\theta^2}}=\frac{2\theta}{1+\omega^2\theta^2} \tag{11.112}$$

Similarly,

$$w_p(\kappa)=\frac{2L}{1+\kappa^2L^2} \tag{11.113}$$

If the vibrator exhibits many nodal line areas, Equation 11.107 applies, and Equation 11.91 becomes:

$$W_\xi(\omega)=\sum_\nu \frac{\langle p^2\rangle\sigma^2}{X_\nu^2}\kappa_\nu^2(\omega)=\sum_\nu \frac{\langle p^2\rangle\sigma}{X_\nu^2}w_p(\omega, \kappa_\nu)$$

$$=\sum_\nu \frac{\langle p^2\rangle\sigma}{|X_\nu^2|}\left(\frac{2\theta}{1+\omega^2\theta^2}\cdot\frac{2L}{1+\kappa^2L^2}\right) \tag{11.114}$$

Each term on the right-hand side of the equation represents the power spectrum of a particular mode of vibration. The contribution of each mode to the mean-square amplitude is found by integrating over the frequency:[11]

$$\frac{2\langle p^2\rangle l\theta\cdot L}{M^2(1+\kappa^2L^2)}\int_{-\infty}^{\infty}\frac{2}{1+\omega^2\theta^2}\,\frac{\frac{d\omega}{2\pi}}{(\omega_\nu^2-\omega^2)^2+4\delta_\nu^2\omega^2} \tag{11.115}$$

[11] Because higher powers of δ are neglected, it does not make any difference whether the losses are due to external or internal friction. For internal friction the last term in the denominator would be $4\delta_\nu^2\omega_\nu^2$ instead of $4\delta_\nu^2\omega^2$.

The integral can be evaluated by contour integration; if we integrate along the real ω-axis from $-\infty$ to $+\infty$ and close the path by an infinite semicircle above the ω-axis, only the poles with positive imaginary parts contribute. It is expedient to write the integral in the following form:

$$I_\omega = \int_{-\infty}^{\infty} \frac{2\beta^2}{\beta^2+\omega^2} \frac{\frac{d\omega}{2\pi}}{(\omega_\nu^2-\omega^2)^2+4\delta_\nu^2\omega^2} \tag{11.116}$$

where

$$\beta = \frac{1}{\theta} \tag{11.117}$$

The magnitude β represents a very characteristic parameter of the force distribution. Its value is the radial frequency (usually 5 to 100 cps), for which the power spectrum has decreased to half its maximum value. The first factor in the integrand introduces the two poles:

$$\omega = \pm j\beta \tag{11.118}$$

The second factor introduces the four poles:

$$(\omega^2-\omega_\nu^2)^2+4\delta_\nu^2\omega^2=0 \qquad \omega^2=\omega_\nu^2 \pm 2j\omega\delta_\nu \qquad \text{and}$$

$$\omega = \pm\omega_\nu\sqrt{1 \pm 2j\frac{\omega}{\omega_\nu^2}\delta_\nu} \tag{11.119}$$

Since damping affects the result only in the resonance range $(\omega/\omega_\nu^2)\delta_\nu \cong (\omega/\omega^2)$, $\omega\eta/2$ may be replaced by $\eta/2$, and the expressions for the four poles of the second factor simplify to:

$$\omega = \pm\omega_\nu\sqrt{1 \pm j\eta} = \pm\omega_\nu\left(1 \pm \frac{j\eta}{2}\right) \tag{11.120}$$

The poles

$$\omega = j\beta \qquad \omega_\nu\left(1+\frac{j\eta}{2}\right) \qquad \text{and} \qquad -\omega_\nu\left(1-\frac{j\eta}{2}\right) \tag{11.121}$$

are above the real axis and contribute to the integral. The residue of the first is:

$$\frac{\beta^2}{j\beta} \cdot \frac{1}{(\omega_\nu^2+\beta^2)^2-4\delta^2\beta^2} \doteq \frac{\beta}{j(\omega_\nu^2+\beta^2)^2} \tag{11.122}$$

In the denominator, the term $4\delta_\nu^2$, which equals $\omega^2\eta^2$, is almost always small as compared to one, and this term is always negligible as compared to the first term of the denominator. The sum of the residues at the two other poles is:

$$\frac{1}{2}\frac{\beta^2}{\beta^2+\omega_\nu^2\left(1+\frac{j\eta}{2}\right)^2}\frac{1}{\omega_\nu^3\left(1+\frac{j\eta}{2}\right)j\eta}+\frac{1}{2}\frac{\beta^2}{\beta^2+\omega_\nu^2\left(1-\frac{j\eta}{2}\right)^2}\frac{1}{\omega_\nu^3\left(1-\frac{j\eta}{2}\right)j\eta}$$

$$=\frac{\beta^2}{j\eta\omega_\nu^3}\frac{\beta^2+\omega_\nu^2}{(\beta^2+\omega_\nu^2)^2+\omega_\nu^4\frac{\eta^2}{4}}$$

$$\doteq\frac{\beta^2}{j\eta\omega_\nu^3}\frac{1}{\beta^2+\omega_\nu^2} \tag{11.123}$$

where squares and higher powers of η have been neglected. The value of the integral is $2\pi j$ times its residues. If the result is still divided by 2π (because the integration is with respect to $\omega/2\pi$), the integral becomes:

$$I_\omega=\frac{\beta}{(\omega_\nu^2+\beta^2)^2}+\frac{\beta^2}{\omega_\nu^3\eta(\beta^2+\omega_\nu^2)} \tag{11.124}$$

The result is very interesting indeed. The second term represents the mean-square vibration amplitude that would have been excited if the power spectrum of the force distribution had been constant and equal to the value at the resonant frequency of the system. This part of the solution represents the contribution of the resonance range and, consequently, is inversely proportional to the loss factor. The mean square of the velocity amplitude is obtained by multiplying the integrand (Eq. 11.116) by ω^2. Since this factor does not generate any new poles or cancel existing poles, it appears as multiplier in the residues. The first term in the solution (Eq. 11.124) then is multiplied by a factor $-\beta^2$; thus the equivalent frequency of this term is not ω_ν, but the much lower frequency β. If the other two pole frequencies $\omega_\nu^2(1\pm j\eta/2)^2$ (Eq. 11.121) are substituted in forming the residues, the $j\eta$ terms drop out, and the second term in the integral solution (Eq. 11.124) becomes multiplied by ω_ν^2.

The first term of the solution represents the effect of the decrease of the power spectrum of the force distribution with frequency. It generates a pole pair outside the resonance range and represents the force excitation of the mode by the part of the force spectrum that is outside the band width of the mode. The equivalent frequency $\beta=1/\theta$ is the frequency at which the force spectrum starts its drastic decrease. Since these contributions are off resonance, damping is not involved, and the velocity amplitude is $\beta\xi$ (not $\omega_\nu\xi$), because the value of the corresponding residue is $\omega=j\beta$. Since $\beta=1/\theta$ is usually much smaller than ω_ν, the contribution of this term to the velocity amplitude is negligible, but it does have a considerable effect on the displacement amplitude. Thus, whenever the mean square of the vibration amplitude is inversely proportional to the loss factor, the natural modes are excited in their resonance range and $\omega_\nu^2\,\xi_\nu^2=\dot{\xi}_\nu^2$. But if the mean square does not depend on the damping, the displacement amplitude is predominantly determined by the off-resonance part of the force spectrum, and

$$\dot{\xi}_\nu^2=\beta^2\xi_\nu^2\neq\omega_\nu^2\xi_\nu^2 \tag{11.125}$$

In all practical cases, the off-resonance term of the mean-square velocity seems to be negligible when compared to the resonance term. It seems that the displacement amplitude of the higher-order modes is primarily due to the excitation of these modes to forced vibration by the low-frequency part of the force spectrum. But the velocity amplitude will usually be predominantly determined by the force spectrum in the resonance range of the mode. Figure 11.3 shows the frequency curves of the power spectrum of the force field, the mode amplitude, and the mode velocity.

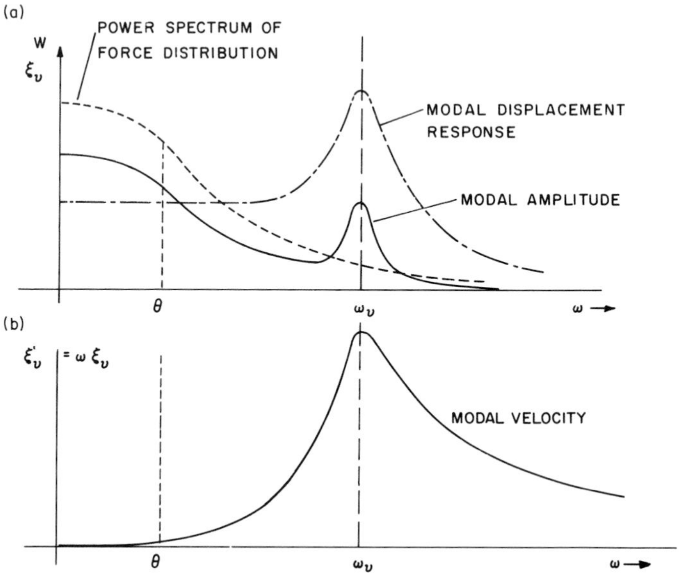

Fig. 11.3 Frequency curves of the power spectrum of the force field, the modal amplitude, and the modal velocity; *a*, *solid curve*, modal amplitude that is generated by the power spectrum; *broken curve*, power spectrum of the average type of statistical force field; *dotted curve*, modal displacement response for constant amplitude driving force; *b*, modal velocity, forced by multiplying the forced modal amplitude by ω (not by ω_ν).

The mean square of the displacement amplitude is obtained by adding the contributions of the various modes:

$$\langle\xi^2\rangle=\sum_\nu\langle\xi_\nu{}^2\rangle=\sum_\nu\frac{2\langle p^2\rangle lL}{M^2(1+\kappa_\nu{}^2L^2)\left(\omega_\nu{}^2+\dfrac{1}{\theta^2}\right)}\left(\frac{1}{\omega_\nu{}^2+\dfrac{1}{\theta^2}}+\frac{\dfrac{1}{\theta}}{\omega_\nu{}^3\eta}\right) \qquad (11.126)$$

If the vibrating system is a one-dimensional strip and if its resonant frequency is high ($\omega_\nu{}^2\gg 1/\theta^2$ and $\omega_\nu\theta\eta\gg 1$), like that of a piezoelectric receiver, the solution (Eq. 11.126) simplifies to $2\langle p^2\rangle lLK^2$, where K is the equivalent compliance, and the lifetime θ of the force pattern has no effect on the frequency response of the receiver.

The mean square of the velocity is deduced in a similar manner; it is given by:

$$\langle\dot{\xi}^2\rangle=\sum_\nu\langle\dot{\xi}_\nu{}^2\rangle=\sum_\nu\frac{2\langle p^2\rangle Ll}{M^2(1+\kappa_\nu{}^2L^2)\left(\omega_\nu{}^2+\frac{1}{\theta^2}\right)}\left(\frac{-\frac{1}{\theta^2}}{\omega_\nu{}^2+\frac{1}{\theta^2}}+\frac{\frac{1}{\theta}}{\omega_\nu\eta}\right) \quad (11.127)$$

Because the first term in the parentheses of the last form on the right-hand side is practically always negligible as compared to the second term,

$$\langle\dot{\xi}^2\rangle=\sum_\nu\frac{2\langle p^2\rangle Ll\theta}{\omega_\nu\eta M^2(1+\kappa_\nu{}^2L^2)(1+\omega_\nu{}^2\theta^2)} \quad (11.128)$$

The factor 2 in the result is due to the fact that $2L$, and not L, is the correlation distance. If the vibration were two-dimensional, a factor $2\ Ll_y/(1+\kappa_y{}^2l_y{}^2)$ would have to be included in the solution.

Thus, the mean-square velocity amplitude is a very simple function of the damping, the correlation distance and correlation time of the force pattern, the mean-square force, and the bending wave numbers κ_ν of the modes that are excited.

Since the velocity amplitude is predominantly determined by the contributions of the resonance ranges of the modes, the smoothed-out power spectrum of the velocity amplitude of a single mode is given by:

$$\langle\dot{\xi}_\nu{}^2\rangle=\int_{-\infty}^{\infty}W_{\dot{\xi}_\nu}(\omega)\frac{d\omega}{2\pi}\cong W_{\dot{\xi}}(\omega)\frac{\epsilon_\nu}{2\pi} \quad (11.129)$$

or

$$W_{\dot{\xi}}(\omega)=\frac{2\pi\langle\dot{\xi}_\nu{}^2\rangle}{\epsilon_\nu}=\frac{2\pi\langle p^2\rangle 2Ll\theta}{\omega_\nu\eta M^2(1+\kappa_\nu{}^2L^2)(1+\omega_\nu{}^2\theta^2)\epsilon_\nu} \quad (11.130)$$

where $\epsilon_\nu/2\pi$ is the average frequency difference between successive modes. Since correlation distance and correlation time are well known for most force fields, the above formulas can be readily evaluated. For instance, if the force field is generated by the turbulent velocity fluctuations in the boundary layer of a moving vehicle,

$$\langle p^2\rangle^{\frac{1}{2}}\doteq 9\cdot 10^{-3}u_0{}^2 \qquad \text{and} \qquad L\cong 5\delta^* \quad (11.131)$$

where δ^* is the displacement thickness of the boundary layer; the lifetime or correlation time of the force pattern is found to be given by $\theta\cong 30\delta^*/u_0$, *ut* being the velocity of the vehicle. However, a warning seems to be justified. The value of correlation analysis is frequently overestimated. Boundary layer turbulence, for instance, is generated in strictly periodic streaks along the wall.[12] An exponential correlation function, then, is a very crude assumption, and considerable discrepancies may be expected, and do occur, between theory and experimental results.

Computation of the Mean-Square Vibration Amplitude of a System on the Basis of Its Impulse Response[13]

The preceding computations were based on the Fourier methods. The solutions were exact except for the assumption of a frequency-independent loss factor and of a frequency-independent external resistance. But the error is negligible if damping is small.

Similar results can be obtained on the basis of the impulse response (Eq. 11.54) of the system. In terms of the impulse response, the square of the vibration amplitude is given by:

$$\xi^2(x,y;t)=\sum_\nu \frac{\varphi_\nu(x,y)}{\omega_\nu{}^*m}\int_\sigma\int_{-\infty}^{t} p(x_F,y_F;t_F)e^{-\delta_\nu(t-t_F)}\varphi_\nu(x_F,y_F)$$

$$\cdot \sin\omega_\nu{}^*(t-t_F)dx_F dy_F dt_F$$

$$\cdot \sum_\mu \frac{\varphi_\mu(x,y)}{\omega_\mu{}^*m}\int_\sigma\int_{-\infty}^{t} p(x_F,y_F;t_F)e^{-\delta_\mu(t-t_F)}\varphi_\mu(x_F,y_F)$$

$$\cdot \sin\omega^*(t-t_F')dx_F'\,dy_F'\,dt_F'$$

$$=\sum_\nu\sum_\mu \frac{\varphi_\nu(x,y)\varphi_\mu(x,y)}{\omega_\nu{}^*\omega_\mu{}^*m^2}\int_\sigma\int_{-\infty}^{t}\int_{-\infty}^{t} p(x_F',y_F';t_F')p(x_F,y_F;t_F)$$

$$\cdot e^{-(\delta_\nu+\delta_\mu)t}\cdot e^{\delta_\nu t_F+\delta_\mu t_F'}\varphi_\nu(x_F,y_F)\varphi_\mu(x_F',y_F')\sin\omega_\nu{}^*(t-t_F)$$

$$\cdot \sin\omega_\nu{}^*(t-t_F')dx_F dy_F dx_F' dy_F' dt_F dt_F' \qquad (11.132)$$

If the excitation is of a statistical nature, the time average $\langle\xi^2(x,y;t)\rangle$ is of interest. The only factor on the right-hand side of this equation that may change with time is the product $\langle p(x_F,y_F;t_F)\cdot p(x_F',y_F';t_F')\rangle$. For a statistically homogeneous force distribution, the average of this product is always a function of the differences of the co-ordinates:

$$\langle p(x_F,y_F;t_F)p(x_F',y_F';t_F')\rangle=\langle p^2\rangle w_p(x_F'-x_F,y_F'-y_F,t_F'-t_F) \qquad (11.133)$$

where $\langle p^2\rangle$ is the mean-square pressure variation and w_p stands for the normalized correlation function. If we are interested only in the mean square of the displacement over the system, the integrals over the products

[12] See S. J. Kline *et al.*, *Reports*, Stanford University, 1964–66.

[13] See I. Dyer, "Sound radiation into a closed space from boundary layer turbulence," in Bolt, Beranek, and Newman Report No. 602 (Cambridge, Mass., 1958); and R. H. Lyon, "Response of strings to random noise fields," *J.A.S.A.*, **28** (1956), 391–98.

$\langle\varphi_\nu\varphi_\mu\rangle$ vanish, and $\langle\varphi_\nu{}^2\rangle = 1/\sigma$ because of the orthogonality conditions. The result then simplifies to:

$$\langle\xi^2\rangle = \sum_\nu \langle\xi_\nu{}^2\rangle = \sum_\nu \frac{\langle p^2\rangle}{\sigma\omega_\nu{}^{2*}m^2} \int w_p(x_F' - x_F, y - y_F, t - t_F')\varphi_\nu(x_F, y_F)\varphi_\nu(x_F', y_F')$$

$$\cdot\, e^{-\delta_\nu(2t - t_F - t_F')} \sin\omega_\nu{}^*(t - t_F) \sin\omega_\nu{}^*(t - t_F')\,dx_F\,dy_F\,dx_F'\,dy_F'\,dt_F\,dt_F' \tag{11.134}$$

Mean Square of the Vibration Amplitude for Statistically Varying Force Distribution

For most practical cases, the correlation function can be approximated by a product of a function of space and a function of time of the following form:

$$w_p(x - x', y - y', t - t') = w_p(x - x', y - y')e^{-|t - t'|/\theta} \tag{11.135}$$

The quantity θ is equal to half the correlation interval (Eq. 11.73); it is called the lifetime of the force pattern. If this correlation function is introduced, space integration and time integration become separable, and

$$\langle\xi_\nu{}^2\rangle = \frac{\langle p^2\rangle}{\sigma m^2} \int_\sigma \int_\sigma w_p(x_F - x_F', y_F - y_F')\varphi_\nu(x_F, y_F)\varphi_\nu(x_F', y_F')\,d\sigma_F\,d\sigma_F'$$

$$\int_{t_F}^{t} \int_{t_F'}^{t} \frac{1}{\omega_\nu{}^2} e^{-\delta_\nu(2t - t_F - t_F') - |t_F - t_F'|/\theta} \sin\omega_\nu{}^*(t - t_F) \sin\omega_\nu{}^*(t - t_F')\,dt_F\,dt_F'$$

$$= \frac{\langle p^2\rangle}{\sigma m^2} I_t I_\sigma \tag{11.136}$$

where I_t stands for the time integral and I_σ, for the space integral. Since books and publications hardly ever discuss the evaluation of integrals like those above, the various steps of the integration procedure is discussed here in detail.

To perform the time integration, the following variables are introduced:

$$\mu = t_F + t_F'$$
$$\tau = t_F - t_F' \tag{11.137}$$

And if we simply write ω for $\omega_\nu{}^*$ and δ for δ_ν, the time integral becomes:

$$I_t = \frac{1}{2\omega^2} \int_{-\infty}^{2t} e^{-\delta(2t - \mu)}d\mu \int_{\mu - 2t}^{2t - \mu} e^{-\beta|\tau|} \sin\omega\left[t - \frac{1}{2}(\mu + \tau)\right] \sin\omega\left[t - \frac{1}{2}(\mu - \tau)\right] d\tau \tag{11.138}$$

where

$$\beta = \frac{1}{\theta} \tag{11.139}$$

The factor $\frac{1}{2}$ is a consequence of the Jacobian of the transformation

$$d\mu d\tau = \begin{vmatrix} \dfrac{\partial\mu}{\partial t_F'}, & \dfrac{\partial\mu}{\partial t_F} \\ \dfrac{\partial\tau}{\partial t_F'}, & \dfrac{\partial\tau}{\partial t_F} \end{vmatrix} dt_F dt_F' = -2dt_F dt_F' \tag{11.140}$$

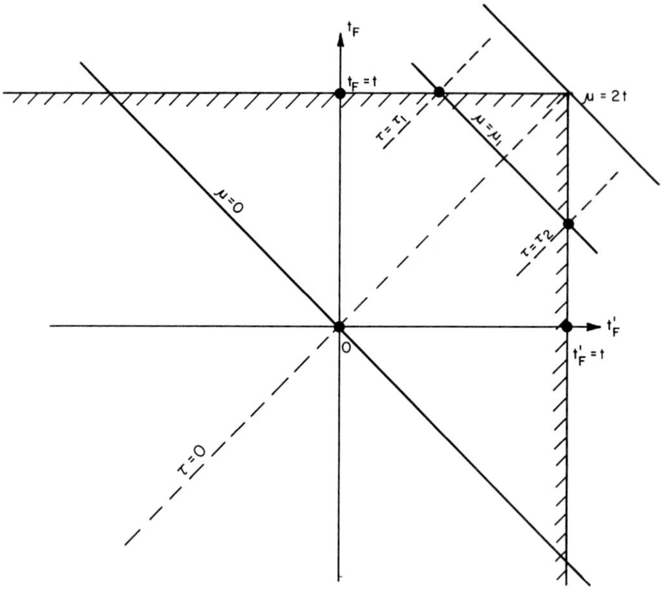

Fig. 11.4 Determination of the limits of integration.

The determination of these limits is somewhat tricky. They are determined with the aid of Figure 11.4, as follows. The locus of $\mu=0$ is the line

$$\mu = 0 = t_F + t_F' \qquad \text{or} \qquad t_F = t_F' \tag{11.141}$$

The lines $\mu=$const are parallel to the line $\mu=0$. The lower limit of μ is $-\infty$, and the upper limit of $\mu = t_F + t_F'$ is $2t$. The line $\tau = t_F - t_F' = 0$ is normal to the line $\mu=0$, and the lines $\tau=$const are parallel to the line $\tau=0$. For any value of $\mu=\mu_1$, τ varies between the limits τ_1 and τ_2. The limit $\tau=\tau_1$ is determined by:

$$\mu = \mu_1 \qquad \text{and} \qquad t_F \leqq t \tag{11.142}$$

And the limit $\tau=\tau_2$ is determined by:

$$\mu = \mu_1 \qquad \text{and} \qquad t_F' \leqq t \tag{11.143}$$

But

$$\mu = t_F + t_F' \tag{11.144}$$

Hence,

$$\tau = t_F - t_F' = 2t_F - (t_F + t_F') = 2t_F - \mu \tag{11.145}$$

or

$$\tau = t_F - t_F' = (t_F + t_F') - 2t_F' = \mu - 2t_F' \tag{11.146}$$

If $t_F = t$ is introduced into Equation 11.145, which gives τ as a function of μ and t_F, the limit τ_1 is obtained:

$$\tau = \tau_1 = 2t - \mu \tag{11.147}$$

Correspondingly, if $t_F' = t$ is introduced into the second equation, which gives τ as a function of μ and t_F,

$$\tau = \tau_2 = \mu - 2t \tag{11.148}$$

A further simplification of the integral is obtained if the variable z is introduced:

$$z = 2t - \mu \qquad \text{and} \qquad dz = -d\mu \tag{11.149}$$

and

$$I_t = \frac{1}{2\omega^2} \int_0^\infty e^{-\delta z} dz \int_{-z}^{z} e^{-\beta|\tau|} \sin \omega \left[t - \frac{1}{2}(\mu + \tau) \right] \sin \omega \left[t - \frac{1}{2}(\mu - \tau) \right] d\tau \tag{11.150}$$

The limits for the τ-integration then become $+z$ and $-z$, and the τ-integral, after the product of the sines is expressed by the difference of the two cosines, becomes:

$$\frac{1}{2} \int_{-z}^{z} d\tau [\cos \omega\tau - \cos \omega(2t - \mu)] e^{-\beta|\tau|} d\tau = \int_0^z d\tau (\cos \omega\tau - \cos \omega z) e^{-\beta\tau} \tag{11.151}$$

The symmetry of the integrand with respect to positive and negative τ made it possible to change the limits to 0 and z and to drop the absolute signs in the exponent. The τ-integration can now be performed with the aid of the standard formulas:

$$\int_0^z \cos \omega\tau e^{-\beta\tau} d\tau = \left(e^{-\beta\tau} \frac{-\beta \cos \omega\tau + \omega \sin \omega\tau}{\omega^2 + \beta^2} \right)_0^z$$

$$= \frac{e^{-\beta z}(-\beta \cos \omega z + \omega \sin \omega z) + \beta}{\omega^2 + \beta^2} \tag{11.152}$$

and

$$\int_0^z e^{-\beta\tau} d\tau = -\frac{1}{\beta}(e^{-\beta z} - 1) = \frac{1}{\beta}(1 - e^{-\beta z}) \tag{11.153}$$

The integral thus reduces to:

$$I_t=\frac{1}{2\omega^2}\int_0^\infty dze^{-\delta z}\left[\frac{(-\beta\cos\omega z+\omega\sin\omega z)e^{-\beta z}+\beta}{\beta^2+\omega^2}+\frac{\cos\omega z}{\beta}\left(e^{-\beta z}-1\right)\right]$$

$$=\frac{1}{2\omega^2}\int_0^\infty dz\left\{\frac{1}{\beta^2+\omega^2}[e^{-\gamma z}(-\beta\cos\omega z+\omega\sin\omega z)+\beta e^{-\delta z}]+\frac{\cos\omega z}{\beta}(e^{-\gamma z}-e^{-\delta z})\right\}$$

(11.154)

where $\gamma=\beta+\delta.$ But

$$\int_0^\infty e^{-\gamma z}\cos\omega z dz=\frac{\gamma}{\gamma^2+\omega^2}\quad\text{and}\quad\int_0^\infty e^{-\gamma z}\sin\omega z dz=\frac{\omega}{\gamma^2+\omega^2}\tag{11.155}$$

and the integral becomes:

$$I_t=\frac{1}{2\omega^2}\left[\frac{1}{\beta^2+\omega^2}\left(\frac{-\beta\gamma+\omega^2}{\gamma^2+\omega^2}+\frac{\beta}{\delta}\right)+\frac{\frac{\gamma}{\beta}}{\gamma^2+\omega^2}-\frac{\frac{\delta}{\beta}}{\delta^2+\omega^2}\right]\tag{11.156}$$

where ω^2 has been written for the frequency ω_ν^{*2} of the decaying vibration, and δ for δ_ν.

In practical cases (if the vibration is not aperiodically damped), $\delta_\nu^2\ll\omega_\nu^2$ and $\omega_\nu^*=\omega_\nu$. If we continue to write ω, δ, and γ for ω_ν^*, δ_ν, and $\gamma_\nu=\beta+\delta_\nu$, respectively, the integral simplifies to:

$$I_t=\frac{1}{2\omega^2}\left\{\frac{1}{\omega^2+\gamma^2}\left[\frac{\omega^2-\beta\gamma+\frac{\gamma}{\beta}(\omega^2+\beta^2)}{\omega^2+\beta^2}\right]+\frac{\frac{\beta}{\delta}}{\omega^2+\beta^2}-\frac{\frac{\delta}{\beta}}{\omega^2+\delta^2}\right\}$$

$$=\frac{1}{2\omega^2}\left[\frac{\omega^2\left(1+\frac{\gamma}{\beta}\right)}{(\omega^2+\gamma^2)(\omega^2+\beta^2)}+\frac{\frac{\beta}{\delta}}{\omega^2+\beta^2}-\frac{\frac{\delta}{\beta}}{\omega^2+\delta^2}\right]$$

$$=\frac{1}{\omega^2+\beta^2}\left[\frac{1}{\omega^2+\gamma^2}+\frac{\delta}{2\beta}\left(\frac{1}{\omega^2+\gamma^2}-\frac{1+\frac{\beta^2}{\omega^2}}{\omega^2+\delta^2}\right)+\frac{\beta}{2\delta\omega^2}\right]\tag{11.157}$$

where

$$\delta^2=\frac{\omega^2\eta^2}{4}\quad\text{and}\quad\omega^2+\gamma^2=\omega^2+(\beta+\delta)^2\cong\omega^2+\beta^2\tag{11.158}$$

This result is rigorous if the energy dissipation is caused by resistances, and it is accurate up to first powers in δ if elastic losses are included. At very low frequencies, the second term in the parentheses cancels with the last term; at the very high frequencies, the terms within the parentheses are zero, provided that $\beta=1/\theta$ is small. In fact, the contribution of the terms within the parentheses is negligible at all frequencies and under all circumstances, provided that $\delta^2=\omega^2\eta^2/4\ll\omega^2$. Except for a factor $1/\beta$, the time integral I_t given by Equation 11.157 thus becomes identical with the time integral given by Equation 11.124, which was derived by Fourier integra-

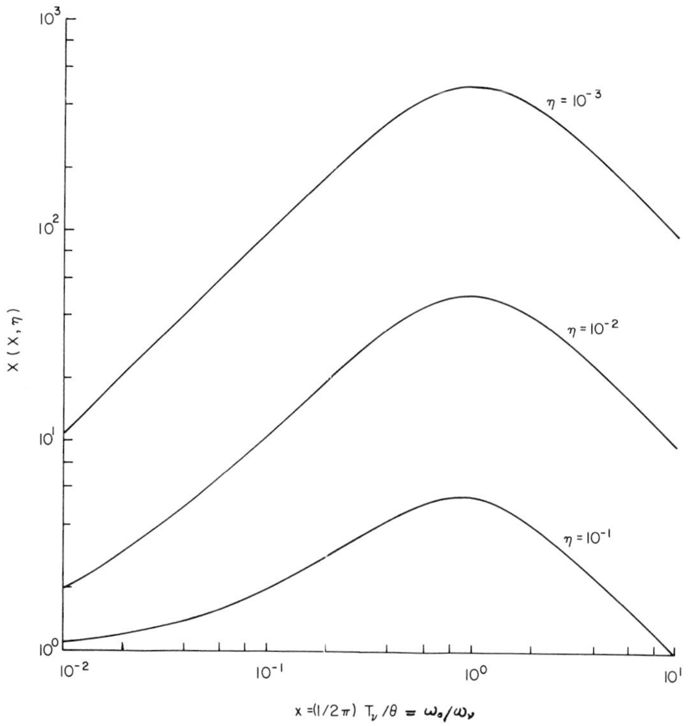

Fig. 11.5 Time integral for various values of damping (as a function of $\alpha=\beta/\omega$).

tion. Figure 11.5 shows I_t as a function of $\alpha=\beta/\omega$ for various values of damping.

The mean-square vibration amplitude, then, is given by:

$$\langle\xi^2\rangle=\frac{\langle p^2\rangle I_t I_x}{\sigma m^2} \tag{11.159}$$

The magnitude I_x represents the space integrals:

$$I_x=\int\int\int\int w_P(x_F-x_F', y_F-y_F')\varphi_\nu(x_F, y_F)\varphi_\nu(x_F', y_F')d\sigma d\sigma' \tag{11.160}$$

The physical meaning of the solution will be discussed below.

Effect of the Nodal Line Pattern on the Mean-Square Vibration Amplitude

To evaluate the integral I_x, the correlation function w_1 and the natural functions of the system must be known. Frequently, the correlation distance is much shorter than the distance between the nodal lines of the vibrator. The natural functions may then be assumed to be constant over the range for which w_P is appreciably different from zero. The σ and σ' integrations can be performed as if φ_ν were constant:

$$I_x = \varphi_\nu(x_F, y_F)\varphi_\nu(x_F', y_F') \int\int w_P(x_F - x_F', y_F - y_F')d\sigma d\sigma' \quad (11.161)$$

and as if x_F, y_F were equal to x_F', y_F' in the factor preceding the integral; for, if this were not so, w_1 would be practically zero because of the assumption of a short correlation distance. Integration then yields two factors: one is the correlation length $2L_x$ or the correlation area $4L_xL_y$; the other is the length l_x or the area $l_xl_y = \sigma$ of the vibrator. Hence,

$$I_x = \langle\varphi_\nu{}^2\rangle\sigma\ \sigma_{\text{cor}} = \sigma_{\text{cor}} \quad (11.162)$$

because $\langle\varphi_\nu{}^2\rangle\sigma = 1$. The mean-square vibration amplitude then becomes:

$$\frac{\langle p^2\rangle\sigma\ \sigma_{\text{cor}} I_t}{\sigma^2 m^2} = \frac{\langle p^2\rangle\sigma\ \sigma_{\text{cor}} I_t}{M^2} \quad (11.163)$$

Frequently, the correlation distance is comparable to or greater than the distance between the nodal lines, and the variations of the natural functions must be taken into account in evaluating the integral I_x. In most cases, the natural functions are of the form:

$$\varphi_\nu(x, y) = \frac{2}{\sqrt{l_x l_y}} \sin \kappa_x x \sin \kappa_y y = \frac{2}{\sqrt{\sigma}} \sin \kappa_x x \sin \kappa_y y \quad (11.164)$$

where

$$\kappa_x = \frac{m\pi}{l_x} \qquad \kappa_y = \frac{n\pi}{l_y} \qquad \sigma = l_x l_y \qquad m = 1, 2, \ldots \quad \text{and} \quad n = 1, 2, \ldots \quad (11.165)$$

For a first estimate of the effect of the finite correlation distance, it is sufficient to choose a correlation function in which the x- and y-parts are separable, such as

$$w_1 = w_2(x_F - x_F')w_3(y_F - y_F') = e^{-(|x_F - x_F'|/L_x + |y_F - y_F'|/L_y} \quad (11.166)$$

The x- and y-integrations can then be performed separately. The x-integration results in the factor:

$$\frac{2}{l_x}\int_0^{l_x}\int_0^{l_x} w_2(x_F - x_F') \sin \kappa_x x_F \sin \kappa_x x_F'\, dx_F\, dx_F'$$

$$= \frac{1}{l_x}\int_0^{l_x}\int_0^{l_x} w_2(x_F - x_F')[\cos \kappa_x(x_F - x_F') - \cos \kappa_x(x_F + x_F')]dx_F dx_F' \quad (11.167)$$

A change of the variables to

$$\xi = x_F - x_F' \qquad \text{and} \qquad \eta = x_F + x_F' \tag{11.168}$$

with the Jacobian

$$d\xi \cdot d\eta \begin{vmatrix} \dfrac{\partial \xi}{\partial x_F}, & \dfrac{\partial \eta}{\partial x_F} \\ \dfrac{\partial \xi}{\partial x_F'}, & \dfrac{\partial \eta}{\partial x_F'} \end{vmatrix} dx_F\, dx_F' = 2dx_F\, dx_F' \tag{11.169}$$

leads to the integral

$$\frac{1}{2}\frac{1}{l_x}\int_0^{2l_x} d\eta \int_{-\eta}^{\eta} w_2(\xi)(\cos \kappa_x \xi - \cos \kappa_x \eta)\, d\xi \tag{11.170}$$

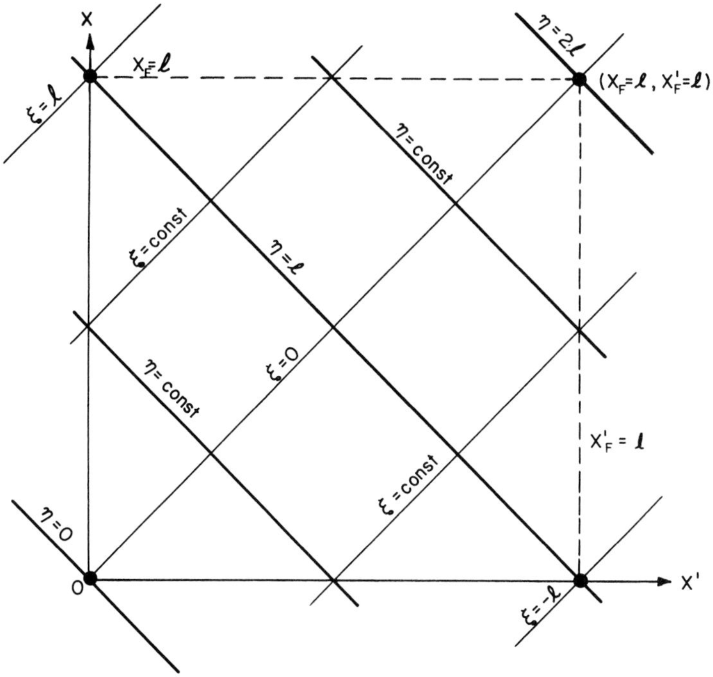

Fig. 11.6 Determination of the limits of integration.

The limits of integration are deduced with the aid of Figure 11.6. The co-ordinates x_F and x_F' vary between 0 and $l_x = l$. The new co-ordinates are given by the lines

$$\xi = x_F - x_F' = \text{const} \tag{11.171}$$

The co-ordinate $\xi = 0$ is represented by the line $x = x_F'$. The lines $\xi = \text{const}$ must be parallel to line $x_F = x_F'$. The ξ-co-ordinate through $x_F = l$ and $x_F' = 0$ is $\xi = l$; the ξ-co-ordinate of the line through $x_F = 0$ and $x_F' = l$ is $-l$.

The line $\eta = x_F + x_F' = 0$ or $x_F = -x_F'$ passes through $x_F = 0$ and $x_F' = 0$; the η-co-ordinate of the opposite corner is $\eta = x_F + x_F' = 2l$. If the outside integration is performed with respect to η, the limits of the η-integration are 0 and $2l_x$. For any given value of η,

$$\eta = x_F + x_F' \tag{11.172}$$

The limits of ξ are given by:

$$\begin{aligned} \eta = \eta \quad &\text{and} \quad x_F' = 0 \\ \eta = \eta \quad &\text{and} \quad x_F = 0 \end{aligned} \tag{11.173}$$

But

$$\xi = x_F - x_F' = x_F + x_F' - 2x_F' = \eta - 2x_F' \tag{11.174}$$

or

$$\xi = -(x_F + x_F') + 2x_F = 2x_F - \eta \tag{11.175}$$

Thus, for $\eta = \eta$ and $x_F' = 0$,

$$\xi = \eta - 2x_F' = \eta \tag{11.176}$$

Similarly, for $\eta = \eta$ and $x_F = 0$,

$$\xi = 2x_F - \eta = -\eta \tag{11.177}$$

and the limits of ξ are $\pm\eta$. The function $w_2(\xi)$ decreases rapidly with $|\xi|$. It makes little difference, therefore, if the limits η and $-\eta$ are replaced by $\pm\infty$. The ξ-integral then becomes:

$$\frac{1}{2l_x}\int_{-\infty}^{\infty} w_2(\xi)(\cos\kappa_x\xi - \cos\kappa_x\eta)d\xi = \frac{1}{l_x}\int_0^{\infty} w_2(\xi)(\cos\kappa_x\xi - \cos\kappa_x\eta)d\xi \tag{11.178}$$

If $w_2 = e^{-|\xi|/L_x}$, this reduces to a standard integral (see Eq. 11.155), and the η-integral becomes:

$$\frac{L_x}{l_x}\int_0^{2l_x}\left(\frac{1}{1+\kappa_x^2L_x^2} - \cos\kappa_x\eta\right)d\eta \tag{11.179}$$

The second term fluctuates with η and does not contribute significantly to the solution. Thus, we obtain the result:

$$I_x = \frac{2L_x}{1+\kappa_x^2L_x^2} \tag{11.180}$$

The result is very similar to that obtained for the effect of the time correlation. The characteristic parameter is $\kappa_x L_x = 2\pi L_x/\lambda_B$, where λ_B is the bending wave length of the vibration. The magnitude $2L_x$ is the correlation length in the x-direction, because

$$\int_{-\infty}^{\infty} e^{-|\xi|/L_x}d\xi = 2L_x \tag{11.181}$$

The y-integration leads to a similar factor,

$$I_y = \frac{2L_y}{1+\kappa_y{}^2 L_y} \tag{11.182}$$

If the correlation distances are small as compared to the distances between the nodal lines,

$$(\kappa_x L_x)^2 \ll 1 \qquad \text{and} \qquad (\kappa_y L_y)^2 \ll 1 \tag{11.183}$$

and the space integral becomes equal to the correlation area. Equation 11.162 is reobtained. The nodal line pattern, then, has no effect on the motion. This again is obvious, since the contributions of the various correlation areas may have either sign with equal probability; the probability that the system is driven by the force on a particular correlation area is ust as great as the probability that the system is retarded. But if the correlation distances become greater than the distance between the nodal lines, the effect of the force decreases. The part of the system that is within a correlation area moves in one direction, the remaining part moves in the other direction, and the force correspondingly drives part of the system and retards the remaining part.

If the above expressions are substituted in Equation 11.159, the mean-square amplitude becomes:

$$\langle \xi^2 \rangle = \frac{\langle p^2 \rangle \sigma \ \sigma_{\text{cor}} I_t}{\omega_\nu{}^2 M^2 (1+\kappa_x{}^2 L_x{}^2)(1+\kappa_y{}^2 L_y)} \tag{11.184}$$

where I_t is given by Equation 11.157 and Figure 11.5. The mean-square velocity amplitude can be computed in a very similar manner. The impulse response for the velocity is given by an equation of the form of Equation 11.56, except that the sine is replaced by the cosine and the denominator $m\omega_\nu$ by m. The various steps in the computation and the integrations then are the same, except for the lack of the factor ω_ν in the denominator and for the opposite sign of the second term in the integrand of Equation 11.151.

In deriving the solution on the basis of the impulse response, it was assumed that the loss factor is the same for steady-state and for decaying vibrations, which is not strictly correct. In the computations that were based on Fourier integration, the loss factor was assumed to be constant. The two assumptions are not exactly equivalent, and the two solutions obtained by the two procedures differ slightly. However, the differences are negligible if damping is small. The preceding computations were based on an exponential correlation function.

The Gaussian correlation function is known to represent a relatively poor approximation to most experimental results, but it has the advantage of leading to integrals that can easily be evaluated. If the correlation function is Gaussian,

$$w(\xi) = e^{-\xi^2/a^2} \tag{11.185}$$

and the significant contribution to the integral is given by:

$$2\int_0^{2l} d\eta \int_0^{\infty} e^{-\xi^2/a^2} \cos \kappa\xi d\xi = 2le^{-\kappa a^2/4} \sqrt{\pi a^2} = 2lLe^{-\kappa^2 a^2/4} \quad (11.186)$$

where

$$L = \int_{-\infty}^{\infty} w(\xi) d\xi = \int_{-\infty}^{\infty} e^{-\xi^2/a^2} d\xi = \sqrt{\pi a^2} \quad (11.187)$$

is the correlation distance and λ_B is, as above, the bending wave length. The result is similar to that for the exponential correlation function, except that the decrease in amplitude is considerably steeper at the higher wave numbers.

Convected Force Patterns

If vibrations are excited by wind or turbulence in the boundary layer of a moving body, a force pattern is generated that is convected with the speed of the mean flow along the surfaces of the vibrator. The correlation function can then be approximated by an expression of the following type:

$$\langle p(x, y; t) p(x', y'; t') \rangle = \langle p^2 \rangle e^{-\beta|t-t'|} e^{-\kappa\sqrt{(\xi - v\tau)^2 + \zeta^2}} = \langle p^2 \rangle R(\xi, \zeta, \tau) \quad (11.188)$$

where

$$\beta = \frac{1}{\theta} \qquad \xi = x - x' \qquad \zeta = y - y' \qquad \text{and} \qquad \tau = t - t' \quad (11.189)$$

and v is the mean convection speed (positive when in the $+x$-direction). The magnitude $2\kappa^{-1}$ is the correlation distance in the radial direction (eddy diameter), and θ is the correlation or lifetime of the flow pattern (or of a turbulent eddy). The correlation area is obtained by integrating the above expression over ζ and ξ:

$$\sigma_{\text{cor}} = \frac{2\pi}{\kappa^2} \quad (11.190)$$

The correlation decays with time according to the factor $e^{-\beta|\tau|}$. Except for this decay, the correlation is the same for all points $\xi - vt = \text{const}$ and $\eta = 0$ that travel with a velocity v in the direction of the main flow.

The effect of the nodal line pattern on the excitation of a vibrator by statistically varying forces has been discussed above. There is no reason to believe that the nodal line pattern will have a different effect on the result if the force pattern is convected over the surfaces of the vibrator; to simplify the computations, we shall assume that the distance between the nodal lines is large as compared to the correlation distance and shall replace the correlation function by a delta function $\underset{\sim}{\delta}$ of the following type:

$$\langle p^2\rangle\sigma_{\text{cor}}\underset{\sim}{\delta}(\xi-v\tau)\cdot\underset{\sim}{\delta}(\zeta)e^{-|\tau|/\theta} \tag{11.191}$$

The mean-square vibration amplitude, then, is determined by:

$$\langle\xi_\nu{}^2\rangle=\sigma_{\text{cor}}\langle p^2\rangle\frac{\varphi_\nu(x,y)\varphi_\nu(x',y')}{\omega^2 m^2}$$

$$\cdot\int_{-\infty}^{t}dt_F\int_{-\infty}^{t}dt_F'\int\int\int\int\varphi_\nu(x_F,y_F)\varphi_\nu(x_F',y_F')e^{-\delta(2t-t_F-t_F')-|\tau_F|/\theta}$$

$$\cdot\sin\omega_\nu(t-t_F)\sin\omega_\nu(t-t_F')\delta(\xi_F-v\tau_F)\delta(\zeta_F)dx_F dy_F dx_F' dy_F' \tag{11.192}$$

The y_F=integration is simple because of the delta function; it simply replaces y_F by y_F' in the integrand. The y_F-integration follows readily:

$$\frac{2}{L_y}\int_0^{L_y}\sin^2\left(\frac{n\pi y_F}{L_y}\right)dy_F=1 \tag{11.193}$$

The x_F-integration is equally simple, if we assume that the distance the force pattern travels until correlation has decayed is small as compared to the distance between the nodal lines, or that

$$L_x\gg v\theta \tag{11.194}$$

This condition is usually fulfilled in practical cases, except at the very high frequencies. This assumption makes it possible to neglect the variation of x_F, y_F during the x_F-integration and to replace x_F, because of the delta function $\underset{\sim}{\delta}(\xi_F-v\tau_F)$, by $x_F'+v\tau_F$. The x_F'-integration then yields the factor

$$\frac{2}{L_x}\int_0^{L_x}\sin\left(\frac{m\pi}{L_x}x_F'\right)\sin\left[\frac{m\pi}{L_x}(x_F'+v\tau_F)\right]dx_F'$$

$$=\frac{1}{L_x}\int_0^{L_x}\left\{\cos\left(\frac{m\pi}{L_x}v\tau_F\right)-\cos\left[\frac{m\pi}{L_x}(2x_F'+v\tau_F)\right]\right\}dx_F'$$

$$=\cos\left(\frac{m\pi v}{L_x}\tau_F\right)-\frac{1}{m\pi}\left\{\sin\left[\frac{m\pi}{L_x}(2x_F'+v\tau_F)\right]\right\}_0^{L_x}$$

$$=\cos\alpha\tau_F \tag{11.195}$$

where

$$\alpha=\frac{m\pi v}{L_x} \tag{11.196}$$

The solution reduces to:

$$\langle\xi_\nu{}^2\rangle=\frac{\sigma_{\text{cor}}\langle p^2\rangle\langle\varphi_\nu(x,y)^2\rangle}{\omega^2 m^2}\cdot I_t=\frac{\sigma_{\text{cor}}\langle p^2\rangle\sigma}{M^2}\cdot I_t \tag{11.197}$$

where

$$\omega^2 I_t = \int_{-\infty}^{t} dt_F \int_{-\infty}^{t} dt_F' \cos \alpha(t-t_F')[\sin \omega(t-t_F) \sin \omega(t-t_F') e^{-\delta(2t-t_F-t_F')}$$

$$\cdot\, e^{-\beta(t_F-t_F')}] = \int_0^{\infty} dz e^{-\delta z} \int_0^{z} (\cos \alpha\tau e^{-\beta\tau} \cos \omega\tau - \cos \omega z) d\tau \tag{11.198}$$

The various steps in the transformation of the above integral are the same as those in the preceding section, and the limits are determined in exactly the same manner; the only difference is the additional factor $\cos \alpha\tau$. The integration leads to:

$$\int_0^z d\tau (\cos \alpha\tau \cos \omega\tau - \cos \omega z \cos \alpha\tau) e^{-\beta\tau}$$

$$= \int_0^z d\tau \left\{ \left[\frac{\cos(\alpha+\omega)\tau + \cos(\alpha-\omega)\tau}{2} \right] - \cos \omega z \cos \alpha\tau \right\} e^{-\beta\tau}$$

$$= \frac{[-\beta \cos(\alpha+\omega)z + (\alpha+\omega) \sin(\alpha+\omega)z] e^{-\beta z} + \beta}{2[\beta^2 + (\alpha+\omega)^2]}$$

$$+ \frac{[-\beta \cos(\alpha-\omega)z + (\alpha-\omega) \sin(\alpha-\omega)z] e^{-\beta z} + \beta}{2[\beta^2 + (\alpha-\omega)^2]}$$

$$- \frac{\cos \omega z[(-\beta \cos \alpha z + \alpha \sin \alpha z) e^{-\beta z} + \beta]}{(\alpha^2 + \beta^2)} \tag{11.199}$$

This expression is to be multiplied by $\frac{1}{2} e^{-\delta z}$ and integrated between 0 and ∞. If the last term is decomposed into sum and differences of cosines and sines, we easily obtain the following result:

$$2\omega^2 I_t = \frac{1}{2[\beta^2 + (\alpha+\omega)^2]} \left[\frac{-\beta\gamma + (\alpha+\omega)^2}{\gamma^2 + (\alpha+\omega)^2} + \frac{\beta}{\delta} \right]$$

$$+ \frac{1}{2[\beta^2 + (\alpha-\omega)^2]} \left[\frac{-\beta\gamma + (\alpha-\omega)^2}{\gamma^2 + (\alpha-\omega)^2} + \frac{\beta}{\delta} \right]$$

$$+ \frac{\beta}{2(\alpha^2+\beta^2)} \left[\frac{\gamma}{\gamma^2 + (\omega+\alpha)^2} + \frac{\gamma}{\gamma^2 + (\omega-\alpha)^2} \right]$$

$$- \frac{\alpha}{2(\alpha^2+\beta^2)} \left[\frac{\omega+\alpha}{\gamma^2 + (\omega+\alpha)^2} - \frac{\omega-\alpha}{\gamma^2 + (\omega-\alpha)^2} \right]$$

$$- \frac{\beta}{\alpha^2+\beta^2} \frac{\delta}{\omega^2+\delta^2} \tag{11.200}$$

We arrive at a very interesting conclusion.[14] The effect of the convection

[14] See I. Dyer, *loc. cit.*

velocity is negligible, and we fall back on our previous results if $\alpha^2 \ll \omega^2$ or $\alpha^2/\omega^2 \ll 1$. But

$$\frac{\alpha}{\omega} = \frac{m\pi v}{L_x\omega} = \frac{mv}{2L_x\dfrac{\omega}{2\pi}} = \frac{v}{c_B} \tag{11.201}$$

where c_B is the velocity for bending waves in the walls of the vibrator, and

$$c_B = \frac{2L_x}{m} \cdot \frac{\omega}{2\pi} \tag{11.202}$$

Thus, the convection of the force pattern has no effect on the vibration amplitude, if the convection velocity is small as compared to the velocity of bending waves in the walls of the vibrator.

Physical Interpretation of the Solution

The results can be interpreted in a very simple manner. The average force that acts on a correlation area is given by:

$$\left(\langle p^2\rangle \sigma^2{}_{\mathrm{cor}}\right)^{\frac{1}{2}} \tag{11.203}$$

This force is coherent over the correlation interval 2θ, and the impulse value of the force is:

$$U_F = \left(\langle p^2\rangle \sigma^2{}_{\mathrm{cor}}\theta^2\right)^{\frac{1}{2}} \tag{11.204}$$

Each impulse U_F may increase or decrease the vibration amplitude, depending on whether it is in phase or out of phase with the motion of the vibrator at the particular correlation area. In fact, the probability that the effect of this force is positive or negative is exactly the same, regardless of the nodal line pattern of the vibrator. Statistical theory shows that in such cases the sum of the squares of all the contributions determines the resultant effect. The square of the effective impulse is given by:

$$F^2{}_{\mathrm{eff}} = \sum \langle p^2\rangle \sigma^2{}_{\mathrm{cor}}\theta^2 = \langle p^2\rangle \sigma^2{}_{\mathrm{cor}}\theta^2 n = \langle p^2\rangle \sigma_{\mathrm{cor}}\sigma\theta^2 \tag{11.205}$$

where $n = \sigma/\sigma_{\mathrm{cor}}$ is the total number of correlation areas. If the duration θ of each impulse is small as compared to the period and to the decay time $t = 1/(2 \cdot \omega\eta/2) = 1/\omega\eta$ of the vibration energy, and if successive pulses are uncorrelated, the energies of the pulses add. The effect is then proportional to the energy of all the t/θ pulses that are generated during an interval equal to the decay time t of the system (because this interval is approximately the time taken by the system to store energy). The square of the resultant effective force is, therefore, given by:

$$\langle p^2\rangle \sigma_{\mathrm{cor}}\sigma\theta^2 \cdot \frac{t}{\theta} = \langle p^2\rangle \sigma_{\mathrm{cor}} \frac{\sigma\theta}{\omega\eta} \tag{11.206}$$

The root-mean-square velocity that is generated by an impulsive force I is

I/M, where M is the total mass of the system. This result can be easily deduced from Equation 11.52 by observing that if referred to the mean-square amplitude or velocity, the mode masses M_ν are equal to the total mass of the system. If Equation 11.206 is substituted as the impulsive force, the mean-square velocity becomes:

$$\langle \dot{\xi}^2 \rangle = \frac{\langle p^2 \rangle \sigma_{\text{cor}} \sigma \theta}{M^2 \omega_\nu \eta} \tag{11.207}$$

The last expression is identical with the exact solution when θ is short as compared to the decay time (and hence to the period of the vibration) of the system.

Because of the unsteadiness of the force pattern, each mode vibrates, not only at its resonance frequency, but in a continuous frequency band that is determined by the band width of the mode and the frequency dependence of the force spectrum. If the power spectrum of the exciting force is approximately constant, mode amplitude ξ_ν and mode velocity $\dot{\xi}_\nu$ are related by the standard relation

$$\dot{\xi}_\nu \approx \omega_\nu \xi_\nu \tag{11.208}$$

As has already been pointed out in connection with Equation 11.124, the mode, then, is predominantly excited in its resonance range, and the result depends on the damping. But if the power spectrum of the force decreases with frequency, like that of the near-field pressure in a flow-noise field, then the mathematical solution consists of two fundamentally different parts. The first is a resonance term that depends on the damping; the second term represents the forced excitation of the mode because of the low-frequency spectrum of the force distribution. This term, then, since it is not a resonance term, does not depend on the damping, and the relation $\dot{\xi}_\nu = \omega_\nu \xi_\nu$ does not hold. Thus, the motion enforced by the low-frequency part of the spectrum usually predominates, the vibration amplitude is independent of the damping, and

$$\langle \dot{\xi}_\nu^2 \rangle = \beta^2 \xi_\nu^2 \tag{11.209}$$

where $\theta = 1/\beta$ is the lifetime of the exciting force distribution. In most cases of interest,

$$\beta^2 \ll \omega_\nu^2 \tag{11.210}$$

and the mean square of the velocity amplitude is obtained by multiplying the mean square of the displacement amplitude by a factor β^2 that may be much smaller then ω_ν^2.

In contrast to the results obtained for the displacement amplitude, the effect of the low-frequency part of the force spectrum on the velocity amplitude is always negligible. The factor ω^2 with which the power spectrum of the displacement has to be multiplied to obtain the power spectrum of the velocity compensates the decrease of the force spectrum, and the velocity contributions of the modes stem predominantly from their resonance range; therefore, in contrast to the mean-square displacement, the mean-square velocity depends only on the force spectrum in the resonance range and on the damping.

Recommended Reading

CALLAGHAN, E. E., HOWES, W. L., AND W. D. COLES, "Near noise field of a jet engine exhaust: II. Cross correlation of sound pressures," *N.A.C.A., T.N.* (1956), 3760.

CORCOS, G. R., AND H. W. LIEPMANN, "On the contribution of turbulent boundary layers to the noise inside a fuselage," *N.A.C.A., T.M.* (1958), 1420.

CRANDALL, S. H., (ed.), *Random Vibrations,* Technology Press of The Massachusetts Institute of Technology, Cambridge, 1958.

DYER, I., "Sound radiation into a closed space from boundary layer turbulence," Bolt, Beranek, and Newman Report No. 602, Cambridge, Mass., O.N.R. Contract Nonr-2321(00), 1958.

———, "Response of plates to decaying pressure field," *J.A.S.A.* **31** (1959), 922–28.

LYON, R. H., "Propagation of correlation functions in continuous media," *J.A.S.A.,* **28** (1956), 76–79.

———, "Response of strings to random noise fields," *J.A.S.A.,* **28** (1956), 391–98.

POWELL, A., "On structural vibrations excited by random pressures, with reference to structural failure and boundary layer noise," Douglas Aircraft Co., Report SM22795, 1957.

———, "On the approximation to the 'infinite' solution by the method of normal modes for random vibrations," *J.A.S.A.,* **30** (1958), 1136–39.

RIBNER, H. S., "Boundary-layer-induced noise in the interior of aircraft," U.T.I.A. Report No. 37, 1956.

THOMSON, W. T., AND M. V. BARTON, "The response of mechanical systems to random excitation," *J Appl. Mech.,* **24** (1957), 248.

XII / SOUND RADIATION OF COMPLEX VIBRATORS

The preceding chapters dealt with the vibrations of simple and complex vibrators. In many instances it is not the vibrations in which we are interested, but the sound radiation. Sound radiation is discussed in books on acoustics that usually confine themselves to the study of the classical cases for which exact mathematical solutions are available. Exact solutions have been derived for spheres and ellipsoids, for cylinders, and for square and circular piston membranes. Unfortunately, these shapes are not typical of the sound radiators encountered in practice. For instance, the most common sound radiator, the loud-speaker, is a cone, which has resisted all attempts at computation. Also, very little is known about the sound radiation of such a simple vibrator as a finite plate with many nodal lines.

The exact computation of the sound field of a complex vibrator is a difficult and laborious task—if it is possible at all. Even if this computation were possible, it is doubtful whether the result would be worth the trouble. A small change in the amplitude distribution over the vibrator, a slight deviation in the properties of the material, small objects in the neighborhood of the vibrator, the characteristics of the enclosure containing the sound generator, and many other details always cause considerable deviations in the sound pressure from the computed values. In most instances, a good estimate of the sound pressure will be close enough to the actual value, and a good estimate can be made if a few fundamental properties of sound generators and sound fields are known. Frequently, the approximate solutions are very simple indeed and turn out to be practically as accurate as the rigorous mathematical ones. It is the objective of this chapter to provide a fundamental understanding of the laws that govern sound radiation, to derive solutions that are useful in practical work, and to review the published work that is not yet available in textbook form.

Fundamentals of Sound Radiation

Wave Equation

Sound does not propagate through a vacuum. The propagation of sound is always associated with some medium. Experience shows that sound is generated when the medium is dynamically disturbed. A rapid disturbance of a fluid affects its pressure, density, particle velocity, and temperature. Our task is to find the relationships between the variables of interest. To simplify this task, relationships that hold for very small elements of volume will be considered first. The relationships we shall derive are differential equations.

All known fluids and solids have a relatively small heat conductivity, so that sound propagation is very nearly adiabatic, even at very low frequencies. A first relation between pressure and density is, therefore, the adiabatic state equation:

$$p = f(\rho) \tag{12.1}$$

Since the changes of pressure and density are small, this equation can be developed into a Taylor series:

$$p = p_0 + \frac{\partial f}{\partial \rho} \cdot \delta\rho + \ldots \tag{12.2}$$

where $\partial f/\partial\rho$ is understood to represent the derivative with respect to ρ for $\rho = \rho_0$ or $p = p_0$. If the higher powers of $\delta\rho$ are neglected, and if $\partial f/\partial\rho$ is abbreviated as

$$c^2 = \frac{\partial f}{\partial \rho} \tag{12.3}$$

the (linearized) state equation becomes:

$$p = p_0 + c^2\delta\rho = p_0 + c^2(\rho - \rho_0) = \text{const} + c^2\rho \tag{12.4}$$

Thus we have replaced the curve (Eq. 12.1) by its tangent at p_0, ρ_0. The constant is eliminated by differentiating the last expression with respect to time, and

$$\frac{\partial p}{\partial t} = c^2 \frac{\partial \rho}{\partial t} \tag{12.5}$$

or

$$\frac{\partial \rho}{\partial t} = \frac{1}{c^2} \frac{\partial p}{\partial t} \tag{12.6}$$

This equation will later be used to eliminate the density changes $\partial\rho/\partial t$.

A second relationship between the variables ρ, p, and v can be obtained by considering a small element of volume that is always made up of the same molecules and that moves with the fluid. We shall assume that this element of volume moves as if it were frozen and that Newton's law ($F = ma$) can be applied to it. This assumption represents a generalization of Newton's law that is equivalent to a new axiom of mechanics, and the resulting equation is no longer called Newton's law but is known as Euler's equation.

To derive Euler's equation for the one-dimensional case, consider an elementary slab of area σ, of thickness dx, oriented perpendicularly to the x-axis. The resultant force on this slab (as illustrated in Fig. 12.1) is given by:

$$[p(x)-p(x+dx)]\sigma=-\frac{\partial p}{\partial x}\cdot dx\sigma \tag{12.7}$$

since, as dx tends toward zero,

$$\frac{p(x+dx)-p(x)}{dx}=\frac{\partial p}{\partial x} \tag{12.8}$$

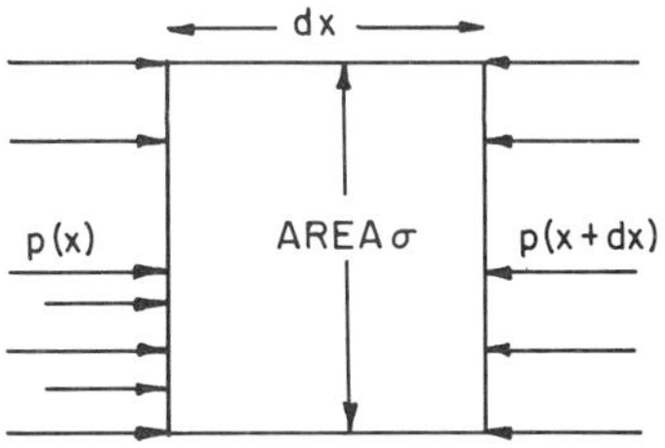

Fig. 12.1 Derivation of Euler's equation.

The resultant force is positive if it points in the positive x-direction. If the pressure increases with increasing x, $\partial p/\partial x$ is positive, and the resultant force $-\partial p/\partial x$ is negative and points in the negative x-direction. In further computations, the signs are taken care of by rules inherent in our notation. According to Newton's principle, the resultant force on the elementary volume of cross section σ and depth dx is equal to the product of its mass and acceleration:

$$\begin{aligned}\sigma\cdot\left(-\frac{\partial p}{\partial x}\right)dx&=\sigma\rho dx\frac{dv_x}{dt}=\sigma\rho dx\left(\frac{\partial v_x}{\partial t}+\frac{\partial v_x}{\partial x}\frac{dx}{dt}\right)\\&=\sigma\rho dx\left(\frac{\partial v_x}{\partial t}+v_x\frac{\partial v_x}{\partial x}\right)\end{aligned} \tag{12.9}$$

The particle velocity is a function of time t and of the co-ordinate x; the chain rule of differentiation leads to the second form of the right-hand side. The third form is obtained by replacing dx/dt by v_x. Since the particle velocity v_x is usually very small, the last term, which is of the second order in v_x, can be neglected, and Euler's equation simplifies to:

$$-\frac{\partial p}{\partial x}=\rho\frac{\partial v_x}{\partial t}=(\rho_0+\partial\rho)\frac{\partial v_x}{\partial t}=\rho_0\frac{\partial v_x}{\partial t} \tag{12.10}$$

In this equation, $\partial\rho$ and $\partial v_x/\partial t$ are of the same order of magnitude as v_x; the density ρ has, therefore, been replaced by its mean value ρ_0, and the second-order term $\partial\rho\,(\partial v_x/\partial t)$ has been neglected.

To determine the three variables p, ρ, and v_x, a third relationship is required. This relationship is set up by considering the continuity of the fluid.

The excess of fluid that is carried into the volume element because of the sound motion must cause a corresponding increase of the density of the fluid in that element, since there are no sources of fluid in it. If we consider a slab similar to the previous one, but fixed in space, the amount of matter entering the slab in the time interval dt is that contained in a cylinder of area σ and thickness $v_x(x)dt$ adjacent to the left-hand face of the slab (Fig. 12.2). This amount of matter is given by:

$$\sigma \cdot \rho(x) v_x(x) dt \tag{12.11}$$

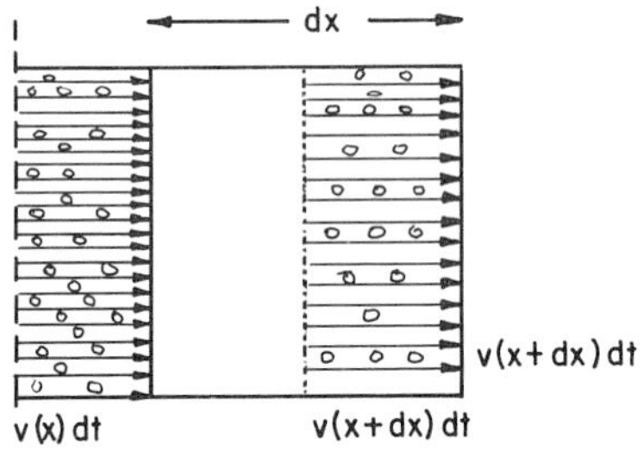

Fig. 12.2 Derivation of the equation of continuity.

The amount of matter leaving the elementary volume through its right-hand face in the time interval dt is that enclosed in a cylinder of area σ and thickness $v_x(x+dx)dt$ to the left of the right-hand face of the elementary slab. This amount of matter is:

$$\sigma \cdot \rho(x+dx) \cdot v_x(x+dx)dt \tag{12.12}$$

The excess of matter entering the slab over that leaving it is:

$$\sigma\rho(x)\, v_x(x)dt - \sigma\rho(x+dx)v_x(x+dx) \cdot dt = -dx \cdot \sigma \frac{\partial(\rho v_x)}{\partial x} dt$$

$$-\sigma\rho_0 \frac{\partial v_x}{\partial x} dt\, dx + \text{second-and higher-order terms} \tag{12.13}$$

The increase of matter is also given by the product of the elementary volume and the increase of its density:

$$\sigma\delta\rho \cdot dx = \sigma \frac{\partial \rho}{\partial t} dt dx \tag{12.14}$$

If Equations 12.13 and 12.14 are equated to one another, the equation of continuity results:

$$\frac{\partial v_x}{\partial x} = -\frac{1}{\rho_0}\frac{\partial \rho}{\partial t} = -\frac{1}{\rho_0 c^2}\frac{\partial p}{\partial t} \tag{12.15}$$

The last form of the right-hand side was obtained by eliminating the density with the aid of the state equation (12.5).

Thus it has been shown that sound propagation is governed by the following equations:

$$p = c^2 \rho + \text{const} \qquad \text{(linearized state equation)} \tag{12.16}$$

$$\frac{\partial v_x}{\partial t} = -\frac{1}{\rho_0}\frac{\partial p}{\partial x} \qquad \text{(linearized Euler's equation)} \tag{12.17}$$

$$\frac{\partial v_x}{\partial x} = -\frac{1}{\rho_0 c^2}\frac{\partial p}{\partial t} \qquad \text{(linearized equation of continuity)} \tag{12.18}$$

If the particle velocity is eliminated by differentiating Euler's equation with respect to x and the equation of continuity with respect to t, the one-dimensional wave equation results:

$$\frac{\partial^2 p}{\partial x^2} = \frac{1}{c^2}\frac{\partial^2 p}{\partial t^2} \tag{12.19}$$

In the three-dimensional case, the derivations are practically the same. The state equation (12.16) applies in the same form. Euler's equations are derived for a cube as elementary volume with the edges dx, dy, and dz, and equations similar to Equation 12.17 are obtained for the y- and the z-directions. In vector form, the three-dimensional Euler's equation reads:

$$-\frac{1}{\rho_0}\,\text{grad}\, p = \frac{\partial \vec{v}}{\partial t} \tag{12.20}$$

A similar elementary cube is considered in deriving the three-dimensional equation of continuity. The inflow in the y- and z-directions contributes two similar terms ($\partial v_y/\partial y$ and $\partial v_z/\partial z$) to the left-hand side of Equation 12.15, which now becomes:

$$\text{div}\, \vec{v} = -\frac{1}{\rho_0}\frac{\partial \rho}{\partial t} = -\frac{1}{\rho_0 c^2}\frac{\partial p}{\partial t} \tag{12.21}$$

The wave equation for the pressure is derived by taking the divergence of Euler's equation and the gradient of the equation of continuity and adding the results:

$$\text{div grad}\, p = \frac{1}{c^2}\frac{\partial^2 p}{\partial t^2} \tag{12.22}$$

or

$$\nabla^2 p = \frac{1}{c^2}\frac{\partial^2 p}{\partial t^2} \tag{12.23}$$

where

$$\text{div grad} = \nabla^2 = \frac{\partial^2}{\partial x^2} + \frac{\partial^2}{\partial y^2} + \frac{\partial^2}{\partial z^2} \tag{12.24}$$

The wave equation is equivalent to the statement that the amount of matter that flows into an elementary volume is reflected as a corresponding change in its density, the density being eliminated with the aid of the state equation and the particle velocity being eliminated with the aid of Euler's equation. The tools of mathematics then lead to the infinite number of different solutions that describe the phenomena of sound and its generation.

The equation for the particle velocity can be derived by taking the gradient of the continuity equation and differentiating Euler's equations with respect to time. The operator grad div is not the same as the operator div grad, but

$$\begin{aligned}\text{grad div} &= \text{div grad} + \text{curl curl}\\ &= \nabla^2 + \text{curl curl}\end{aligned} \tag{12.25}$$

and the equation for the particle velocity becomes:

$$\nabla^2 \vec{v} + \text{curl curl } \vec{v} = \frac{1}{c^2}\frac{\partial^2 v}{\partial t^2} \tag{12.26}$$

Differential equations for vectors are usually hard to solve, since the three vector components have to be adapted to the boundary conditions. There is great need to simplify the procedure whenever possible. One method is to derive the solution from a scalar potential by setting:

$$\begin{aligned} v_x &= -\frac{\partial \Phi}{\partial x}\\ v_y &= -\frac{\partial \Phi}{\partial y}\\ v_z &= -\frac{\partial \Phi}{dz}\\ \text{or } \vec{v} &= -\text{grad } \Phi \end{aligned} \tag{12.27}$$

The minus sign is a matter of convention; it is of no particular significance. The logic of this step is obvious in the one-dimensional case; Φ is simply equal to the integral of the particle velocity v_x:

$$\Phi = -\int v_x dx + \text{const} \tag{12.28}$$

In the three-dimensional case, however, this step reduces the generality of our solution, for if the first of the equations (12.27) is differentiated with respect to y, the second, with respect to x, and the results are subtracted,

$$\frac{\partial v_x}{\partial y} - \frac{\partial v_y}{\partial x} = \frac{\partial^2 \Phi}{\partial y \partial x} - \frac{\partial^2 \Phi}{\partial x \partial y} = 0 \tag{12.29}$$

Two similar equations are obtained if this procedure is continued with the first and the third and with the second and the third of the equations (12.27). The resulting equations can then be condensed to:

$$\text{curl } \vec{v} = -\text{curl (grad } \Phi) = 0 \tag{12.30}$$

which is Stokes's theorem: The curl of a gradient is identically zero. In consequence, the introduction of the velocity potential Φ permits only rotationless solutions. Fortunately, acoustic motions in liquids and gases are always rotationless, even if viscosity effects are considered.[1] It can be shown that there is always a vortical layer near solid boundaries, but this boundary layer is extremely thin (less than 0.001 mm. in air at a frequency of 1,000 cps).

If the velocity potential is introduced into Euler's equation, it takes the form:

$$\text{grad } p = -\rho_0 \frac{\partial \vec{v}}{\partial t} = \rho_0 \frac{\partial(\text{grad } \Phi)}{\partial t} = \rho_0 \text{ grad} \frac{\partial \Phi}{\partial t} \tag{12.31}$$

Integration leads to the important relation

$$p = \rho_0 \frac{\partial \Phi}{\partial t} + \text{const} \tag{12.32}$$

Thus, not only the three components of the particle velocity, but also the sound pressure can be derived from the velocity potential by simple differentiation. If Equation 12.32 is introduced into the wave equation (12.19) for the pressure, a similar equation results for the velocity potential after integration with respect to time and by dropping the insignificant integration constant:

$$\nabla^2 \Phi = \frac{1}{c^2} \frac{\partial^2 \Phi}{\partial t^2} \tag{12.33}$$

The physical meaning of the velocity potential is meager;[2] it is best to consider it as a mathematical formalism. For periodic motion, the velocity potential can be replaced by the pressure because of the relationship:

$$\tilde{p} = \rho_0 \frac{\partial \tilde{\Phi}}{\partial t} = \rho_0 j\omega \tilde{\Phi} \tag{12.34}$$

Hence,

$$\tilde{\Phi} = \frac{\tilde{p}}{\rho_0 j\omega} = \frac{\tilde{p}}{jk\rho_0 c} \tag{12.35}$$

where $k = \omega/c$. The particle velocity then follows from the pressure:

$$\tilde{\vec{v}} = -\text{grad } \tilde{\Phi} = \frac{j}{k\rho_0 c} \text{grad } \tilde{p} \tag{12.36}$$

The last relation can also be derived directly from Euler's equation (12.20) by replacing $\rho_0 (\partial/\partial t)\, \tilde{v}$ by $\rho_0 j\omega \tilde{v} = j\rho_0 ck\tilde{v}$.

One-Dimensional Wave Equation and Its Solutions

The one-dimensional wave equation

$$\frac{\partial^2 p}{\partial x^2} = \frac{1}{c^2} \frac{\partial^2 p}{\partial t^2} \tag{12.37}$$

[1] If the motion were not rotationless, its vortical part would have to be described by a vector potential $\vec{A}$, as will be shown in Chapter XIV for shear deformations.

[2] See Lord Rayleigh, *The Theory of Sound* (New York, II,(1954), p. 15.

is of the same form as the equation for transverse vibrations of a string, and the solutions are the same. We are now predominantly interested in solutions that represent propagating waves. If the motion is restricted to periodic vibrations, the wave equation can be written as follows:

$$\frac{\partial^2 p}{\partial x^2}+k^2p=0 \tag{12.38}$$

and the solution becomes:

$$p=(Ae^{-jkx}+Be^{jkx})e^{j\omega t} \tag{12.39}$$

The first term represents a periodic wave that propagates in the positive x-direction:

$$Ae^{j(\omega t-kx)}=Ae^{j(\omega/c)(ct-x)} \tag{12.40}$$

It is of the form $f(ct-x)$. Similarly, the second term represents a wave that propagates in the negative x-direction.[3] Solutions of the given form are called plane waves; they do not depend on the two co-ordinates y and z, and the motion is the same in all planes for which $x=\text{const}$.

The wavelength is defined as the distance traveled by the progressive wave in one period:

$$\lambda=cT=\frac{c}{f}=\frac{2\pi c}{\omega} \tag{12.41}$$

The wave number can be expressed in terms of the wavelength:

$$k=\frac{\omega}{c}=\frac{2\pi f}{c}=\frac{2\pi}{\lambda} \tag{12.42}$$

The wave number represents a measure of the frequency, since it is proportional to the frequency; it can also be interpreted as the phase difference (in radians) between two points of a harmonic wave that are unit distance apart. The real solution is given by the real part of the above solution (Eq. 12.39):

$$p=A\cos(\omega t-kx)+B\cos(\omega t+kx) \tag{12.43}$$

However, it will seldom be necessary to use the solution in its real form.

The particle velocity follows from differentiation of the pressure (see Eq. 12.36):

$$\begin{aligned}\tilde{v}&=\frac{j}{k\rho c}\frac{\partial\tilde{p}}{\partial x}=\frac{j}{k\rho c}(-jkAe^{-jkx}+jkBe^{jkx})e^{j\omega t}\\&=\left(\frac{A}{\rho c}e^{-jkx}-\frac{B}{\rho c}e^{jkx}\right)e^{j\omega t}\end{aligned} \tag{12.44}$$

For a wave that progresses in the positive x-direction,

$$\tilde{v}=\frac{\tilde{p}}{\rho c} \tag{12.45}$$

[3] See p. 145.

For a wave that travels in the negative x-direction,

$$\tilde{v} = -\frac{\tilde{p}}{\rho c} \tag{12.46}$$

These results follow from Equations 12.39 and 12.44 if $B=0$ and $A=0$ are assumed successively and the ratio $\tilde{p}/\tilde{v}$ is computed.

The ratio of the pressure to the particle velocity is real and positive if the propagation is in the positive x-direction, and

$$\frac{p}{v} = \rho c \text{ kg. per m}^3 \cdot \text{m. per sec.} = \text{kg. per sec. m}^2 \tag{12.47}$$

The quantity ρc is called the wave resistance of the medium; it has the dimensions of a resistance per unit area. For air, $\rho = 1.29$ kg. per m^3, $c = 330$ m. per second, and $\rho c = 440$ kg. per sec. per m^2; for water, $\rho = 10^3$ kg. per m^3, $c = 1{,}500$ m. per second, and $\rho c = 1{,}500{,}000$ kg. per sec. per m^2.

For a fixed co-ordinate $x = \text{const}$, the fluid particles perform harmonic oscillations:

$$v = \frac{A}{\rho c}\cos(\omega t + \varphi) + \frac{B}{\rho c}\cos(\omega t + \varphi) \tag{12.48}$$

For a wave propagating in the positive x-direction, $B=0$. If an infinitely thin and infinitely light membrane is placed through the fluid particles, it will not disturb the motion. The medium may even be removed from the right of the membrane without changing the motion in front of it; therefore, the velocity of the membrane and the pressure on it wi'l still be described by the plane wave relation,

$$p = \rho c v \tag{12.49}$$

The magnitude ρc then describes the mechanical resistance per unit area that the membrane has to overcome to generate a sound wave. Since viscosity and other mechanisms that give rise to energy losses have been neglected, the resistance ρc can be only a radiation resistance. And the energy dissipated in ρc is identical with the sound energy that is generated by the moving membrane per unit of its area; it is the energy associated with the traveling wave. Thus, the radiation resistance of an infinitely large membrane is ρc per unit area. It will be shown later that "infinitely large"—from the point of sound generation—means that the diameter is larger than the wave length.

The average power generated per unit area of the membrane is given by:

$$\frac{1}{T}\int_0^T p v\,dt = \frac{\rho c}{T}\int_0^T v^2\,dt = \frac{1}{T}\int_0^T \frac{p^2}{\rho c}\,dt$$

$$= \frac{\rho c V^2}{2} = \frac{P^2}{2\rho c} \tag{12.50}$$

where P and V are the amplitudes of the pressure and the particle velocity, and $P/\sqrt{2}$ and $V/\sqrt{2}$ are the root-mean-square values of the amplitudes. The formulas are similar to those for electrical systems; the electrical power, for instance, is:

$$Ri^2 = \frac{u^2}{R} \tag{12.51}$$

where u and i are understood to represent the root-mean-square values.

Spherical Waves

Sound rays, sound beams, plane waves, and cylindrical waves are possible only near a sound source. According to Huygens' principle, every point in a wave front acts as a secondary source and propagates energy into all directions. This spreading out of the sound energy leads to a divergence of the sound waves, so that eventually, at great distances from the source, all sound waves turn into spherical waves. From a great distance, every sound source appears as the center of outgoing spherical waves.

Obviously, spherical sound propagation is very important, and we are very interested in deriving its laws. We shall have to start by finding the solutions of the wave equation (12.33) in the general spherical co-ordinates r, θ, and φ. These solutions form a complete set of spherical wave functions that are orthogonal over all space, and every wave field can be expressed as an infinite series of such functions. Details of this analysis are given in books on acoustics (see recommended literature at end of this chapter). The first term in the solution can be interpreted as a sound field that is generated by a pulsating sphere (monopole); the second, as a sound field that is generated by an oscillating solid sphere (dipole); the third, as the combined field of a pulsating sphere, an oscillating solid sphere (dipole), and a sphere with two nodal circles (a quadrupole); and so on.[4]

To derive the solutions of the wave equation in spherical co-ordinates, we shall use here a simpler and more physical procedure. We shall start with the simplest possible solution, the monopole solution, which depends only on the distance from the source, and not on the angles θ and φ; and we shall derive additional solutions by forming multipoles with this solution. It will be shown in the following that for small sound sources the monopole or pulsating sphere term of the solution predominates overwhelmingly whenever the source generates sound by periodic changes of volume. Therefore, the study of the pulsating sphere is of particular importance.

The wave equation can be obtained in spherical co-ordinates by trans-

[4] The fields generated by higher-order multipoles are not orthogonal. The wave functions are obtained by orthogonalizing the set of multipole solutions; consequently, (except for the zero- and first-order wave functions), the higher-order wave functions are made up of a number of multipole terms.

forming the Cartesian co-ordinates into spherical co-ordinates, but the procedure is lengthy and difficult. It is much easier to derive the equation of continuity for an elementary spherical shell and to eliminate the density with the aid of the state equation. The wave equation then is obtained by expressing the radial particle velocity as the radial derivative of a velocity potential. We only need to consider radially symmetrical vibrations.

The equation of continuity for a spherical shell, assuming radial symmetry, is derived by computing the excess of fluid mass that enters the shell over the mass leaving it in the time interval dt (see Fig. 12.3):

$$4\pi r^2\rho(r)v_r(r)dt-4\pi(r+dr)^2\rho(r+dr)v_r(r+dr)dt=-4\pi\frac{\partial(r^2\rho v_r)}{\partial r}drdt \quad (12.52)$$

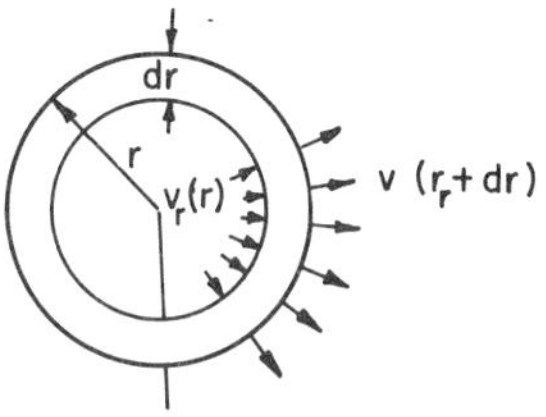

Fig. 12.3 Derivation of the equation of continuity in spherical co-ordinates.

The increase in mass can also be formulated in terms of the increase of the density of the shell:

$$\partial\rho\cdot 4\pi r^2dr=4\pi r^2\frac{\partial\rho}{\partial t}dtdr=\frac{4\pi r^2}{c^2}\frac{\partial p}{\partial t}dtdr \quad (12.53)$$

If the last two expressions are equated to one another, the wave equation is obtained in spherical co-ordinates:

$$\frac{\partial\left(r^2\dfrac{\partial\Phi}{\partial r}\right)}{\partial r}=\frac{r^2}{\rho_0c^2}\frac{\partial p}{\partial t}=\frac{r^2}{c^2}\frac{\partial^2\Phi}{\partial t^2} \quad (12.54)$$

where, as before (Eq. 12.32), Φ is the velocity potential. By performing the various differentiations and adding and subtracting terms, the above expression can be written in the following form:

$$\frac{\partial^2(r\Phi)}{\partial r^2}=\frac{1}{c^2}\frac{\partial^2(r\Phi)}{\partial t^2} \quad (12.55)$$

This result is best proved by working backward from Equation 12.55 and, after performing the differentiations in Equations 12.55 and 12.54, by comparing the resulting expressions.

The wave equation for spherical sound propagation is the same as that for plane waves, except that the variable Φ is replaced by $r\Phi$ and that the differentiation with respect to x has been replaced by differentiation with respect to r. Hence, the solution is:

$$r\Phi = f_1(ct-r) + f_2(ct+r) \tag{12.56}$$

or

$$\Phi = \frac{1}{r} f_1(ct-r) + \frac{1}{r} f_2(ct+r) \tag{12.57}$$

The first term represents a wave that originates from a point source and travels in the positive r-direction; the second term represents a wave that travels in the negative r-direction and converges to a point.[5]

Since we are mainly interested in waves that diverge from a source, attention will be restricted primarily to the first term of the solution:

$$\Phi = \frac{f(ct-r)}{r} \tag{12.58}$$

or

$$p = \rho \frac{\partial \Phi}{\partial t} = \rho r \frac{\partial f(u)}{\partial u} \frac{\partial u}{\partial t} = \frac{\rho c f'}{r} \tag{12.59}$$

where u has been written for $ct-r$, and f', for the derivative of f with respect to its argument $u = ct - r$. The particle velocity is:

$$v = -\frac{\partial \Phi}{\partial r} = \frac{1}{r} f' + \frac{1}{r^2} f = \frac{p}{\rho c} + \frac{1}{\rho r} \int p dt \tag{12.60}$$

The first term represents the far-field particle velocity, which is in phase with the pressure and, consequently, is responsible for the energy transport in the sound wave. The second term, which depends on r^2, predominates close to the source, but is negligible as compared to the far-field term at great distances from the source. For sinusoidal vibrations,

$$p = \frac{P_0}{r} \cos(\omega t - kr) \tag{12.61}$$

$$v_{\text{far}} = \frac{P_0}{r\rho c} \cos(\omega t - kr) \qquad v_{\text{near}} = \frac{P_0}{\omega \rho r^2} \sin(\omega t - kr) \tag{12.62}$$

where P_0 is a constant. The near-field term is 90° out of phase with the pressure and describes a sound field that does not contribute to the power of the source. It is frequently called the wattless component of the sound field, and it represents a flow of fluid in the proximity of the sound source. The near-field term increases inversely with frequency and the square of the distance from the source. If the source generates more than one frequency, the lower frequencies predominate in the vicinity of the source (because of the factor $1/\omega$ in Eq. 12.62), and the frequency spectrum of the velocity field changes with the distance from the source. If the sound pressure varies in a non-sinusoidal manner, then the sound impression, and not only the loudness, varies with the distance from the source. This variation is very pronounced

[5] See pp. 145.

if the near-field term f/r^2 is large in comparison to the far-field term f'/r, that is, if the rate of change f' of the function f with time is slow. The low-frequency phenomena, therefore, lead to a particularly great change in the sound picture with the distance from the source (that is, with the curvature of the sound wave). The ear responds to a certain extent to the particle velocity and, consequently, receives a true distance sensation if the sound source generates low-frequency transients or other low-frequency phenomena that differ from sinusoidal vibrations. Sinusoidal vibrations remain sinusoidal even if the distance from the source is altered; the loudness changes, but otherwise there is no radical change in the nature of the sounds with the distance from the source. Therefore, sinusoidally vibrating sources cannot generate a true distance sensation.[6] But for nonsinusoidally vibrating sources, the sound impression is proportional to $p(t)$ at a great distance from the source, whereas near the source it is proportional to the integral of $p(t)$, which may be very different. This phenomenon is illustrated for two pulses in Figure 12.4.

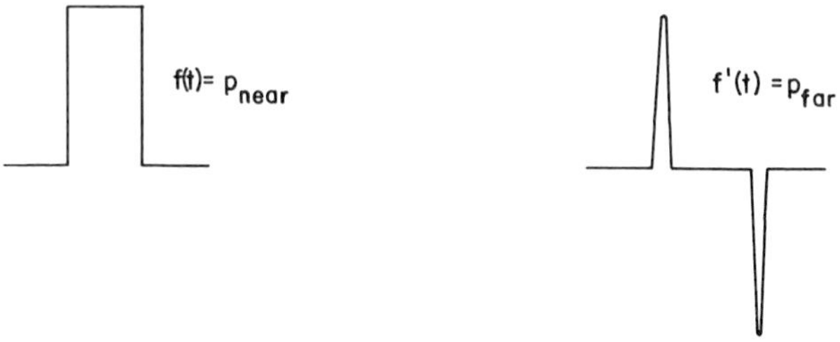

Fig. 12.4 Variation of the sound pressure with time near and far from the sound source (if $f(t)$ is a pulse).

Spherical Wave Impedance and Radiation of Small Sound Sources

Simple sources (*monopoles*). For harmonic variations, the velocity potential may be expressed in terms of the pressure (Eq. 12.36), and the following relations hold:

$$\bar{P} = \frac{\bar{P}_0 e^{-jkr}}{r} \tag{12.63}$$

$$\bar{V}_r = \frac{j}{k\rho c}\frac{\partial \bar{P}}{\partial r} = \frac{j}{k\rho c}\left(-\frac{jk}{r} - \frac{1}{r^2}\right)\bar{P}_0 e^{-jkr}$$

[6] For more information about the distance sensation, see G. von Békésy's fundamental paper "Ueber die Entstehung der Entfernungsempfindung beim Hoeren," *Akustische Zeits,* **3** (1938), 21–31.

$$=\frac{\bar{P}_0}{\rho c r}\left(1+\frac{1}{jkr}\right)e^{-jkr} \tag{12.64}$$

The wave impedance in the spherical wave or any other type of wave (like that in a plane wave) is defined as the ratio of the pressure to the particle velocity. This ratio is given by:

$$\bar{z}=\frac{\bar{P}}{\bar{V}}=\frac{\dfrac{\bar{P}_0 e^{-jkr}}{r}}{\dfrac{\bar{P}_0 e^{-jkr}}{r\rho c}\left(1+\dfrac{1}{jkr}\right)}=\rho c\frac{1}{1+\dfrac{1}{jkr}}=\rho c\frac{(1-jkr)jkr}{1+k^2r^2}$$

$$=\rho c\frac{k^2r^2}{1+k^2r^2}+\frac{j\omega\rho r}{1+k^2r^2}=r_{\mathrm{rad}}+j\omega m_{\mathrm{eff}} \tag{12.65}$$

For large values of r,

$$\bar{z}=\frac{\bar{P}}{\bar{V}}=\rho c \tag{12.66}$$

as in the plane wave. The real part of the wave impedance

$$r_{\mathrm{rad}}=\rho c\frac{k^2r^2}{1+k^2r^2} \qquad (\doteq \rho c k^2 r^2 \quad \text{if} \quad k^2r^2 \ll 1)$$
$$(\doteq \rho c \quad \text{if} \quad k^2r^2 \gg 1) \tag{12.67}$$

represents the radiation resistance in the spherical wave. The imaginary part can be interpreted as the reactance of a frequency-dependent mass of the magnitude:

$$m_{\mathrm{eff}}=\frac{\rho r}{1+k^2r^2} \qquad (\doteq \rho r \quad \text{if} \quad k^2r^2 \ll 1)$$
$$\left(\doteq \frac{\rho r}{k^2r^2} \quad \text{if} \quad k^2r^2 \gg 1\right) \tag{12.68}$$

It can easily be shown[7] that this mass, when multiplied by half the square of the particle velocity and $4\pi r^2$, represents the kinetic energy of the near field of the radiator. The second form of the right-hand sides of the last two equations is only valid at low frequencies, when

$$k^2r^2=\frac{4\pi^2r^2}{\lambda^2}\ll 1 \tag{12.69}$$

For practical purposes, the weaker conditions, $kr<1$ or $2r/\lambda<\frac{1}{3}$, are usually accurate enough. Thus, a pulsating source may be approximated by a small sphere, if its diameter is less than one third of the wave length. The wave impedance (Eq. 12.68) is identical with the impedance that a spherical source has to overcome per unit of its area.

The wave or radiation resistance multiplied by the square of the effective velocity (root-mean-square velocity $V/\sqrt{2}$) represents the power that is generated per unit area of the sound source. Figure 12.5 shows a plot of this

[7] See E. J. Skudrzyk, *Grundlagen der Akustik* (Vienna, 1954), p. 167.

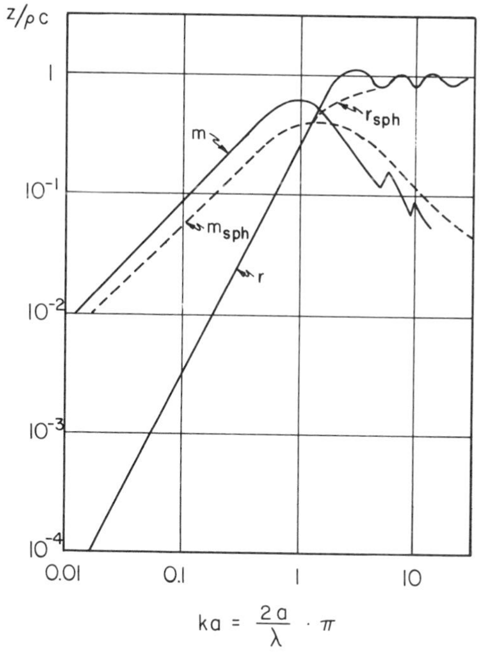

Fig. 12.5 Comparison of the radiation resistance and of the effective vibrating mass of a sphere (of radius r_{sph} and mass m_{sph}) with the corresponding magnitudes of a circular piston membrane (of radius r and mass m); plotted as a function of ka, where a is the radius of the sphere or that of the equivalent sphere (the sphere of the same surface area as the piston membrane).

radiation resistance r_{sph} and the effective mass m_{sph} for a sphere and of the corresponding quantities m and r for a piston membrane. Because of the small radiation resistance at low frequencies,

$$r_{rad} \doteq \rho c k^2 r^2 = \rho c \pi^2 \left(\frac{2r}{\lambda}\right)^2 \tag{12.70}$$

a small sphere is a very poor sound radiator.

The strength of a pulsating sound source (monopole) can be expressed by the volume flow it generates. This volume flow Q is defined as the product of the surface area of the source and its velocity (Eq. 12.64):

$$\bar{Q} = 4\pi r^2 \bar{V}_r = 4\pi \frac{\bar{P}_0}{\rho c j k}(1 + jkr)e^{-jkr} \tag{12.71}$$

If the diameter of the sound source is smaller than one third of the wave length (or $kr \ll 1$), the far-field term can be neglected, and the exponential e^{-jkr} can be replaced by one. The radial velocity, then, is:

$$\bar{V}_r = \frac{\bar{P}_0}{\rho c r} \cdot \frac{1}{jkr} \tag{12.72}$$

and

$$\bar{Q}=\frac{4\pi\bar{P}_0}{j\rho ck} \quad \text{or} \quad \bar{P}_0=j\rho c\frac{k\bar{Q}}{4\pi} \tag{12.73}$$

The sound pressure (Eq. 12.63) is thus proportional to the volume rate at which fluid is introduced or withdrawn by the source; it is given by:

$$\tilde{p}=\frac{\bar{P}_0}{r}e^{-jkr+j\omega t}=\frac{jk\rho c\bar{Q}e^{-jkr+j\omega t}}{4\pi r} \tag{12.74}$$

The sound pressure of a small spherical source is determined by its volume flow, and by nothing else. It is obvious that the shape of a small source will not influence the pressure it generates at a sufficiently great distance from it and that sources producing equal volume flow will generate the same sound pressure and the same sound energy.[8]

Equivalent sound sources and radiation resistance of small sound sources. The preceding conclusion leads to a considerable simplification of the theory of sound radiation of small sources. Two sources that have the same area and vibrate with the same velocity generate the same volume flow. A sphere of the same surface area σ as the vibrator under consideration generates the same sound pressure and the same sound power if both vibrators have the same volume flow (or the same surface area and velocity amplitude). Since they have the same area and generate the same sound power, they necessarily have the same radiation resistance per unit area and the same total radiation resistance. The radiation resistance per unit area of any vibrator is, therefore, the same as the radiation resistance per unit area of a sphere with the same area σ. Since the radius of a sphere of an area σ is given by:

$$\sigma=4\pi r^2 \quad \text{or} \quad r=\sqrt{\frac{\sigma}{4\pi}} \tag{12.75}$$

the radiation resistance (per unit area) of any vibrator that is small as compared to the wavelength is:

$$r_{\text{rad}}=\rho ck^2r^2=\rho ck^2\frac{\sigma}{4\pi} \tag{12.76}$$

For a piston membrane in a baffle, $\sigma=2\pi a^2$ (both sides), where a is the radius of the membrane and where the radiation resistance per unit area is:

$$r_{\text{rad}}=\rho ck^2\frac{a^2}{2} \tag{12.77}$$

This expression is valid as long as the diameter of the membrane is less than one third of the wave length. If, on the other hand, the diameter of the

[8] This statement can be proved by showing that the energy contributions of the higher-order wave functions that are generated by a small source are negligible as compared to that of the zero-order wave function, whenever $Q\neq 0$. See, for instance, Eq. 12.92 and the corresponding equations for the radiation resistance of the higher-order sources.

membrane is greater than a wave length,

$$r_{\text{rad}} = \rho c \tag{12.78}$$

A good approximation for the range between these limits can be obtained by using the formula for the radiation resistance of the equivalent sphere, which is a sphere of the same surface area as the vibrator. Figure 12.5 compares the radiation resistance of the equivalent sphere with the exact computed value for a piston membrane.

Acoustic dipoles and oscillating rigid bodies. The second term in the series solution of the wave equation (12.33) in radial co-ordinates can be interpreted as a sound field that is generated by an acoustic dipole. If a positive

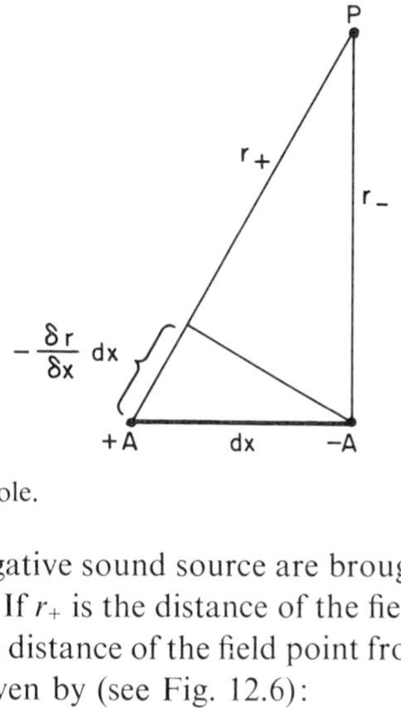

Fig. 12.6 An acoustic dipole.

sound source and a negative sound source are brought near each other, an acoustic dipole results. If r_+ is the distance of the field point from the positive source and r_- is the distance of the field point from the negative source, the resultant field is given by (see Fig. 12.6):

$$\bar{P} = A\left(\frac{e^{-jkr_+}}{r_+} + \frac{e^{-jkr_-}}{r_-}\right) \tag{12.79}$$

where P stands for the pressure or velocity potential. As the distance between the two sources becomes smaller, the above difference can be replaced by the differential,[9] and

$$\begin{aligned} P &= A\frac{\partial}{\partial x}\left(\frac{e^{-jkr}}{r}\right)dx = -A\frac{\partial}{\partial r}\left(\frac{e^{-jkr}}{r}\right)\frac{\partial r}{\partial x}dx \\ &= \frac{jkAdx}{r}\left(1+\frac{1}{jkr}\right)e^{-jkr}\frac{\partial r}{\partial x} = \frac{\bar{B}}{r}\left(1+\frac{1}{jkr}\right)e^{-jkr}\cos\theta \end{aligned} \tag{12.80}$$

[9] The minus sign in the result is due to the fact that r is a vector from the source point to the field point. The magnitude $\partial r/\partial x$ is the derivative of r at the field point. But the $\partial/\partial x$ refers to a differentiation at the source point. Therefore, the direction of r has to be reversed, and the derivative changes sign. This conclusion is trivial if Cartesian coordinates are used. If $r = \sqrt{(x-x_0)^2 + \ldots}$ then $\partial r/\partial x = -\partial r/\partial x_0$, etc.

where

$$\bar{B}=jkAdx \qquad \text{and} \qquad \frac{\partial r}{\partial x}=\cos\theta \tag{12.81}$$

and θ is the angle between the direction of the axis of the dipole (which has been assumed to have the direction of the x-axis) and the radius vector to the point of observation. To generate a dipole of finite moment $\bar{B}$, the strength $\bar{A}$ of the sources that make up the dipole has to become infinite. Thus, one differentiation with respect to a co-ordinate of a source field results in a dipole field.

The characteristic features of the dipole are the directivity factor $\cos\theta$ and the very small sound radiation whenever the frequency is low or the distance is small between the two sources that form the dipole (the length of the dipole axis).

The radial component of the particle velocity that is generated by the dipole is obtained by differentiation:

$$\bar{V}_r=\frac{j}{k\rho c}\frac{\partial\bar{P}}{\partial r}=\frac{\bar{B}}{\rho cr}\left[1+\frac{2}{jkr}+\frac{2}{(jkr)^2}\right]\cos\theta\cdot e^{-jkr} \tag{12.82}$$

and the acoustic impedance per unit area becomes:

$$\bar{z}=\frac{\bar{P}}{\bar{V}}=\frac{\rho cjkr(1+jkr)}{2-k^2r^2+2jkr}=\rho c\frac{k^4r^4}{4+k^4r^4}+j\omega\rho r\frac{2+k^2r^2}{4+k^4r^4} \tag{12.83}$$

The real part of this expression represents the radiation resistance; the sound power that is produced by the dipole is proportional to it. For the small pulsating sphere, the radiation resistance is proportional to k^2r^2; for the small dipole, it is proportional to k^4r^4. Thus, whenever the sound source is small or the frequency low ($k^2r^2 \ll 1$), the pulsating-sphere component of the sound energy is two orders of magnitude greater than the dipole component. A small rigid body that oscillates about a mean position acts like an acoustic dipole; it can be shown that it generates the sound pressure:[10]

$$\tilde{p}=-\frac{\rho c}{4\pi}k^2\tilde{v}_0\left(\frac{M_s}{\rho}+\tau\right)\cos\theta\cdot\left(1+\frac{1}{jkr}\right)\frac{e^{-jkr}}{r} \tag{12.84}$$

where v_0 is the axial velocity of the vibrator, M_s is the effective mass of the surrounding medium (which can readily be computed by the methods used in hydrodynamics), τ is the volume of the vibrator, θ is the angle between the direction of vibration and the point of observation, and r is the distance from the vibrator. For a solid sphere of radius R,

$$M_s=\frac{2\pi R^3\rho}{3} \qquad \tau=\frac{4\pi R^3}{3} \tag{12.85}$$

For a plate of radius a,

$$M_s=\frac{8\rho a^3}{3} \qquad \tau\doteq 0 \tag{12.86}$$

[10] See E. J. Skudrzyk, *op. cit.*, p. 237.

ρ being the density of the surrounding medium. The radiation resistance for such a rigid body R_s referred to its whole area is:

$$R_s = \frac{\rho c}{12\pi} k^4 \left(\frac{M_s}{\rho} + \tau \right)^2 \tag{12.87}$$

This result is obtained by integrating the sound power $P^2/2\rho c$ over a large sphere (integrating over $\cos^2\theta \sin\theta$) and by dividing by V_0^2 (V_0 being the velocity of the body). Because of the factor k^4, an oscillating rigid body is a very poor sound radiator at low frequencies.

Far-field and sound power generated by multipoles. The quadrupole solution is obtained by differentiating the dipole solution with respect to any one of the three Cartesian co-ordinates. If the axis of the dipole has the same direction as the direction of differentiation, a longitudinal quadrupole is obtained; if it is at right angles, a so-called lateral quadrupole will result. If we neglect the near-field terms, differentiation can be confined to the exponential factor. Differentiation then yields a factor $-jk$ and a factor $-\partial r/\partial x_n = -\cos(r, x_n)$, where x_n is the co-ordinate that is differentiated.

If we start with the source solution:

$$P_s = jk\rho c \frac{Q}{4\pi r} e^{-jkr} \tag{12.88}$$

the dipole far-field solution becomes:

$$P_d = -k^2 \rho c \frac{Q}{4\pi r} e^{-jkr} \cos(n, x) dx \tag{12.89}$$

A lateral quadrupole far-field solution is obtained by differentiating with respect to y:

$$P_Q = -jk^3 \frac{\rho c Q}{4\pi r} dx dy \cos(n, x) \cos(n, y) \tag{12.90}$$

The corresponding sound powers are obtained by integrating the squares of the sound pressure over a sphere of large radius. The total sound power generated by a source is:

$$N_s = \frac{1}{2} P_s^2 \frac{4\pi r^2}{\rho c} = \frac{1}{2} \frac{k^2 \rho c Q^2}{4\pi} \tag{12.91}$$

The corresponding result for a dipole differs by a factor $k^2 dx^2$ and a factor equal to the mean square over the surface of a sphere $\langle \cos^2(r, x) \rangle = \frac{1}{3}$. Thus,

$$N_d = \frac{1}{3} k^4 \frac{\rho c Q^2 dx^2}{8\pi} \tag{12.92}$$

Correspondingly, the sound power generated by a quadrupole is:

$$N_Q = \gamma k^6 \frac{\rho c Q^2 dx^2 dy^2}{8\pi} \tag{12.93}$$

where $\gamma=\frac{1}{5}$ for longitudinal quadrupoles (both differentiations along the same co-ordinate, and $\gamma=\frac{1}{15}$ for lateral quadrupoles.

Sound radiation at high frequencies. The solutions of the wave equation that describe the sound fields generated by monopoles, dipoles, quadrupoles, and higher-order multipoles are of the form:

$$\frac{\tilde{p}}{\tilde{v}}=\rho c\frac{1}{a+\dfrac{b}{jkr}+\ldots\dfrac{f}{(jkr)^n}} \tag{12.94}$$

where n is the order of the multipole. They all approach the value ρc asymptotically when $(kr)^2 \gg 1$, that is, when the diameter of the vibrator approaches or exceeds one wave length. The sound field generated by the vibrator then obeys the laws of geometrical optics, as if the wave length were infinitely small. Diffraction effects need not be taken into account, and the intensity can be computed by assuming that $p=\rho cv$ at the surface of the vibrator and by considering only the divergence of the sound waves.

Radiation resistance and sound power. The power generated by unit surface area of any vibrator is given by the product of its surface velocity and the component of the pressure in phase with it:

$$N_0=\frac{1}{T}\int_0^T P\cos(\omega t+\varphi_p)V\cos(\omega t+\varphi_v)dt$$

$$=\frac{1}{2T}\int_0^T PV[\cos(2\omega t+\varphi_p+\varphi_v)+\cos(\varphi_p-\varphi_v)]\,dt$$

$$=\frac{PV}{2}\cos(\varphi_p-\varphi_v)=\frac{1}{2}Re\left(\bar{P}\,\bar{V}^*\right) \tag{12.95}$$

But

$$\bar{P}=\bar{V}(r+j\omega m) \tag{12.96}$$

where r is the radiation resistance and m is the effective mass per unit area; hence,

$$N_0=\frac{1}{2}Re[\bar{V}\bar{V}^*(r+j\omega m)]=\frac{1}{2}rV^2 \tag{12.97}$$

For a small sphere, $r_{rad}=\rho ck^2a^2$, and the total power N generated by it is:

$$N=4\pi r^2\cdot\rho ck^2r^2\frac{V^2}{2} \tag{12.98}$$

Interaction between Sound Sources

The fundamental sound-field equations are linear. If p_1 is the pressure that is generated by one of two sources and p_2 is the pressure generated by the second source, the resultant pressure is equal to the sum of the two pressures. However, the resultant sound intensity is not equal to the sum of the sound powers that each source would generate individually, but is proportional to:

$$|\bar{P}_1+\bar{P}_2|^2=(\bar{P}_1+\bar{P}_2)(\bar{P}_1^*+\bar{P}_2^*)=P_1^2+P_2^2+2Re(\bar{P}_1\bar{P}_2^*) \qquad (12.99)$$

The double product represents the effect of the interaction between the two sound sources.

The total sound power that is generated by the two sources is obtained by integrating the square of the pressure over a spherical surface of large radius. If the two sources are sufficiently far away from each other (or if their frequencies are sufficiently different), the product $\bar{P}_1\bar{P}_2$ is as frequently positive as it is negative during this integration and does not contribute to the integral. The sound pressures generated by the two sources, then, are incoherent (over the integration surface), and the resultant sound power is equal to the sum of the sound powers that are generated by each source alone. But if the sound sources are of the same frequency and are very close to each other, the resultant sound power may be very different. For instance, if $P_1=P_2$, the resultant sound power is four times as large as that of one source alone. The explanation for this phenomenon is very simple. Each source has to work against its own sound pressure (which represents the reaction of the medium to its motion) as well as against the sound pressure that is generated by the source near it. It happens that for the two equal point sources the work performed by each against its own pressure is equal to the work performed against the pressure at its surface that is generated by the second source. This is demonstrated by considering two small pulsating spheres of equal intensity of radius r_0 at a distance d. If V_0 is its surface velocity, $Q=4\pi r_0^2 V_0$, and the sound pressure generated by each source is given by:

$$P=j\frac{k\rho c Q e^{-jkr}}{4\pi r}=j\frac{k\rho c 4\pi r_0^2 V_0}{4\pi r}(1-jkr+\ldots)$$
$$=\frac{k\rho c r_0^2 V_0}{r}(kr+j\ldots) \qquad (12.100)$$

where

$$e^{-jkr}=1-jkr+\ldots \qquad (12.101)$$

The power generated by each source is given by half the product of its surface area with its surface velocity and the component of the pressure in phase with its surface velocity. Hence, in overcoming its own sound pressure, it generates the power:

$$N_1=\frac{1}{2}\cdot 4\pi r_0^2\cdot\frac{k\rho c r_0^2 V_0}{r_0}kr_0V_0=\frac{\rho c}{2}\cdot 4\pi r_0^2 k^2 r_0^2 V_0^2 \qquad (12.102)$$

In overcoming the sound pressure p (Eq. 12.100) of the second source, at a distance $r=d$ from it, it generates the power:

$$N_{12}=\frac{\rho c}{2}\cdot 4\pi r_0^2 V_0 Re(P)=\frac{\rho c}{2}\cdot 4\pi r_0^2 k\rho c\frac{r_0^2 V_0}{d}kd\cdot V_0$$

$$=\frac{\rho c}{2}\cdot 4\pi r_0^2 k^2 r_0^2 V_0^2=N_1 \tag{12.103}$$

Because the values d cancel, this work is independent of the distance of the second source as long as

$$k^2d^2\ll 1 \qquad \text{or} \qquad d^2\ll\left(\frac{\lambda}{2\pi}\right)^2 \tag{12.104}$$

Thus, if sound sources are close to one another, they react with each other, and the two sources may generate up to two times more sound energy than if they were far apart. It is imperative for practical work to know how far the sources must be apart, so that the sound fields are incoherent and their powers can simply be added. A good estimate of this distance is obtained by repeating the preceding computation without developing the exponentials into a series (which is equivalent to replacing the factor jkd by $j\sin kd$). The result is:

$$N=N_1\left(1\pm\frac{\sin kd}{kd}\right) \tag{12.105}$$

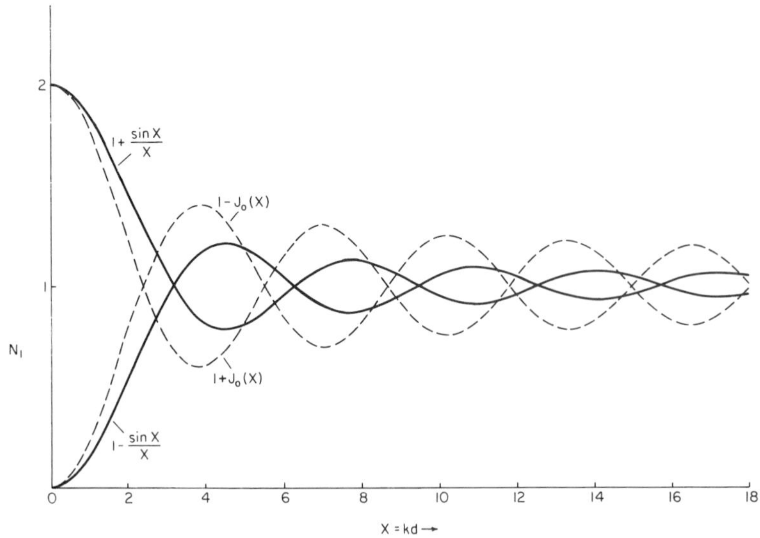

Fig. 12.7 Sound power generated by each of two equal point sources, (thin curves) and line sources (thick curves) as a function of their separation; *a*, when they vibrate in phase; *b*, when they vibrate in antiphase.

The negative sign applies if the two sources vibrate in phase opposition. Figure 12.7 shows N/N_1 as a function of kd. For $kd>1$, $N\cong N_1$. Thus, two sound sources do not interact whenever their distance is greater than one sixth of the wave length. It is surprising that the interaction between two sound sources is limited to such small distances. The computation shows that this interaction is a consequence only of the near field. The computation and the results are very similar for other sound sources.

A similar result is obtained for the sound power generated by two parallel line sources (sources distributed with constant intensity along an infinite line). The computation then leads to the expression $N=N_1[1\pm J_0(kd)]$, where J_0 is the Bessel function of zero order. This result is also plotted in Figure 12.7. Because of the slower divergence of the field that is generated by line sources, interaction extends over a much wider range.

Cylindrical Sound Radiation

Sound fields generated by sources distributed along a line can be analyzed with the aid of cylindrical wave functions. By deriving the equation of continuity for an infinite cylindrical shell the wave equation is easily obtained. If axial symmetry is assumed, the continuity equation is:

$$\frac{1}{2\pi r dr dz}\left[2\pi\frac{\partial(rv_r)}{\partial r}drdz+\frac{\partial v_z}{\partial z}2\pi r dr dz\right]=-\frac{1}{\rho_0}\frac{\partial\rho}{\partial t}=-\frac{1}{\rho_0 c^2}\frac{\partial p}{\partial t} \qquad (12.106)$$

If the velocity potential

$$\bar{V}=-\text{grad}\,\Phi \qquad (12.107)$$

is introduced, the wave equation results:

$$\frac{\partial^2\Phi}{\partial r^2}+\frac{1}{r}\frac{\partial\Phi}{\partial r}+\frac{\partial^2\Phi}{\partial z^2}=\frac{1}{c^2}\frac{\partial^2\Phi}{\partial t^2} \qquad (12.108)$$

For an infinitely long pulsating cylinder, whose velocity potential varies like $\cos(\beta z+\alpha)e^{-j\omega t}$ in the z-direction, the above equation reduces to:

$$\frac{\partial^2\Phi}{\partial r^2}+\frac{1}{r}\frac{\partial\Phi}{\partial r}+(k^2-\beta^2)\Phi=0 \qquad (12.109)$$

where

$$k^2=\frac{\omega^2}{c^2} \quad \text{and} \quad k'^2=k^2-\beta^2 \qquad (12.110)$$

The pressure satisfies a similar differential equation, and the solution for the pressure is given by the Hankel functions

$$\bar{P}=[\bar{A}H_0^{(1)}(k'r)+\bar{B}H_0^{(2)}(k'r)]\cos(\beta z+\alpha) \qquad (12.111)$$

For large $k'r$, these functions can be replaced by their asymptotic expressions:

$$H_0^{(1)}(k'r)=\sqrt{\frac{2}{\pi k'r}}e^{j(k'r-\pi/4)} \qquad H_0^{(2)}(k'r)=\sqrt{\frac{2}{\pi k'r}}e^{-j(k'r-\pi/4)} \qquad (12.112)$$

and the solution becomes:

$$\bar{P}=\left[\bar{A}\sqrt{\frac{2}{\pi k'r}}e^{j(k'r-\pi/4)}+\bar{B}\sqrt{\frac{2}{\pi k'r}}e^{-j(k'r-\pi/4)}\right]\cos(\beta z+\alpha) \quad (12.113)$$

whereas for small $k'r$,

$$J_0(z)\doteq 1-\frac{z^2}{4} \qquad N_0(z)=-\frac{2}{\pi}\ln\frac{2}{\gamma z} \qquad H_0^{(1)}(z)=J_0(z)+jN_0(z)$$
$$H_0^{(2)}(z)=J_0(z)-jN_0(z) \quad (12.114)$$

and

$$\bar{P}=\left[\bar{A}\left(1-j\frac{2}{\pi}\ln\frac{2}{\gamma k'r}\right)+\bar{B}\left(1+j\frac{2}{\pi}\ln\frac{2}{\gamma k'r}\right)\right]\cos(\beta z+\alpha) \quad (12.115)$$

where γ is the Euler's number ($\gamma=1.781072$) and $J_0(z)$ and $N_0(z)$ are the Bessel functions of the first and second kind.

If the cylinder is a source and no energy returns to it, $A=0$. If the radius of the cylindrical source becomes very small ($k'r \ll 1$), the radial velocity at its surface is:

$$\bar{V}_r=\frac{j}{k\rho c}\frac{\partial\bar{P}}{\partial r}=\bar{B}\cos(\beta z+\alpha)\frac{2}{\pi k\rho cr} \quad (12.116)$$

and the volume flow per element of length dz at the surface $r=r_0$ becomes:

$$\frac{dQ}{dz}=2\pi r_0(V_r)_{r=r_0}=\frac{4}{k\rho c}\bar{B}\cos(\beta z+\alpha) \quad (12.117)$$

Hence,

$$\bar{B}\cos(\beta z+\alpha)=\frac{k\rho c}{4}Q_0 \quad (12.118)$$

If this value is substituted in the solution ($\bar{A}$ being zero), the following result is obtained for the sound pressure at greater distances from the pulsating cylinder:

$$\bar{P}=\bar{P}_{\text{source}}=\frac{k\rho c}{4}Q_0\sqrt{\frac{2}{\pi k'r}}e^{-j(k'r-\pi/4)}$$
$$=\frac{k\rho c}{4}Q_0\sqrt{\frac{2}{\pi k'r}}e^{-j(k'r-\pi/4)} \quad (12.119)$$

where $Q_0(z)$ is the volume flow per unit length of the cylinder (the unit length being assumed to be small as compared to the wave length). The field generated by a dipole cylindrical source (oscillating rigid cylinder) is obtained by combining two cylindrical zero-order sources of opposite sign. The mathematical solution can be obtained by a procedure similar to that used for deriving the dipole source and by dropping a near-field term that results from differentiating $1/\sqrt{r}$:

$$\bar{P}_{\text{dip}}=-\frac{\partial\bar{P}}{\partial r}\frac{\partial r}{\partial x}dx=-dx\frac{\partial r}{\partial x}\frac{k\rho c}{4}Q_0\sqrt{\frac{2}{\pi k'r}}e^{-j(k'r-\pi/4)}\cdot(-jk')$$
$$=[jQ_0 dx\cos(r,x)]\frac{\rho ckk'}{4}\sqrt{\frac{2}{\pi k'r}}e^{-j(k'r-\pi/4)} \quad (12.120)$$

It can be shown by comparing the asymptotic solution (Eq. 12.120) with Equation 12.111 that the true axial velocity of the dipole is $Q_0 dx/2\pi R^2$.

A further differentiation leads to a quadrupole field. A so-called lateral quadrupole is obtained if this differentiation is performed in the y-direction:

$$P_{\text{quad}} = Q_0(k'^2 dxdy) \cos(r, x) \cos(r, y) \frac{\rho ck}{4} \sqrt{\frac{2}{\pi k' r}} e^{-j(k'r - \pi/4)} \quad (12.121)$$

The sound power that is generated per unit length of a pulsating cylinder is given by:

$$N_1 = \frac{1}{2} \frac{P^2 \cdot 2\pi r}{\rho c} \cos\theta = \frac{1}{2} \frac{k\rho c}{4} \hat{Q}_0^2 \cos^2(\beta z + \alpha) \quad (12.122)$$

In this last expression θ denotes the angle of the direction of propagation of the outgoing waves with the normal to the surface of the cylinder. This is proved by decomposing $\cos(\beta z + \alpha)$ into its exponential constituents exp $[\pm(\beta z + \alpha)]$ and combining them with the exponential in front of it in Equation 12.119: $e^{-jk'r} \cdot e^{\pm j(\beta z + \alpha)} = e^{-j(k'r \pm \beta z)}$. Such terms represent waves that travel normal to the direction $k'r \pm \beta z = k(r \cos\theta + z \sin\theta) = \text{const}$, where $\cos\theta = k'/k$, $\sin\theta = \beta/k$ and $\cos^2\theta + \sin^2\theta = k'^2/k^2 + \beta^2 k^2 = 1$. Without the factor $\cos\theta$, Equation 12.122 would represent the power per unit area of the wave front. However, we are interested in the power generated per unit length of the cylinder. Similarly, we obtain for the sound power that is generated by an oscillating cylinder:

$$N_1 = \frac{1}{2} \frac{k'^2 k}{4} \rho c \hat{Q}_0^2 dx^2 \cdot \frac{1}{2} \cos^2(\beta z + \alpha) \quad (12.123)$$

where $Q_0 = \hat{Q}_0 \cos(\beta z + d)$.

Huygens' Principle

The sound radiation of a plane membrane in a baffle can be computed with the aid of the preceding results. If the membrane is subdivided into small elements $d\sigma$, each of these elements generates volume flow $v d\sigma$ and represents a sound source of strength $dq = v d\sigma$ that radiates into the space angle 2π (or a sound source of strength $2v d\sigma$ that radiates into the solid angle 4π). Since the dimensions of the elementary sources are very small, the dipole and higher-order components of the sound radiation of each element are negligibly small, and the sound pressure generated by such an elementary source is given by:

$$d\tilde{p} = j \frac{k\rho c(2d\sigma)\tilde{v}}{4\pi} \frac{e^{-jkr}}{r} = jk\rho c\left(\frac{2d\sigma}{4\pi}\right)\tilde{v} \frac{e^{-jkr}}{r} \quad (12.124)$$

(the total volume flow into the space angle 4π being $2\sigma v$). Because of the baffle, the radiations from the front and back do not interact, and reflection and diffraction phenomena do not occur. The resulting sound pressure is obtained by adding up the contributions (Eq. 12.124) of all these elementary areas:

$$\tilde{p}=\frac{jk\rho c}{2\pi}\int \tilde{v}d\sigma\frac{e^{-jkr}}{r}=\frac{jk\rho c e^{jkr_0}}{2\pi r_0}\int \tilde{v}d\sigma e^{-jk(x\cos\theta+y\cos\varphi)} \tag{12.125}$$

where $\cos\theta=\cos(x, r_0)$, $\cos\varphi=\cos(y, r_0)$, and r_0 is the distance from the center of the vibration to the field point. This integral is called Rayleigh's integral. It represents a special case of Huygens' principle that every point in a wave front may be considered as the center of an outgoing wave. Rayleigh's integral is exact if the radiating surface is plane and is enclosed in a baffle, so that no sound is reflected or diffracted at the boundaries. Rayleigh's integral can be transformed into an integral over the pressure distribution:[11]

$$\tilde{p}=\frac{jk}{2\pi}\int \tilde{p}\cos(n, r)\frac{e^{-jkr}}{r}\cdot d\sigma \tag{12.126}$$

where $\cos(n, r)$ is the direction cosine between the radius vector and the outside normal of the surface. The last form of Huygens' integral is valuable if the boundary is rigid and the pressure distribution over it is known (for instance, for computing the effect of a baffle on the sound field generated by a small source at its center). If the boundary is not plane, then Kirchhoff's integral has to be used for computing the sound field.[12] This integral is:

$$\tilde{p}=-\frac{1}{4\pi}\int\left(\tilde{p}\frac{\partial\frac{e^{-jkr}}{r}}{\partial n}-\frac{e^{-jkr}}{r}\frac{\partial\tilde{p}}{\partial n}\right)d\sigma \tag{12.127}$$

The second term in this integral represents the effect of the velocity of the boundary; the first, that of the pressure field near it. For a plane vibrating surface, pressure and velocity are closely related, and Kirchhoff's integral can be transformed into Rayleigh's integral.

Another very useful diffraction integral has been derived by Rubinovicz.[13] It represents the sound field by two components, one (p_g, the geometric optical component) being obtained by completely neglecting diffraction (as if the wave length were very small), the other (p_{dif}, the diffraction component) representing the effect of the boundary line of the radiator. Rubinovicz' integral is very useful, since it shows that diffraction can be fully accounted for by assuming a source distribution along the boundary line of the vibrator.

[11] See B. B. Baker and E. T. Copson, *The Mathematical Theory of Huygens' Principle* (Oxford, 1950), or E. J. Skudrzyk, *op. cit.*, p. 225.

[12] See Lord Rayleigh, *op. cit.*, II, p. 144.

[13] This integral, like Rayleigh's integral, applies only to plane radiators or plane screens. See A. Rubinovicz, "Die Beugungswelle in der Kirchhoffschen Theorie der Beugungserscheinungen," *Ann. Physik*, **53** (1917), 257, and E. J. Skudrzyk, *op. cit.*, p. 239.

Vibrators with Nodal Lines

Many of the vibrators exhibit nodal line patterns, and their sound radiation is too complex to be treated by accurate methods. But valuable information about such vibrators is obtained by studying the sound radiation of an infinite plate and that of finite plates that perform bending vibrations. Accurate solutions can then be derived, and these solutions can be used to test the accuracy of asymptotic or other approximate methods.

Infinite Plate, Vibrating in a Rectangular Nodal Line Pattern

Nodal line pattern, independent of the frequency. The simplest vibrator with a nodal line pattern is an infinite plate that is excited in a rectangular nodal line pattern:

$$v = V_0 \cos \kappa_x x \cos \kappa_y y \qquad (12.128)$$

where κ_x and κ_y are the bending-wave numbers in the x- and y-directions, respectively. It shall be assumed that the plate vibration is of a fixed nodal line pattern, so that κ_x and κ_y are independent of the frequency. The factors $\cos \kappa_x x$ and $\cos \kappa_y y$ satisfy the wave equation individually, and an expression of the form

$$p = (\cos \kappa_x x \cos \kappa_y y)\, F(z) \qquad (12.129)$$

satisfies it, if

$$\frac{d^2F(z)}{dz^2} = -k^2 n_z^2 F(z) \qquad (12.130)$$

or

$$F(z) = Ae^{-jkn_z z} + Be^{jkn_z z} \qquad (12.131)$$

and if

$$k^2 = \kappa_x^2 + \kappa_y^2 + k^2 n_z^2 \qquad (12.132)$$

or if

$$n_z = \sqrt{1 - \left(\frac{\kappa}{k}\right)^2} \quad \text{and} \quad \kappa^2 = \kappa_x^2 + \kappa_y^2 \qquad (12.133)$$

The magnitude n_z represents the direction cosine of the sound waves that are generated by the plate, the proof will be given below.

The bending wave length in the plate is obtained by decomposing its vibration pattern (Eq. 12.128) into progressive waves, as follows:

$$\tilde{v} = A \cos \kappa_x x \cos \kappa_y y e^{j\omega t} = \sum \frac{A}{2} e^{j(\pm\kappa_x x \pm \kappa_y y + \omega t)} \qquad (12.134)$$

Each term then represents a two-dimensional progressive wave:

$$\frac{A}{2} e^{-j\vec{\kappa} \cdot \vec{r} + j\omega t} \qquad (12.135)$$

where $\vec{r}\,(x, y)$ is the radius vector in the plate, $\vec{\kappa}$ is the wave vector of the plate vibration, whose direction is the same as the direction of propagation, and κ_x and κ_y are the components of the wave vector. If $k=\kappa$, n_z is zero, the bending wavelength in the plate is equal to the sound wave length in the surrounding medium, and the bending-wave velocity for the plate c_B is equal to the sound velocity c in the medium. The frequency

$$f_0=\frac{kc}{2\pi}=\frac{\kappa c}{2\pi} \tag{12.136}$$

for which $k=k_0=\kappa$ is defined as the coincidence frequency.

If the sound field is generated by the vibration of the plate, there is no incident wave, and $B=0$; the constant A is determined by the boundary conditions at the plate:

$$\begin{aligned}(\bar{V})_{z=0} &= V_0 \cos \kappa_x x \cos \kappa_y y=\frac{j}{k\rho c}\left(\frac{\partial \bar{P}}{\partial z}\right)_{z=0}\\ &=A\frac{n_z}{\rho c}\cos \kappa_x x \cos \kappa_y y\end{aligned} \tag{12.137}$$

or

$$A=V_0\frac{\rho c}{n_z} \tag{12.138}$$

The sound pressure, therefore, is:

$$\tilde{p}=\frac{\rho c}{n_z}V_0 \cos \kappa_x x \cos \kappa_y y e^{-jn_z kz+j\omega t} \tag{12.139}$$

and the acoustic impedance per unit area of the plate becomes:

$$\frac{\tilde{p}}{\tilde{v}_0}=\frac{\rho c}{n_z}=\frac{\rho c}{\sqrt{1-\left(\frac{\kappa}{k}\right)^2}}=\frac{\rho c}{\sqrt{1-\left(\frac{f_0}{f}\right)^2}} \tag{12.140}$$

At low frequencies, $f/f_0<1$, and n_z is imaginary:

$$\begin{aligned}kn_z &= k\sqrt{1-\left(\frac{f_0}{f}\right)^2}=\pm jk\sqrt{\left(\frac{k_0}{k}\right)^2-1}\doteq \pm jk_0\\ &=\pm j\frac{2\pi}{\lambda_0}\end{aligned} \tag{12.141}$$

where

$$\lambda_0=\frac{c}{f_0}=\frac{2\pi}{\kappa}=\frac{2\pi}{k_0} \tag{12.142}$$

is the characteristic wavelength, that is, the wavelength in the medium that corresponds to the coincidence frequency (Eq. 12.136) of the plate. For frequencies below the coincidence frequency, the sound pressure decreases exponentially with the distance from the plate:

$$\begin{aligned}\tilde{p} &= \frac{\rho c}{n_z}V_0 \cos \kappa_x x \cos \kappa_y y e^{-kn_z z+j\omega t}\\ &\doteq \frac{\rho c}{n_z}V_0 e^{-2\pi z/\lambda_0} \cos \kappa_x x \cos \kappa_y y e^{j\omega t}\end{aligned} \tag{12.143}$$

Thus, at low frequencies the sound pressure decreases by a factor of $e^{-2\pi} \approx \frac{1}{500}$ if the distance from the plate is increased by one characteristic wavelength λ_0. The sound field is a wattless near field, no energy being radiated to great distances. This case is called the acoustic short circuit. The distances between the maxima and minima of the vibrator are short enough so that the pressure variations over the surface can set up a pure flow of fluid from the compressed portions to the rarefied portions. We note that the exponential decrease of the near field with distance is governed by the characteristic wavelength of the plate, and not by the sound wavelength. The characteristic frequency is usually a high frequency (a few kilocycles for an aluminum plate $\frac{1}{4}$ in. thick), and the characteristic wavelength is not much greater than a few inches; the near field is, therefore, confined to the immediate vicinity of the plate surface. Experimental results show that if a plate is excited by white noise, the near field is usually negligible at distances of more than a foot from the plate. In the frequency range of the acoustic short circuit ($f/f_0 < 1$), the acoustic impedance becomes a mass impedance:

$$\bar{z} = \frac{\rho c}{n_z} = \frac{j\rho c}{\sqrt{\left(\frac{\omega_0}{\omega}\right)^2 - 1}} = j\omega m \tag{12.144}$$

where

$$m = \frac{\rho c}{\omega\sqrt{\left(\frac{\omega_0}{\omega}\right)^2 - 1}} = \frac{\rho c}{\sqrt{\omega_0^2 - \omega^2}} \tag{12.145}$$

is the effective mass per unit area of the plate. Figure 12.8 shows the impedance $|z|$ as a function of the frequency; it is relatively small at low frequencies, but becomes infinite at the frequency ω_0. At frequencies $\omega \ll \omega_0$, we have:

$$z \cong \frac{j\omega\rho c}{\omega_0} \quad \text{and} \quad m \cong \frac{\rho c}{\omega_0} \tag{12.146}$$

For a ship's hull, $\omega_0 \approx 10^4$ per second, and the effective mass m is relatively small ($m \approx 1.5 \cdot 10^2$ kg. per/sq. m.). But for a loud-speaker membrane, $\omega_0 \approx 10^2$ per second, and $m \approx 4.3$ kg./per sq. m. ($=0.43$ g./per sq. cm.); this mass is of the same magnitude as that of the membrane itself.

If the frequency f is greater than the coincidence frequency f_0 for the bending-wave pattern of the plate, the time available for the fluid to flow from the compressed to the rarefied region is no longer sufficient to permit the pressure differences to equalize, and a true sound field is set up. The factor n_z in the exponent is real, and the acoustic impedance becomes a radiation resistance:

$$z = \frac{\rho c}{n_z} = \frac{\rho c}{\sqrt{1 - \left(\frac{f_0}{f}\right)^2}} \doteq \rho c \tag{12.147}$$

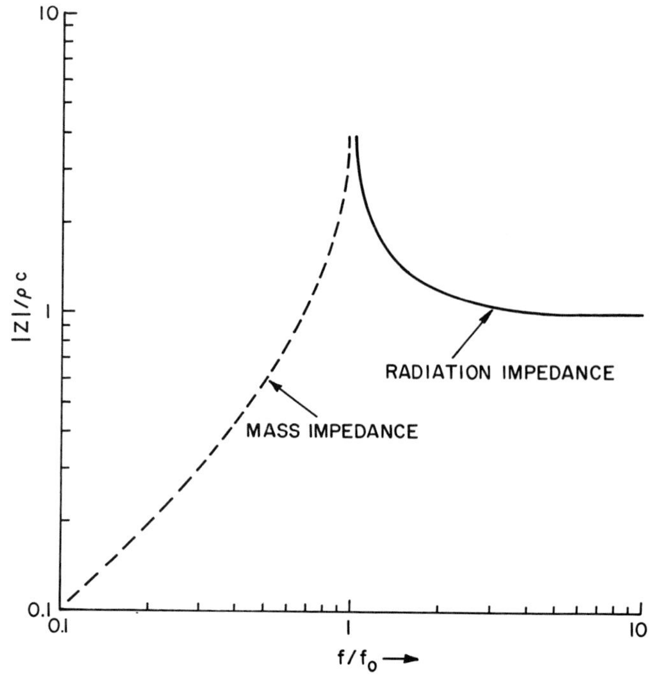

Fig. 12.8 Radiation impedance of an infinite plate excited to a sinusoidal vibration pattern; *solid curve*, radiation impedance; *broken curve*, mass impedance.

This radiation resistance is infinite at the coincidence frequency (Fig. 12.8)' but it becomes practically equal to the wave resistance of the medium if the frequency is more than twice the coincidence frequency. The sound pressure, then, is given by:

$$p = \frac{\rho c}{n_z} V_0 \cos \kappa_x x \cos \kappa_y y e^{-jkn_z z + j\omega t} \tag{12.148}$$

The pressure field can be decomposed into eight progressive waves:

$$\sum \frac{\rho c V_0}{4n_z} e^{j(\pm\kappa_x x \pm \kappa_y y - kn_z z) + j\omega t} \tag{12.149}$$

with the direction cosines:

$$\cos(n, z) = \pm \frac{\kappa_x}{k}$$

$$\cos(n, y) = \pm \frac{\kappa_y}{k}$$

$$\cos(n, z) = \pm \sqrt{1 - \left(\frac{\kappa_x{}^2}{k}\right)^2 - \left(\frac{\kappa_y{}^2}{k}\right)^2} = n_z \tag{12.150}$$

The projection of the direction of propagation of the waves on the vibrating surface has the direction of the diagonal of the nodal squares. At the characteristic frequency $k^2 = \kappa_x^2 + \kappa_y^2 = \kappa_z^2$, $\cos(n, z) = 0$ (see Eqs. 12.133 and 12.150), and the waves propagate parallel to the surface. The sound energy generated by the portions of the plate at infinite distance propagates with a grazing angle to the plate and contributes to the sound field; the sound pressure and the acoustic impedance become infinite. Since all vibrating plates are finite, this infinite value will never be actually observed. With increasing frequency, the direction of propagation of the waves that are generated by the plate turns away from the plate until, at the high frequencies, the waves propagate normal to the plate, and the radiation impedance becomes ρc.

Nodal line pattern, not fixed, but due to bending vibrations of a plate of constant thickness. If the plate is homogeneous and the vibration pattern a natural one (in contrast to a forced pattern, which results if the plate is clamped along various lines or is excited in a particular mode of vibration), the distance between the nodal lines and also the bending-wave number are functions of the frequency. It has been shown (Eq. 8.35)) that the bending wave velocity is:

$$c_B = \alpha\sqrt{\omega} \tag{12.151}$$

where

$$\alpha^4 = \frac{\lambda_E h^2}{12(1-\nu^2)\rho} = \frac{c_p^2 h^2}{12(1-\nu^2)} \tag{12.152}$$

and where

$$c_p = \sqrt{\frac{\lambda_E}{\rho}} \tag{12.153}$$

is the second velocity for longitudinal waves in a thin rod of the same material as the plate; h is the thickness of the plate, and ν is Poisson's contraction. The bending-wave number κ_0 now is a function of the frequency:

$$\kappa_0 = \frac{\omega}{c_B} = \frac{\omega}{\alpha\sqrt{\omega}} = \frac{\sqrt{\omega}}{\alpha} \tag{12.154}$$

and

$$\left(\frac{\kappa_0}{k}\right)^2 = \frac{\left(\dfrac{\sqrt{\omega}}{\alpha}\right)^2}{\left(\dfrac{\omega}{c_0}\right)^2} = \frac{c_0^2}{\alpha^2\omega} \tag{12.155}$$

Because of the frequency dependence of the nodal line pattern—$\kappa = \kappa(\omega)$—and the coincidence frequency, ω_0 is determined by the relation:

$$\kappa_0(\omega_0) = k_0 \tag{12.156}$$

where

$$\kappa_0(\omega_0) = \frac{\sqrt{\omega_0}}{\alpha} \quad \text{and} \quad k_0 = \frac{\omega_0}{c_0} \tag{12.157}$$

Hence,

$$\omega_0 = \frac{c_0^2}{\alpha^2} \tag{12.158}$$

and

$$\frac{\kappa_0^2}{k^2} = \frac{\dfrac{\omega}{\alpha^2}}{\dfrac{\omega^2}{c_0^2}} = \frac{\dfrac{c_0^2}{\alpha^2}}{\omega} = \frac{\omega_0}{\omega} \tag{12.159}$$

All the equations derived in the preceding section apply for the case of a natural (bending-wave) nodal line pattern, provided that κ_0^2/k^2 or ω_0^2/ω^2 is replaced by ω_0/ω and that $(1-\omega_0^2/\omega^2)$ is replaced by $(1-\omega_0/\omega)$.

For many materials, $\nu \approx \frac{1}{3}$, and

$$\frac{\omega_0}{2\pi} = \frac{c_0^2\sqrt{12(1-\nu^2)}}{2\pi\sqrt{\dfrac{\lambda_E}{\rho}}} = \frac{3.26}{2\pi}\frac{c_0^2}{c_p h} \doteq \frac{c_0^2}{c_p^2}\frac{c_p}{2h} = \frac{c_0^2}{c_p^2} f_{th} \tag{12.160}$$

where $f_{th} = c_p/2h$ is the resonant frequency of a thin rod of the same material as the plate, whose length is equal to the thickness of the plate. Figure 12.9 shows the coincidence frequency of an aluminum or iron plate in water and air, as a function of its thickness.

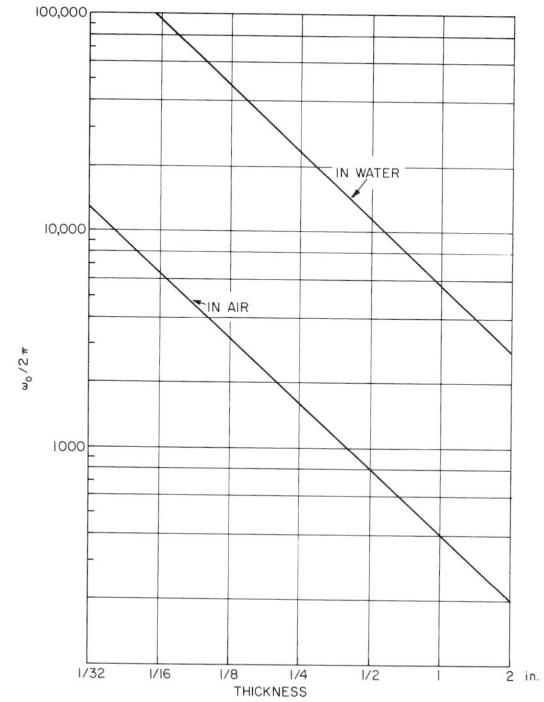

Fig. 12.9 Coincidence frequency of an aluminum or iron plate in air and water, as a function of its thickness.

The preceding theory can be impressively demonstrated by striking a thin and a thick plate and immersing the two plates in water. The thin plate will continue to vibrate and sound like a bell, even when immersed under water. Its coincidence frequency is very high, and its vibration is not radiation-damped. In contrast, the coincidence frequency of the thick plate is low, and most of its modes are radiation-damped. Therefore, the sound of the thick plate, when it is immersed under water, will die out immediately.

Sound Radiation of an Infinite Plate, Excited to a One-Dimensional Vibration Pattern by a Linear Force Distribution of Constant Intensity

An infinite plate that vibrates in one of its natural bending wave patterns radiates or does not radiate sound according to whether the bending wavelength is greater or smaller than the sound wavelength. In contrast, an infinite plate that is excited by an external force distribution radiates sound at all frequencies because of the distorsion of the sinusoidal vibration pattern by the applied force distribution.

If the external force is a line force (that is, a force distributed with constant intensity over a line), a one-dimensional vibration pattern is excited. Such a plate vibrates in an infinite number of modes. The high-order modes are acoustically short-circuited and generate only a near field. But the low-order modes radiate sound, because the distance between their nodal lines is much greater than the sound wavelength. The velocity distribution can be represented by a one-dimensional Fourier integral:[14]

$$v(x)=\int_{-\infty}^{\infty} S_v(\kappa)e^{j\kappa x}\frac{d\kappa}{2\pi} \tag{12.161}$$

where

$$S_v(\kappa)=\int_{-\infty}^{\infty} v(x)e^{-j\kappa x}dx \tag{12.162}$$

The magnitude κ is the space Fourier wave number of the vibration pattern, and $S_v(\kappa)$ is the magnitude of the spectral component at this wave number (κ is not a function of the frequency here, but corresponds to an independent variable).

The sound pressure can be represented by a Fourier integral of the following form:

$$p(x, z)=\frac{1}{2\pi}\int_{-\infty}^{\infty} S_p(\kappa)e^{-j\kappa x-jk_z z}d\kappa \tag{12.163}$$

[14] See M. Heckl, "Schallabstranlung von Platten bei punktförmiger Anregung," *Acustica*, **9** (1959), 372.

This integral satisfies the wave equation:

$$\nabla^2 p + k^2 p = 0 \tag{12.164}$$

(where k is the wave number in the medium in front of the plate), if

$$k^2 = \kappa^2 + k_z^2 \quad \text{or} \quad k_z = \sqrt{k^2 - \kappa^2} \tag{12.165}$$

and it satisfies the boundary condition for the normal component of the velocity at the plate, if (see Eq. 12.36)

$$\tilde{v}(x) = \frac{j}{k\rho c}\left(\frac{\partial \tilde{p}}{\partial z}\right)_{z=0} \tag{12.166}$$

The last relation can be expressed in terms of the Fourier components, and

$$S_p(\kappa) = \rho c \frac{k}{\sqrt{k^2 - \kappa^2}} S_v(\kappa) = \frac{\rho c}{\sqrt{1 - \dfrac{\kappa^2}{k^2}}} S_v(\kappa) \tag{12.167}$$

We could substitute this value of $S_p(\kappa)$ into the integral (Eq. 12.163) and try to perform the κ-integration. But because of the $k_z = \sqrt{k^2 - \kappa^2}$ in the exponent and in the denominator, integration could only be performed by series developments or by using computers. However, most of the information that is contained in this integral can be obtained by computing the sound power that is generated at the surface of the plate. The integral then does not contain the complex exponent and is of much simpler form. The sound power that is generated per unit width of the infinitely long plate is given by:

$$N_1 = \frac{1}{2} Re\left(\int_{-\infty}^{\infty} \bar{P}\bar{V}^* dx\right) \tag{12.168}$$

where $\bar{V}^*$ is the conjugate complex value of $\bar{V}$. If Fourier transforms are introduced,

$$N_1 = \frac{1}{2} Re\left\{\int_{-\infty}^{\infty} S_p(\kappa) S_v^*(\kappa')\left[\int_{-\infty}^{\infty} e^{-j(\kappa-\kappa')x} \frac{dx}{2\pi}\right] \frac{d\kappa\, d\kappa'}{2\pi}\right\} \tag{12.169}$$

The integral in the bracket has the same properties as the Dirac's delta function $\delta(\kappa - \kappa')$:

$$\delta(0) = \infty \qquad \delta(\kappa - \kappa') = 0 \qquad \kappa \neq \kappa'$$

$$\int_{-\infty}^{\infty} \delta(\kappa - \kappa')\, d\kappa = 1 \tag{12.170}$$

The κ'-integration is equivalent to replacing the integral in the bracket by one and κ', by κ. If $S_p(\kappa)$ is replaced by its Fourier integral and $S_p(\kappa)$ is expressed in terms of $S_v(\kappa)$ (Eq. 12.167), the sound power that is generated per unit width of the infinitely long plate becomes:

$$N_1 = \frac{1}{2}\rho c \int_{-k}^{k} \left| S_v(\kappa) \right|^2 \frac{k}{\sqrt{k^2-\kappa^2}} \frac{d\kappa}{2\pi} \tag{12.171}$$

The limits of the last integral are $\pm k$, because (see Eq. 12.168):

$$Re\left(\frac{k}{\sqrt{k^2-\kappa^2}}\right)=0 \quad \text{for} \quad |\kappa|>k \tag{12.172}$$

Equation 12.171 represents the sound power that is generated by a prescribed one-dimensional velocity distribution.

The velocity distribution that is excited by a line force in an infinite plate can be computed with the aid of the one-dimensional plate equation (see Eq. 8.1):

$$\alpha^4 \Gamma^4 \xi + \frac{\partial^2 \xi}{\partial t^2} = \frac{F(x)}{m} = \frac{F_0 \delta(x)}{m} \tag{12.173}$$

which, in terms of the velocity, takes the following form:

$$\Gamma^4 v(x) - \kappa_0^4 v(x) = \frac{j\omega}{\alpha^4 m} F_0 \delta(x) \tag{12.174}$$

where

$$\kappa_0 = \frac{\sqrt{\omega}}{\alpha} \tag{12.175}$$

is the bending-wave number in the plate at the force frequency ω, $\delta(x)$ is Dirac's function, α is the constant given by Equation 8.1, m is the mass of the plate per unit area, and F_0 is the force per unit length. We may assume that v vanishes when x tends toward infinity; if $v(x)$ and $\delta(x)$ are replaced by their Fourier integrals,

$$S_\delta(\kappa) = \int_{-\infty}^{\infty} \delta(x) e^{-j\kappa x} dx = 1 \tag{12.176}$$

the differential equation reduces to the relation:

$$S_v(\kappa) = \frac{j\omega F_0}{m\alpha^4(\kappa^4 - \kappa_0^4)} \tag{12.177}$$

Thus, the line force excites a space spectrum that is constant at the lower wave numbers when $\kappa^4 \ll \kappa_0^4$ (because of the motion of the center of gravity, as if the plate were perfectly rigid), that has an infinite peak of the wave number κ_0 of the bending wave that is excited by a force of the frequency ω, and that decreases in inverse proportion to the fourth power of the wave number κ when $\kappa^4 \gg \kappa_0^4$. The line force excites a one-dimensional vibration pattern that is similar to that excited by a point force acting on an infinite beam. The velocity distribution can be calculated by Fourier integration; however, damping must be taken into account. Thus,

$$\bar{V}(x)=\frac{j\omega\bar{F}_0}{2\pi m\alpha^4}\int_{-\infty}^{\infty}\frac{d\kappa e^{j\kappa x}}{\kappa^4-\kappa_0^4(1-j\eta)}=\frac{\bar{F}}{4mc_B}(-je^{-\kappa_0 x}+e^{-j\kappa_0 x}) \quad (12.178)$$

where κ_0^4 in Equation 12.177 has been replaced by $\kappa_0^4\ (1-j\eta)$ to account for damping. Since the frequency of the force is positive, η is also positive during the whole integration. The path of integration can be closed by a semicircle of infinite radius, which for positive x is above the real axis and for negative x is below the real axis. Contour integration then leads to the last form on the right-hand side of Equation 12.178. If damping is neglected, a third pole ($\kappa=\kappa_0$) moves into the integration range, and a wrong result is obtained. This shows that damping must be included in Fourier integrals that have poles in the integration range, and solutions for no damping have to be derived by transition to the limit $\eta\to 0$. The solution of Equation 12.178 shows that the line force excites a progressive wave and a distortion near field. The progressive wave represents the contribution of the pole $\kappa=-j\kappa_0$; the distortion field is a consequence of the pole $\kappa=-\kappa_0$. The expression (Eq. 12.177) can now be substituted in the sound integral (Eq. 12.171):

$$N_1=\frac{\rho c}{4\pi}\frac{\omega^2 F_0^2}{m^2\alpha^8}\int_{-k}^{k}\frac{k}{(\kappa^4-\kappa_0^4)^2\sqrt{k^2-\kappa^2}}d\kappa \quad (12.179)$$

If $k\geq\kappa_0$, the plate modes for which $\kappa=\kappa_0$ vibrate against infinite radiation resistance, become infinitely damped, and generate a finite sound pressure. The reaction to sound radiation can be taken into account by introducing the sound pressure as a negative driving force. Equation 12.174 then has to be replaced by:

$$\nabla^4 v(x)-\kappa_0^4 v(x)=\frac{j\omega}{\alpha^4 m}\left[F_0\delta(x)-p(x)\right] \quad (12.180)$$

and Equation 12.177, by:

$$S_v(\kappa)=\frac{j\omega}{m\alpha^4\left(\kappa^4-\kappa_0^4+\dfrac{j\omega\rho c}{m\alpha^4\sqrt{1-\dfrac{\kappa^2}{k^2}}}\right)}$$

$$=\frac{j\omega F_0}{m\alpha^4(\kappa^4-\kappa_0^4+jb)} \quad (12.181)$$

where

$$b=\frac{\omega\rho c}{m\alpha^4\sqrt{1-\dfrac{\kappa^2}{k^2}}}=\frac{\rho c\kappa_0^4}{\omega m\sqrt{1-\dfrac{\kappa^2}{k^2}}} \quad \text{and} \quad \kappa_0=\frac{\omega}{\sqrt{\alpha}} \quad (12.182)$$

In Equation 12.180, $v(x)$ and $p(x)$ have been expressed by their Fourier transforms (Eqs. 12.161 and 12.163). Thus, the reaction of the sound radiation to the vibration of the plate leads to the damping term jb, and the sound pressure is finite for all wave numbers.

The sound power becomes:

$$N_1 = \frac{\rho c}{2} \frac{\omega^2 F_0^2}{m^2 \alpha^8} \int_{-k}^{k} \frac{\frac{d\kappa}{2\pi}}{[(\kappa^4 - \kappa_0^4)^2 + b^2]\sqrt{1 - \frac{\kappa^2}{k^2}}} \tag{12.183}$$

Let is be stated again that κ_0 is the bending-wave number in the plate at the frequency ω (the natural wave number for bending vibrations); κ is the space wave number of a Fourier component of the vibration pattern that is excited by the external force; and k is the wave number of the sound that is generated in the medium surrounding the plate.

At very high frequencies,

$$k = \frac{\omega}{c_0} \gg \kappa_0 = \frac{\sqrt{\omega}}{\alpha} \tag{12.184}$$

and the limits of integration can be replaced by $\pm\infty$; the main contribution of the integrand then originates for $\kappa \approx \kappa_0$, and κ can be replaced by κ_0 in b^2 and under the square root. The magnitude b is usually very small and limits the peak of the integrand to a finite value. The integration can be performed by partial-fraction development, as follows:

$$N_1 = \frac{\rho c \omega^2 F_0^2}{4\pi m^2 \alpha^8 \sqrt{1 - \frac{\kappa_0^2}{k^2}}} \int_{-\infty}^{\infty} \frac{d\kappa}{2jb} \left(\frac{1}{\kappa^4 - \kappa_0^4 - jb} - \frac{1}{\kappa^4 - \kappa_0^4 + jb} \right)$$

$$= \frac{\rho c \omega^2 F_0^2}{4\pi m^2 \alpha^8 b \sqrt{1 - \frac{\kappa_0^2}{k^2}}} Im \left(\int_{-\infty}^{\infty} \frac{d\kappa}{\kappa^4 - \kappa_0^4 - jb} \right) \tag{12.185}$$

The integral is known[15] and equal to:

$$\frac{\pi}{\sqrt{2}\left(-\kappa_0^4 - jb\right)^{\frac{3}{4}}} \tag{12.186}$$

Its imaginary part is:

$$Im\left[\frac{\pi}{\sqrt{2}\,\kappa_0^3} \left(1 - \frac{3jb}{4\kappa_0^4} + \dots \right) e^{j\pi 3/4} \right] = \frac{\pi}{\sqrt{2}\,\kappa_0^3} \sin\frac{3\pi}{4} = \frac{\pi}{2\kappa_0^3} \tag{12.187}$$

We have assumed that $b \ll 1$ or $\rho c/\omega m \ll 1$.

The sound power per unit width thus becomes:

$$N_1 = \frac{\rho c F_0^2}{4\pi m^2} \frac{\pi \omega^2}{\alpha^8 b 2\kappa_0^3 \sqrt{1 - \frac{\kappa_0^2}{k^2}}} = \frac{F_0^2}{8\alpha\sqrt{\omega}\, m} = N_{\text{driv}} \tag{12.188}$$

[15] See B. DeHahn, *Nouvelles tables d'intégrales définies* (New York, 1939), p. 47, Integral 6.

where

$$N_{\text{driv}}=\frac{1}{2}\frac{F_0^2 Re(Z_c)}{|Z_c|^2}=\frac{1}{2}\cdot\frac{F_0^2}{4mc_B} \tag{12.189}$$

is the driving power, F_0 is the force per unit width, $\bar{Z}_c=2\,(1+j)\,mc_B$ (see Eq. 6.90) is the characteristic bending-wave impedance of the plate when it is excited at the center or at a point elsewhere inside to a one-dimensional vibration (this value of the characteristic impedance can be readily deduced by integrating the amplitude spectrum, Eq. 12.181, over the infinite wave number range), and $c_B=\alpha\sqrt{\omega}$ (see Eq. 8.35) is the bending-wave velocity in the plate. Thus, if damping is neglected, $\rho c/\omega m \ll 1$, and the plate is infinitely large, all the driving power is transformed into sound, and no vibrational energy escapes to infinity through the acoustically short-circuited modes.

If the effect of internal friction is to be taken into account, κ_0^4 has to be replaced by $\kappa_0^4\,(1+j\eta)$, and b has to be correspondingly increased by $\kappa_0^4\eta$. The integral then is of the same form as before, and the sound power becomes equal to $\rho c/(\rho c+m\omega\eta)$ times the driving power:

$$N=\frac{\rho c}{m\omega\eta+\rho c}N_{\text{driv}} \tag{12.190}$$

The magnitude $m\omega\eta$ represents the loss resistance per unit area; the magnitude ρc, the radiation resistance per unit area; and the factor $\rho c/(m\omega\eta+\rho c)$, the fraction of the total energy that is dissipated into sound.

If an infinite plate vibrates in a vacuum and if internal friction is negligible, the energy supplied by the force propagates to infinity. If the plate vibrates in air, its modes are damped because of sound radiation, and, for sufficiently great distances from the driver, their energy decreases exponentially with distance. Because an exponential function decreases faster than any inverse power law, the energy of the radiating modes does not leak to infinity, but is completely transformed into sound. If the plate is excited high above its coincidence frequency, an overwhelmingly greater portion of its modes is radiation-damped, and practically all the driving power is transformed into sound.

If the frequency is equal to the coincidence frequency, $k=\kappa_0$, and by integration between 0 and κ_0, Equation 12.183 becomes:

$$N_1=\frac{\rho c\omega^2 F_0^2}{2\pi m^2\alpha^8}\int_0^{\kappa_0}\frac{d\kappa}{(\kappa^4-\kappa_0^4)^2\sqrt{1-\dfrac{\kappa^2}{\kappa_0^2}}+\dfrac{\beta^2\kappa_0^8}{\sqrt{1-\dfrac{\kappa^2}{\kappa_0^2}}}}$$

$$=\frac{\rho c\omega^2 F_0^2}{2\pi m^2\alpha^8\kappa_0^7}\int_0^1\frac{dz}{(1-z^4)^2\sqrt{1-z^2}+\dfrac{\beta^2}{\sqrt{1-z^2}}}$$

$$=\frac{\rho c F_0^2}{2\pi\omega m c^2{}_B}\int_0^1 \frac{dz\,\sqrt{1-z^2}}{(1-z^4)^2\,(1-z^2)+\beta^2} \tag{12.191}$$

where

$$\beta=\frac{\omega\rho c}{m\alpha^4\kappa_0^4}=\frac{\rho c}{\omega m} \quad \text{and} \quad z=\frac{\kappa}{\kappa_0} \tag{12.192}$$

If β^2 is large as compared to one, the denominator of the integrand is practically equal to $1+\beta^2$, and the integral reduces to:

$$\frac{1}{1+\beta^2}\int_0^1 \sqrt{1-z^2}\,dz=\frac{\pi}{4(1+\beta^2)} \tag{12.193}$$

The sound power then becomes:

$$N_1=\frac{1}{2}\,\frac{F_0^2}{4mc_B}\,\frac{\beta}{1+\beta^2} \quad (\text{for } \beta>2) \tag{12.194}$$

For smaller values of β, the integration has to be performed graphically The result is represented in Figure 12.10 (*broken curve*). Most of the modes that radiate sound are vibrating at frequencies below their resonant frequency. For these modes, the plate impedance is $j\omega m$, and optimum matching occurs when $\rho c/\omega m \approx 1$.[16] Sound radiation decreases relatively little if $\omega m > \rho c$, but it decreases considerably if ωm becomes much smaller than ρc. For minimum sound radiation, ωm should be as small as possible (so that most of the space Fourier components of the plate vibration are acoustically short-circuited). If the frequency of the force is equal to, or lower than, the coincidence frequency, many modes of the plate are in acoustic short circuit and not radiation-damped; a considerable amount of the energy supplied by the driver then is propagated to infinity, and sound radiation becomes much smaller.

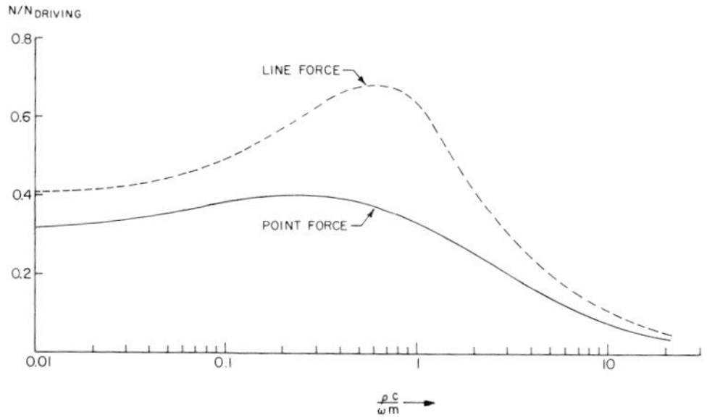

Fig. 12.10 Fraction of the driving power that is transformed into sound by an infinite plate at the coincidence frequency for a line force (*broken curve*) and a point force (*solid curve*).

[16] See pp. 18–20.

The power output at low frequencies is of particular interest. Since only those Fourier components (for infinite plate modes) whose bending wave length is longer than the sound wave length generate sound, only the wave number range $-k<\kappa<k$ contributes to the integral (Eq. 12.179). Because $\kappa \leqq k$ and k is assumed to correspond to a frequency below the coincidence frequency $\kappa^2 \ll \kappa_0^2$. The low wave numbers (Fourier components, infinite plate modes), therefore, are excited with constant amplitude.

For very low frequencies, $\kappa \ll \kappa_0$, and the integral for the sound power in Equation 12.179 reduces to:

$$N_1 = \frac{\rho c}{4\pi} \frac{\omega^2 F_0^2}{m^2 \alpha^8} \int_{-k}^{+k} \frac{d\kappa}{\kappa_0^8 \sqrt{1-\dfrac{\kappa^2}{k^2}}}$$

$$= \frac{\rho c}{4\pi} \frac{F_0^2}{m^2 \omega c} \int_{-1}^{+1} \frac{dz}{\sqrt{1-z^2}} = \frac{\rho c F_0^2}{4m^2 \omega c} \qquad (12.195)$$

where N_1, as before, is the sound power per unit width of the infinitely long plate.

The preceding computations apply to an infinite plate and for low frequencies. They may be expected to hold approximately for a finite plate, if its linear dimension is large as compared to the sound wavelength. The total sound power generated by a finite plate of length l_1 and width l_2 may be expected to be:

$$N = l_2 N_1 = \frac{\sigma \rho c F^2 l_1}{2\omega c M^2} \frac{\pi}{2\pi} = \frac{\sigma \rho c F^2}{2\omega \omega_{l1} M^2} \frac{\pi}{2} \qquad (12.196)$$

where $\sigma = l_1 l_2$ is the area of the plate, $\omega_{l1} = \pi c / l_1$ is the resonant frequency of a pipe of a length equal to that of the plate, and $F = F_0 l_2$ is the total force that is applied to the plate.

The above results have been derived in terms of modes and Fourier components. They can also be interpreted in terms of the bending waves; the force excites a one-dimensional bending wave that travels toward infiinity in both co-ordinate directions (see Eq. 12.144). A bending wave does not radiate sound if its wavelength is smaller than the sound wavelength. Consequently, any sound radiation can only be a consequence of the deviation of the amplitude distribution from the strictly sinusoidal space pattern. The amplitude does indeed deviate from this pattern in the vicinity of the point of attack of the force because of the distortion term $-je^{-\kappa_0 x}$ in Equation 12.178. This distortion field generates a volume flow $\int_0^\infty V dx = 2F/4mc_B\kappa_0$ per unit width of the plate and corresponds to a line source that radiates into the half space. This power turns out to be $\frac{1}{2} N_1$, as has been computed above for the one-dimensional plate. The plate radiation, because of the nonacoustically short-circuited modes at the low frequencies, is thus equivalent to the sound generated by the out-of-balance volume flow that results from the distortion of the sinusoidal amplitude distribution by the boundary or driving conditions. To obtain the correct result, we have to take the coupling into account between the near-field generated by the bending wave and the distortion field.

Sound Radiation of an Infinite Plate, Excited by a Point Force

The derivations of the preceding section can easily be generalized for a point force. The velocity distribution is radially symmetrical; the natural functions are the Bessel's functions $J_0(\kappa r)$; and the Fourier integrals are replaced by Hankel's transforms:

$$v(r)=\int_{-\infty}^{\infty} S_v(\kappa)\, J_0(\kappa r)\, \kappa d\kappa \tag{12.197}$$

$$p(r, z)=\int_{0}^{\infty} S_p(\kappa)\, J_0(\kappa r)\, \kappa d\kappa e^{-jk_z z} \tag{12.198}$$

The power N that is radiated by the whole plate is computed in the same manner as in the preceding case, except that integration is performed over a circular area, as follows:

$$N=\pi\rho c\int_{0}^{k} |S_v(\kappa)|^2 \frac{k}{\sqrt{k^2-\kappa^2}}\, \kappa d\kappa \tag{12.199}$$

The spectrum function $S_v(\kappa)$ is computed with the aid of the plate equation. If sound radiation is taken into account, this equation is:

$$\nabla^4\tilde{v}(r)-\kappa_0{}^4\tilde{v}(r)=\frac{j\omega}{\alpha^4 m}(\tilde{p}_A-\tilde{p}) \tag{12.200}$$

where

$$p_A=0 \quad \text{for} \quad r>0 \tag{12.201}$$

and

$$\int_{0}^{\infty} p_A 2\pi r dr=F \tag{12.202}$$

is the total force applied to the plate. The force distribution can be written as a Hankel's transform:

$$p_A=\int_{0}^{\infty} J_0(\kappa r)\, S_{p_A}(\kappa)\kappa d\kappa \tag{12.203}$$

where

$$S_{p_A}(\kappa)=\int_0^\infty p_A J_0(\kappa r) r dr=\frac{F}{2\pi} \tag{12.204}$$

If Hankel's integrals (Eqs. 12.197, 12.203, and 12.204) are entered into the plate equation, we obtain:

$$S_v(\kappa)\left(\kappa^4-\kappa_0{}^4+\frac{j\omega}{\alpha^4 m}\frac{\rho c}{\sqrt{1-\frac{\kappa^2}{k^2}}}\right)=\frac{j\omega}{\alpha^4 m}\frac{F}{2\pi} \tag{12.205}$$

The sound power becomes:

$$N=\rho c F^2\frac{\omega^2}{\alpha^8 m^2 4\pi}\int_0^k \frac{\kappa d\kappa}{\sqrt{1-\frac{\kappa^2}{k^2}}\,[(\kappa^4-\kappa_0{}^4)^2+b^2]} \tag{12.206}$$

where

$$b=\frac{\omega}{\alpha^4 m}\frac{\rho c}{\sqrt{1-\frac{\kappa^2}{k^2}}}=\frac{\rho c}{\omega m}\frac{\kappa_0{}^4}{\sqrt{1-\frac{\kappa^2}{k^2}}} \tag{12.207}$$

At low frequencies, $\kappa_0 \gg k$, $\kappa \leq k \ll \kappa_0$, and b^2 can be neglected. The integral then simplifies to:

$$k^2\int_0^k \frac{\frac{1}{2}\frac{d\kappa^2}{k^2}}{\kappa_0{}^8\sqrt{1-\frac{\kappa^2}{k^2}}}=\frac{k^2}{2\kappa_0{}^8}\int_0^1 \frac{dz}{\sqrt{1-z}}=\frac{k^2}{\kappa_0{}^8} \tag{12.208}$$

and

$$N=\frac{\rho c F^2\omega^2 k^2}{\alpha^8 m^2 4\pi\kappa_0{}^8}=\frac{\rho c}{4\pi}F^2\frac{k^2}{\omega^2 m^2}=\frac{\rho c F^2}{4\pi c^2 m^2} \tag{12.209}$$

Equation 12.205 shows that at low frequencies a point force also excites the small wave number modes with constant intensity. These modes, and only these, radiate sound. Because of the increase of the radiation resistance toward the coincidence frequency (see Eq. 12.141), the average radiation resistance is $2\rho c$ rather than ρc; this conclusion follows from the value of the integral in Equation 12.208. Again, as for the line source (Eq. 12.195), this sound source can also be interpreted as the result of the out-of-balance volume flow near the driving point. The velocity amplitude at the center of the plate is $V_0=F/Z_c=F/8\alpha^2 m$. The above expression for the sound power can thus be written in the form:

$$N=\frac{1}{2}\rho c\frac{F^2 k^2}{(8\alpha^2 m)^2}\frac{(8\alpha^2 m)^2}{2\pi\omega^2 m^2}=\frac{1}{2}\rho c V_0{}^2\frac{64\alpha^4}{2\pi c^2} \tag{12.209a}$$

On the other hand, the sound power radiated into the half space by a source that generates the volume flow $Q_H = V_0\sigma$ in the half space is (see Eq. 12.91)

$$N_H = \frac{1}{2}\frac{\rho c k^2}{4\pi} 2Q_H{}^2 = \frac{1}{2}\rho c V_0{}^2 \frac{\omega^2\sigma^2}{2\pi c^2} \tag{12.209b}$$

Equating N to N_H yields:

$$\sigma^2 = \frac{64\alpha^4}{\omega^2} = \frac{64}{k_B{}^4} = (\pi a^2)^2 \tag{12.209c}$$

where a is the radius of the equivalent disk that vibrates with the velocity of the driving point and generates the same sound power as the infinite plate. Hence,

$$a = \sqrt{\frac{2}{\pi^3}}\lambda_B = 0.254\,\lambda_B \approx \frac{\lambda_B}{4} \tag{12.209d}$$

This result is very gratifying. It shows that the situation is fundamentally the same as when Huygens' principle is applied. The point force generates bending waves with a circular wave front. If we divide the circles into rings of a width $\lambda_B/2$, then at low frequencies each half ring of width $\lambda_B/4$ will cancel the contribution of the adjacent one, and we are finally left with the contribution of half the central zone, whose radius is $\lambda_B/4$.

If the plate is thin, its bending wavelength is small, and the vibration amplitude decreases greatly with the distance from the driving point.[17] Very little sound will then be generated by the regions farther away from the driving point, and the solution for the infinite plate may be expected to represent a good approximation for the finite plate. If the mass per unit area is replaced by the total mass of the plate, the sound power becomes:

$$N = \frac{\rho c F^2}{4\pi m^2 c^2}\frac{l_1{}^2 l_2{}^2}{l_1{}^2 l_2{}^2} = \frac{1}{2}\sigma\rho c\frac{l_1 l_2 F^2}{2\pi c^2 M^2} = \frac{1}{2}\frac{\sigma\rho c F^2}{\omega_{l_1}\omega_{l_2} M^2}\frac{\pi}{2} \tag{12.210}$$

Thus, a very large plate excited by a point force at its center, except for a factor $\pi/2$, generates the same sound power as a piston membrane of the same mass and area at a frequency

$$\omega = \sqrt{\omega_{l_1}\omega_{l_2}} \tag{12.211}$$

where ω_{l_1} and ω_{l_2} are the resonant frequencies of two organ pipes whose lengths are equal to the length and width, respectively, of the plate.

At very high frequencies, when $k^2 \gg \kappa_0{}^2$, the square root may be replaced by one in the wave number range ($\kappa \approx \kappa_0$) that contributes most to the integral, and

$$N = \frac{\rho c \omega^2 F^2}{\alpha^8 m^2 8\pi}\int_0^k \frac{d\kappa^2}{(\kappa^4 - \kappa_0{}^4)^2 + b^2} \tag{12.212}$$

The upper limit of integration can again be replaced by ∞, and b^2 may be considered a small quantity. If z is written for κ^2, the integral becomes:[18]

[17] See pp. 254–55.
[18] See B. DeHahn, *loc. cit.*

$$\int_0^\infty \frac{dz}{(z^2-z_0^2)^2+b^2} = \int_0^\infty \frac{dz}{z^4-2z_0^2z^2+(z_0^4+b^2)}$$

$$= \frac{\pi}{2bz_0} + \text{terms with higher powers of } b \quad (12.213)$$

In evaluating this integral, we have assumed that $\rho c/\omega m \ll 1$ (or $b^2 \ll z_0^4$). If this value is substituted, the sound power that is radiated by the whole plate becomes:

$$N = \frac{\rho c \omega F^2}{\alpha^4 m \cdot 16\kappa_0^2 \rho c} = \frac{F^2}{2 \cdot 8\alpha^2 m} = \frac{1}{2}\frac{F^2}{Z_c} = N_{\text{driv}} \quad (12.214)$$

where $Z_c = 8\alpha^2 m$ is the characteristic impedance of the plate and N_{driv} is the driving power. Thus, if internal friction is neglected, and if the plate is infinitely large, all the input power is converted into sound. Friction can easily be taken into account; it reduces the sound power by the factor $\rho c/(\eta\omega m+\rho c)$.

At the coincidence frequency, Equation 12.206 becomes:

$$N = \frac{\rho c}{2} F^2 \frac{\omega^2}{\alpha^8 m^2 4\pi\kappa_0^6} \int_0^1 \frac{dz}{\sqrt{(1-z)}\,(1-z^2)^2 + \dfrac{\left(\dfrac{\rho c}{\omega m}\right)^2}{\sqrt{1-z}}}$$

$$= \frac{F^2}{2Z_c} \cdot \frac{\rho c}{\omega m}\frac{2}{\pi} \int_0^1 \frac{dz\,\sqrt{1-z}}{(1-z^2)^2\,(1-z) + \left(\dfrac{\rho c}{\omega m}\right)^2} \quad (12.215)$$

For light plates, $\rho c/\omega m > 1$, and the first term in the denominator can be set equal to one. Thus,

$$N = \frac{F^2}{2Z_c}\frac{\rho c}{\omega m} \frac{1}{1+\left(\dfrac{\rho c}{\omega m}\right)^2} \doteq N_{\text{driv}} \cdot \frac{\omega m}{\rho c} \quad (12.216)$$

For smaller values of $\rho c/\omega m$, the integral has to be evaluated graphically. The resulting curve is plotted in Figure 12.10 (*solid curve*). Friction would, again, reduce the sound power by a factor $\rho c/(\eta\omega m+\rho c)$.

Sound Radiation of a Rectangular Plate, Excited by a Point Force or a Line Force[19]

Freely suspended plate. The sound radiation of a finite plate can be approximated by the sound radiation of a plate enclosed in an infinitely long rigid channel of rectangular cross section. The walls of the channel act like acoustic mirrors, and the computation becomes identical with that for a

[19] See M. Heckl, *loc. cit.*

periodically repeated rectangular plate pattern. Because of the periodicity of the vibration pattern, the Fourier integrals of the preceding sections are replaced by Fourier series.

Some very interesting results can be obtained in this way. We shall show (and shall later verify by accurate computations for a finite plate) that the sound radiation of a plate consists of three components. One component is the same as the radiation of an infinite plate; the second component is generated by the edges of the plate. We shall show that if the edge distortion is neglected, so that the amplitude distribution is strictly sinusoidal, this edge effect is negligible for a freely suspended plate, but finite and not negligible for a simply supported plate. The third component has already been discussed in the preceding section. It is the sound that is produced by the distortion of the vibration field in the region of the driver.

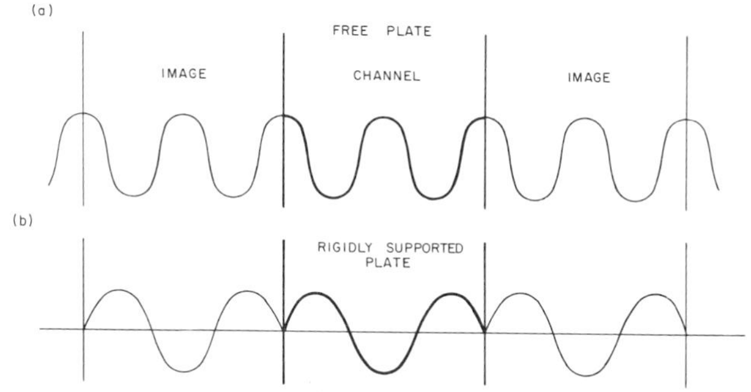

Fig. 12.11 Approximation of finite plate by image method; *a*, plate with free ends; *b*, ridigly supported plate.

Let us first consider a freely suspended plate; its edges, then, are lines of maximum velocity. The channel walls act like ideal acoustic mirrors, and the resulting pressure and vibration pattern generated by the plate and all its images are symmetrical with respect to the imaginary channel walls (see Fig. 12.11). Because of symmetry, the normal component of the velocity vanishes at the walls, and the boundary condition for the velocity

$$0=v_n=\frac{j}{k\rho c}\frac{\partial p}{\partial x} \qquad \left(\text{for } x=0, \quad x=\frac{l_x}{2}, \quad x=l_x, \quad x=\frac{3l_x}{2}\right) \quad (12.217)$$

is automatically satisfied. A similar condition applies for variations in the y-direction. As pointed out in Chapter VIII, the natural functions for a freely suspended rectangular plate are unknown. But they can be approximated very accurately, except for a region near the edges of the plate, by sinusoidally varying terms of the form

$$\phi_{mn}=\sqrt{\frac{4}{l_x l_y}}\cos\frac{m\pi x}{l_x}\cos\frac{n\pi y}{l_y} \quad (12.218)$$

(The effect of the edge distortion, if great accuracy is required, can be determined by a separate computation, and the two sound fields can be added because of the linearity of the phenomenon.) The velocity of the plate is then given by the Fourier series:

$$\bar{V}=\sum_m\sum_n \bar{V}_{mn}\varphi_{mn} \tag{12.219}$$

The natural functions for the pressure field inside a rectangular channel are of the same form, except for an exponential factor that accounts for the z-variation:

$$\bar{P}=\sum_m\sum_n \bar{P}_{mn}\varphi_{mn}e^{-jk_{mn}z} \tag{12.220}$$

where

$$k_{mn}{}^2=k^2-\frac{m^2\pi^2}{l_x{}^2}-\frac{n^2\pi^2}{l_y{}^2}=k^2-\kappa_{mn}{}^2 \tag{12.221}$$

and

$$\kappa_{mn}{}^2=\frac{m^2\pi^2}{l_x{}^2}+\frac{n^2\pi^2}{l_y{}^2} \tag{12.222}$$

The last relation is derived by substituting the above expression for p in the wave equation; it represents the condition that the individual terms of p satisfy in the wave equation. The coefficients P_{mn} are derived from the boundary condition for $z=0$:

$$\tilde{v}=\frac{j}{k\rho c}\frac{\partial\tilde{p}}{\partial z} \tag{12.223}$$

or

$$\sum_m\sum_n \bar{V}_{mn}\varphi_{mn}=\sum_m\sum_n\frac{k_{mn}}{k\rho c}\bar{P}_{mn}\varphi_{mn} \tag{12.224}$$

Since the terms φ_{mn} are independent of one another, the coefficients of φ_{mn} must satisfy the relation:

$$\bar{P}_{mn}=\frac{\rho ck}{k_{mn}}\bar{V}_{mn}=\frac{\rho ck}{\sqrt{k^2-\kappa_{mn}{}^2}} \tag{12.225}$$

The sound power generated by the whole plate is given by:

$$N=\int\frac{1}{2}Re(\bar{P}\bar{V}^*)d\sigma=\frac{\rho c}{2}\int Re\Big(\sum_m\sum_n\frac{k}{k_{mn}}\bar{V}_{mn}\varphi_{mn}\Big)\sum_m\sum_n\bar{V}_{mn}{}^*\varphi_{mn}d\sigma$$

$$=\frac{\rho c}{2}Re\sum_m\sum_n\frac{k}{k_{mn}}V_{mn}{}^2\int\varphi_{mn}{}^2d\sigma$$

$$=\sum_m\sum_n\frac{\rho c}{2}V_{mn}{}^2Re\frac{1}{\sqrt{1-\frac{\kappa_{mn}{}^2}{k^2}}} \tag{12.226}$$

because of the orthogonality condition for the φ_{mn}.

Our next task is to determine the velocity spectrum of the plate vibrations for a plate that is excited by a point force. The theory of Chapter VII leads to the following expression for the velocity amplitude of the plate:

$$\hat{\dot{\xi}}_{mn}=j\omega\hat{\xi}_{mn}=V_{mn}\varphi_{mn}=\frac{j\omega F\varphi_{mn}(F)\varphi_{mn}}{m(\bar{\omega}_{mn}{}^2-\omega^2)}$$
$$=\frac{j\omega F\varphi_{mn}(F)\sigma\varphi_{mn}}{M(\bar{\omega}_{mn}{}^2-\omega^2)} \qquad (12.227)$$

where

$$M=\sigma m \qquad (12.228)$$

The sound power becomes:

$$N=\sum_m\sum_n\frac{\rho c}{2}\frac{\omega^2F^2\varphi_{mn}{}^2(F)\sigma^2}{M^2|\bar{\omega}_{mn}{}^2-\omega^2|^2}Re\frac{1}{\sqrt{1-\dfrac{\kappa_{mn}{}^2}{k^2}}} \qquad (12.229)$$

where κ_{mn} is the wave number of the bending-wave pattern of the plate for the mn^{th} mode (see Eq. 12.222). The contribution of each normal mode is proportional to the square of the natural function at the excitation point. If the position of the driving point (F) is continuously varied, $\sigma\varphi_{mn}{}^2(F)=1$, and the average sound power per unit area for an average position of the driving point is given by:

$$N_0=\sum_m\sum_n\frac{\rho c}{2}\frac{\omega^2F^2}{M^2|\bar{\omega}_{mn}{}^2-\omega^2|^2}Re\frac{1}{\sqrt{1-\dfrac{\kappa_{mn}{}^2}{k^2}}}$$
$$=\sum_m\sum_n\frac{\rho c}{2}\frac{F^2}{\omega^2M^2}\frac{1}{\left|\left(\dfrac{\omega_{mn}}{\omega}\right)^2(1+j\eta)-1\right|^2}Re\frac{1}{\sqrt{1-\dfrac{\kappa_{mn}{}^2}{k^2}}}$$
$$=\frac{\rho c}{2}\frac{F^2}{\omega^2M^2}\sum_m\sum_n\frac{1}{\left[\left(\dfrac{\omega_{mn}}{\omega}\right)^2-1\right]^2+\left(\dfrac{\omega_{mn}}{\omega}\right)^4\eta^2}Re\frac{1}{\sqrt{1-\dfrac{\kappa_{mn}{}^2}{k^2}}} \qquad (12.230)$$

Because $Re\sqrt{1-\kappa_{mn}{}^2/k^2}$ is zero if $\kappa_{mn}>k$, only those modes contribute for which $\kappa_{mn}\leq k$. The condition $\kappa_{mn}{}^2\leq k^2$ or $c^2(\kappa_x{}^2+\kappa_y{}^2)\leq\omega^2$ implies that the wave length must be smaller than the so-called coincidence wave length:

$$\lambda\leq\frac{2\pi}{\sqrt{\dfrac{m^2}{l_x{}^2}+\dfrac{n^2}{l_y{}^2}}} \qquad (12.231)$$

The last condition also determines the maximum values of m and n (the maximum order of the modes) that contribute to the sound power.

In the one-dimensional case, if the force is a line force, $m=0$, and the maximum value of n is determined by the number of nodal lines that can be formed so that the separation between them is half a sound wave length. Thus,

$$m_{\max}=\frac{l_x}{\frac{\lambda}{2}}=\frac{\omega l_x}{\pi c} \qquad (12.232)$$

Sound radiation is due to the modes whose distance between the nodal lines is greater than half a sound wave length. If the frequency of the force is low, most of the modes will not radiate sound, because the bending wave length in the plate will be much shorter than the sound wave length. Only the low-order modes, which also are excited by the line force and whose resonant frequencies will be lower than the fixed frequency, generate sound. For these modes $(\omega_{mn}/\omega)^2$ is negligible as compared to one, and the sound power that is generated by the plate becomes (see Eq. 12.230):

$$N=\sigma N_0=\frac{\sigma\rho c}{2}\frac{F^2}{\omega^2 M^2}\sum_{1}^{m\max}\frac{1}{\sqrt{1-\dfrac{m^2\pi^2}{l_x^2k^2}}} \qquad (12.233)$$

The square root describes the increased radiation of the infinite plate as the distance between the nodal lines approaches half the sound wave length of the surrounding medium. The above sum can be replaced by an integral, as follows:

$$\sum_{1}^{m\max}\frac{1}{\sqrt{1-\dfrac{m^2\pi^2}{l_x^2k^2}}}=\frac{l_xk}{\pi}\int_0^{m\pi/kl_x=1}\frac{d\dfrac{m\pi}{l_xk}}{\sqrt{1-\dfrac{m^2\pi^2}{l_x^2k^2}}}=\frac{l_xk}{\pi}\cdot\frac{\pi}{2}=\frac{l_xk}{2} \qquad (12.234)$$

and the sound power that is generated by the plate becomes:

$$N=\sigma\frac{\rho c}{2}\frac{F^2}{\omega^2M^2}\frac{l_xk}{2}=\sigma\frac{\rho c}{2}\frac{F^2 l_x\pi}{\omega M^2 c\pi 2}=\sigma\frac{\rho c}{2}\frac{F^2}{\omega_{l_x}\omega M^2}\frac{\pi}{2} \qquad (12.235)$$

where

$$\omega_{l_x}=\frac{\pi c}{l_x} \qquad (12.236)$$

is the resonant frequency of a column of fluid of length l_x. The last formula is the same as that for the infinite plate (Eq. 12.196).[20]

[20] If the plate were not enclosed in a rectangular channel, the infinite peak in the radiation resistance at the coincidence frequency would be finite and approximately equal to $\rho c n_{\max}/2$ (see p. 413, 406). To derive an approximation for a finite plate, the square root under the integrand (Eq. 12.234) is replaced by $\sqrt{1-(m\pi/l_xk)^2+\alpha^2}$, where $\alpha^2=1/(m_{\max}/2)^2$, so that the pole of the integrand is reduced to a maximum of height $\rho c m_{\max}/2$. If the variable m is replaced by $m'=n/\sqrt{1+\alpha^2}$, an integral results that is of the same form as before, except that the upper limit is $1/\sqrt{1+\alpha^2}=m_{\max}/\sqrt{m_{\max}{}^2+1}$. This result shows that the infinity of the integrand is very weak and that it makes hardly any difference if the infinite peak is replaced by a peak of finite height. We thus arrive at the conclusion that a plate whose length is greater than a few bending wavelengths radiates sound with practically the same efficiency as an infinite plate. If the plate were very large, its reaction to the sound radiation would have to be taken into account, as in the preceding section.

If the effect of coincidence and the increase of the radiation resistance near this frequency were neglected, the radiation resistance of each mode would be ρc, and the square root would have to be replaced by one, and the sound power would be smaller by a factor $2/\pi$.

In the two-dimensional case, when the exciting force is a point force, the number of modes that can radiate sound is given by the number of grid points in a quadrant of a circle with a radius

$$\omega = \omega_{mn} = \pi c \sqrt{\left(\frac{m}{l_x}\right)^2 + \left(\frac{n}{l_y}\right)^2} \tag{12.237}$$

The area of this quadrant is $\frac{1}{4}\pi\omega^2$. Every grid point corresponds to a cell of length $\Delta\omega = \pi c/l_x$ and of width $\Delta\omega = \pi c/l_y$, and, consequently, to an area

$$\Delta\sigma = \frac{\pi^2 c^2}{l_x l_y} \tag{12.238}$$

Thus, the number $\nu_{\max}$ of grid points is:

$$\nu_{\max} = \frac{1}{4}\frac{\pi\omega^2}{\Delta\sigma} = \frac{1}{4}\frac{\pi\omega^2 l_x l_y}{\pi^2 c^2} = \frac{\pi}{4}\frac{\omega^2}{\omega_{l_x}\omega_{l_y}} \tag{12.239}$$

where $\omega_{l_x} = \pi c/l_x$ and $\omega_{l_y} = \pi c/l_y$ are the resonant frequencies of a column of fluid of length l_x and l_y, respectively. If every one of these modes radiated sound, as if the radiation impedance were ρc, the square root in Equation 12.230 could be replaced by one, and

$$N_0 \cong \frac{\rho c}{2}\frac{F^2}{\omega^2 M^2}\frac{\pi}{4}\frac{\omega^2}{\omega_{l_x}\omega_{l_y}} = \frac{1}{2}\rho c \frac{F^2}{\omega_{l_x}\omega_{l_y} M^2}\frac{\pi}{4} \tag{12.240}$$

If the square root is not neglected, but the sum in Equation 12.230 is approximated by an integral, we obtain:

$$\sum_1^m \sum_1^n \frac{1}{\sqrt{1-\left(\frac{m\pi}{l_x k}\right)^2 - \left(\frac{n\pi}{l_y k}\right)^2}} \cong \int\int \frac{dmdn}{\sqrt{1-\left(\frac{m\pi}{l_x k}\right)^2 - \left(\frac{n\pi}{l_y k}\right)^2}}$$
$$= \frac{l_x l_y k^2}{\pi^2}\int\int \frac{dudv}{\sqrt{1-u^2-v^2}} \tag{12.241}$$

If $u = \rho\cos\theta$, $v = \rho\sin\theta$, and $dudv = \rho d\rho d\theta$, the sum becomes:

$$\frac{l_x l_y k^2}{\pi^2}\int_0^{\pi/2} d\theta \int_0^1 \frac{\rho d\rho}{\sqrt{1-\rho^2}} = \frac{l_x l_y k^2}{2\pi} \tag{12.242}$$

and the total sound power is given by:

$$N = \sigma\frac{\rho c}{2}\frac{F^2}{\omega^2 M^2}\frac{l_x l_y k^2}{2\pi} = \frac{1}{2}\rho c \frac{F^2}{\omega_{l_x}\omega_{l_y}}\frac{\pi}{2} \tag{12.243}$$

Thus, taking account of the increase of the radiation resistance near the coincidence frequency for two-dimensional vibration patterns leads to an increase of the sound power by a factor of two. Again, because of the weakness of the infinity in the integrand, this result also applies with excellent approximation to a finite plate whose linear dimensions exceed a few bending wave lengths at the coincidence frequency.

The mirror images of the rigidly supported vibrating plate lead to a continuous vibration pattern like that of the infinite plate, with no discontinuity in either the plate velocity or the slope of the deflection curve. Therefore, the edges of the plate do not contribute to the sound energy that is generated by the plate, and the sound radiation per unit area of a finite rigidly supported plate that forms the rear wall of a rectangular channel is the same as that of an infinitely large plate.

If the plate is not in a rectangular channel, then the pressure will be smaller near the edges because of radiation into the space that surrounds the plate. The sound pressure at the surface of the plate then can no longer be represented by the same natural functions as the plate vibration (see Eqs. 12.219 and 12.220); the more accurate computation, which follows, will show that the edges then give rise to an additional component of sound radiation.

Plate rigidly supported at the edges. The image method can also be used to find an approximate solution for a plate that is supported rigidly at its edges (Fig. 12.11). The natural functions of the plate then are given by:

$$v_{\mu\nu}=V_{\mu\nu}\sin\frac{\mu\pi x}{l_x}\sin\frac{\nu\pi y}{l_y}=V_{\mu\nu}\varphi_{\mu\nu} \tag{12.244}$$

and

$$v=\sum_{\mu}\sum_{\nu}V_{\mu\nu}\varphi_{\mu\nu} \tag{12.245}$$

But the pressure distribution in front of the plate is no longer the same as the velocity distribution (see Fig. 12.11). The plate velocity vanishes at the edges $x=\pm l_x/2$, but the pressure is finite at this point, and the natural functions that are used to describe the pressure distribution must be finite for $x=\pm l_x/2$. Since they must also satisfy the boundary condition of zero normal velocity at the channel surfaces, they can only be of the form:

$$\Psi_{mn}=\frac{2}{\sqrt{l_x l_y}}\cos\frac{m\pi x}{l_x}\cos\frac{n\pi y}{l_y}e^{-jk_z z} \tag{12.246}$$

where

$$k_z=k_{mn}=\sqrt{k^2-\left(\frac{m\pi}{l_x}\right)^2-\left(\frac{n\pi}{l_y}\right)^2} \tag{12.247}$$

and

$$P=\sum_{m}\sum_{n}P_{mn}\Psi_{mn} \tag{12.248}$$

The coefficients P_{mn} are obtained from the boundary conditions at $z=0$:

$$\tilde{v}=\frac{j}{k\rho c}\frac{\partial\tilde{p}}{\partial z} \tag{12.249}$$

or

$$\sum_{\mu}\sum_{\nu} V_{\mu\nu}\varphi_{\mu\nu} = \frac{1}{k\rho c}\sum\sum P_{mn}k_{mn}\Psi_{mn} \tag{12.250}$$

In this equation, the functions P_{mn} have to be determined as functions of V_{mn}. The functions Ψ_{mn} represent solutions of the wave equation that satisfy the boundary conditions at $x=0$ and $x=l$. They also represent a system of functions that is complete and orthogonal over the plate. The last equation can, therefore, be multiplied by Ψ_{mn} and integrated over the plate. Because of the orthogonality conditions, the mixed products in $\Psi_{mn}\Psi_{mn}$ vanish during the integration over the plate surface, and

$$P_{m} = \sum_{\mu}\sum_{\nu} \frac{\rho c k}{k_{mn}} V_{\mu\nu} \frac{\int \varphi_{\mu\nu}\Psi_{mn} d\sigma}{\int \Psi_{mn}^2 d\sigma} \tag{12.251}$$

In the preceding case, when the plate was free at the edges, the natural functions of the pressure field were the same as those for the velocity field. For the simply supported plate, the two sets of natural functions are different. The pressure amplitude P_{mn} then is related not only to one, but to all the natural functions $V_{\mu\nu}$ of the velocity field. The sound power per unit area is given, as before, by:

$$N_0 = \frac{1}{2} Re(\bar{P}\bar{V}^*) = \frac{1}{\sigma}\int \frac{1}{2} Re \sum_{m}\sum_{n} P_{mn}\Psi_{mn} \sum_{\mu}\sum_{\nu} V_{\mu\nu}^*\varphi_{\mu\nu} d\sigma \tag{12.252}$$

and if Equation 12.255 is substituted for P_{mn},

$$N_0 = \frac{1}{\sigma}\frac{\rho c}{2} Re \sum_{m}\sum_{n}\left(\frac{k}{k_{mn}}\right)\sum_{\mu}\sum_{\nu} V_{\mu\nu}^2 \frac{\left(\int \Psi_{mn}\varphi_{\mu\nu} d\sigma\right)^2}{\int \Psi_{mn}^2 d\sigma} \tag{12.253}$$

The magnitude $V_{\mu\nu}$ is again replaced by the solution of the plate equation (Eq. 8.1), and the sound power thus becomes:

$$N_0 = \frac{\rho c}{2}\frac{F^2}{M^2}\sum_{m}\sum_{n}\sum_{\mu}\sum_{\nu} \frac{\left(\int \varphi_{\mu\nu}\Psi_{mn} d\sigma\right)^2}{\int \varphi_{\mu\nu}^2 d\sigma \int \Psi_{mn}^2 d\sigma} \cdot \frac{\omega^2}{(\bar{\omega}_{\mu\nu}^2 - \omega^2)^2} Re \frac{k}{k_{mn}} \tag{12.254}$$

In the one-dimensional case (line force), we have:

$$\Psi_m = \sqrt{\frac{2}{l}}\cos\frac{m\pi x}{l} \qquad \varphi_\mu = \sqrt{\frac{2}{l}}\sin\frac{\mu\pi x}{l} \quad \text{and} \quad k_m = \sqrt{k^2 - \frac{m^2\pi^2}{l^2}} \tag{12.255}$$

and

$$N = \frac{\rho c}{2}\frac{16}{\pi^2}\frac{F^2}{M^2}\sum_{m=0}^{m}\sum_{\mu=1}^{\infty} \frac{n^2}{(\mu^2 - m^2)^2} \cdot \frac{\omega^2}{(\bar{\omega}_{\mu}^2 - \omega^2)^2} \cdot \frac{k}{\sqrt{k^2 - \frac{m^2\pi^2}{l^2}}} \tag{12.256}$$

where M is the mass per unit width of the plate and $m+n$ is odd. The evaluation of the above summations is difficult, and only approximate results can be derived.[21] The resultant sound field consists of two parts, one being generated by the forced excitation of the low-order modes (as in the preceding case), the other being a result of the discontinuity of the slope of the mirror image at the edges of the plate. The first part is obtained by summing the contributions of those modes, whose wavelength is greater than or at least equal to the sound wave length. This part of the solution, then, turns out to be the same as that for the image pattern of the freely suspended plate (Eq. 12.196). The second part of the solution represents the contributions of the modes whose bending wavelength is smaller than the sound wavelength ($\mu > m$). These modes radiate sound only because of the discontinuity at the edges of the plate—because $\int \varphi_\mu \Psi_m \, d\sigma \neq 0$ for $\mu > m$. Thus, if the plate is rigidly supported, sound is generated, not only by the low-order modes whose bending wavelength is greater than the sound wavelength, but also by the high-order modes, because of the discontinuity at the edges. We shall later derive simple methods for determining this component of sound radiation. M. Heckl[22] obtains the following expression for the sound power that is due to the edge effect[23] (the same as that given by Eq. 12.295):

$$N_0' \approx \frac{1}{\sigma} \rho c \left(\frac{\tilde{V}^2}{2} \right) \frac{k}{k_0^2} \tag{12.257}$$

The same result will subsequently be obtained by a different method.

Sound Power Generated by a Rectangular Plate—Fourier Method

Fundamental formulas. The preceding computations can be generalized for a finite plate that is not enclosed in an infinite channel. The velocity distribution then is expressed by its Fourier transform:

$$v(x, y) = \int_{-\infty}^{\infty} \int_{-\infty}^{\infty} \bar{S}_v(\kappa_x, \kappa_y) e^{j(\kappa_x x + \kappa_y y)} \frac{d\kappa_x d\kappa_y}{4\pi^2} \tag{12.258}$$

and the pressure distribution, by the corresponding integral:

[21] See M. Heckl, *op. cit.*, p. 371.
[22] *Ibid.*
[23] The preceding conclusions lead to an understanding of the Huygens' zone construction in optics. The radiating surface is divided into strips or circles whose mean distance from the point of observation differs by half a wavelength. To get the correct result it is necessary to assume that the second half of the first zone cancels the first half of the second zone, and so on. It is not permissible to assume that the first zone cancels the effect of the second zone, etc., although this procedure would be expected to work equally well. The reason that it does not work in the second case is that (as for the rigidly supported plate) the canceling effect is much poorer, so that the contributions from the boundaries between the zones are not negligible.

$$p(x, y, z) = \int_{-\infty}^{\infty} \int_{-\infty}^{\infty} \bar{S}_p(\kappa_x, \kappa_y) e^{j(\kappa_x x + \kappa_y y) - jk_z z} \frac{d\kappa_x d\kappa_y}{4\pi^2} \tag{12.259}$$

where

$$k_z^2 = k^2 - \kappa_x^2 - \kappa_y^2 = k^2 - \kappa^2 \tag{12.260}$$

The boundary condition for $z=0$, $\tilde{v} = (j/k\rho c)(\partial \tilde{p}/\partial z)$, leads to the relation:

$$\bar{S}_p(\kappa_x, \kappa_y) = \rho c \frac{k}{k_z} \bar{S}_v(\kappa_x, \kappa_y) = \frac{\rho c}{\sqrt{1 - \frac{\kappa^2}{k^2}}} \bar{S}_v(\kappa_x, \kappa_y) \tag{12.261}$$

and the sound power per unit area of the plate becomes:

$$N_0 = \frac{1}{\sigma} \cdot \frac{1}{2} Re \int_\sigma \bar{P} \bar{V}^* d\sigma$$

$$= \frac{\rho c}{2\sigma} Re \int_{-l_1/2}^{l_1/2} dx \int_{-l_2/2}^{l_2/2} dy \left[\int_{-\infty}^{\infty} \int_{-\infty}^{\infty} \frac{k}{k_z} \bar{S}_v(\kappa_x, \kappa_y) e^{-j(\kappa_x x + \kappa_y y)} \frac{d\kappa_x d\kappa_y}{4\pi^2} \right.$$

$$\left. \cdot \int_{-\infty}^{\infty} \int_{-\infty}^{\infty} \bar{S}_v^*(\kappa_x', \kappa_y') e^{j(\kappa_x' x + \kappa_y' y)} \frac{d\kappa_x' d\kappa_y'}{4\pi^2} \right]$$

$$= Re \frac{\rho c}{2} \int \int \int_{-\infty}^{\infty} \int \frac{k}{k_z} \frac{\bar{S}_v(\kappa_x, \kappa_y) \bar{S}_v^*(\kappa_x', \kappa_y')}{\sigma} \frac{d\kappa_x d\kappa_y}{4\pi^2} d\kappa_x' d\kappa_y'$$

$$\cdot \int_{-l_1/2}^{l_1/2} \int_{-l_2/2}^{l_2/2} e^{-j[(\kappa_x - \kappa_x')x + (\kappa_y - \kappa_y')y]} \frac{dxdy}{4\pi^2} \tag{12.262}$$

If the dimensions of the plate are very large as compared to the bending wave length, the limits $\pm l_1/2$ and $\pm l_2/2$ can be replaced by $\pm\infty$; then the double integral on the right acts like a delta function[24] and replaces κ_x', κ_y' by κ_x, κ_y. This statement is proved as follows:

[24] This condition is equivalent to the orthogonality condition for the discrete set of natural functions of the periodic plate pattern in the preceding section. It means that the space Fourier components are orthogonal when integrated over an infinite range.

The main contribution of the integrand to the integral arises from the wave numbers $k \doteq \kappa$ because of the factor k_z in the denominator; if $k > \kappa_0$, there is also a contribution from the wave numbers $\kappa = \kappa_0$, for which the bending wave length is equal to or smaller than the sound wave length. The x, y-integral is equal to:

$$\frac{l_1 l_2}{4\pi^2} \frac{\sin(\kappa_x' - \kappa_x)\frac{l_1}{2}}{(\kappa_x' - \kappa_x)\frac{l_1}{2}} \cdot \frac{\sin(\kappa_y' - \kappa_y)\frac{l_2}{2}}{(\kappa_y' - \kappa_y)\frac{l_2}{2}}$$

Each factor decreases rapidly as its argument is increased. The large plate approximation

$$\int_{l/2}^{l/2} \frac{1}{2\pi} e^{-j(\kappa-\kappa')x}\, dx = \frac{\sin (\kappa-\kappa')\frac{l}{2}}{\pi(\kappa-\kappa')} \tag{12.263}$$

If l is very large, this function fluctuates rapidly, and integrands with this function as a factor contribute only for $\kappa=\kappa'$. In the nonfluctuating factors of the integrand, κ' can be replaced by κ, and the κ'-integration then yields the factor -1, and two such integrations yield the factor $+1$:

$$\lim_{l\to\infty} \int_{-l/2}^{l/2} f(\kappa)\frac{\sin (\kappa-\kappa')\frac{l}{2}}{\pi(\kappa-\kappa')} d(\kappa-\kappa') = f(\kappa)\int_{-l/2}^{l/2} \frac{-1}{\pi}\frac{\sin u du}{u} = -f(\kappa) \tag{12.264}$$

The integral for the power then simplifies to:

$$N_0 = Re\frac{\rho c}{2}\int\int_{-\infty}^{\infty} \frac{\bar{S}_v\bar{S}_v{}^*}{\sigma}\frac{k}{k_z}\frac{d\kappa_x d\kappa_y}{4\pi^2}$$

$$= Re\frac{\rho c}{2}\int\int_{-\infty}^{\infty} \frac{W_v(\kappa_x,\kappa_y)}{\sqrt{1-\frac{\kappa_x{}^2}{k^2}-\frac{\kappa_y{}^2}{k^2}}}\frac{d\kappa_x}{2\pi}\frac{d\kappa_y}{2\pi} \tag{12.265}$$

where

$$W_v(\kappa_x,\kappa_y) = \frac{\langle \bar{S}_v\bar{S}_v{}^*\rangle}{\sigma} \tag{12.266}$$

is the power spectrum of the velocity distribution. For a one-dimensional vibration, a similar result is obtained:

$$N_0 = \frac{\rho c}{4\pi}\int_{-k}^{k} \frac{W_v(\kappa)d\kappa}{\sqrt{1-\frac{\kappa^2}{k^2}}} \tag{12.267}$$

Sound radiation at very high frequencies. The power spectrum of a vibrating plate is predominantly made up of spectral components whose wave length is of the order of magnitude of the bending wave length in the plate. It usually decreases rapidly for higher space wave numbers. If the frequency of the exciting forces is much greater than the coincidence frequency ($\kappa/k \ll 1$), the power spectrum of the plate is practically zero for $k \gg \kappa_0$, and the square root in the integrand (Eq. 12.265) can be replaced by one. The integral for the sound power then simplifies to:

$$N_0 = \frac{\rho c}{2}\int_{-\infty}^{\infty}\int_{-\infty}^{\infty} W_v(\kappa_x,\kappa_y)\frac{d\kappa_x d\kappa_y}{4\pi^2} = \frac{\rho c}{2}\langle V^2\rangle \tag{12.268}$$

may, therefore, be expected to apply whenever the linear dimensions of the plate exceed about five wave lengths. Comparison of the results of this section with the accurate computations of the next section shows that the large plate approximation applies fairly accurately if the dimensions of the plate exceed one sound wavelength.

where

$$\langle V^2 \rangle = \int_{\infty}^{\infty}\int_{\infty}^{\infty} W(\kappa_x, \kappa_y)\frac{d\kappa_x d\kappa_y}{4\pi^2} \tag{12.269}$$

The sound power, then, becomes proportional to the mean-square velocity over the plate, as was to be expected. Every plate mode radiates sound as if its radiation impedance were ρc, and the total sound power is proportional to the vibrational energy of the plate.

Infinitely long vibrating strip. The previous integral was derived for plates that are long and wide as compared to the bending wave length. But it is valid also for an infinitely long strip of width dx that moves periodically in a baffle like a rigid piston; the space-power spectrum is constant—$S(\kappa') = S(\kappa)$—and the delta function integral is not needed. For such a strip we find that

$$S_v = V dx \tag{12.270}$$

(see Eq. 11.30) and

$$W_v = V^2 \frac{dx^2}{dx} = V^2 dx \tag{12.271}$$

The power that is generated (in the half space) by the unit length of the strip is:

$$N = N_0 dx = \frac{\rho c}{4\pi} V^2 dx^2 \int_{-k}^{k} \frac{1}{\sqrt{1 - \frac{\kappa^2}{k^2}}} d\kappa$$

$$= \frac{k}{4} \rho c V^2 dx^2 = \frac{k \rho c (2Q)^2}{4 \cdot 4} \tag{12.272}$$

where $Q = V dx$ is the volume flow. This result is identical with the classical computation for half the sound power of an infinitely thin cylinder of volume flow $2Q$ that radiates into the full space or of a cylinder of volume flow Q that radiates into the half space (see Eq. 12.122).

Finite Plate Excited in a Single Vibrational Mode: Edge Radiation—Power Spectrum Method

Bending waves of shorter wavelength than sound waves of the same frequency do not generate sound. A vibrator generates sound because of the deformation of the vibration field around the region of the driving force.

For a point force, the vibration amplitude is approximately constant and has a maximum value near the driver; but, from a certain distance on, it decreases crudely proportionally to $1/\sqrt{r}$. For a one-dimensional bending pattern, the driving force generates an exponentially decreasing distortion. This type of sound radiation has been investigated in the preceding sections. We were not interested in the effect of the boundaries and consequently have assumed that the vibrator was infinitely extended, or we have extended the vibrator to infinity by introducing its mirror images.

A second component of low-frequency sound radiation is due to the discontinuity of the vibration field near the edges of the vibrator. This type of sound radiation is particularly important when the vibrator is driven at a resonance. At a resonance, the vibration field is essentially that of a single mode, i.e., of the mode that is excited at its resonant frequency. To investigate this type of sound radiation, we assume the system to be excited in a single mode.

We shall assume that the plate is rigidly supported at its edges ($v=0$) or freely suspended and that the vibration is symmetrical around the center line of the plate. The center may be a zero point of velocity or a point of maximum velocity. In the first case,

$$V = V_0 \sin \kappa_0 x = \frac{V_0}{2j}(e^{j\kappa_0 x} - e^{-j\kappa_0 x}) \tag{12.273}$$

In the second case,

$$V = V_0 \cos \kappa_0 x = \frac{V_0}{2}(e^{j\kappa_0 x} + e^{-j\kappa_0 x}) \tag{12.274}$$

for $-l/2 \leq x \leq l/2$. If $V = V_0 \sin \kappa_0 x$, the velocity spectrum then is:

$$\begin{aligned}
\bar{S}_v(\kappa) &= \int_{-l/2}^{l/2} V_0 \frac{e^{j\kappa_0 x} - e^{-j\kappa_0 x}}{2j} e^{-j\kappa x} dx \\
&= \frac{V_0}{2j}\left[\frac{e^{j(\kappa_0-\kappa)l/2} - e^{-j(\kappa_0-\kappa)l/2}}{j(\kappa_0-\kappa)} - \frac{e^{-j(\kappa_0+\kappa)l/2} - e^{j(\kappa_0+\kappa)l/2}}{-j(\kappa_0+\kappa)}\right] \\
&= \frac{V_0}{j}\left[\frac{\sin(\kappa_0-\kappa)\frac{l}{2}}{(\kappa_0-\kappa)} - \frac{\sin(\kappa_0+\kappa)\frac{l}{2}}{(\kappa_0+\kappa)}\right] \\
&= \frac{2V_0}{j(\kappa_0^2-\kappa^2)}\left[\kappa \sin\frac{\kappa_0 l}{2}\cos\frac{\kappa l}{2} - \kappa_0 \cos\frac{\kappa_0 l}{2}\sin\frac{\kappa l}{2}\right]
\end{aligned} \tag{12.275}$$

If the edges of the plate are rigidly supported:

$$\sin\frac{\kappa_0 l}{2} = 0 \qquad \cos\frac{\kappa_0 l}{2} = \pm 1 \tag{12.276}$$

and

$$\bar{S}_v(\kappa) = \pm\frac{2V_0\kappa_0 \sin\frac{\kappa l}{2}}{j(\kappa_0^2-\kappa^2)} \tag{12.277}$$

If the edges of the plate are free and if the end distortion of the vibration is neglected:

$$\sin\frac{\kappa_0 l}{2}=\pm 1 \qquad \cos\frac{\kappa_0 l}{2}=0 \tag{12.278}$$

and

$$\bar{S}_v(\kappa)=\pm\frac{2\kappa V_0 \cos\dfrac{\kappa l}{2}}{j(\kappa_0{}^2-\kappa^2)} \tag{12.279}$$

The correctness of this result can be easily checked. The Fourier integral over a function $f(t)$ for the frequency zero is equal to the mean value of the function. This follows directly from the defining equation (11.57). Because the mean value of V over the plate is zero, both spectral functions are zero for $\kappa=0$.

If the center of the plate is a point of maximum motion, the minus sign in the integrand (Eq. 12.275) has to be replaced by a plus sign, and one of the j's has to be omitted. The velocity spectrum then becomes:

$$\bar{S}_v(\kappa)=\frac{2V_0}{\kappa_0{}^2-\kappa^2}\left(\kappa_0 \sin\frac{\kappa_0 l}{2}\cos\frac{\kappa l}{2}-\kappa\cos\frac{\kappa_0 l}{2}\sin\frac{\kappa l}{2}\right) \tag{12.280}$$

If the edges of the plate are rigidly supported, $\cos \kappa_0 l/2=0$, $\sin \kappa_0 l/2=\pm 1$, and

$$\bar{S}_v(\kappa)=\pm\frac{2V_0\kappa_0 \cos\dfrac{\kappa l}{2}}{\kappa_0{}^2-\kappa^2} \tag{12.281}$$

The mean velocity now is not zero, and, as a consequence, the spectral amplitude $S_v(\kappa)$ is finite for $\kappa=0$. If the edges of the plate are free and end distortion is neglected, $\cos \kappa_0 l/2=\pm 1$, $\sin \kappa_0 l/2=0$, and

$$\bar{S}_v=\pm\frac{2V_0\,\kappa \sin\dfrac{\kappa l}{2}}{\kappa_0{}^2-\kappa^2} \tag{12.282}$$

The four cases are represented in Figure 12.12. The power spectrum is given by:

$$W_v(\kappa)=\frac{\bar{S}_v\bar{S}_v{}^*}{l} \tag{12.283}$$

Figure 12.13 shows the power spectrum $W_v(\kappa)$ for a rigidly supported plate as a function of κ/κ_0, with the number of half waves as parameter. If κ_0 is large, the maximum is attained for $\kappa_0=\kappa$. It is given by: $\kappa l=(\kappa_0+\epsilon)l=(\nu\pi+\epsilon l)$, $\epsilon\to 0$. Hence,

$$W_v(\kappa_0+\epsilon)=\frac{V_0{}^2 l\kappa_0{}^2\dfrac{l^2}{4}\epsilon^2\dfrac{l^2}{4}}{\dfrac{4\kappa_0 l}{2}\left(\dfrac{\epsilon l}{2}\right)^2}=\frac{V_0{}^2 l}{4} \tag{12.284}$$

To determine the sound radiation at low frequencies, $\kappa^2\leq k^2\ll\kappa_0{}^2$ and $\kappa^2\ll\kappa_0{}^2$ can be neglected in the denominator of the power spectrum. Also,

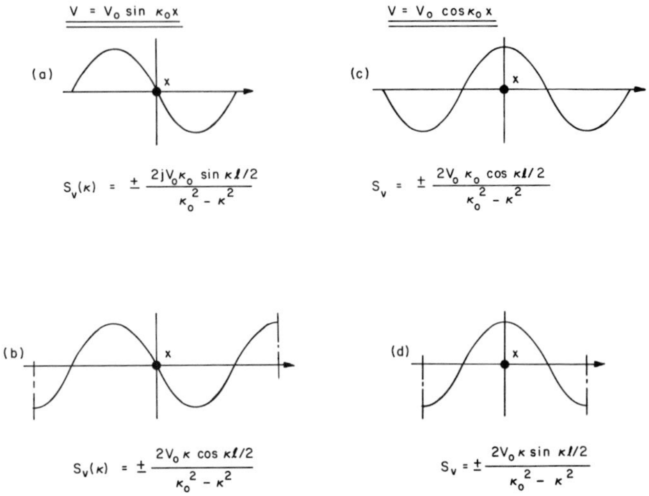

Fig. 12.12 Various types of vibration of a plate and the corresponding velocity spectra.

since the dimensions of the plate have been assumed to be large, $\sin^2 \kappa l/2$ or $\cos^2 \kappa l/2$ can be replaced in the integrand by one half. The cases in which the ends of the plate are free (Fig. 12.12*b* and *d*) then lead to the same result. If the Fourier spectrum is substituted in Equation 12.283 and the power spectrum thus obtained is substituted in Equation 12.267, the sound power per unit area of the plate becomes:

$$N_0 = \frac{\rho c}{4\pi} \int_{-k}^{k} \frac{W_\nu(\kappa) d\kappa}{\sqrt{1 - \frac{\kappa^2}{k^2}}} = \frac{\rho c}{2\pi} \int_0^k \frac{4 V_0^2 \kappa^2 \cdot \frac{1}{2} d\kappa}{(\kappa_0^2 - \kappa^2)^2 \sqrt{1 - \frac{\kappa^2}{k^2}}}$$

$$\cong \frac{\rho c V_0^2}{\pi \kappa_0^4} \int_0^k \frac{\kappa^2 d\kappa}{\sqrt{1 - \frac{\kappa^2}{k^2}}} = \frac{\rho c V_0^2 k^3}{\pi \kappa_0^4} \int_0^1 \frac{z^2 dz}{\sqrt{1 - z^2}}$$

$$= \frac{\rho c V_0^2}{2} \frac{k^3}{2\kappa_0^4} = \frac{\rho c V_0^2}{2} \frac{\omega \alpha^4}{2c^3} \tag{12.285}$$

where

$$z = \frac{\kappa}{k} \quad \text{and} \quad \kappa_0 = \frac{\sqrt{\omega}}{\alpha} \tag{12.286}$$

The low-frequency sound power per unit width of the plate is independent of the length l of the plate. This result proves that the low-frequency sound radiation of a plate is a consequence of the discontinuity of the vibration pattern at the edges and, consequently, is an edge effect. Each of the two

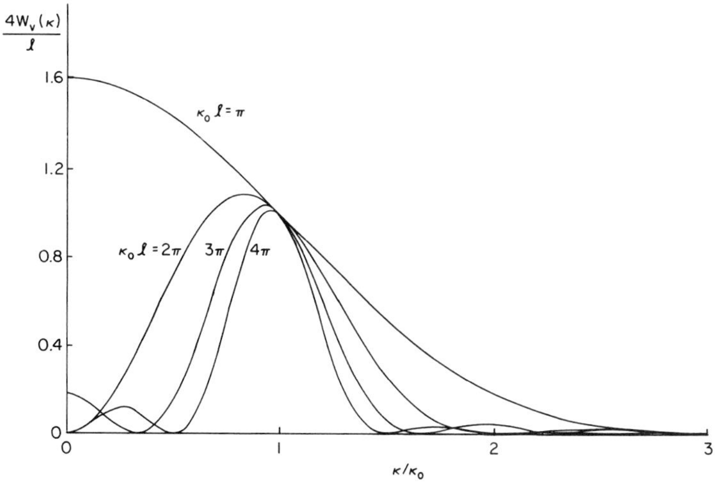

Fig. 12.13 Velocity spectrum of plate vibration

infinitely long edges that are parallel to the nodal lines radiates the sound energy:

$$\frac{1}{2}N_0 = \frac{\rho c V_0^2}{2}\frac{k^3}{4\kappa_0^4} \tag{12.287}$$

per unit length, as if the edges were a cylindrical dipole source (see Eq. 12.123). This formula is identical with that for the sound power of a cylindrical dipole source of constant moment along its axis ($k = k'$). If $Q_0 = 2Q_H$, where Q_H is the volume flow generated in the semispace, the power radiated into the semispace N_H by such a source is (see Eq. 12.123):

$$N_H = \frac{1}{2}N_0 = \frac{1}{2}\frac{k^3 \rho c}{16}(2Q_H dx)^2 \tag{12.288}$$

Comparison of the last two expressions shows that the moment of the equivalent dipole is:

$$Q_H dx = \frac{V_0}{\kappa_0^2} = \frac{2}{\pi}V_0\frac{\lambda_B}{2}\frac{\lambda_B}{4\pi} \tag{12.289}$$

where λ_B is the bending wave length in the plate. The sound radiation of an edge of such a freely vibrating plate is the same as that of a cylindrical dipole that is made up of two sources, both of which have a volume flow equal to that of a strip of the plate of width $\lambda_B/2$ at a distance $\lambda_B/4\pi$. It is obvious that the sound radiation of a freely supported plate is very small at low frequencies.

At the coincidence frequency, $\kappa_0 = k_0$; the boundary conditions have practically no effect on the sound power, that is radiated by a plate that is large compared to the sound wavelength, this is easily proved by substituting the respective expressions for the power spectrum into the integral for the radiated sound power. We shall therefore use Equation 12.286 as a starting point. The corresponding spectrum is given by Equation 12.277 and the sound power (Eq. 12.267) becomes:

$$N=\frac{\rho c V_0^2}{4\pi l} 2 \int_0^{\kappa_0} \frac{4\kappa_0^3 \sin^2 \kappa l/2 \; d\kappa \cdot (l/2)^4}{(\kappa_0^2-\kappa^2)^{5/2} \qquad (l/2)^4}$$

$$=\frac{\rho c V_0^2}{\pi} \int_0^{z_0} \frac{z_0^3 \sin^2 z dz}{(z_0^2-z^2)^{5/2}}$$

$$=\frac{\rho c V_0^2 z_0^3}{\pi} \int_0^{z_0} \frac{\sin^2 u dz}{(2z_0 u-u^2)^{5/2}}$$

$$\simeq \frac{\rho c V_0^2 z_0^3}{2z_0 2z_0 \pi} \int_0^{\infty} \frac{\sin^2 u du}{u^{5/2}} = \frac{\rho c V_0^2 z_0^{3/2}}{2\sqrt{2\pi}} \left[\frac{4}{3}\sqrt{\pi}\right]$$

$$=\frac{\rho c V_0^2}{2} \cdot 3 \left(\frac{l}{\lambda_B}\right)^{3/2} \qquad (12.290)$$

where $z_0=\nu\pi=\kappa_0 l/2$, and $u=z_0-z$. At the coincidence frequency, the sound power generated by a one dimensionally vibrating plate is proportional to the one and a half power of the ratio of its length to the bending wave length.

A similar computation is possible for two-dimensional vibrations. The expression for the power spectrum then contains a factor (Eq. 12.283) for the variations in the y-direction (with the numerical factor 2^2). Because the new integration variable is $d\kappa_y/2\pi$, a factor $1/2\pi$ is generated, and by changing twice the limits of integration to 0 and ∞, a factor 4 is generated. The total sound power thus is given by:

$$N_2=\frac{2\rho c}{4\pi^2} \int_0^{k} \int_0^{\sqrt{k^2-\kappa_y^2}} \frac{V_0^2 4^2 \kappa_x^2 \kappa_y^2 d\kappa_x d\kappa_y \cdot \frac{1}{2} \cdot \frac{1}{2}}{\kappa_0^4 \cdot \kappa_0^4 \sqrt{1-\frac{\kappa_x^2}{k^2}-\frac{\kappa_y^2}{k^2}}}$$

$$=\frac{2\rho c V_0^2 k^6}{\pi^2 \kappa_0^8} \int_0^1 y^2 dy \int_0^{\sqrt{1-y^2}} \frac{z^2 dz}{\sqrt{(1-y^2)-z^2}}$$

$$=\frac{2\rho c V_0^2 k^6}{\pi^2 \kappa^8} \int_0^1 y^2 dy \left[(1-y^2)\frac{\pi}{2} \cdot \frac{1}{2}\right] = \frac{\rho c V_0^2}{2} \frac{2k^6}{\kappa_0^8 15\pi}$$

$$=\frac{\rho c V_0^2}{2} \left(\frac{\omega \alpha^4}{c^3}\right)^2 \cdot \frac{2}{15\pi}$$

where

$$z=\frac{\kappa_x}{k} \qquad y=\frac{\kappa_y}{k} \qquad \text{and} \qquad \kappa_{0x}=\kappa_{0y}=\kappa_0 \tag{12.291}$$

The sound power now is independent of the dimensions of the plate. Because of the canceling effect, the edges do not contribute, and the radiation can be considered as made up of the contributions of the four corners of the plate. The structure of Equation 12.290 is the same as that for the sound radiation of a quadrupole. Every corner of the plate acts like a lateral quadrupole and generates the sound power

$$\frac{1}{4}\cdot\frac{1}{2}\rho c V_0^2\frac{2}{15\pi}\frac{k^6}{\kappa_0^8}=\frac{1}{2}\cdot\frac{1}{8\pi}k^6\rho c(2Q_H)^2dx^2dy^2\frac{1}{15} \tag{12.292}$$

where the right-hand side represents the power radiated into the half square by a quadrupole made up of sources of the volume flow Q_H into half space. The equivalent quadrupole moment of a plate corner thus is given by:

$$Q_H dxdy=\frac{V_0}{\kappa_0^4}=\left[\left(\frac{2}{\pi}\right)^2 V_0\left(\frac{\lambda_B}{2}\right)^2\right]\cdot\frac{\lambda_B^2}{16\pi^2} \tag{12.293}$$

where

$$Q_{pl}=V_0\left(\frac{\lambda_B}{2}\right)^2\cdot\frac{4}{\pi^2} \tag{12.294}$$

This result shows that the volume flow of each of the equivalent sources is that of a nodal area of the plate vibration and that the length of each axis of the quadrupole is about one fortieth of the bending wave length in the plate. Thus, the sound radiation of a freely suspended plate is extremely small.

In the cases in which the edges of the plate are rigidly supported (Fig. 12.12*a* and *c*), the factor κ^2 in the integrand has to be replaced by κ_0^2. For one-dimensional vibrations, the sound power per unit area becomes:

$$N_0=\frac{\rho c V_0^2}{4\pi\kappa_0^4}\int_{-k}^{k}\frac{4\kappa_0^2\frac{d\kappa}{k}\cdot\frac{1}{2}\cdot k}{\sqrt{1-\frac{\kappa^2}{k^2}}}=\frac{\rho c}{2}V_0^2\frac{k}{\kappa_0^2}=\frac{\rho c}{2}V_0^2\frac{\alpha^2}{c} \tag{12.295}$$

Sound radiation now is considerably greater. Each edge acts like a simple line source (see Eq. 12.122) and radiates the power

$$\frac{\rho c}{2}V_0^2\frac{k}{2\kappa_0^2}=\frac{1}{2}\cdot\frac{1}{2}(2Q_H)^2\frac{k\rho c}{4} \tag{12.296}$$

into the semispace. The equivalent line source has the volume flow

$$Q_H=\frac{V_0}{\kappa_0}=\frac{2V_0}{\pi}\frac{\lambda_B}{4} \tag{12.297}$$

since it corresponds to the volume flow generated by a strip of width $\lambda_B/4$ near the edge of the plate.

For two-dimensional vibrations of a plate with simply supported edges,

$$N=\frac{\rho c V_0^2}{2\pi^2\kappa_0^8}\int_0^k\int_0^{\sqrt{k^2-\kappa_y^2}}\frac{4^2\kappa_0^4 d\frac{\kappa_x}{k}\,d\frac{\kappa_y}{k}\cdot k^2\cdot\frac{1}{2}\cdot\frac{1}{2}}{\sqrt{1-\frac{\kappa_x^2}{k^2}-\frac{\kappa_y^2}{k^2}}}$$

$$=\frac{\rho c V_0^2 k^2}{\pi^2\kappa_0^4}\int_0^1 2dy\int_0^{\sqrt{1-y^2}}\frac{dx}{\sqrt{1-y^2-x^2}}=\frac{\rho c V_0^2 k^2}{\pi^2\kappa_0^4}\int_0^1 2dy\frac{\pi}{2}$$

$$=\frac{\rho c V_0^2 2k^2}{2\pi\kappa_0^4}=\frac{1}{2}\rho c V_0^2\frac{2\alpha^4}{\pi c^2} \tag{12.298}$$

Each corner of the plate radiates sound as if it were a simple source radiating into semispace (see Eq. 12.91):

$$N_s=\frac{1}{4}\cdot\frac{\rho c V_0^2}{2\pi}\frac{2k^2}{\kappa_0^4}=\frac{1}{2}\cdot\frac{1}{2}k^2\frac{\rho c(2Q_H)^2}{4\pi} \tag{12.299}$$

Hence,

$$Q_H=\frac{V_0}{\kappa_0^2}=\left(\frac{2}{\pi}\right)^2 V_0\left(\frac{\lambda_B}{4}\right)^2 \tag{12.300}$$

Each corner radiates as if its volume flow were that of a quarter of a nodal area of the plate.

The frequency dependence of κ_0 compensates that of the source or dipole, and the resultant sound power generated by the free or the rigidly supported plate is independent of the frequency. The last results show that the rigidly supported plate is a much better sound radiator at low frequencies than the freely suspended plate. Because of the supported edges, the canceling effect between successive maxima and minima is smaller,[25] and sound radiation is considerably greater.

Sound Radiation of a Finite Plate, Excited in Single Vibrational Mode—Exact Computation

In the preceding sections, the sound radiation of a plate was computed on the basis of the power spectrum of the plate vibration. The results were exact if $\kappa l/2 \gg 1$ in the integrand for the sound power, so that the x, y-integral in Equation 12.262 could be replaced by a delta function. This assumption was equivalent to assuming that the main contribution of the power spectrum of the plate vibration arises from wave numbers whose wavelength is not very different from the sound wave length and that the plate has a length and width greater than the sound wavelength. The sound power, then, is a function only of the power spectrum of the velocity distribution and of the sound wavelength. The advantage of the preceding

[25] See p. 404, Fig. 12.12.

derivations is their generality; their disadvantage is that they do not apply to small plates.

In this section we are concerned with the accurate determination of the sound radiation of plates of any size that vibrate in only one plate mode. The computations can then be based on Rayleigh's integral (Eq. 12.125), and the resulting integrals can be evaluated in a relatively simple manner. If more than one plate mode is excited, the sound pressure is obtained (because of the linearity of the equations) by adding the pressures generated individually by each plate mode. However, the sound power is no longer equal to the sum of the sound powers that would be generated separately by each plate mode. The terms that describe the space distribution of the sound pressures generated by single modes are no longer simple natural functions (and consequently are not orthogonal over the plate area, unless the large plate approximation is introduced), and the mixed products, when integrated over space, do not vanish. The sound power, then, is dependent not only on the power spectrum of the plate vibration, but on all the details of the vibration pattern of the plate.

For a one-dimensional vibration pattern that is symmetrical with respect to $x=0$ and has a minimum or maximum at $x=0$, the velocity amplitude of the plate vibration can be represented by:

$$v(x)=V_0\cos\kappa_0 x \qquad \text{or} \qquad v(x)=V_0\sin\kappa_0 x \tag{12.301}$$

The sound pressure at a great distance from the plate is given by Rayleigh's integral (Eq. 12.125 and Fig. 12.14):

$$r\bar{P}=\frac{jk\rho ce^{-jkr}}{2\pi}\int_{-l_1/2}^{l_1/2}\int_{-l_2/2}^{l_2/2} v(x)e^{-jk(\alpha x+\beta y)}\,dxdy$$

$$=j\frac{k\rho c}{2\pi}e^{-jkr}\,l_2\frac{\sin\dfrac{k\beta l_2}{2}}{\dfrac{k\beta l_2}{2}}\int_{-l_1/2}^{l_1/2} v(x)e^{-jk\alpha x}\,dx \tag{12.302}$$

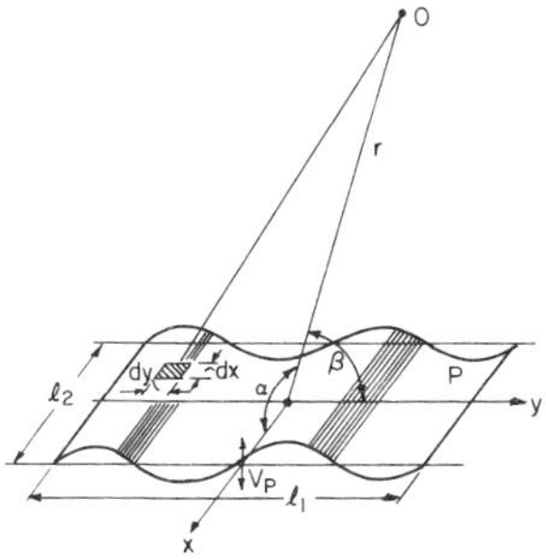

Fig. 12.14 Co-ordinate system for computing the radiated pressure field.

and

$$|rP| = \left| \frac{k\rho c}{2\pi} l_2 \frac{\sin \frac{k\beta l_2}{2}}{\frac{k\beta l_2}{2}} S_v(k\alpha) \right| \tag{12.303}$$

where $S_v(k\alpha)$ is the Fourier transform of the plate velocity for the wave number $\kappa \rightarrow k\alpha$, as given in Figure 12.12 for the various cases; l_1 is the length of the plate in the direction of the vibration pattern, and l_2 is its width; $\alpha = \cos(x, r_0) = \cos\theta$, $\beta = \cos(y, r_0)$, and r_0 is the radius vector to the center of the plate. $S_v(k\alpha) = S_v(k\cos\theta)$ is identical with the directivity factor of the sound radiation of the plate.

Directivity characteristics are discussed in detail in most of the textbooks on acoustics. In the theory of noise and vibration isolation we usually do not care about the detailed pattern of the radiated sound, but are predominantly concerned with the total sound power generated by the vibrator. We shall, therefore, confine ourselves here to the computation of the sound power. Let the x-axis be the polar axis of a polar co-ordinate system, let θ be the angle between this axis and the radius vector r, and let φ be the azimuth (Fig. 12.15). We then have:

$$y = r \sin\theta \sin\varphi$$

$$\beta = \cos(y, r) = \vec{r} \cdot \vec{y}_0 = \frac{y}{r} = \sin\theta \sin\varphi \tag{12.304}$$

where $\vec{y}_0$ is the unit vector in the y-direction. The elementary space angle then is:

$$d\Omega = \sin\theta \, d\theta d\varphi \tag{12.305}$$

The sound power is obtained by integrating the square of the far-field pressure over a hemisphere of radius r:[26]

$$N = \int_0^{2\pi} d\varphi \int_0^{\pi/2} \frac{P^2 r^2}{2\rho c} \sin\theta d\theta$$

$$= \frac{k^2 \rho c}{8\pi^2} l_2^2 \int_0^{2\pi} d\varphi \int_0^{\pi/2} \left[\frac{\sin\left(\frac{kl_2}{2} \sin\theta\cos\varphi\right)}{\frac{kl_2}{2}\sin\theta\cos\varphi} \right]^2 |S_v^2(k\cos\theta)| \sin\theta d\theta \tag{12.306}$$

The φ-integral can be evaluated by series development and by integrating term by term.[27] For small values of $kl_2/2$, the following result is valuable:

[26] This computation was performed by K. Gösele, "Schallabstrahlung von Platten, die zu Biegeschwingungen angeregt sind," *Acustica*, **3** (1953), 243. Gösele did not include the factor sin θ and integrated the angles over φ and $\sphericalangle(r, y)$ between 0 and π.

This procedure leads to the correct result in the one-dimensional case, because the factors sin θ cancel; but for two-dimensional vibrations, integration must be performed over a hemisphere.

[27] See H. Stenzel, *Leitfaden zur Berechnung von Schallvorgangen* (Berlin, 1939), p. 44.

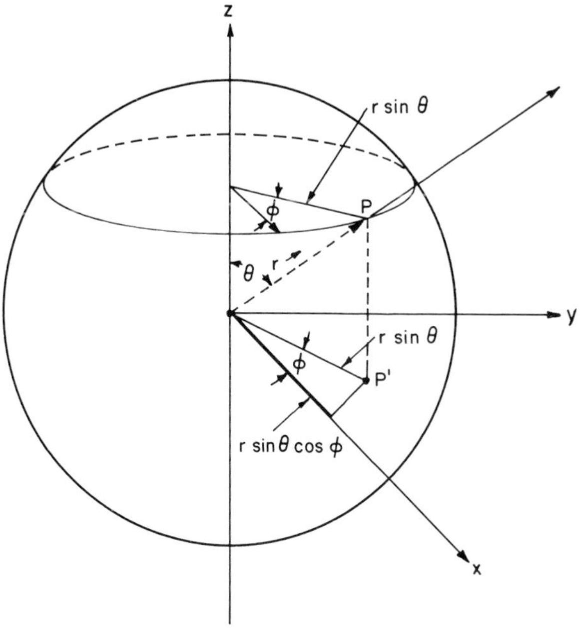

Fig. 12.15 Spherical co-ordinates.

$$\phi=\frac{2}{\pi}\int_0^{\pi/2}\frac{\sin^2\left(\frac{kl_2}{2}\sin\theta\cos\varphi\right)}{\left(\frac{kl_2}{2}\sin\theta\cos\varphi\right)^2}d\varphi=1-\frac{\left(\frac{k'l_2}{2}\right)^2}{3\cdot 1!2!}+\frac{\left(\frac{k'l_2}{2}\right)^4}{5\cdot 2!3!}-\frac{\left(\frac{k'l_2}{2}\right)^6}{7\cdot 3!4!} \tag{12.307}$$

where

$$k'=k\sin\theta \tag{12.308}$$

For larger values of $kl_2/2$, development into Bessel's functions leads to a series that converges very fast:

$$\phi=\frac{1}{\frac{kl_2}{2}}[J_1(k'l_2)+2J_3(k'l_2)+2J_5(k'l_2)+\ldots] \tag{12.309}$$

Figure 12.16 represents $x\phi(x)$ as a function of $x=(kl_2/2)\sin\theta$. The curve

Fig. 12.16 Solution of the ϕ-integral.

shows that whenever $x > 1$, the integral is very nearly equal to $1/x$. This result is very plausible: Whenever the linear dimensions of a radiator exceed half the wave length, the radiation impedance becomes constant and very nearly equal to ρc. Thus, the integral $(0 \leq \varphi \leq 2\pi)$ is very nearly equal to $2\pi\psi \doteq (4\pi/kl_2) \sin \theta$. We are left with the θ-integration. The factors sin θ cancel, and

$$N = \frac{\rho c k l_2}{2\pi} \int_0^{\pi/2} |S_v{}^2(k \cos \theta)| d\theta \tag{12.310}$$

Let us consider the case illustrated in Figure 12.12*a*, where the plate velocity is $V_0 \sin \kappa_0 x$ and the plate is rigidly supported at its edges. The integral then becomes:

$$\int_0^{\pi/2} \frac{4V_0{}^2 \kappa_0{}^2 \sin^2\left(\frac{kl}{2} \cos \theta\right) d\theta}{(\kappa_0{}^2 - k^2 \cos^2 \theta)^2} \tag{12.311}$$

For low frequencies, $\kappa_0{}^2 \gg (k^2 l^2/2) \cos^2 \theta$, and the integral simplifies to:

$$\frac{4V_0{}^2}{\kappa_0{}^2} \int_0^{\pi/2} \sin^2\left(\frac{kl}{2} \cos \theta\right) d\theta = \frac{4V_0{}^2}{\kappa_0{}^2} \int_0^{\pi/2} \frac{1 - \cos(kl \cos \theta)}{2} d\theta$$

$$= \frac{V_0{}^2 \pi}{\kappa_0{}^2} [1 - J_0(kl)] \tag{12.312}$$

and the sound power generated per unit width of the plate becomes:

$$N_0 = \frac{N}{l_2} = \frac{1}{2} \rho c \frac{k V_0{}^2}{\kappa_0{}^2} [1 - J_0(kl)] \tag{12.313}$$

If the velocity distribution has a maximum at $x = 0$ $(V = V_0 \cos \kappa_0 x)$ and the plate is rigidly supported, a similar result is obtained, except that the minus sign in front of the Bessel's function is replaced by a plus sign:

$$N_0 = \frac{N}{l_2} = \frac{1}{2} \frac{\rho c k V_0{}^2}{\kappa_0{}^2} [1 + J_0(kl)] \tag{12.314}$$

Because the mean velocity over the plate is different from zero, the sound power now is finite at very low frequencies, when $kl \ll 1$.

If the plate is free at its edges and has zero velocity at the center, so that the mean plate velocity is zero, the sound power follows from Equation 12.310 with S_v $(k \cos \theta)$ as given by Figure 12.16*b* and $\kappa = k \cos \theta$:

$$N = \frac{4\rho c k^2 l_2 V_0{}^2}{2\pi} \int_0^{\pi/2} \frac{\cos^2 \theta \cos^2\left(\frac{kl}{2} \cos \theta\right) d\theta}{(\kappa_0{}^2 - k^2 \cos^2 \theta)^2} \tag{12.315}$$

Integration can be performed if $\kappa_0{}^2 \gg k^2$. The integral then becomes:

$$\frac{1}{\kappa_0{}^4}\int_0^{\pi/2} (1-\sin^2\theta)\frac{1+\cos(kl\cos\theta)}{2}d\theta=\frac{1}{4\kappa_0{}^4}\left[\pi-\frac{\pi}{2}+\pi J_0(kl)-\frac{\pi\cdot 3}{2kl}J_1(kl)\right]$$

$$=\frac{\pi}{8\kappa_0{}^4}\left[1+2J_0(kl)-\frac{3J_1(kl)}{kl}\right] \quad (12.316)$$

and the sound power is given by the following expression, with the non-bracketed signs:

$$N_0=\frac{N}{l_2}=\frac{\rho ck^3V_0{}^2}{4\kappa_0{}^4}[1(\pm)2J_0(kl)(\mp)3J_1(kl)] \quad (12.317)$$

If the center of the plate is a velocity maximum, the mean plate velocity is finite, and the sound power is given by the above expression, with the bracketed signs.

The results in this section (Equations 12.313 and 12.317 are identical to those of the preceding section (Equations 12.295 and 12.287), except for the Bessel's functions. These terms decrease rapidly with kl; they represent the interaction of the two edges of the plate whenever their distance is small. The situation is very similar to that depicted in Figure 12.7 for two line sources.

We note that the sound radiation at very low frequencies depends on the out-of-balance volume flow. If the total volume flow that is generated by the vibrating plate is zero, the Bessel's functions in the solution cancel the constant term, and the sound power generated by the plate is zero. But if the total volume flow is different from zero, and the edges of the plate are closer to each other than half a sound wavelength, then the sound pressures generated by the two edges interact, and the sound generated by the plate is twice as great as when the two edges are far apart.

At high frequencies, the radiation impedance is ρc, and the sound power is:

$$N_0=\frac{1}{2}\rho c\frac{V_0{}^2}{2} \quad (12.318)$$

for one-dimensional vibration patterns, and half as much for two-dimensional patterns.

The integrals can be evaluated only approximately at the coincidence frequency, and it seems that the radiation resistance then is $n\rho c$,[28] where n is the number of wave lengths of the vibration pattern of the plate. Figure 12.17 shows the directivity pattern $S_v(\kappa\cos\theta)$ for a plate that is excited to progressive waves ($\bar{V}=V_0\,e^{j\kappa_0 x}$); Figures 12.18 and 12.19 show the sound power that is radiated by a plate excited to standing and progressive waves, as derived by K. Gösele.[29]

[28] See K. Gösele, *loc. cit.*
[29] *Ibid.*

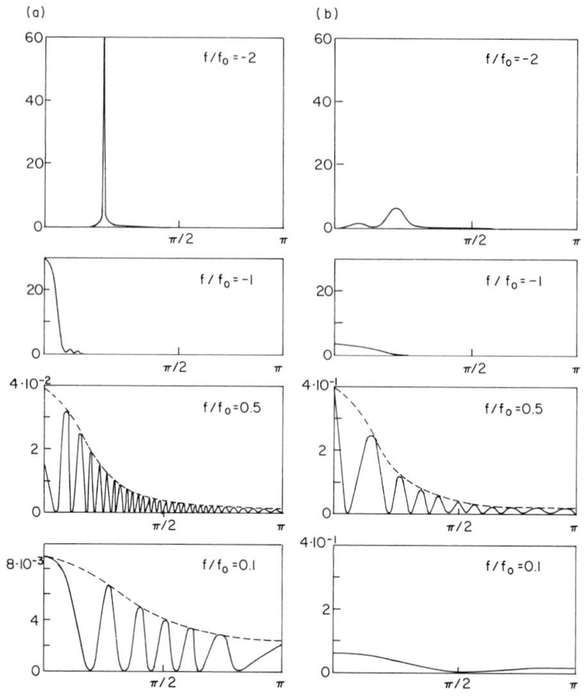

Fig. 12.17 Angular distribution of radiated energy for a finite plate at various frequencies; *a*, large plate ($l/\lambda_0=30$); *b*, small plate ($l/\lambda_0=3$). From K. Gösele, *loc. cit.*

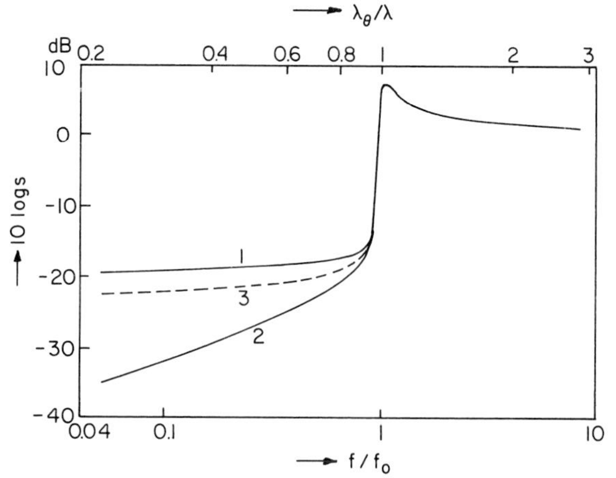

Fig. 12.18 Comparison of the radiated power of a finite plate ($l/\lambda_0=30$) for standing and progressive waves; *a*, standing waves, node at plate edge; *b*, progressive waves; *c*, standing waves, loop at plate edge. From K. Gösele, *loc. cit.*

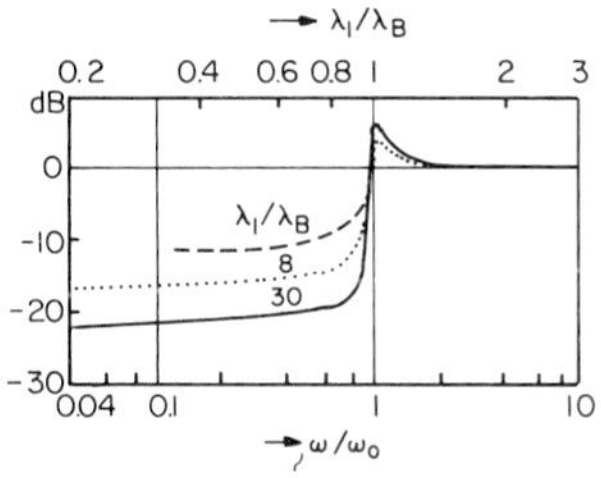

Fig. 12.19 Relation between the radiated sound energy and the normalized frequency (f/f_0) for three different lengths of a plate; *broken curve*, $l_1/\lambda_0=3$; *dotted curve*, $l_1/\lambda_0=8$; *solid curve*, $l_1/\lambda_0=30$. From K. Gösele, *loc. cit.*

Two-Dimensional Plate Vibrations

If the plate vibration is two-dimensional, the sound pressure is given by:

$$p=\frac{k\rho cV_0}{2\pi}\int\int v(x)v(y)e^{-jk(\alpha x-\beta y)}\,dxdy=\frac{k\rho c}{2\pi}V_0S_{v(x)}(k\alpha)S_{v(y)}(k\beta) \quad (12.319)$$

where

$$V=V_0v(x)v(y) \quad (12.320)$$

is the prescribed plate velocity and $S_{v(x)}$ and $S_{v(y)}$ are the Fourier coefficients of the plate vibration. The sound power then is given by:

$$N=\frac{1}{2}\int\frac{p^2}{\rho c}\,d\Omega$$

$$=\frac{k^2\rho cV_0{}^2}{8\pi^2}\int_0^{2\pi}d\varphi\int_0^{\pi/2}[S_{v(x)}(k\cos\theta)]^2\sin\theta d\theta[S_{v(y)}(k\sin\theta\sin\varphi)]^2 \quad (12.321)$$

The rigorous evaluation of this integral is very difficult, but an approximate solution can be obtained by replacing $\sin^2(kl/2\cos\theta)$ and $\sin^2[kl/2\cos(r,y)]$ by one half. The results, then, are the same as those obtained in the preceding sections.

Circular Membrane or a Plate Vibrating in One of Its Radial Modes

The velocity of a membrane or of a circular plate of radius a at a radial mode is given with good approximation by:

$$v_\nu=V_\nu J_0\left(\frac{\gamma_\nu\rho}{a}\right) \quad (12.322)$$

where the terms γ_ν are the roots of the equation $J_0(\gamma_\nu)=0$ and ρ is the length of the radius vector from the center of the plate. The sound pressure at a great distance from the plate or membrane is:

$$e^{jkr}r\bar{P} = j\frac{k\rho c}{2\pi}\int_0^{\alpha}\int_0^{2\pi} V_\nu J_0\left(\frac{\gamma_\nu \rho}{a}\right)\rho d\rho e^{-jk\rho \sin\theta \cos\varphi}\, d\varphi dr \qquad (12.323)$$

where θ and φ are spherical co-ordinates of the field point and ρ is the radius vector in the disk or membrane. The φ-integral is a Bessel's function,[30] and

$$e^{jkr}r\bar{P} = jk\rho c V_\nu \int_0^a J_0\left(\frac{\gamma_\nu \rho}{a}\right) J_0(k\rho \sin\theta)\rho d\rho$$

$$= \frac{k\rho c V_\nu a^2 \gamma_\nu J_1(\gamma_\nu) J_0(ka \sin\theta)}{\gamma_\nu^2 - k^2 a^2 \sin^2\theta} \qquad (12.324)$$

since $J_0(\gamma_\nu)=0$ because of the boundary condition for the membrane or the rigidly supported plate.

The smallest root of $J_0(\gamma)=0$ represents the first radial mode; the second smallest, the second radial mode; and so on. For the second and the higher radial modes, the Bessel's functions can be replaced by their asymptotic expressions:

$$J_0(ka \sin\theta) = \left(\frac{2}{\pi ka \sin\theta}\right)^{\frac{1}{2}} \cos\left(ka \sin\theta - \frac{\pi}{4}\right)$$

$$J_1(\gamma_\nu) = \left(\frac{2}{\pi\gamma_\nu}\right)^{\frac{1}{2}} \cos\left(\gamma_\nu - \frac{3\pi}{4}\right)$$

$$= \left(\frac{2}{\pi\gamma_\nu}\right)^{\frac{1}{2}} \cos(\nu - 1)\pi = \pm\left(\frac{2}{\pi\gamma_\nu}\right)^{\frac{1}{2}} \qquad (12.325)$$

The roots γ_ν then are given with sufficient accuracy by:

$$\gamma_\nu = \left(\nu - \frac{1}{4}\right)\pi \cong \nu\pi \quad \text{and} \quad \omega_\nu = \frac{\gamma_\nu^2 \omega_{1p}}{\gamma_1^2} \qquad (12.326)$$

where ω_{1p} is the fundamental resonance of the membrane (see Eq. 9.55). We shall assume that the sound wavelength is much greater than the distance between the nodal circles, so that $\gamma_\nu^2 \gg k^2a^2$.

The directivity pattern will then be given by:

$$|rP| = \rho c V_\nu \frac{a^2}{\gamma_\nu^{\frac{3}{2}}} \sqrt{\frac{2}{\pi}} J_0(ka \sin\theta) \qquad (12.327)$$

The sound power is found by integrating the square of the far-field pressure over a hemisphere:

[30] See E. Jahnke and F. Emde, *Tables of Functions* (New York, 1945).

$$N=\int_0^{2\pi}\int_0^{\pi/2}\frac{r^2P_1^2}{2\rho c}\sin\theta d\theta d\varphi$$

$$=\frac{\rho c V_\nu^2}{2}\cdot\frac{4a^4k^2}{\gamma_\nu^3}\int_0^{\pi/2}J_0^2(ka\sin\theta)\sin\theta d\theta \tag{12.328}$$

For a loud-speaker membrane ka is usually small, and the cosine factor that asymptotically represents $J_0(ka \sin\theta)$ can be replaced by one. The integral then is one, and the sound power becomes:

$$N=\left(\frac{\rho c}{2}V_\nu^2\pi a^2\cdot\frac{k^2a^2}{2}\right)\frac{8}{\pi\gamma_\nu^3}=N_p\cdot\frac{8}{\pi\gamma_\nu^3} \tag{12.329}$$

The expression in the bracket represents the sound power that is generated by a piston membrane, and the factor, the reduction of the sound power because of the nodal circles. For the fundamental, this factor is 0.183 (because $\gamma_1=2.405$); for the higher-order modes $\gamma_\nu\approx\nu\pi$, and this factor is $0.081/\nu^3$. Equation 12.329 could also have been derived by integrating Equation 12.322 over the membrane and determining the volume flow:

$$Q_H^2=8\pi a^4\frac{V_\nu^2}{\gamma_\nu^3} \tag{12.330}$$

Because in this computation the membrane is assumed to be small ($k^2a^2\ll 1$), the various Huygens' zones and the central zone are strongly coupled, and the sound power turns out to be greater by a factor $(\pi/2)^2$ than the power generated by half the outermost Huygens' zones.

If the diameter of the membrane is greater than about half the sound wavelength, the Bessel's function in the integral (12.328) can be replaced by its asymptotic development. The integral is then $1/ka$ (the same result is obtained by a more accurate evaluation, if $k^2a^2\gg 1$), and the sound power becomes:

$$N=\frac{k\rho c V_\nu^2}{2}\frac{4a^3}{\gamma_\nu^3}=\frac{k\rho c}{2}\frac{Q_H^2}{2}\cdot 2\pi a \tag{12.331}$$

The frequency variation is the same as that of a line source (Eq. 12.122) that is represented by the sound form of the right-hand side. Here we assume that the length of the line source is that of the circumference of the membrane. The volume flow per unit length of the equivalent line source thus is given by:

$$Q_H^2=\frac{8a^3V_\nu^2}{2\pi a\gamma_\nu^3}=\left(\frac{2}{\pi\gamma_\nu}V_\nu^2\right)\frac{4a^2}{\gamma_\nu^2}$$
$$=V_{\text{edge}}^2\cdot\left(\frac{\lambda_B}{\sqrt{2\pi}}\right)^2=V_{\text{edge}}^2\cdot\left(\frac{\lambda_B}{4.44}\right)^2 \tag{12.332}$$

where $\lambda_B=2\pi a/\gamma_\nu$ is the bending wavelength in the membrane. Again, the sound power is given by the unbalanced half of the outermost Huygens' zone. Because the boundary is circular, the effective width of this half zone is not exactly $\lambda_B/4$, but is $\lambda_B/4.44$. This result also shows that a circular line source of large diameter radiates by a factor $8/\pi^2$ less power per unit length than an infinitely long and straight line source of the same volume flow.

The central Huygens' half zone radiates power that, as can easily be shown, is smaller by a factor $(ka/\gamma_\nu)\cdot\pi^6/128=0.75\ \lambda_B/\lambda$ than the power that is generated by the edge effect.

If the edge is free, and we neglect the edge distortion, the edge corresponds to a maximum of the velocity amplitude and $\partial J_0(\kappa r)/\partial r=0$. The resultant volume flow then is zero and the edge radiation approaches that of a dipole source.

The volume flow that is generated by the plate up to a radius r is proportional to $J_1(\kappa r)$ (see Eq. 9.56) and the contribution of successive Huygens zones cancel each other, if their width Δr is equal to the distance between two successive zeroes of the function $J_1(\kappa r)$, or what amounts to the same, if their limits are between two successive vibration maxima of opposite phase. Asymptotically, this distance is equal to half a bending wavelength.

Because no driving force is applied at the center, the natural mode pattern is not disturbed, and provided $n>1$ the region near the center of the plate does not radiate sound, whether the plate is driven at a resonance or not. The sound radiation of the region in the immediate vicinity of the force, therefore, is not affected by the contribution of higher order circular plate modes. In computing this radiation, the velocity $v_c=F_0/Z_c$ has to be substituted that would be generated if the plate were infinite. This result can easily be verified by considering the solution (Eq. 8.71) for a point force that is applied to a circular plate. The constant B′ is very small and can be neglected. The solution then consists of the contribution of a natural mode $J_0(\kappa r)$ and of the Y_0 and $2K_0$ terms in the bracket. The bracket approaches the function $H_0^{(2)}(\kappa r)$ as soon as $\kappa r>\pi$ or $r>\lambda_B/2$, but the motion described by $H_0^{(2)}(\kappa r)$ does not generate sound at low frequencies. Therefore, the sound that is generated because of the distortion of the natural vibration pattern by the applied point force originates from the region $r=0$, to $r\approx\lambda_B/2$.

If the membrane exhibits nodal lines, $v_\nu=V_{\nu n}J_n(\gamma_{n\nu}\ r/a)$. cos $(n\varphi)$, where $J_n(\gamma_{n\nu})=0$; $J_1(\gamma_\nu)$ on the right-hand side of Equation 12.324 has to be replaced by $J_{n-1}\ (\gamma_{n\nu})$, and $J_0(ka \sin\theta)$ by $J_n(ka\sin\theta)$. The computations then can be performed in practically the same manner.

Summary of Sound Radiation

The sound field produced by a complex vibrator always consists of a near field, resulting from the streaming motion and the pressure equalization between the adjacent areas that move in opposition to one another, and of an energy-carrying sound field that is radiated to greater distances. The near-field sound pressure decreases at least as rapidly as $1/r^2$, if the generator is a dipole source; and it decreases exponentially with distance (by 2π Nepers every time the distance is increased by one bending wavelength at the coincidence frequency), if the generator exhibits many nodal lines and the sound wavelength is greater than twice the distance between the nodal lines. The near field depends on the shape of the vibrator and on all the details of the velocity distribution; it can be estimated, but it can rarely be computed accurately. The near-field sound pressure seems to be responsible for the low-frequency noise in the immediate vicinity of the vibrator, but it is unimportant at distances greater than a coincidence bending wavelength from the vibrator.

The sound pressure radiated to greater distances is due to the generation of sound energy by the vibrating surface against the component of pressure in phase with its velocity amplitude. The sound fields generated by vibrators more than half a wavelength apart can be considered as spatially uncorrelated (Fig. 12.7), and the energies add as if there were no interaction between the various vibrators. This fact makes it possible to compute the sound radiation of a complex system by adding up the energy contributions of the individual radiating elements. The task is to determine the sound-radiating elements and to analyze them.

The sound field produced by a sound vibrator may be developed into a series of spherical waves. If the dimensions of the vibrator are small, i.e., if

$$kR<1 \qquad \text{or} \qquad R<\frac{\lambda}{2\pi} \tag{12.333}$$

(where $2R$ is the greatest linear dimension of the vibrator, $k=2\pi/\lambda$ is the wave number, and λ is the wavelength), and if the vibrator generates sound because of a periodic change in its volume, the lowest term in the series expansion is found to predominate. This term is given by:

$$p=\frac{jk\rho c Q e^{-jkr}}{4\pi r} \tag{12.334}$$

where Q is the total volume flow of the source (surface area multiplied by the average velocity v over the area) and r is the distance from the vibrator. This source generates the power

$$N=\sigma r_s \langle V^2 \rangle \tag{12.335}$$

where

$$r_s=\frac{\rho c k^2 \sigma}{4\pi} \tag{12.336}$$

is the radiation resistance per unit area referred to the average velocity V of the vibrator and σ is the area of the vibrator.

If the vibrator is rigid and does not change its volume during vibration, the second term is the leading term in the series expansion of the sound field. This term is given by Equation 12.87 and has been discussed above.[31]

At higher frequencies, i.e., when

$$kr>2 \quad \text{and} \quad k>\frac{\lambda}{\pi} \tag{12.337}$$

the radiation impedance becomes equal to ρc for all spherical wave components in the series development of the sound field. We may, therefore, assume that the radiation impedance is ρc whenever the diameter of the sound source is larger than the wavelength or whenever the distance between the nodal lines of the vibrator is greater than the wavelength.

Between the low-frequency and the high-frequency solutions given above there is a transition range, almost an octave wide, where the radiation resistance depends on the particular shape of the vibrator and the details of its velocity distribution. Rubinovicz has shown[32] that for a plane vibrator of constant velocity amplitude over its surface or for an opaque screen the sound field always consists of two components. One component is determined by the laws of geometrical optics; the second is a diffraction component generated by the boundary of the vibrator, as if this boundary consisted of a linear source distribution. The boundary field gives rise to interferences that cause oscillations in the frequency curve, but on the average have only little effect on the intensity. Seemingly, similar laws would also apply to nonplanar vibrators, too, provided that they do not exhibit a nodal line pattern, and it appears justified to theorize that every sound field consists of a simple field produced by the bulk area of the vibrator and an interference field that originates at the boundary of the vibrator.

Because a sphere has no abrupt boundary curve, its interference field is particularly small. We may, therefore, expect the sphere to represent the prototype of a vibrator without nodal lines and expect the sound field of any other similar vibrator to deviate from that of the sphere by unimportant fluctuations in the transition range between the low- and the high-frequency solution. This contention does hold, as illustrated by Figure 12.5, which shows the radiation resistance of a sphere and of a piston membrane as a function of the frequency. Even the equivalent masses are found to be nearly the same, although there is no theoretical background for this result. It is hardly worthwhile to consider the intricate solution of the piston membrane and other vibrators, since a simple sphere gives as good a solution, and, moreover, it is free from details that have no bearing on practical cases.

The prototype of a vibrator with many nodal lines is the rectangular or circular plate excited to bending vibrations; important information about

[31] See pp. 365.
[32] *Loc. cit.*

such vibrations can be obtained from an analysis of the sound field of an infinite plate. The infinite and the finite plates have been studied in detail in the preceding sections.

Bending vibrations whose amplitude varies sinusoidally with distance generate sound only if the space wavelength of the bending pattern is greater than the sound wavelength. If this is the case, the radiation impedance is very nearly equal to ρc per unit area. If the bending wavelength is shorter than the sound wavelength (which happens at low frequencies), a wattless type of flow, that is not accompanied by sound radiation is generated. The vibrator is said to work in acoustic short circuit. But even such a vibrator generates some sound, because of the distortion of the sinusoidal vibration field in the vicinity of the point of attack of the driving force and because of the discontinuity of the vibration field near the edges of the vibratoı.

The distortion of the vibration field by the driving force generates an extra volume flow, which in the one-dimensional case is equivalent to a simple line source. In the two-dimensional case, a modified Huygens' principle is found to apply. A point force generates outgoing bending waves; successive annular zones of a width of half a bending wavelength have opposite phase. Successive halves of such zones are found to cancel each other in their effect on sound radiation. The sound power then is exclusively due to the volume flow generated by the first half of the first circular zone, which is left over in this canceling process; it can easily be computed. This contribution is equivalent to the sound field that is directly generated by the low-order modes that are not acoustically short-circuited. It can also be computed statistically.

If the external force is of the nature of a point force or a line force, it excites practically all the natural modes of the svstem to forced vibrations. It excites the low-order modes that resonate at frequencies considerably below the frequency of the force. For these modes the distance between the nodal lines is considerably larger than half the sound wavelength.[33] They are not acoustically short-circuited, and their radiation resistance is very nearly equal to ρc. The sound pressure can, therefore, be computed by summing up the contributions of the low-order modes up to the mode number at which they enter the acoustic short circuit; that is, at which their radiation resistance becomes zero. This number is determined by the number of grid points in the frequency plane inside a quadrant (m, n-positive) of a circle of radius ω, where

$$\omega^2 = \left(\frac{m^2}{l_1^2} + \frac{n^2}{l_2^2}\right) \cdot \pi^2 c^2 \qquad m, n = 1, 2, 3, \ldots \tag{12.338}$$

From a practical viewpoint, it does not make much difference at the higher

[33] Since the bending-wave velocity $c_B = \alpha\sqrt{\omega}$ is proportional to the square root of the frequency, high-order modes need not be acoustically short-circuited, if the frequency of the driving force is sufficiently high.

frequencies whether the driver is exactly at the center of the plate or somewhat away from it. The sound power will be practically the same. We may, therefore, assume that the plate or the vibrator is driven exactly at its center, so that only odd natural modes ($m, n=1, 3, 5, 7, \ldots$) are excited.[34] The excitation constant κ_ν then is equal to one. The total number n of modes is found by dividing one quarter of the area of the circle of radius ω by the elementary area $2\pi c/l_1 \cdot 2\pi c/l_2$ that corresponds to the natural (odd) mode in the gird representation. Thus,

$$n=\frac{\pi}{4}\frac{\omega^2}{\pi^2 c^2}\frac{l_1 l_2}{4}=\frac{\pi}{16}\frac{\omega^2}{\omega_a \omega_b} \tag{12.339}$$

where

$$\omega_a=\frac{\pi c}{l_1} \quad \text{and} \quad \omega_b=\frac{\pi c}{l_2} \tag{12.340}$$

For a one-dimensional vibration pattern, this number is obtained by counting the number of the nodal lines:

$$n=\frac{l_1}{\lambda}=\frac{\omega}{2}\frac{l_1}{\pi c}=\frac{1}{2}\frac{\omega}{\omega_a} \tag{12.341}$$

The magnitude c is the sound velocity in the surrounding medium, and ω_a and ω_b are the fundamental resonant frequencies of two pipes filled with this medium. One pipe has a length equal to the length of the vibrator, and the other has a length equal to the width of the vibrator.

It has been shown that unless the linear dimensions of a vibrator are smaller than the wavelength, the sound power is proportional to the space-average square of the amplitude of the radiation modes. The resonant frequencies of the radiating modes are considerably lower than the frequency of the force. Their contributions, therefore, reduce to the parallel connection of the first N mode masses—M_ν in the equivalent electrical circuit (Fig. 1.11) that represents the mechanical system. Every mode corresponds to a series-resonant circuit, and all these circuits are in parallel. For sinusoidal vibration patterns, the mode masses are all equal, and the mean-square value becomes proportional to (see Eq. 7.52):

$$\sum\langle\xi_\nu^2\rangle=\sum\xi_\nu^2(A)\left|\frac{\langle\xi_\nu^2\rangle}{\xi_\nu^2(A)}\right|=\sum\xi_\nu^2(A)q_\nu \tag{12.342}$$

or to N times the value of one contribution, because for a point force or a line force the mode masses are equal, or nearly equal (see Fig. 1.11). The contribution of each radiating mode is the same, and since the density of the sound-radiating modes of a plate or a similar vibrator is constant in frequency space, the increase of the radiation resistance toward the coincidence frequency can easily be taken into account by assuming the value:

$$\sigma\rho c\int_0^1\frac{dz}{\sqrt{1-z^2}}=\rho c\frac{\pi}{2} \tag{12.343}$$

[34] The same result is obtained if we average over the various positions of the driving point, as done in the derivation of Eq. 12.235.

for the average radiation resistance per unit area of a one-dimensional mode. A similar result is obtained for a two-dimensional mode:

$$\frac{1}{4}\frac{\sigma\rho c}{\pi r^2}\int\int\frac{dxdy}{\sqrt{1-x^2-y^2}} \qquad r^2=x^2+y^2 \tag{12.344}$$

or for polar co-ordinates:

$$\frac{\sigma\rho c}{\pi}\int_0^1\frac{rdr2\pi}{\sqrt{1-r^2}}=\frac{2\pi\rho c}{\pi}=2\rho c \tag{12.345}$$

Since infinity for $r=1$ or $z=1$ is very weak, it does not really matter whether the radiation resistance actually becomes infinite at the coincidence frequency or stays finite, as it does for a vibrator of finite size; this can be illustrated with the aid of the curves shown in Figure 12.18. The radiation resistance represented in this figure can be approximated by the following expressions:

$$r_{\text{rad}}=\frac{\rho c}{\sqrt{1-\left(\frac{f_0}{f}\right)^2}} \qquad \text{if} \quad \frac{f}{f_0}<\alpha \tag{12.346}$$

and

$$r_{\text{rad}}=\frac{\rho c}{\sqrt{1-\alpha^2}} \qquad \text{if} \quad (1-\alpha)<\frac{f}{f_0}<1 \tag{12.347}$$

where α is a constant that has to be deduced from Figures 12.18 and 12.19. If this value is used in the integrand of Equation 12.343, the following value can be deduced for the radiation resistance:

$$r_{\text{rad}}=\rho c\left(\sin^{-1}\alpha+\frac{1-\alpha}{\sqrt{1-\alpha^2}}\right) \tag{12.348}$$

The curves in Figure 12.19 lead to $\alpha\approx 0.87$ for $l_1/\lambda_0=30$ (or $\alpha\approx 0.41$ for $l/\lambda_0=3$); the corresponding value of the radiation resistance is 1.32 ρc (or 1.07ρc) which is close enough to $(\pi/2)$ ρc, particularly if the plate is

The sound power that is generated by a one-dimensional vibrator of area σ at low frequencies is thus given by:

$$N=\frac{\sigma\rho c}{2}\frac{\pi}{2}\frac{F^2}{\omega^2M^2q_\nu}\frac{1}{2}\frac{\omega}{\omega_a}=\frac{1}{2}\rho c\frac{\sigma\pi F^2}{2\omega_a\omega M^2} \tag{12.349}$$

that generated by a two-dimensional vibrator, by:

$$N=\frac{\sigma\rho c}{2}\cdot 2\frac{F^2}{\omega^2M^2q_\nu}\cdot\frac{\pi}{16}\frac{\omega^2}{\omega_a\omega_b}=\frac{\sigma\pi\rho cF^2}{4\omega_a\omega_bM^2} \tag{12.350}$$

as has already been proved for the special case of a vibrating plate (Eqs. 12.196 and 12.210).

The sound radiation of a cylinder seems to be somewhat different from that of a plate, at least at first sight. The plate does not radiate sound whenever the sound wave number k is smaller than the resultant bending wave number $\kappa = (\kappa_x^2 + \kappa_y^2)^{\frac{1}{2}}$; thus whenever

$$k^2 < \kappa_x^2 + \kappa_y^2 \tag{12.351}$$

this case is called the acoustic short circuit. It seems that for the cylinder the acoustic short circuit was solely determined by the bending wave number in the axial direction, because the infinitely long cylinder does not radiate sound at all whenever

$$k^2 < \kappa_x^2 \tag{12.352}$$

regardless of the value of $\kappa_y = 2\pi/\lambda_y = 2\pi/2\pi R/n = n/R$.

However, the sound radiation of a cylinder (Eq. 12.111) is also proportional to the Hankel's function $H_n(\gamma r)$, and this function is very small if its argument is smaller than n, particularly if n is large (where $2n$ is the number of nodal lines in the circumferential direction). The reason that the sound radiation of the infinitely long cylinder is not zero, even if κ_y is very large, is the finite diameter of the cylinder. In fact, the sound radiation described by the Hankel's function $H_n(\gamma R)$ for $\gamma R < n$ is equivalent to the sound radiation at low frequencies of a plate of finite size, because of the discontinuity of the vibration pattern at its edges. Since for the cylinder canceling out can always be performed in $\lambda/4$ steps, the sound radiation of a cylinder with circumferential modes is extremely small at low frequencies and needs to be considered only if the driving force excites such modes in their resonance range so that their amplitude is many times larger than that of the axially symmetrical modes. In fact, the condition that the Hankel's function H_n^2 (γr) is not very small:

$$\gamma^2 R^2 < n^2$$

or

$$k^2 - \kappa_x^2 < \frac{n^2}{R^2} = \kappa_y^2,\ k^2 \cdot < \kappa_x^2 + \kappa_y^2 \tag{12.353}$$

is the same as the condition that describes the acoustic short circuit of a plate.

The sound radiation of a finite cylinder can be computed by the same method as for a plate. We can assume that the acoustic radiation resistance is zero, if

$$k^2 < \kappa_x^2 + \frac{n^2}{R^2} = \kappa_x^2 + \kappa_y^2 \tag{12.354}$$

because of the small value of the Hankel's function for $\gamma R < n$, and consequently integration for computing the sound power extends only from

$$\kappa_x = -\sqrt{k^2 - \kappa_y^2} \quad \text{to} \quad \sqrt{k^2 - \kappa_y^2} \tag{12.355}$$

instead of from $-k$ to $+k$, so that the pole $\gamma = 0$ in the radiation resistance $r_{\text{rad}} \approx k/\gamma \cdot \rho c$ is outside the range of integration. In the case of a plate, the pole in the radiation resistance is due to the sound energy that comes from infinite regions and travels grazingly to the plate. For a finite plate, such regions do not occur, and the radiation resistance is finite at all frequencies. (Its finite value is enforced in some of the computations by introducing a constant α under the square root, which has exactly the same effect as κ_y in the above formula.) The magnitude κ_y then determines the height of the peak in the radiation resistance. Because of the degeneracy of the modes of a cylinder, even-and odd-order modes being excited by a point force in the circumferential direction, Equation 12.350 has to be multiplied by a factor 2 for the cylinder. Thus, the same formulas apply for the sound radiation of a cylinder except for a factor 2 for the point force.

It is important that the sound power that is generated by a point or a line force at low frequencies is independent of the damping. Sound radiation at low frequencies is due to the forced excitation of the low-order modes at a frequency considerably below their resonant frequency. The loss resistance, therefore, does not affect the sound radiation.

The force also excited modes whose resonance frequency is similar to the frequency of excitation. Such modes vibrate with very large amplitudes and will contribute to sound radiation by secondary effects, such as the "edge effect." Because of the discontinuity of the vibration pattern at the edge of the plate, the space spectrum of the vibration field contains space-Fourier components form infinity to zero. The acoustically nonshort-circuited Fourier modes then generate sound. The detailed computation showed (see p. 405–408) that this sound radiation can be described by sources distributed along the edges of the vibrator, if the edge of the plate is rigidly supported, and by dipole sources if the edge is free. Since dipole sources are very poor sound radiators, such sources may be neglected whenever other sound sources are present. The result of the accurate computation shows that at low frequencies the same modified Huygens' principle seems also to apply for such modes. The contributions of the successive rings or strips of a width one fourth the bending wave length cancel each other, and we are left with the contributions of the zones near the boundary of the vibrator that did not cancel out in this process. Again, the computation of the sound power becomes very simple. For a one-dimensionally vibrating plate, regions of positive and of negative volume flow cancel each other, if their width is $\frac{1}{4}$ the bending wavelength or less (Fig. 12.20). This is also the principle that is basic to Huygens' zone constructions (Fig. 12.21). The

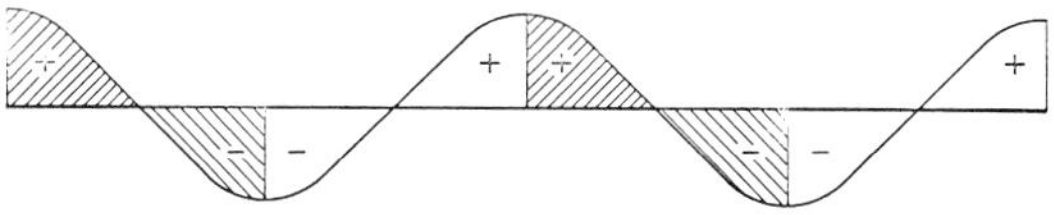

Fig. 12.20 Freely suspended plate radiates very little sound at low frequencies. Deviation of the sinusoidal vibration pattern near the edges of the plate leads to increased sound radiation because it is not balanced by a corresponding change of volume flow in the adjacent nodal area.

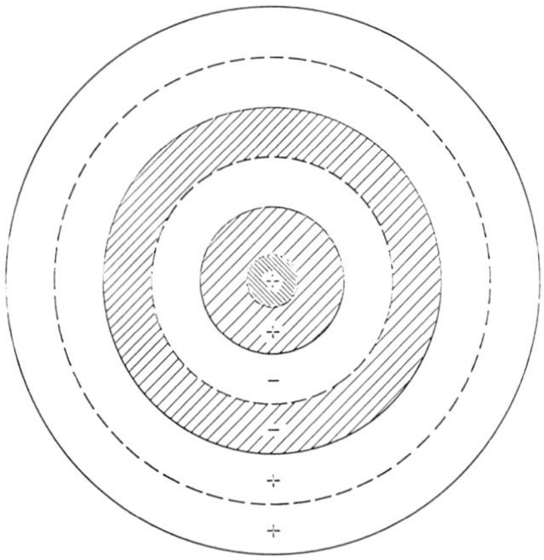

Fig. 12.21 Huyghens zone construction only works if second half of central (first) zone is balanced against first half of second zone, and second half of second zone against first half of third zone, etc.

second half of the first zone cancels the effect of the first half of the second zone, and so on. Finally we are left with the full effect of the first half zone and the unbalanced effect of the last zone. In applying Huygens' principle, it is not permissible to balance the effect of the whole first zone against that of the whole second zone, and so on. The reason is that zones of a width of $\lambda/2$ are already too wide to cancel each other completely; this is proved by computing the sound radiation of a plate. Sources of a width of $\lambda/2$ and of opposite sign contribute also by a boundary term. They act like line sources that are distributed over the two boundaries; they are not negligible (canceling a region of width $\lambda/4$ leads only to dipole sources at the boundaries, whose effect is evancescent if λ_B is small as compared to the sound wave length).

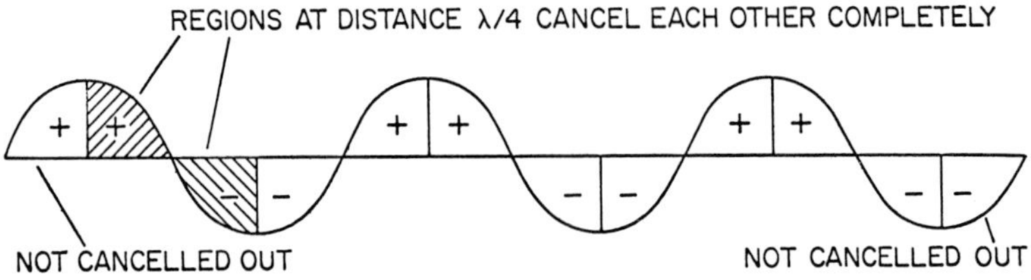

Fig. 12.22 Plate rigidly supported at its edges radiates sound at low frequencies.

If a one-dimensionally vibrating plate is supported at its edges (Fig. 12.22), regions of width $\lambda/4$ at its edges are uncanceled and act like line sources.

Because of the coupling between the two line sources, each source radiates an energy that differs by the factor:

$$1 \pm J_0(kl) \tag{12.356}$$

from what it would radiate if there were no coupling. This result has also been deduced by computing the sound radiation of a finite plate.

The above procedure can be easily generalized for two-dimensionally vibrating plates. Nodal areas of width and length $\lambda/4$ can be canceled against each other, and the edge effect is practically zero if the edges are free and the distribution of the vibration is strictly sinusoidal. If the edges are supported, all that is left is the corners, each of which contributes with the volume flow of one 1/16th nodal area.

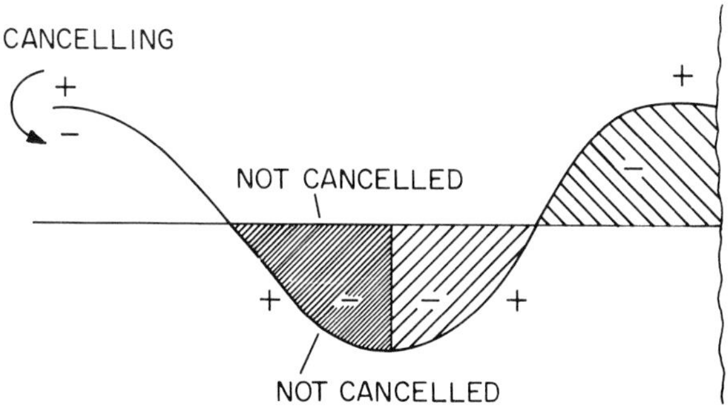

Fig. 12.23 Freely suspended plate not in a baffle generates sound at low frequencies, because regions of width $\lambda_B/4$ at a distance $\lambda_B/4$ from the edge at its upper and at its lower surface are unbalanced.

A similar method can be used to determine the sound radiation of a rectangular plate that is not enclosed in a baffle. If the edges are rigidly supported, the region next to the edge of width $\lambda/4$ will cancel the contribution of a similar region on the second surface of the plate. The remaining pattern on the surface of the plate can then be subdivided into regions of a width $\lambda/4$, and canceling out is compete. Therefore, such a plate will not radiate sound at low frequencies (see Fig. 12.23). In contrast, if the plate is vibrating in a one-dimensional pattern and has its edges free, we are left with two regions of width $\lambda/4$ at a distance $\lambda/4$ from each edge that act like line sources (as shown in Fig. 12.24), both at a distance $\lambda/4$ from the edge of the plate, one at its upper surface and the other at its lower surface. It can be shown that these two line sources interact as if they were approximately a distance $\lambda/2$ apart. Such a plate radiates sound, even at low frequencies.

In practice it will be sufficient to determine the edge effect for modes that are excited at or near these resonant frequencies and to neglect all the others. A line through the troughs of the frequency curve (see Fig. 12.24) of the

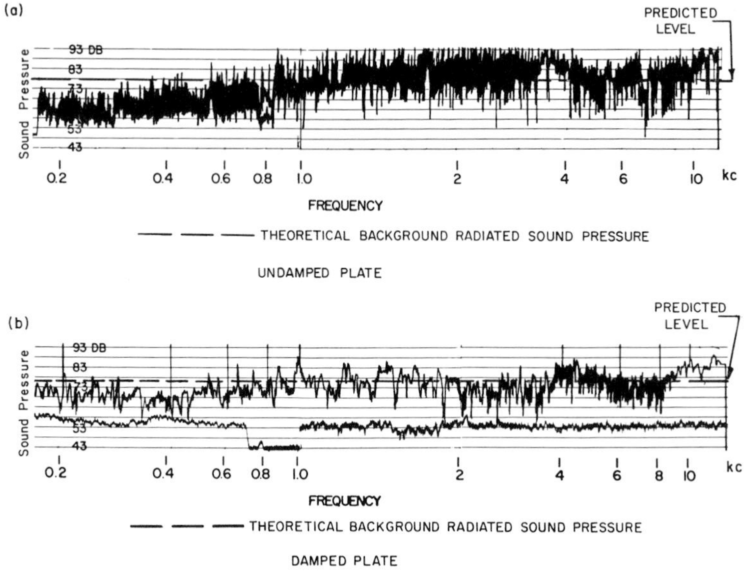

Fig. 12.24 Frequency curves of the sound pressure radiated by a large damped and a large undamped plate (reference sound-pressure level, 0.000204 dyne/cm^2); *a*, large undamped plate; *b*, large damped plate. From D. Greene, Master's thesis (1960), The Pennsylvania State University.

sound radiation will then represent the radiation of the low-order sound-radiating modes, and peaks will occur at all the resonant frequencies because of the edge effects of the resonating modes. If the amplitude distribution were also strictly sinusoidal near the edges, the edge would be negligible for a freely supported plate, for which the velocity at the edges is a maximum.

The bending-wave velocity in a plate increases proportionally to the square root of the frequency and at high frequencies exceeds the sound velocity in the adjacent medium. All modes then radiate as if the radiation impedance were ρc.

Damping will not affect the line through the troughs of the sound-pressure frequency curve, but it will reduce the height of the peaks (Fig. 12.24). If the vibrator acts in water, radiation damping will be very effective, and damping coatings will hardly affect sound radiation, unless they have very high damping qualities.

Recommended Reading

BAKER, B. B., AND E. T. COPSON, *The Mathematical Theory of Huygens' Principle,* Clarendon Press, Oxford, 1950.

BERANEK, L. L., *Acoustics,* McGraw-Hill, Inc., New York, 1954.

GÖSELE, K., "Schallabstrahlung von Platten, die zu Biegeschwingungen angeregt sind," *Acustica,* **3** (1953), 243.

HECKL, M., "Schallabstrahlung von Platten bei punktförmiger Anregung," *Acustica,* **9** (1959), 371–80.

HUNTER, J. L., *Acoustics,* Prentice-Hall, Inc., Englewood Cliffs, N. J., 1957.

KINSLER, L. E., AND R. FREY, *Fundamentals of Acoustics,* John Wiley & Sons, Inc., New York, 1962.

RAYLEIGH, LORD, *The Theory of Sound,* Macmillan and Co., Ltd., London, 1894.

RUBINOVICZ, A., "Die Beugungswelle in der Kirchhoffschen Theorie der Beugungserscheinungen," *Ann. Physik,* **53** (1917), 257; "Zur Kirchhoffschen Beugungstheorie," *Ann. Physik,* **73** (1924), 339.

SKUDRZYK, E. J., *Grundlagen der Akustik,* Springer Verlag, Vienna, 1954.

———, "Sound radiation of a system with a finite or infinite number of resonances," *J.A.S.A.,* **30** (1958), 1152.

STEPHENS, R. W. B., AND A. E. BATE, *Wave Motion and Sound,* Arnold, London, 1950.

XIII / THEORY OF VIBRATION INSULATION FOR A SYSTEM WITH MANY RESONANCES

Classical Theory

The classical theory of vibration insulation considers systems with only one resonant frequency. The source of vibration is usually pictured as an eccentric rotating shaft that generates a periodic force. The machinery is mounted on a heavy base, and the base is insulated from the ground by a layer of compliant material or by springs, as shown in Figure 13.1. The force that the compliant element transmits to the floor excites the walls and remote parts of the building. It is assumed that the system has only one resonance or that the external force excites only one of the natural modes of the system. The behavior of such a system is similar to that of a simple point-mass compliant element vibrator.

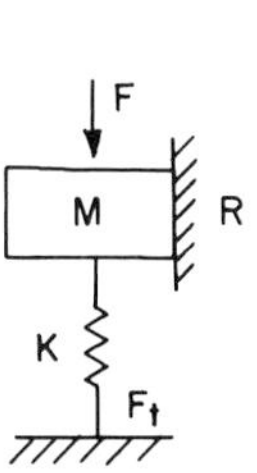

Fig. 13.1 Classical vibration insulation.

If the loss resistance of the compliant material is small as compared to its mechanical impedance ($R \ll 1/\omega K$), the magnitude of the transmitted force is given by the product of the deflection of the spring and its stiffness constant:

$$\bar{F}_t = \frac{1}{K}\hat{\xi} = \frac{\bar{V}}{j\omega K} = \frac{\bar{F}}{j\omega K\bar{Z}} \tag{13.1}$$

and the frequency curve of the transmitted force and that of the deflection are the same except for a factor $1/K$.

The transmission factor $\bar{T}$ is defined as the ratio of the transmitted force to the driving force. It is given by:

$$\bar{T}=\frac{\bar{F}_t}{\bar{F}}=\frac{1}{j\omega K\bar{Z}}=\frac{1}{j\omega K\left(R+j\omega M+\dfrac{1}{j\omega K}\right)}$$

$$=\frac{1}{j\omega KR+1-\omega^2 MK}=\frac{1}{j\eta+1-\dfrac{\omega^2}{\omega_0{}^2}} \tag{13.2}$$

as can be deduced directly from the circuit diagram shown in Figure 2.2. The velocity is equal to $\tilde{f}/\bar{Z}$, and the transmitted force (which corresponds to the electrical voltage across K) is equal to the product of the velocity and the impedance $1/j\omega K$. At low frequencies, $\omega \ll \omega_0$, and

$$\bar{T}=\frac{\bar{F}_t}{\bar{F}}\doteq 1 \tag{13.3}$$

The acceleration of the mass is very small, and only a negligible fraction of the driving force is neutralized by its inertia. The motion then is determined by the spring, as if the system were massless, and the vibration amplitude is equal to the static amplitude:

$$\hat{\xi}=\frac{1}{j\omega\left(R+j\omega M+\dfrac{1}{j\omega K}\right)}\doteq\frac{\bar{F}}{j\omega\dfrac{1}{j\omega K}}=KF \tag{13.4}$$

that is, to the amplitude that would be produced by the same force F, if its frequency were zero. As the frequency increases, the mechanical impedance of the system decreases, and displacement amplitude and transmitted force increase. At resonance,

$$\left|\frac{\bar{F}_t}{\bar{F}}\right|=\frac{1}{\eta}=Q \tag{13.5}$$

Because of the resonance effect, the transmitted force becomes Q times larger than the force that excites the vibration.

At frequencies sufficiently above the resonant frequency, the damping resistance has little effect on the motion; the magnitudes 1 and $j\omega KR$ can be neglected in the denominator of Equation 13.2, and

$$\bar{T}=\frac{\bar{F}_t}{\bar{F}}=\frac{\omega_0{}^2}{\omega^2} \tag{13.6}$$

Most of the force is used for moving the mass, and the transmitted force decreases inversely with the square of the frequency. The curve of Figure 13.2 shows that the compliant element reduces the transmitted force, if

$$\frac{1}{1-\dfrac{\omega^2}{\omega_0{}^2}}>1 \tag{13.7}$$

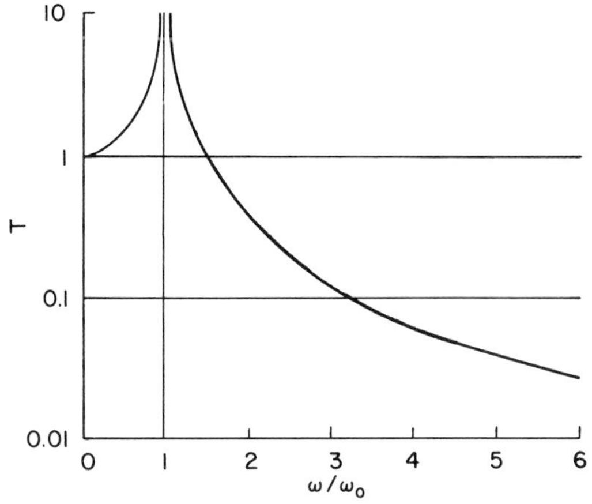

Fig. 13.2 Frequency curve of the transmission factor of a simple point-mass compliance system.

or if

$$\omega > \sqrt{2}\,\omega_0 \tag{13.8}$$

In the above computations it was assumed that the loss resistance R has no effect on the magnitude of the mechanical impedance of the spring, and R was neglected in computing the transmitted force. If the loss resistance of the compliant material is not small, Equation 13.1 has to be replaced by:

$$\bar{F}_t = \left(R + \frac{1}{j\omega K}\right)\dot{\bar{\xi}} = \frac{\bar{F}(1 + j\omega KR)}{j\omega K\bar{Z}} = \frac{\bar{F}(1 + j\eta)}{j\omega K\bar{Z}} \tag{13.9}$$

where

$$\eta = \omega KR = \frac{1}{Q} \tag{13.10}$$

For elastic damping, η is usually less than one fourth, and Equations 13.1 and 13.9 lead to practically the same result. But if the system is heavily damped by a dashpot, so that $\eta = \omega KR \gg 1$, the equation for the high-frequency behavior of the system (Eq. 13.6) has to be replaced by:

$$\frac{\bar{F}_t}{\bar{F}} = \frac{1 + j\omega KR}{j\omega K\left(-R + j\omega M + \dfrac{1}{j\omega K}\right)} = \frac{j\omega KR}{-\omega^2 MK} = \frac{-jKR\omega_0^2}{\omega} \tag{13.11}$$

and the transmission factor then decreases in inverse proportion only to the first power of ω.

The resonant frequency is a function of the compliance of the system.

The compliance K can be expressed by the deflection of the system ξ_W under its own weight:

$$\xi_W = K \cdot Mg \qquad \text{or} \qquad K = \frac{\xi_W}{Mg} \tag{13.12}$$

where g is the acceleration due to gravity and Mg is the static force exerted on the springs by the weight of the mass M. The expression for the resonant frequency takes the following form:

$$\omega_0{}^2 = \frac{1}{MK} = \frac{g}{MgK} = \frac{g}{\xi_W} \tag{13.13}$$

Thus, the resonant frequency is inversely proportional to the square root of the deflection ξ_W of the system under its own weight. Figure 13.3 shows a graph of the resonant frequency as a function of the deflection ξ_W.

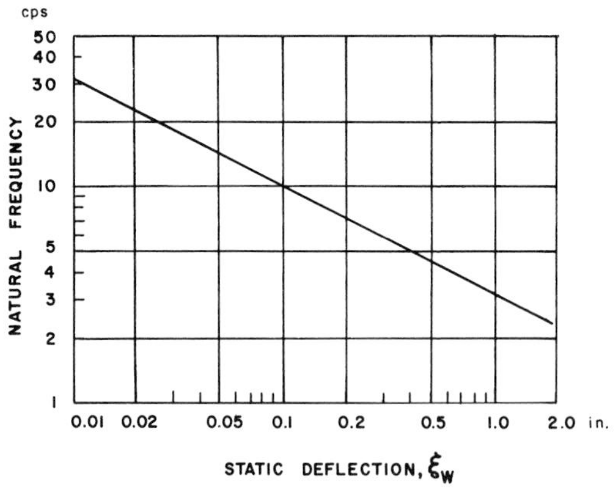

Fig. 13.3 Natural frequency as a function of the static deflection produced by the weight of the machine and its base.

For effective vibration damping, the system should have a low resonant frequency. Frequently, it is impossible to make the resonant frequency sufficiently low; the spring mounting would have to be impractically soft, and the system would be insufficiently constrained. The best that can be done in such a situation is to make sure that the exciting frequency is sufficiently below the resonant frequency. Frequently, the floor or foundation upon which the machinery stands acts as a compliance. If the machinery is mounted on a heavy base, the resonant frequency of the total mass of the system with the compliance of the floor can easily fall in the frequency range that is excited by the machinery. In such a case it is better to mount the machinery on a large, but very light (hollow), base that is secured directly to the floor, so that the resonant frequency is higher than the frequency of the machine vibration. High-speed machines can always be spring-mounted, but low-speed machines usually have to be attached to the floor without mounting.

When an instrument must be vibration-insulated, it is often mounted on a heavy base that is suspended from the ceiling. The system then is excited by the deflections of the ceiling, and the velocity of the suspended mass can be deduced from the equivalent circuit shown in Figure 13.4; it is given by (see Eq. 1.67):

$$v_M = \frac{v_0\left(R+\dfrac{1}{j\omega K}\right)}{R+j\omega M+\dfrac{1}{j\omega K}} \tag{13.14}$$

If the system is not heavily damped, R can be neglected in the numerator; then,

$$\frac{v_M}{v_0} = \frac{1}{j\omega K\bar{Z}} = \frac{1}{j\omega K\left(R+j\omega M+\dfrac{1}{j\omega K}\right)} = \frac{1}{j\eta+1-\dfrac{\omega^2}{\omega_0^{\,2}}} \tag{13.15}$$

The form of this expression is the same as that for the transmitted force in a spring-mounted series-resonant system. This result is a consequence of the duality of the two circuits and of the duality of the excitation (the ceiling represents a velocity generator).

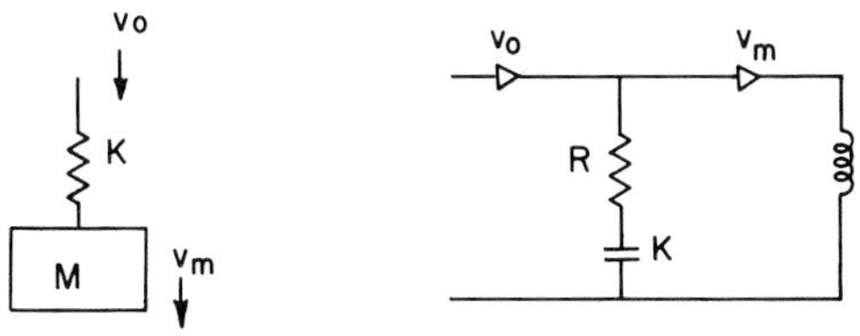

Fig. 13.4 Vibrating system excited by a prescribed velocity of the compliant element.

The same result can be derived with the aid of the differential equation. To obtain it, the velocity in the compliance and the resistance term are replaced by the relative velocity $\dot{\xi}-\dot{\xi}_0=\dot{\xi}_r$

$$M\ddot{\xi}+R(\dot{\xi}-\dot{\xi}_0)+\frac{1}{K}(\xi-\xi_0)=0 \tag{13.16}$$

or

$$M\ddot{\xi}_r+R\dot{\xi}_r+\frac{1}{K}\xi_r=-M\ddot{\xi}_0 \tag{13.17}$$

The solution is:

$$\tilde{\xi}=\tilde{\xi}_r+\tilde{\xi}_0=\tilde{\xi}_0\left(1-\frac{j\omega M}{R+j\omega M+\dfrac{1}{j\omega K}}\right)=\frac{\tilde{\xi}_0\left(R+\dfrac{1}{j\omega K}\right)}{R+j\omega M+\dfrac{1}{j\omega K}} \tag{13.18}$$

which is the same as Equation 13.14.

The spring suspension protects the instrument from short or rapid shocks, but does not insulate it from slow vibrations with periods of the magnitude of, or greater than, the natural period of the system.

Resonances in the Masses of the System

At higher frequencies, machine and base always exhibit internal resonances. The equivalent circuit for a system with several resonances is illustrated in Figure 13.5. For the low frequencies, the circuit is similar to that of a mass point, and the vibration insulation is predicted by the classical theory.

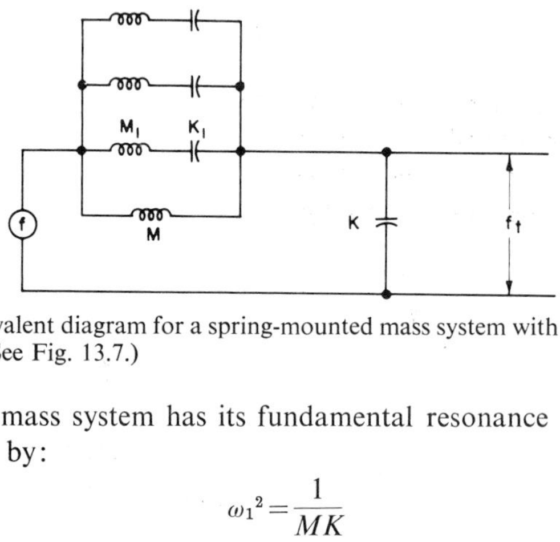

Fig. 13.5 Equivalent diagram for a spring-mounted mass system with many resonances in the masses. (See Fig. 13.7.)

The spring mass system has its fundamental resonance at a frequency given roughly by:

$$\omega_1^2 = \frac{1}{MK} \tag{13.19}$$

A parallel resonance always separates two series resonances (Foster's theorem), and the first parallel resonance occurs between the mass M and the parallel connection of all the mode compliances $K_{st} = \Sigma_\nu K_\nu$ (the mass impedances ωM_ν being negligible in comparison to the compliance impedances $1/j\omega K_\nu$ at frequencies below the series resonances ω_ν). The sum K_{st} is identical with the static compliance of the system. If Q is the average quality factor of the mode compliances and R is the corresponding average dissipation resistance, the impedance becomes:

$$\bar{Z} = \frac{R + \dfrac{j\omega_0 M}{j\omega_0 K}}{R + j\omega_0 M + \dfrac{1}{j\omega_0 K}} = \frac{R + j\omega_0 M}{1 - \omega_0^2 MK + j\omega_0 RK} \doteq \omega_0 MQ \tag{13.20}$$

and the noise reduction of the mass circuit increases approximately by a factor of Q. The last form of the right-hand side is obtained by neglecting

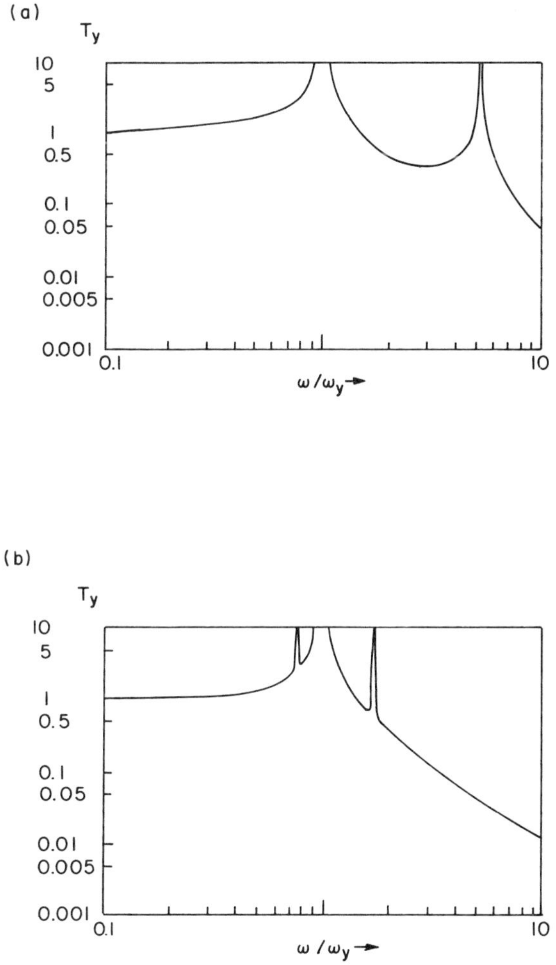

Fig. 13.6 Examples of the transmission curves of a system with one fully and two weakly excited modes.

R in the numerator and by making use of the resonance condition $\omega_0{}^2 = 1/MK$.

At the next series resonance of the mass system, the impedance breaks down to approximately $\omega M/Q$, and the vibration insulation becomes poorer by a factor of Q. The width of the peaks and troughs that are generated by the internal modes of vibration of the mass system depends greatly on whether these modes are fully or weakly excited. For weak excitation, the excitation constant κ is small, and the corresponding mode masses and resistances become very large. They contribute, therefore, to the resultant motion only at or near their resonance peaks. Figure 13.6 shows the frequency curves of the transmission factor for a system with weakly excited internal modes of vibration. The insulation becomes considerably smaller at the resonance frequencies, but its effectiveness is only slightly reduced in the frequency range between the peaks. However, the situation becomes completely different if the internal resonances are fully excited (Fig. 13.7). The peaks then become very large and broad, and the noise insulation is poor over the entire frequency range.

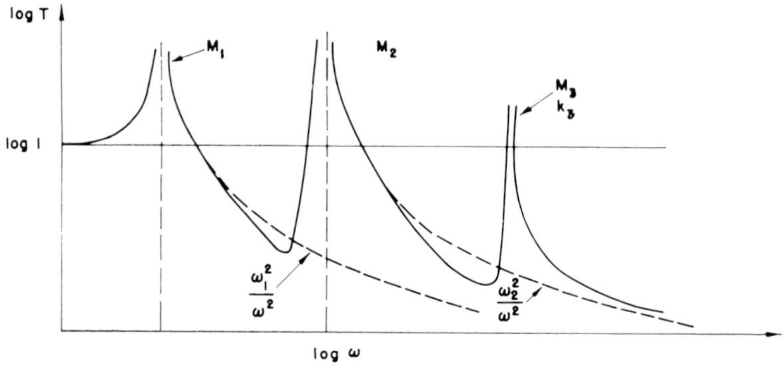

Fig. 13.7 Transmission curve of a spring-mounted mass system with many resonances in the masses. (See Fig. 13.5.)

Sometimes, the machinery and its base have fully excited internal modes of vibration in the frequency range in which the insulation mounting is supposed to function. These internal modes decrease the insulation by a factor Q, which for internal modes is usually very high. These modes completely annihilate the effect of the spring mounting. This situation is illustrated in Figure 13.7. Figure 13.8*a* shows some measurements of the mechanical admittance (mobility) of a small motor. This motor behaves like a mass only at very low frequencies. At about 90 cps, the first parallel resonance occurs, and as the frequency is increased, the motor exhibits the impedance of a compliance. The next series resonance is at 100 cps. Figure 13.8*b* represents the vibration insulation when this motor is attached to a table by a stiff rod.

It is often thought that vibration insulation can be realized if the machine is separated from its base plate by a layer of cork or by springs and the base plate is separated from the foundation by a special vibration mounting (Fig. 13.9). Actually, this procedure may be disastrous, because a second higher resonance (mass of machine resonating with the compliance of the cork) is introduced in the frequency range above the fundamental resonance at which the insulator is supposed to be effective. Hence, the effect of the vibration insulation may be completely destroyed.

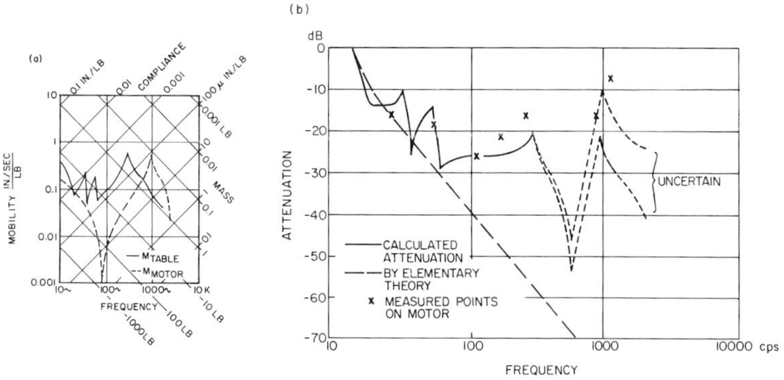

Fig. 13.8 Mechanical admittance (mobility) and the measured vibration insulation of a small motor and rod (used for spring-mounting the motor); *a*, mobility; *solid curve*, rod; *broken curve*, motor; *b*, comparison of the measured (*solid curve*) and the computed (*broken curve*) vibration insulation (crosses indicate measured points on motor). From R. Plunkett, *Noise Control*, **4** (1958), 18–22.

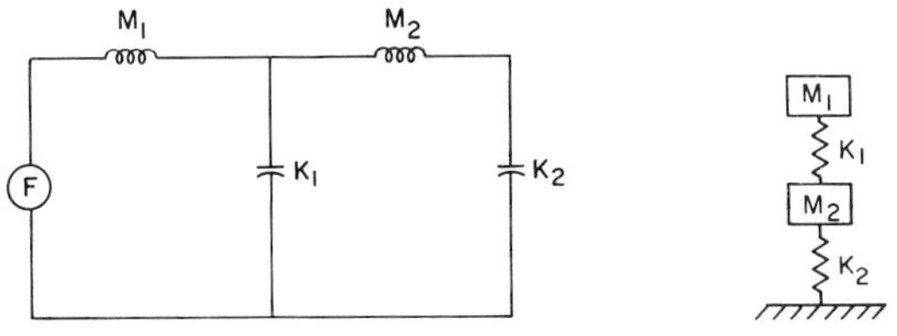

Fig. 13.9 Equivalent diagram for a generator mounted on springs on a spring-insulated base plate.

Resonances in the Springs of the Vibration Insulator

If the mass of the system behaves like a point mass and the spring exhibits resonances in the range of interest because of its distributed mass, the equivalent circuit will then be of the type illustrated in Figure 13.10. At the various series resonances of the spring mounting, the impedance of the mounting becomes particularly small, and vibration insulation is very good. At the antiresonances, vibration insulation is expected to become poorer; however, it can be shown that the maximum impedance that the mounting may exhibit is given by:

$$\omega M'Q' \tag{13.21}$$

where M' is the total mass of the mounting and Q' is the quality factor of the mounting at the frequency of the force. If the mass of the spring mounting is sufficiently small and the mounting is reasonably damped, the antiresonant impedance of the mounting is still very small in comparison with the impedance of the masses, and the vibration insulation is still fairly good. Resonances in the spring support at higher frequencies, then, are unimportant, provided that the mass of the machine is large in comparison with that of the springs.

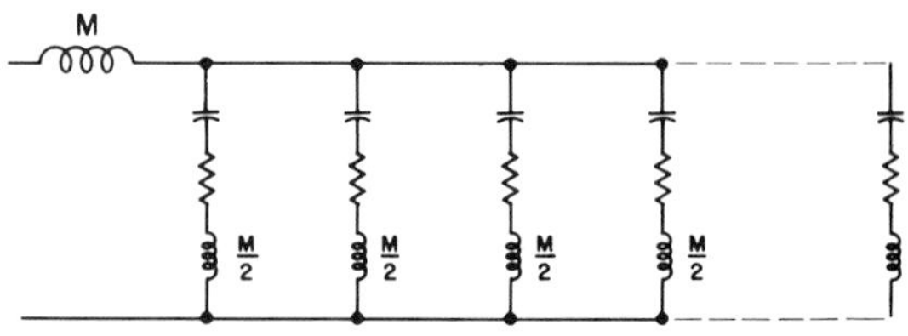

Fig. 13.10 Mass insulated by a spring with several resonances.

Fan or Motor Spring-Mounted in a Housing or in a Shell

Generally, the vibrator is spring-mounted on a plate or in a housing that exhibits many resonances. The mechanical behavior of the plate of the housing can then be represented by its driving-point impedance (which is approximately equal to its characteristic impedance Z_c, and the equivalent circuit becomes identical with the circuit shown in Figure 13.11. A simple computation gives the velocity of the driving point:

$$\bar{V}_d = \frac{F_0 \dfrac{1}{j\omega K}}{\left(\dfrac{1}{j\omega K} + Z_d\right)\left(j\omega M + \dfrac{\dfrac{1}{j\omega K} Z_d}{\dfrac{1}{j\omega K} + Z_d}\right)} \cong \frac{F_0}{Z_d + j\omega M - \dfrac{Z_d \omega^2}{\omega_0^2}} \tag{13.22}$$

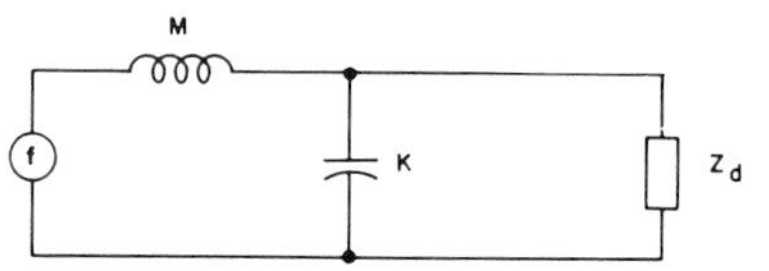

Fig. 13.11 Vibrator insulated by a spring system from a plate or a shell.

where $\omega_0^2 = 1/MK$ is the resonant frequency of the mass and the compliance, as if the spring were mounted on the ideal rigid base and not on the shell. The insulation becomes effective as soon as the last term in the denominator starts to predominate over the other two terms, that is, when the frequency becomes larger than the value ω_0 given by:

$$Z_d \approx \omega_0 M \tag{13.23}$$

In practical cases, this frequency turns out to be of the same order of magnitude as the resonance frequency ω_0 of the mass spring system when the spring is mounted on a rigid base. Equation 13.22 then simplifies to:

$$V_d \doteq F_0 \frac{\omega_0^2}{\omega^2 Z_d} \tag{13.24}$$

The root-mean-square velocity is found by multiplying the driving-point velocity by the factor (see Eq. 7.70):

$$\frac{V_{\text{eff}}}{V_d} = \frac{Z_d}{M}\left(\frac{\pi \kappa_\nu M}{2\varepsilon_\nu M_\nu^* \omega \eta}\right)^{\frac{1}{2}} \tag{13.25}$$

The result is:

$$V_{\text{eff}} = \frac{\omega_0^2 F_0}{\omega^2 M}\left(\frac{\pi}{2} \frac{\kappa_\nu M}{\varepsilon_\nu M_\nu \omega \eta}\right)^{\frac{1}{2}} \tag{13.26}$$

Thus, the insulation improves—as the mass of the housing increases, as the fundamental resonant frequency of the mass spring system becomes lower, and as the frequency difference between successive resonances increases. This frequency difference is usually proportional to the fundamental frequencies of the system; hence, it seems expedient to subdivide the housing into as many parts as possible and to introduce as many stiffening rings as possible. Another possibility is to simulate a one-dimensional force distribution, since the frequency differences between the one-dimensional modes are always considerably greater than those for a two-dimensional vibration pattern. A one-dimensional pattern can be attained by spring-mounting the vibrator on rigid girders and welding the girders on the plate or the shell from which the vibration has to be insulated. A third possibility is to apply a two-dimensional system of joints and stiffening rings and thereby reduce the transmission of the vibration to other parts of the system.

Sound Radiation of a Housing Excited by a Spring-Mounted Vibrator

With the aid of the results of Chapter XII, the sound radiation to greater distances can be computed. If the force F_0 is replaced by the force

$$F_0' = Z_d v_d = F_0 \frac{\omega_0^2}{\omega^2} \tag{13.27}$$

that is exerted by the spring mounting on the housing, this force, as derived in the last equation, is the same as the transmitted force in the classical theory. In the frequency range in which the spring mounting is effective, the impedance of the housing or shell is sufficiently large so that the transmitted force is practically the same as if the housing were perfectly rigid. The sound power generated by the region near the point or line of attack of the general force distribution thus becomes:

$$N=\frac{\pi\sigma\rho c F_0^2 \omega_0^4}{4\omega_a\omega_b M^2\omega^4} \tag{13.28}$$

for a point force or a two-dimensional vibration pattern and

$$N=\frac{\pi\sigma\rho c F_0^2 \omega_0^4}{4\omega_a\omega M^2\omega^4} \tag{13.29}$$

for a force distribution along a line or a circumference of the shell.

Again, the linear force distribution leads to the smaller sound pressure. This kind of sound power is independent of the damping, a result that is in perfect agreement with the experimental evidence. The only efficient way to reduce the sound is to increase the mass of the shell or the housing and to decrease its dimensions. The spring insulation of the vibrator is about as effective as it is in the classical case. To this result must still be added the component of the sound that is generated because of the discontinuity of the vibration field at the edge of the vibrator;[1] this sound field represents predominantly the contribution of the modes that are excited by the external force in their resonance region. These contributions seem to be relatively small at higher frequencies, provided that the vibrator is reasonably damped.

Damping

Because of the wattless near field and the sound radiation of the resonating modes that greatly depend on it, damping does require attention. Airplane bodies, car bodies, and ship hulls always require good damping, and machine parts also have to be damped in order to minimize resonances that might cause breakage. The kind of damping materials is less important than how they are used; most commercial damping materials are adequate for most purposes.

Damping means absorption of energy, but energy can be absorbed by a damping material only when it is in good contact with the object to be damped. This contact is considerably harder to attain than one would guess. For instance, an acoustic tube that is soldered into a lead shell is, within wide frequency ranges, hardly damped at all. The shell, though

[1] See pp. 408–18.

soldered to the tube, vibrates almost independently of it at the higher frequencies because of the inhomogeneity of the connecting boundary layer. A supersonic crystal is completely unaffected by a dry lead damping plate; a microscopic film of air between the two makes contact extremely poor. A small amount of Vaseline or oil, however, makes the contact perfect and decreases the oscillation of the crystal. But the sound must also penetrate the absorbent, and an absorbent of small ρc would be no good at all. Sheets of paper or felt can never damp a vibrating plate unless they are soaked with tar or some similar material that matches their impedance to that of the object to be damped. In this case, it is usually the tar that produces the damping, and the paper or felt serves only as a convenient carrier.

Usually one tries to employ as little damping material as possible. If this material is to generate a reasonable damping resistance, it must be fairly stiff, because its damping resistance is only η times its mechanical impedance; and this damping resistance must match the wave impedance or the mechanical impedance of the object to be damped. A layer of light material glued to a plate vibrates with the plate, but produces little or no damping. The mechanical impedance of the damping material should be even greater than that of the object to be damped, so that it can be applied in a thin layer. This, however, is a demand that can hardly ever be fullfilled in practice.

The recently developed car-damping coats, Aquaplas, and some of the other plastics, when dissolved to make a varnish, are about as good a material as can be obtained. But, to be really effective, they have to be applied in a thick layer. Paper, felt, and other sheets soaked with tar are likewise effective. Metal dust incorporated into such mixtures or into rubber considerably increases the damping because of the microscopic inhomogeneity of the internal stress field and the additional friction.

Metal Sheets with Damping Layers

Metal sheets with damping layers between them are frequently used to damp bending vibrations, and a number of publications have appeared on the subject. An example of such a computation[2] shows some of the results that can be obtained.

If a metal sheet of thickness d_1 is covered by a damping layer of thickness d_2 (Fig. 13.12), the bending stiffness and the loss factor of the combination can then be computed in a manner similar to that for the bending of a

[2] From H. Oberst, Dämpfung der Biegeschwingungen dünner Bleche, *Acustica*, **2** (1952), 181.

beam. According to Bernoulli's theory of bending, the strain is given by:

$$\sigma_{11}=\lambda_E y\frac{\partial^2\xi}{\partial x^2} \tag{13.30}$$

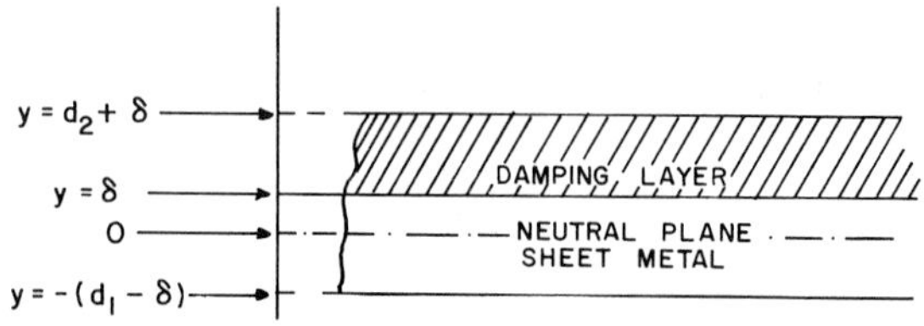

Fig. 13.12 Co-ordinates of a metal sheet with damping layer.

The neutral plane is defined as the plane that is not extended during the process of bending. If δ is the y-co-ordinate of this plane (Fig. 13.12), then the forces on the beam above this plane are equal to the forces below this plane, and the stress integral vanishes. If λ_1 is Young's modulus for the metal and $\bar{\lambda}_2$ that for the damping layer, then,

$$\int_{-(d_1-\delta)}^{d_2+\delta}\bar{\sigma}_{11}dy=0=\int_{-(d_1-\delta)}^{\delta}\lambda_1 y\frac{\partial^2\xi}{\partial x^2}dy+\int_{\delta}^{d_2+\delta}\bar{\lambda}_2 y\frac{\partial^2\xi}{\partial x^2}dy$$

$$=\frac{1}{2}\frac{\partial^2\xi}{\partial x^2}[\lambda_1 d_1(2\delta-d_1)+\bar{\lambda}_2 d_2(d_2+2\delta)]=0 \tag{13.31}$$

The y-co-ordinate of the neutral layer, therefore, is:

$$\delta=\frac{\lambda_1 d_1^2-\lambda_2 d_2^2}{\lambda_1 d_1+\lambda_2 d_2} \tag{13.32}$$

The bending moment is given by:

$$M=\int_{-(d_1-\delta)}^{d_2+\delta} y\sigma_{11}dy \tag{13.33}$$

The losses in the base layer (sheet metal) can be neglected:

$$\bar{\lambda}_1=\lambda_1 \tag{13.34}$$

but they must be accounted for in the damping layer:

$$\bar{\lambda}_2=\lambda_{20}(1+j\eta_2) \tag{13.35}$$

After substitution of the value of σ_{11} (Eq. 13.30), the bending moment then becomes:

$$M=\bar{\lambda}_1\int_{-(d_1-\delta)}^{\delta} y^2\frac{\partial^2\xi}{\partial x^2}dy+\bar{\lambda}_2\int_{\delta}^{d_2+\delta} y^2\frac{\partial^2\xi}{\partial x^2}dy \tag{13.36}$$

The evaluation of this integral leads to the result:

$$M = B\frac{\partial^2 \xi}{\partial x^2} \tag{13.37}$$

where

$$B = \frac{\lambda_1 I_1 \left[1 + 2\frac{\bar{\lambda}_2}{\lambda_1}(2\xi + 3\xi^2 + 2\xi^3) + \left(\frac{\bar{\lambda}_2}{\lambda_1}\right)^2 \xi^4\right]}{1 + \frac{\bar{\lambda}_2}{\lambda_1}\xi} \tag{13.38}$$

and

$$\xi = \frac{d_2}{d_1} \tag{13.39}$$

and

$$I_1 = \frac{d_1^3}{12} \tag{13.40}$$

is the moment of inertia of the cross section of the plate per unit width without the damping layer. The real part of this expression gives the stiffness of the combined layer:

$$\frac{B}{\lambda_1 I_1} = \frac{1 + \frac{2\lambda_2}{\lambda_1}(2\xi + 3\xi^2 + 2\xi^3) + \left(\frac{\lambda_2}{\lambda_1}\right)^2 \xi^4}{1 + \frac{\xi_2}{\lambda_1}\xi} \tag{13.41}$$

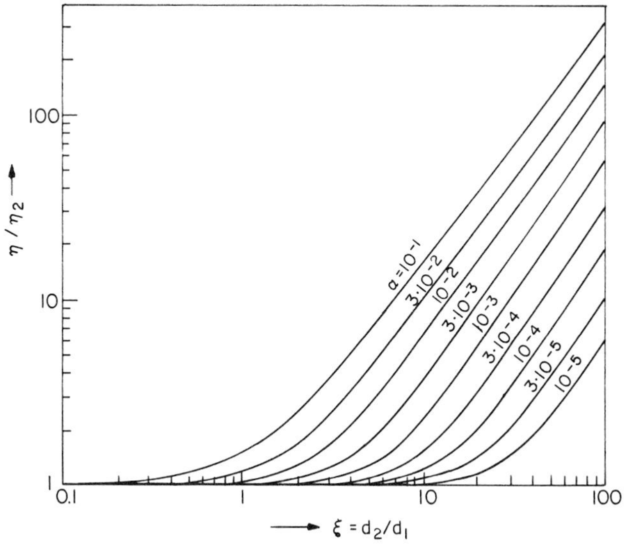

Fig. 13.13 Bending stiffness of a metal sheet with damping layer (relative to that of the undamped layer, as a function of the thickness ratio $\lambda_2/\lambda_1 = b$ for various ratios $\alpha = \lambda_2/\lambda_1$ as parameters. From H. Oberst, *loc. cit.*

The imaginary part represents the loss factor of the plate with the damping layer:

$$\frac{\eta}{\eta_2}=\frac{\frac{\lambda_2}{\lambda_1}\xi\left[3+6\xi+4\xi^2+\frac{2\lambda_2}{\lambda_1}\xi^3+\left(\frac{\lambda_2}{\lambda_1}\right)^2\xi^4\right]}{\left(1+\frac{\lambda_2}{\lambda_1}\xi\right)\left[1+2\frac{\lambda_2}{\lambda_1}\left(2\xi+3\xi^2+2\xi^3\right)+\left(\frac{\lambda_2}{\lambda_1}\right)^2\xi^4\right]} \tag{13.42}$$

provided that $\eta_2{}^2 \ll 1$. Figure 13.13 shows the resulting bending stiffness as a function of the ratio d_2/d_1, and Figure 13.14 shows the loss factor for various values of λ_2/λ_1. The softer the damping layer, the greater is the required thickness. As the thickness of the damping layer is increased, the loss factor approaches the value η_2 of the damping material; further increase of the thickness of the damping layer has no advantage.

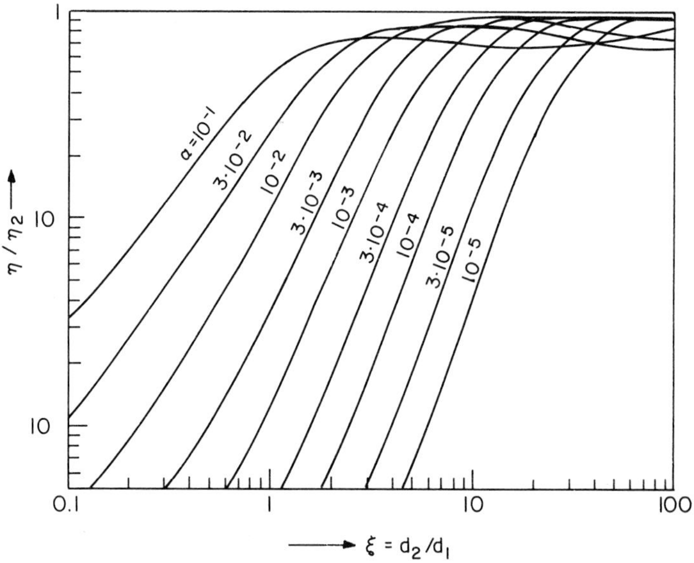

Fig. 13.14 Loss factor ratio (η/η_2) of a metal sheet with damping layer (for various values of the thickness ratio, with $\lambda_2/\lambda_1=\alpha$ as parameter. From H. Oberst, *loc. cit.*

Figure 13.15 shows some of the results that can be obtained with various damping materials, if the thickness of the damping layer is 50 per cent greater than that of the metal sheet. These curves illustrate the great difficulty of obtaining reasonably high values of damping with only one damping layer. Considerably more satisfactory results can be obtained with materials in which many sheets of the material to be damped are cemented together with alternate damping layers. Loss factors greater than 0.1 can then easily be obtained.

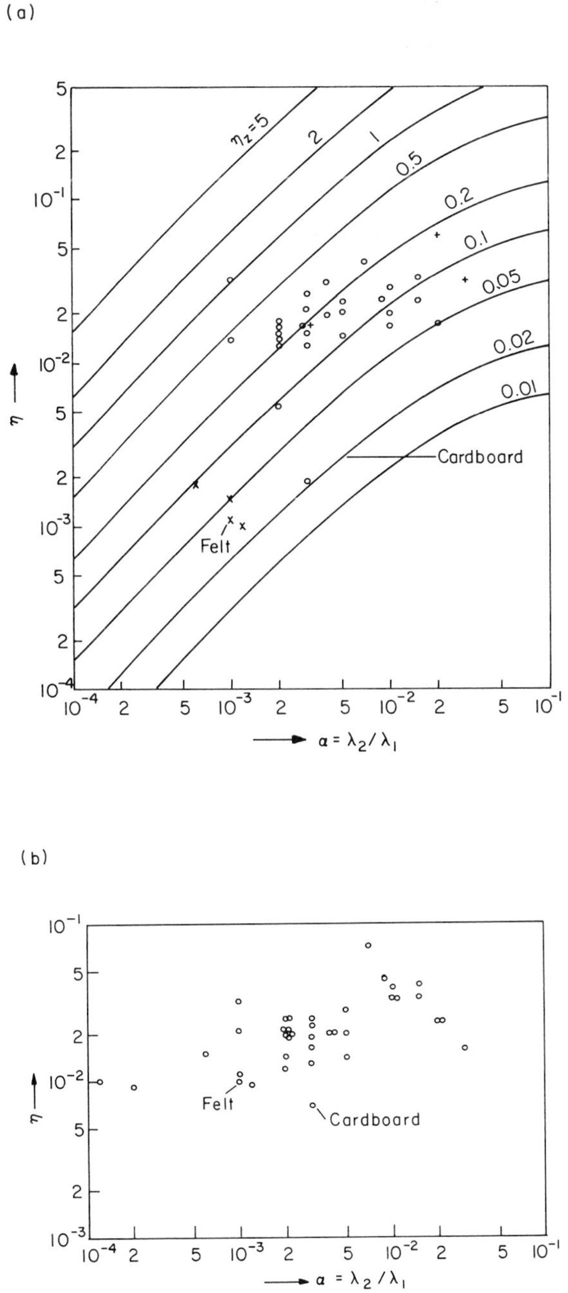

Fig. 13.15 Loss factors (η) for various damping materials (at 200 cps); *a*, for a thickness ratio $d_2/d_1 = 1.5$, as a function of the stiffness ratio λ_2/λ_1; *b*, for a mass ratio $m_2/m_1 = 0.2$. From H. Oberst, *loc. cit.*

Recommended Reading[3]

CREDE, C. E., *Vibration and Shock Isolation*, John Wiley & Sons, Inc., New York, 1951.

OBERST, H., "Dämpfung der Biegeschwingungen dünner Bleche," *Acustica,* **2** (1952), 181.

———, "Werkstoffe mit extrem hoher innere Dämpfung," *Acustica,* **6** (1956), 144. (This paper contains a list of valuable references.)

PLUNKETT, R., *Noise Control,* **4** (1958), 18–22.

[3] A considerable amount of work on damping and damping layers has been performed by the members of the company Bolt, Beranek, and Newman, Cambridge, Mass., and is published in its reports.

XIV / ELASTIC EQUATIONS AND THEIR SOLUTIONS

The preceding parts of this book are based on the classical theory of rods and plates. In this theory the stresses are assumed to be constant over the cross section of the rod or plate, and rotary inertia and mode transformation at the boundaries of the vibrator are neglected. Such a simplified description is permissible at very low frequencies and in the audio-range, but never at very high frequencies.

It is beyond the scope of this text to present a detailed study of the classical and modern elastic theories and their implications for the subject of vibrations. However, the following pages should provide some insight into several of the phenomena that are observed at the higher audio-frequencies and in the ultrasonic frequency range.

Fundamental Elastic Equations

Equilibrium of an Elementary Volume and the Stress Tensor

The derivation of the elastic equation is similar to that of the equations of sound propagation. Let us consider an elementary parallelepiped with the edges dx, dy, and dz; and let us consider the equilibrium of the forces that act on its surfaces. Let the first subscript denote the axis on which the surface element is perpendicular and the second denote the direction of the stress. Let the normal at any point to the surface of the elementary volume point from its inside to its outside, and let the stress be positive and tensile if it points in the positive direction of the co-ordinates. The elastic forces that act on this elementary parallelepiped in the the x-direction are given by the following three contributions. The first contribution is given by the normal stress on surfaces $dy\ dz$ at x and $x+dx$ (Fig. 14.1):

$$\sigma_{xx}(x+dx)dydz-\sigma_{xx}(x)dydz=dydz\frac{\partial\sigma_{xx}}{\partial x}dx \tag{14.1}$$

The first of the left-hand terms describes the pull on the right-hand face of the cube in the positive x-direction; the second term, the reaction to this pull at the left-hand face of the cube. The second contribution is generated

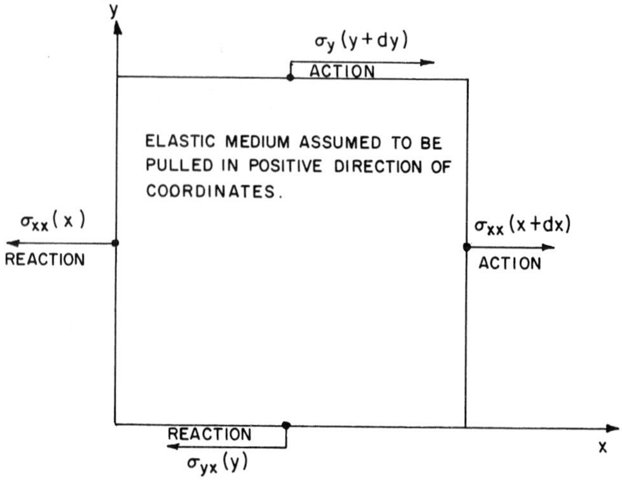

Fig. 14.1 Equilibrium on an elementary parallelepiped; elastic medium is assumed to be pulled in the positive direction of the co-ordinates.

by the shear force that acts in the x-direction on the surfaces of the elementary cube that are perpendicular to the y-axis; it is given by:

$$\sigma_{yx}(y+dy)dxdz-\sigma_{yx}(y)dxdz=dxdz\frac{\partial\sigma_{yx}}{\partial y}dy \tag{14.2}$$

The first term represents the shear force on the surface element at $y+dy$ in the positive x-direction; the second, the reaction of the medium behind the elementary volume to this shear force at the surface element at y. The third contribution is due to the shear stress on the surface perpendicular to the z-axis:

$$\sigma_{zx}(z+dz)dxdy-\sigma_{zx}(z)dxdy=dxdy\frac{\partial\sigma_{zx}}{\partial z}dz \tag{14.3}$$

All these forces act in the positive x-direction, and their sum is:

$$\left(\frac{\partial\sigma_{xx}}{\partial x}+\frac{\partial\sigma_{yx}}{\partial y}+\frac{\partial\sigma_{zx}}{\partial z}\right)dxdydz \tag{14.4}$$

The resultant force—this sum—must be equal to the product of the mass and the acceleration of the elementary volume in the x-direction:

$$\frac{\partial\sigma_{xx}}{\partial x}+\frac{\partial\sigma_{yx}}{\partial y}+\frac{\partial\sigma_{zx}}{\partial z}=\rho\frac{\partial^2\xi}{\partial t^2} \tag{14.5}$$

Two corresponding equations are derived for y and z:

$$\frac{\partial\sigma_{xy}}{\partial x}+\frac{\partial\sigma_{yy}}{\partial y}+\frac{\partial\sigma_{zy}}{\partial z}=\rho\frac{\partial^2\eta}{\partial t^2} \tag{14.6}$$

and

$$\frac{\partial\sigma_{xz}}{\partial x}+\frac{\partial\sigma_{yz}}{\partial y}+\frac{\partial\sigma_{zz}}{\partial z}=\rho\frac{\partial^2\zeta}{\partial t^2} \tag{14.7}$$

The derivations can be considerably condensed by using the following notation:

$$x = x_1 \qquad y = x_2 \qquad z = x_3$$
$$\sigma_{xx} = \sigma_{11} \qquad \sigma_{xy} = \sigma_{12} \qquad \sigma_{xz} = \sigma_{13} \ldots$$
$$\xi = \xi_1 \qquad \eta = \xi_2 \qquad \zeta = \xi_3 \tag{14.8}$$

Equations 14.5, 14.6, and 14.7 then reduce to:

$$\sum_j \frac{\partial \sigma_{ji}}{\partial x_j} = \rho \frac{\partial^2 \xi_i}{\partial t^2} \qquad i = 1, 2, \text{ or } 3 \tag{14.9}$$

The left-hand side of this equation has to be summed for all values of j ($j = 1, 2, 3$). For equilibrium, the turning moments (for instance those acting about the point $x=0$, $y=0$, and $z=0$) must be zero. To derive the moments, the stresses are multiplied by the differentials of the co-ordinates.

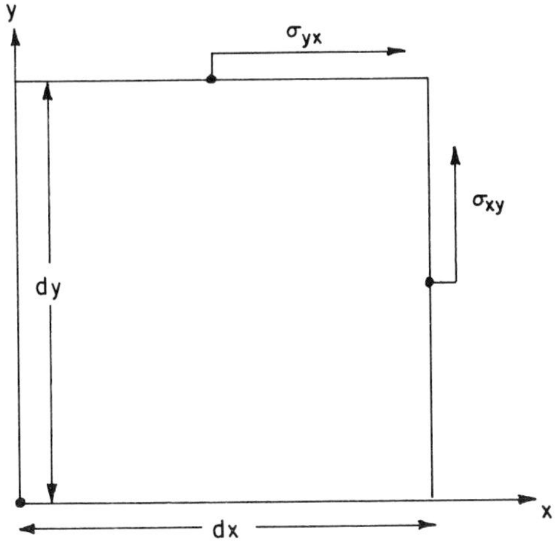

Fig. 14.2 Equilibrium for the moments.

The z-component of the moment (the moment around the z-axis in Fig. 14.2) is:

$$(\sigma_{xy} dz dy) \cdot dx - (\sigma_{yx} dx dy) \cdot dz = (\sigma_{xy} - \sigma_{yx}) dx dy dz \tag{14.10}$$

This moment is zero, if

$$\sigma_{yx} = \sigma_{xy} \tag{14.11}$$

Similarly, the y- and z-components of the moment are zero, if

$$\sigma_{yz} = \sigma_{zy} \qquad \text{and} \qquad \sigma_{xz} = \sigma_{zx} \tag{14.12}$$

The sequence of the subscripts of the stresses is, therefore, insignificant.

Stress Tensor

A vector is a quantity whose components transform like the co-ordinates of a point whenever the co-ordinate system is rotated. We shall consider only rectangular co-ordinate systems here. Let the vector $\vec{A}$ have the components x, y in the old co-ordinate system; its components in the new system are given by (Fig. 14.3):

$$x' = x \cos(x', x) + y \cos(y', y) \tag{14.13}$$

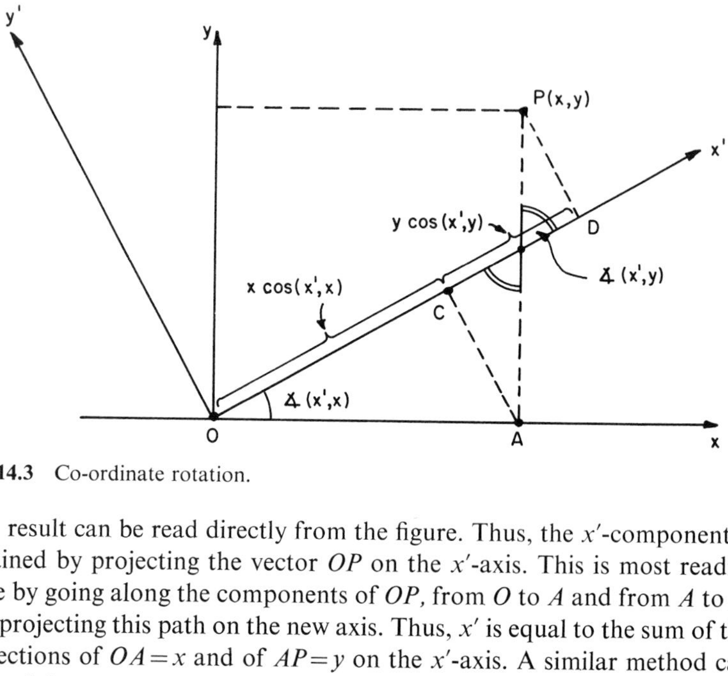

Fig. 14.3 Co-ordinate rotation.

This result can be read directly from the figure. Thus, the x'-component is obtained by projecting the vector OP on the x'-axis. This is most readily done by going along the components of OP, from O to A and from A to P, and projecting this path on the new axis. Thus, x' is equal to the sum of the projections of $OA = x$ and of $AP = y$ on the x'-axis. A similar method can be used for any number of dimensions. Thus,

$$x_i' = \sum_j x_j \cos(x_i', x_j) = \sum_j x_j e_{ij} \tag{14.14}$$

where

$$e_{ij} = \cos(x_i', x_j) \tag{14.15}$$

Einstein simplified the notation by omitting the summation sign and introduced the convention that, unless otherwise stated, double indices mean summation. For three dimensions,

$$x_i' = x_j e_{ij} = x_1 e_{i1} + x_2 e_{i2} + x_3 e_{i3} \tag{14.16}$$

In performing co-ordinate transformations, it is helpful to distinguish between the new and the old co-ordinates by using the Greek subscripts

$\alpha, \beta, \gamma, \ldots$ for the new co-ordinates and the Latin subscripts $i, j, k, \ldots$ for the old co-ordinates. The primes on the new co-ordinates can then be dropped, and Equation 14.16 reads:

$$x_\alpha = e_{\alpha j} x_j \tag{14.17}$$

where

$$e_{\alpha j} = \cos(x_\alpha, x_j) = \cos(x_j, x_\alpha) = e_{j\alpha} \tag{14.18}$$

Since the co-ordinates $e_{\alpha j}$ describe a rotation of the co-ordinate system, the length of a vector is invariant. Thus,

$$x_1^2 + x_2^2 + x_3^2 = x_1'^2 + x_2'^2 + x_3'^2 \tag{14.19}$$

or, in abbreviated form,

$$x_i^2 = x_\alpha^2 \tag{14.20}$$

If x_α is expressed in terms of x_i:

$$x_\alpha = e_{\alpha i} x_i \qquad \text{and} \qquad x_\alpha^2 = e_{\alpha i} x_i e_{\alpha k} x_k = x_i^2 \tag{14.21}$$

The coefficients of the mixed products x_i must vanish; thus,

$$e_{\alpha i} e_{\alpha k} = \delta_{ik} \tag{14.22}$$

The last relation makes it possible to solve the equation $x_\alpha^2 = e_{\alpha j} x_j$ for x_j by multiplying, left and right, by $e_{\alpha k}$ and summing over α:

$$e_{\alpha i} x_\alpha = e_{\alpha i} e_{\alpha j} x_j = \delta_{ij} x_j = x_i \tag{14.23}$$

or

$$x_i = e_{\alpha i} x_\alpha = x_\alpha e_{\alpha i} \tag{14.24}$$

If x_i is expressed in terms of x_α in Equation 14.20, we obtain, similarly to the above relation,

$$e_{\alpha i} e_{\beta i} = \delta_{\alpha\beta} \tag{14.25}$$

A tensor is a magnitude whose components transform like the co-ordinates of a point for each of its subscripts. Thus, the element $A_{\alpha\beta\gamma\ldots}$ in the new co-ordinate system is derived by the following operation:

$$A_{\alpha\beta\gamma\ldots} = e_{\alpha i} e_{\beta j} e_{\gamma k \ldots} \ldots A_{ijk\ldots} \ldots \tag{14.26}$$

Each of the elements of a tensor obeys this rule, and, conversely, elements that obey this rule represent a tensor.

The transformation rules for the stress components σ_{ij} are derived by considering the equilibrium of an elementary tetrahedron (Fig. 14.4). If the elementary volume is sufficiently small, volume forces (which are proportional to dx^3) can be neglected as compared to the forces acting on the surfaces (which are proportional to dx^2). The surface element, in which we are particularly interested, is perpendicular to the direction n. The surface area of this element is $d\sigma$, and the x-component of the force that acts on it is $d\sigma \cdot \sigma_{nx}$. The area of the surface of the elementary tetrahedron that is perpendicular to the x-axis is $d\sigma \cos(n, x)$, and the x-component of the force that acts on it is $d\sigma \cos(n, x) \cdot \sigma_{xx}$. Corresponding expressions are obtained

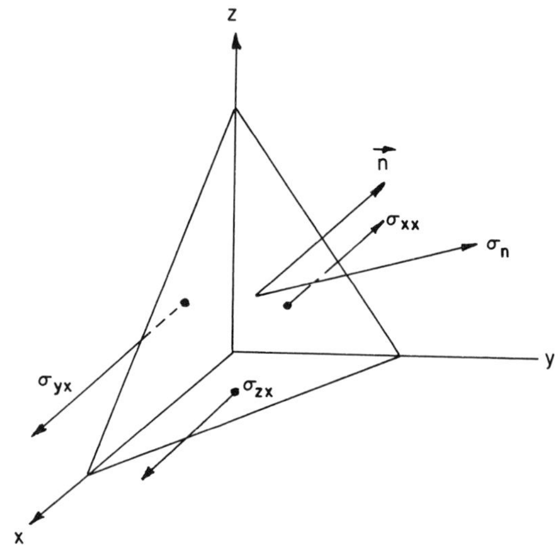

Fig. 14.4 Equilibrium on an elementary tetrahedron.

for the x-components of the force on the two other faces of the tetrahedron. For equilibrium,

$$\sigma_{nx}\cdot d\sigma=\sigma_{xx}d\sigma\cos(n,x)+\sigma_{yx}d\sigma\cos(n,y)+\sigma_{zx}d\sigma\cos(n,z) \tag{14.27}$$

We may interpret n as the direction of a co-ordinate axis of a new system of co-ordinates and, consequently, replace n by x_α. After canceling $d\sigma$, the last equation reads:

$$\sigma_{\alpha 1}=\sigma_{11}\cos(x_\alpha,x_1)+\sigma_{21}\cos(x_\alpha,x_2)+\sigma_{31}\cos(x_\alpha,x_3) \tag{14.28}$$

Similar equations are obtained for the y- and z-components of the force that acts on the elementary area $d\sigma$. The resulting equations can then be condensed into the following form:

$$\sigma_{\alpha i}=e_{\alpha j}\sigma_{ji} \tag{14.29}$$

where

$$e_{\alpha j}=\cos(x_\alpha,x_j) \tag{14.30}$$

and x_α represents the direction of the normal of the elementary area α.

The components of a force transform like the components of a vector; thus, the component of the force $(\sigma_{\alpha 1}, \sigma_{\alpha 2}, \sigma_{\alpha 3})$ that acts on the unit area normal to the α-axis in the direction β is given by:

$$\sigma_{\alpha\beta}=\sigma_{\alpha 1}\cos(\beta,x_1)+\sigma_{\alpha 2}\cos(\beta,x_2)+\sigma_{\alpha 3}\cos(\beta,x_2)=\sigma_{\alpha j}e_{\beta j} \tag{14.31}$$

But

$$\sigma_{\alpha j}=\sigma_{ij}e_{\alpha i} \qquad \text{and} \qquad \sigma_{\alpha\beta}=\sigma_{\alpha j}e_{\beta j}=\sigma_{ij}e_{\alpha i}e_{\beta j} \tag{14.32}$$

And this is exactly the transformation rule that defines a tensor; therefore, $\sigma_{\alpha\beta}$ is a tensor.

Strain Tensor

The elastic stresses are not affected by translations or rotations of the elementary volume and its surroundings; translations and solid body rotations can be disregarded. If ξ_0, η_0, and ζ_0 represent the displacement of a point $x_0y_0z_0$ of an elementary volume, the displacement of a point xyz of that volume is given by:

$$\xi=\xi_0+\frac{\partial\xi}{\partial x}dx+\frac{\partial\xi}{\partial y}dy+\frac{\partial\xi}{\partial z}dz$$

$$\eta=\eta_0+\frac{\partial\eta}{\partial x}dx+\frac{\partial\eta}{\partial y}dy+\frac{\partial\eta}{\partial z}dz$$

$$\zeta=\zeta_0+\frac{\partial\zeta}{\partial x}dx+\frac{\partial\zeta}{\partial y}dy+\frac{\partial\zeta}{\partial z}dz \tag{14.33}$$

The magnitudes ξ_0, η_0, and ζ_0 represent a pure translation. They are of no interest here and can be discarded. The last three equations can then be written as follows:

$$\xi=\frac{\partial\xi}{\partial x}dx+\frac{1}{2}\left(\frac{\partial\xi}{\partial y}+\frac{\partial\eta}{\partial x}\right)dy+\frac{1}{2}\left(\frac{\partial\xi}{\partial z}+\frac{\partial\zeta}{\partial x}\right)dz+\frac{1}{2}\left(\frac{\partial\xi}{\partial y}-\frac{\partial\eta}{\partial x}\right)dy+\frac{1}{2}\left(\frac{\partial\xi}{\partial z}-\frac{\partial\zeta}{\partial x}\right)dz$$
$$=\epsilon_{xx}dx+\epsilon_{xy}dy+\epsilon_{xz}dz+\omega_z dy+\omega_y dz \tag{14.34}$$

where

$$\epsilon_{xx}=\frac{\partial\xi}{\partial x}\qquad \epsilon_{yy}=\frac{\partial\eta}{\partial y}\qquad \text{and}\qquad \epsilon_{zz}=\frac{\partial\zeta}{\partial z} \tag{14.35}$$

and[1]

$$\epsilon_{xy}=\frac{1}{2}\left(\frac{\partial\xi}{\partial y}+\frac{\partial\eta}{\partial x}\right)\qquad \epsilon_{xz}=\frac{1}{2}\left(\frac{\partial\xi}{\partial z}+\frac{\partial\zeta}{\partial x}\right)\qquad \text{and}\qquad \epsilon_{yz}=\frac{1}{2}\left(\frac{\partial\eta}{\partial z}+\frac{\partial\zeta}{\partial y}\right) \tag{14.36}$$

The magnitudes ϵ_{ij} are the so-called deformations or strains. The components ϵ_{ii} that contain two equal subscripts describe the dilatations in the directions of the co-ordinate axes; the strains $\epsilon_{ij}(i\neq j)$ describe the shear deformation. The elements ϵ_{ij} represent the symmetrical part of the strain matrix (that is, $\epsilon_{ij}=\epsilon_{ji}$). The magnitudes

$$\omega_x=\frac{1}{2}\left(\frac{\partial\zeta}{\partial y}-\frac{\partial\eta}{\partial z}\right)\qquad \omega_y=\frac{1}{2}\left(\frac{\partial\xi}{\partial z}-\frac{\partial\zeta}{\partial x}\right)\qquad \text{and}\qquad \omega_z=\frac{1}{2}\left(\frac{\partial\eta}{\partial x}-\frac{\partial\xi}{\partial y}\right) \tag{14.37}$$

are the rigid body rotations—that is, the components of the (axial) vector

$$\vec{\omega}=\frac{1}{2}\text{ curl }\vec{s} \tag{14.38}$$

where $\vec{s}$ is the vector with the components ξ, η, and ζ. They represent the

[1] The factor $\frac{1}{2}$ is essential if the matrix ϵ_{xy} is to represent a tensor; if this factor is moitted, the deformation matrix does not transform like a tensor.

antisymmetrical part of the displacement matrix in a rigid body. These rotations do not produce elastic stresses.

To prove that the deformations are the elements of a tensor, let

$$A_{ij}=\frac{1}{2}\left(\frac{\partial \xi_i}{\partial x_j}+\frac{\partial \xi_j}{\partial x_i}\right) \tag{14.39}$$

If the co-ordinate system is rotated, and if the old co-ordinates are given as a function of the new co-ordinates ξ_α,

$$\xi_i=e_{\alpha i}\xi_\alpha \tag{14.40}$$

where

$$e_{\alpha i}=\cos\,(x_\alpha, x_i) \tag{14.41}$$

and

$$\frac{\partial \xi_i}{\partial x_j}=\frac{\partial e_{\alpha i}\zeta_\alpha}{\partial x_j}=e_{\alpha i}\frac{\partial \zeta_\alpha}{\partial x_\beta}\frac{\partial x_\beta}{\partial x_j} \tag{14.42}$$

Also,

$$x_\beta=e_{\beta k}x_k \qquad \text{and} \qquad \frac{\partial x_\beta}{\partial x_j}=e_{\beta j} \tag{14.43}$$

Hence,

$$\frac{\partial \xi_i}{\partial x_j}=e_{\alpha i}\frac{\partial \xi_\alpha}{\partial x_\beta}e_{\beta j} \tag{14.44}$$

The magnitudes $\partial\xi_j/\partial x_i$ are given by a similar expression, with i and j interchanged. Hence,

$$A_{ij}=\frac{1}{2}\left(\frac{\partial \xi_i}{\partial x_j}+\frac{\partial \xi_j}{\partial x_i}\right)=\frac{1}{2}\left(e_{\alpha i}e_{\beta j}\frac{\partial \xi_\alpha}{\partial x_\beta}+e_{\alpha j}e_{\beta i}\frac{\partial \xi_\alpha}{\partial x_\beta}\right) \tag{14.45}$$

In the second term on the right, α and β are summation indices, and because they are dummy indices, we are permitted to write β for α and α for β. Hence,

$$2A_{ij}=e_{\alpha i}e_{\beta j}\left(\frac{\partial \xi_\alpha}{\partial x_\beta}+\frac{\partial \xi_\beta}{\partial x_\alpha}\right)=e_{\alpha i}e_{\beta j}A_{\alpha\beta} \tag{14.46}$$

Thus, the components A_{ij} transform like the components of a tensor. If the factors $\frac{1}{2}$ were omitted in the definitions of the shear strains ϵ_{ij}, then ϵ_{ij} would not be equal to ϵ_{ii} for $i=j$, and ϵ_{ii} and ϵ_{ij} would obey different transformation rules.

In the older literature,[2] the factor $\frac{1}{2}$ is omitted in the definition of the shear strains, whereas the longitudinal strains are defined as above. This definition leads to different transformation rules for the strain elements.

Since stress and strain are tensors, stress and strain relations can be written in a form that is independent of the co-ordinate system. Standard formulas can be used to obtain their elements in any co-ordinate system.

[2] E.g., in A. E. H. Love, *A Treatise on the Mathematical Theory of Elasticity* (New York, 1944).

Stress-Strain Relations

Since the translations and rotations of an elementary volume as a whole (rigid body motions) do not produce elastic stresses, the elastic stresses can be considered as functions only of the six components of strain. Hence,

$$\sigma_{ij}=\sigma_{ij}(\epsilon_{xx}, \epsilon_{xy}, \epsilon_{xz}, \epsilon_{yy}, \epsilon_{yz}, \epsilon_{zz}) \tag{14.47}$$

Each of the six stresses may be developed into a Taylor series of the six strains. Since Hooke's law may be assumed, only linear terms need be retained. The Taylor coefficients can then be interpreted as elastic constants. Thus, there are $6 \cdot 6=36$ elastic constants. Because of the existence of a unique energy function (as is proved in the standard treatises on elasticity), the stresses can be derived by differentiating the potential energy with respect to the strains. Since the potential energy is a quadratic function of the strains, only 21 coefficients occur in this function, and the number of independent elastic constants reduces to 21. Furthermore, for an isotropic substance, the stresses cannot depend on the orientation of the elastic element, and their magnitudes remain unchanged if x is changed to $-x$ or if the x-axis is rotated until it coincides with one of the other two axes. The relations that can be constructed in this way can be used to eliminate the unnecessary elastic constants. For an isotropic substance, we obtain two independent elastic constants, λ and μ, and the stress-strain relation simplifies to:

$$\begin{aligned} \sigma_{xx}&=\lambda\Delta+2\mu\epsilon_{xx} & \sigma_{xy}&=2\mu\epsilon_{xy} \\ \sigma_{yy}&=\lambda\Delta+2\mu\epsilon_{yy} & \sigma_{xz}&=2\mu\epsilon_{xz} \\ \sigma_{zz}&=\lambda\Delta+2\mu\epsilon_{zz} & \sigma_{yz}&=2\mu\epsilon_{yz} \end{aligned} \tag{14.48}$$

The magnitude

$$\Delta=\epsilon_{xx}+\epsilon_{yy}+\epsilon_{zz}=\operatorname{div}\vec{s} \tag{14.49}$$

is the dilatation. Equation 14.48 can be condensed into one equation:

$$\sigma_{ij}=\lambda\Delta\delta_{ij}+2\mu\epsilon_{ij} \tag{14.50}$$

where

$$\delta_{ij}=1 \quad \text{if } i=j \quad \text{and} \quad \delta_{ij}=0 \quad \text{if } i\neq j \tag{14.51}$$

Elastic Constants of Solids and Liquids

The elastic constants λ and μ in the stress-strain relations (Eq. 14.48) are called Lamé's constants. The constant λ is Lamé's dilatation modulus; it describes the component of the stress that is produced by a change of volume Δ if the shear forces are neglected ($\mu=0$). The second Lamé's constant μ is the shear modulus. This is readily deduced from Equation 14.48 by assuming that $\eta=0$ in the relation

$$\sigma_{xy}=2\mu\epsilon_{xy}=2\mu\frac{1}{2}\left(\frac{\partial\xi}{\partial y}+\frac{\partial\eta}{\partial x}\right)=\mu\frac{\partial\xi}{\partial y} \tag{14.52}$$

The right-hand side defines the shear modulus. The two Lamé's constants define completely the elastic behavior of the medium. For convenience, however, four interrelated elastic constants are usually used; these are Young's modulus λ_E, Poisson's ratio ν, the bulk modulus λ_K, and the shear modulus μ.

Young's modulus is defined as the ratio of the longitudinal stress to the longitudinal strain of a thin rod. If x is the co-ordinate along the axis of the rod, then

$$\sigma_{xx}=\lambda(\epsilon_{xx}+\epsilon_{yy}+\epsilon_{zz})+2\mu\epsilon_{xx} \tag{14.53}$$

Because of the axial symmetry, $\epsilon_{yy}=\epsilon_{zz}$, and

$$\sigma_{xx}=\lambda(\epsilon_{xx}+2\epsilon_{yy})+2\mu\epsilon_{xx} \tag{14.54}$$

The normal stress perpendicular to the axis of the rod is zero at the surface of the rod, because no transverse force is applied to it, and it is practically zero everywhere inside the rod, because the rod is assumed to be thin. Hence,

$$\sigma_{yy}=\sigma_{zz}=0=\lambda(\epsilon_{xx}+2\epsilon_{yy})+2\mu\epsilon_{yy} \tag{14.55}$$

or

$$\epsilon_{yy}=\frac{-\lambda\epsilon_{xx}}{2(\lambda+\mu)}=\nu\epsilon_{xx} \tag{14.56}$$

where

$$\nu=\frac{\lambda}{2(\lambda+\mu)}=\frac{1}{2\left(1+\frac{\mu}{\lambda}\right)} \tag{14.57}$$

represents the ratio of the transverse contraction to the longitudinal dilatation. This ratio is known as Poisson's constant. Young's modulus λ_E is obtained by eliminating ϵ_{yy} from the first equation of Equation 14.48:

$$\lambda_E=\frac{\sigma_{xx}}{\epsilon_{xx}}=\frac{\mu(3\lambda+2\mu)}{\lambda+\mu}=\frac{\mu\left(2\frac{\mu}{\lambda}+3\right)}{1+\frac{\mu}{\lambda}} \tag{14.58}$$

The bulk modulus λ_K is obtained by assuming uniform stress:

$$\sigma_{xx}=\sigma_{yy}=\sigma_{zz} \quad \text{and} \quad \epsilon_{xx}=\epsilon_{yy}=\epsilon_{zz} \tag{14.59}$$

If these values are substituted, Equation 14.48 simplifies to:

$$\sigma_{xx}=\lambda\cdot 3\epsilon_{xx}+2\mu\epsilon_{xx} \tag{14.60}$$

or

$$\lambda_K=\frac{\sigma_{xx}}{3\epsilon_{xx}}=\frac{\sigma_{xx}}{\Delta}=\lambda+\frac{2}{3}\mu \tag{14.61}$$

If the medium is a liquid, the real part α of the shear modulus $\mu=\alpha+j\beta$ is zero, and the complex bulk modulus becomes:

$$\lambda_K=\lambda_0(1+j\eta_\lambda)+\frac{2}{3}j\beta=\lambda_0\left[1+j\left(\eta_\lambda+\frac{2}{3}\eta_\mu\right)\right] \tag{14.62}$$

where $\beta=\lambda_0\eta_\mu$ is written for the imaginary part of the shear modulus.

The classical Stokes-Kirchhoff theory of internal friction assumes that $\eta_\lambda+\frac{2}{3}\eta_\mu=0$, which is equivalent to assuming that compression does not generate friction losses, regardless of whether the fluid is a sticky liquid or an ideal gas. Obviously, the classical theory of internal friction is not correct, and even a fluid is characterized by two constants of internal friction, such as the loss factor for shear deformations and the loss factor for volume changes or a shear viscosity and a volume viscosity.

Differential Equations of an Elastic Medium

If the stresses are expressed by the strains in Equation 14.9 with the aid of Equation 14.48, the equations of motion become:

$$\rho\frac{\partial^2\xi_i}{\partial t^2}=(\lambda+\mu)\frac{\partial\Delta}{\partial x_i}+\mu\nabla^2\xi_i \tag{14.63}$$

or, in vector form,

$$\rho\frac{\partial^2\vec{s}}{\partial t^2}=(\lambda+\mu)\,\mathrm{grad}\;\mathrm{div}\vec{s}+\mu\nabla^2\,\vec{s} \tag{14.64}$$

where ρ is the density of the medium. With the aid of the vector relation

$$\mathrm{curl}\;\mathrm{curl}\;\vec{s}=\nabla\cdot\nabla\cdot\vec{s}=\nabla(\nabla\vec{s})-\nabla^2\cdot\vec{s}=\mathrm{grad}\;\mathrm{div}\;\vec{s}-\nabla^2\vec{s} \tag{14.65}$$

the equations of motion can be transformed into the following two forms:

$$\rho\frac{\partial^2\vec{s}}{\partial t^2}=(\lambda+2\mu)\nabla^2\vec{s}+(\lambda+\mu)\;\mathrm{curl}\;\mathrm{curl}\;\vec{s} \tag{14.66}$$

$$\rho\frac{\partial^2\vec{s}}{\partial t^2}=(\lambda+2\mu)\;\mathrm{grad}\;\mathrm{div}\;\vec{s}-\mu\;\mathrm{curl}\;\mathrm{curl}\;\vec{s} \tag{14.67}$$

The second term on the right is zero whenever the motion is rotationless.

The displacement vector $\vec{s}$ (with the components ξ, η, and ζ) can always be derived from a scalar potential Φ and a vector potential $\vec{A}$:

$$\vec{s}=-\mathrm{grad}\;\Phi+\mathrm{curl}\;\vec{A} \tag{14.68}$$

The scalar potential describes the part of the motion that is produced by sources; the vector potential describes the part of the motion that is generated by vortexes. Substitution of Equation 14.68 in Equation 14.64 results in:

$$-\rho\frac{\partial^2\;\mathrm{grad}\;\Phi}{\partial t^2}+\rho\frac{\partial^2}{\partial t^2}\mathrm{curl}\;\vec{A}=-(\lambda+\mu)\;\mathrm{grad}\;(\nabla^2\Phi)-\mu\nabla^2\;\mathrm{grad}\;\Phi+\mu\nabla^2\;\mathrm{curl}\;\vec{A} \tag{14.69}$$

Because of the relations curl grad $=0$, div curl $=0$, and div grad $=\nabla^2$, the last equation can be split up into two simpler equations. The first is obtained by applying the curl to Equation 14.69. Since curl grad $=0$, applying the curl yields:

$$\rho\frac{\partial^2}{\partial t^2}\mathrm{curl}\;\mathrm{curl}\;\vec{A}=\mu\nabla^2\;\mathrm{curl}\;\mathrm{curl}\;\vec{A} \tag{14.70}$$

Integration leads to:

$$\rho \frac{\partial^2}{\partial t^2} \operatorname{curl} \vec{A} = \mu \nabla^2 \operatorname{curl} \vec{A} + \operatorname{grad} \Phi \tag{14.71}$$

Integration of the above equation with respect to the curl does not yield the complete solution, but only that part, A', of it whose curl is not zero. Since the curl of a gradient is always zero, the solution $A' + \operatorname{grad} \Phi$ also satisfies the above solution if Φ is any arbitrary function of the co-ordinate and the time. We may consider grad Φ as the integration constant in the curl integration.

The second equation is obtained by applying the divergence to Equation 14.66. Since div curl$=0$, this equation takes the form:

$$\rho \frac{\partial^2 \operatorname{div} \vec{s}}{\partial t^2} = (\lambda + 2\mu) \operatorname{div} \nabla^2 \vec{s} \tag{14.72}$$

Applying the divergence has destroyed the curl part of the solution. Thus the solution of the last equation is undetermined for a curl of an arbitrary function of the co-ordinates. If we integrate with respect to the divergence,

$$\rho \frac{\partial^2 \vec{s}}{\partial t^2} = (\lambda + 2\mu) \nabla^2 \vec{s} + \operatorname{curl} \vec{A} \tag{14.73}$$

The term curl A appears in place of an integration constant. Thus, applying the divergence to the general differential equation yields an equation for the divergence part of the solution (i.e., the field that is generated by sources); applying the curl yields the curl part of the solution (generated by eddies). Thus, the function that plays the role of an integration constant in one of the two equations is identical with the solution of the other equation. We may consider the equation

$$\frac{1}{c_s^2} \frac{\partial^2 \vec{A}}{\partial t^2} = \nabla^2 \vec{A} \tag{14.74}$$

where

$$c_s^2 = \frac{\mu}{\rho} \tag{14.75}$$

as the differential equation for the curl part of the solution, and we may consider the equation

$$\frac{1}{c_d^2} \frac{\partial^2 \Phi}{\partial t^2} = \nabla^2 \Phi \tag{14.76}$$

where

$$c_d^2 = \frac{\lambda_E + 2\mu}{\rho} \tag{14.77}$$

as the differential equation for the divergence part of the solution.

The vector equation (14.74) and the scalar equation (14.76) represent four equations—one for Φ and one for each of the components of $\vec{A}$. The Φ-equation has rotationless solutions; therefore, it describes a dilatational wave propagating with the velocity $c_d=[(\lambda+2\mu)/\rho]^{\frac{1}{2}}$. Solutions of the $\vec{A}$-equations have zero divergence, and Equation 14.74 represents three pure shear waves, each traveling with the velocity $c_s=(\mu/\rho)^{\frac{1}{2}}$.

Taking the divergence of Equation 14.67 or operating with ∇^2 on Equation 14.76 shows that the dilatation ∇ satisfies the same differential equation as the scalar potential φ:

$$\rho\frac{\partial^2\Delta}{\partial t^2}=(\lambda+2\mu)\nabla^2\Delta \tag{14.78}$$

where

$$\Delta=\operatorname{div}\vec{s}=-\operatorname{div}\operatorname{grad}\Phi=-\nabla^2\Phi \tag{14.79}$$

Similarly, eliminating Δ between both pairs of the equations that can be formed from Equation 14.63 or operating with the curl on Equation 14.72 proves that the rotation vector $\vec{\omega}$ satisfies the same differential equation as the vector potential $\vec{A}$:

$$\rho\frac{\partial^2\vec{\omega}}{\partial t^2}=\mu\nabla^2\vec{\omega} \tag{14.80}$$

The general solution for the dilatation is, therefore, identical in form to that for the scalar potential, and the general solution for the rotation is identical in form to that for the vector potential. However, the two sets of quantities Φ, Δ and $\vec{A}$, $\vec{\omega}$ must not be confused with one another, since they satisfy different boundary conditions.

Deformation of an Infinitely Extended Medium

Deformation in One Dimension

For an infinite medium, the simplest possible solution for the scalar and the vector potentials is that for plane progressive waves. The solution then depends on only one co-ordinate.

The scalar potential Φ describes a dilatational sound wave that travels with the sound velocity

$$c_d{}^2=\frac{(\lambda+2\mu)}{\rho} \tag{14.81}$$

through the medium. The medium is deformed in the direction of propagation. The vector potential describes shear waves; it may be decomposed into its components a_x and a_y in the direction of propagation and perpendicular to it. If x is the direction of propagation, the solution for a_x is:

$$\tilde{a}_x=A_x e^{-jk_s x+j\omega t} \tag{14.82}$$

The corresponding deformation is given by:

$$\vec{s}=\operatorname{curl}\vec{A} \tag{14.83}$$

or

$$s_x = \frac{\partial a_z}{\partial y} - \frac{\partial a_y}{\partial z} = 0$$

$$s_y = \frac{\partial a_x}{\partial z} - \frac{\partial a_z}{\partial x} = 0$$

$$s_z = \frac{\partial a_y}{\partial x} - \frac{\partial a_x}{\partial y} = 0 \qquad (14.84)$$

The last set of equations can be easily remembered if they are written as a determinant:

$$\begin{vmatrix} \vec{e}_1 & \vec{e}_2 & \vec{e}_3 \\ \dfrac{\partial}{\partial x} & \dfrac{\partial}{\partial y} & \dfrac{\partial}{\partial z} \\ a_x & a_y & a_z \end{vmatrix} \qquad (14.85)$$

where $\vec{e}_1$, $\vec{e}_2$, and $\vec{e}_3$ represent the unit vectors in the directions of the co-ordinate. Thus, the resulting deformation is zero. A component of the vector potential in the direction of propagation does not generate a deformation. The contribution of the component perpendicular to the direction of propagation is:

$$\tilde{a}_y = A_y e^{-jk_s x + j\omega t} \qquad (14.86)$$

The corresponding displacements are:

$$s_x = 0$$

$$s_y = 0$$

$$\tilde{s}_z = \frac{\partial \tilde{a}_y}{\partial x} = jk_s A_y e^{-jk_s x + j\omega t} \qquad (14.87)$$

The component of the vector potential at right angles generates a deformation in the plane normal to the direction of propagation and normal to the component of the vector potential. The direction of propagation, the direction of the component of the vector potential, and deformation (like the axes x, y, and z) form a right-handed system.

Deformation in Two Dimensions

If the solution does depend on two co-ordinates, say x and z, and does not depend on y, all derivatives with respect to y are zero; and the contributions of the vector potential $a(x, z)$ reduce to:

$$s_x' = \frac{\partial a_z}{\partial y} - \frac{\partial a_y}{\partial z} = -\frac{\partial a_y}{\partial z} = \frac{\partial \Psi}{\partial z}$$

$$s_y' = \frac{\partial a_x}{\partial z} - \frac{\partial a_z}{\partial x} = \text{const or zero} \qquad \text{(by definition)}$$

$$s_z' = \frac{\partial a_y}{\partial x} - \frac{\partial a_x}{\partial y} = \frac{\partial a_y}{\partial x} = \frac{-\partial \Psi}{\partial x} \qquad (14.88)$$

where

$$\Psi = -a_y \tag{14.89}$$

Thus, only the component a_y normal to the plane of the motion contributes to the motion. Since constant deformations are of little interest, we may assume that

$$s_y' = 0 \qquad \text{and} \qquad a_x = a_z = 0 \tag{14.90}$$

The total deformation as given by the scalar and the vector potentials is, therefore,

$$\begin{aligned} s_y &= 0 \\ s_x &= -\frac{\partial \Phi}{\partial x} + \frac{\partial \Psi}{\partial z} \\ s_z &= -\frac{\partial \Phi}{\partial z} - \frac{\partial \Psi}{\partial x} \end{aligned} \tag{14.91}$$

It is easy to see that Ψ is similar to the streaming potential in hydrodynamics. We easily deduce the following relations:

$$\begin{aligned} \Delta = \operatorname{div} \vec{s} = \operatorname{div}(-\operatorname{grad} \Phi + \operatorname{curl} \vec{A}) = \operatorname{div}(-\operatorname{grad} \Phi) = -\nabla^2 \Phi \\ \operatorname{curl} \vec{s} = \operatorname{curl}(-\operatorname{grad} \Phi + \operatorname{curl} \vec{A}) = \operatorname{curl} \operatorname{curl} \vec{A} \end{aligned} \tag{14.92}$$

Also, because $s_y = 0$, and because all derivatives with respect to y are zero,

$$\begin{aligned} (\operatorname{curl} \vec{s})_x &= \frac{\partial s_z}{\partial y} - \frac{\partial s_y}{\partial z} = -\frac{\partial s_y}{\partial z} = 0 \\ (\operatorname{curl} \vec{s})_y &= \frac{\partial s_x}{\partial z} - \frac{\partial s_z}{\partial x} = \nabla^2 \Psi \\ (\operatorname{curl} \vec{s})_z &= \frac{\partial s_y}{\partial x} - \frac{\partial s_x}{\partial y} = 0 \end{aligned} \tag{14.93}$$

Equation 14.74 now becomes:

$$\mu \nabla^2 \operatorname{curl} \vec{s} = \rho \frac{\partial^2 \operatorname{curl} \vec{s}}{\partial t^2} \tag{14.94}$$

or

$$\mu \nabla^2 \Psi = \rho \frac{\partial^2 \Psi}{\partial t^2} \tag{14.95}$$

which shows that Ψ also obeys the wave equation.

Deformation of a Semi-Infinite Medium—Rayleigh Waves

Whenever the medium is a solid and is bounded, both types of waves, shear waves and dilatational waves, are needed to satisfy the boundary conditions. Whenever a shear wave impinges on a solid-to-solid or solid-to-liquid interface, it is reflected partially as a shear wave and partially as a dilatational wave. Similarly, a dilatational wave is reflected partially as a dilatational wave and partially as a shear wave. Reflection may even completely transform one type of wave into some other type of wave. Such phenomena are discussed in books on wave propagation in solids and in some of the books on acoustics.

In general, shear and dilatational waves have different velocities, and the energy spreads inhomogeneously over the medium; the phenomenon is unsteady and inherent in itself. In certain cases, shear and dilatational deformations combine and travel with the same velocity, as if the phenomenon were a simple wave. These types of vibrations, which maintain their nature as they travel, are called natural modes; they are very similar to the natural modes of a finite vibrator and represent steady states of the semi-infinite medium.

A Rayleigh wave is a deformation that consists of shear and dilatation and that propagates along the surface of solids or liquids. For instance, the surface waves of the sea are a special type of Rayleigh waves. The wave length of the Rayleigh waves is always smaller than the sound wave length (so-called acoustic short circuit). The vibrating surface does not radiate sound energy into the interior of the medium, and the amplitude of the Rayleigh waves decreases exponentially with the distance from the surface, like that of the near field of a vibrating plate. Since Rayleigh waves spread only in two dimensions, they fall off more slowly with distance than shear or dilatational waves. Because of this, they are very important in the study of such seismic phenomena as earthquakes. The first waves that arrive are usually dilatational waves; they have the greatest sound velocity. Shear waves arrive next, followed by Rayleigh waves with amplitudes that are usually much larger than those of the first two groups of waves.

Rayleigh waves are very important in the theory of vibrations. At high frequencies, when the dimensions of a vibrator are large relative to the wave length, the lower-order modes of three-dimensional vibrators, such as rods and plates, turn into Rayleigh waves. Rayleigh waves are usually polarized elliptically, but the vertical component of vibration is frequently absent; and the horizontal component, instead of having the direction of propagation, may be perpendicular to it. Love showed[3] that such waves can be generated if the density and the elasticity of the earth decrease toward the surface. These waves are usually called Love waves.

Rayleigh waves are surface waves that decrease exponentially with the depth z. They are described by the following expressions:

$$\Phi = F(z)e^{-jkx+j\omega t} \tag{14.96}$$

$$\Psi = G(z)e^{-jkx+j\omega t} \tag{14.97}$$

By substituting these expressions into the corresponding wave equations (Eqs. 14.74 and 14.76), the following conditions are deduced:

$$F''(z) - (k^2 - k_d^2)F(z) = 0 \tag{14.98}$$

[3] A. E. H. Love, *op. cit.*

or

$$F''(z)-q^2F(z)=0 \tag{14.99}$$

where

$$k_d=\frac{\omega}{c_d} \quad \text{and} \quad q^2=k^2-k_d{}^2 \tag{14.100}$$

and

$$G''(z)-(k^2-k_s{}^2)G(z)=0 \tag{14.101}$$

or

$$G''(z)-\underline{s}^2G(z)=0 \tag{14.102}$$

where

$$k_s{}^2=\frac{\omega^2}{c_{\underline{s}}{}^2} \quad \text{and} \quad \underline{s}^2=k^2-k_s{}^2 \tag{14.103}$$

The above differential equations for $F(z)$ and $G(z)$ are solved by exponential functions, and the solutions become:

$$\Phi=Ae^{-qz+j(\omega t-kx)} \tag{14.104}$$

$$\Psi=Be^{-\underline{s}z+j(\omega t-kx)} \tag{14.105}$$

The dilatational waves and the shear waves are connected by the boundary conditions. If the surface $z=0$ is a free surface, all the normal components of the stress and the shear stresses must be zero at the surface. Thus,

$$\sigma_{zz}=\lambda \operatorname{div} \vec{s}+2\mu\frac{\partial s_z}{\partial z}=(\lambda+2\mu)\frac{\partial s_z}{\partial z}+\lambda\frac{\partial s_x}{\partial x}=0 \tag{14.106}$$

$$\sigma_{zx}=\mu\left(\frac{\partial s_z}{\partial x}+\frac{\partial s_x}{\partial z}\right)=0 \tag{14.107}$$

If the Equations 14.91 are substituted, the above equations become:

$$\sigma_{zz}=(\lambda+2\mu)\frac{\partial^2\Phi}{\partial z^2}+\lambda\frac{\partial^2\Phi}{\partial x^2}-2\mu\frac{\partial^2\Psi}{\partial x\partial z}=0 \tag{14.108}$$

$$\sigma_{zx}=\mu\left(2\frac{\partial^2\Phi}{\partial x\partial z}-\frac{\partial^2\Psi}{\partial x^2}+\frac{\partial^2\Psi}{\partial z^2}\right)=0 \tag{14.109}$$

These two equations determine the ratio A/B and the wave number k:

$$[(\lambda+2\mu)q^2-\lambda k^2]A-j2\mu skB=0 \tag{14.110}$$

$$2jkqA+(k^2+s^2)B=0 \tag{14.111}$$

A nontrivial solution ($A\neq 0$, $B\neq 0$) can exist only if the determinant of the last two equations is zero or if

$$[(\lambda+2\mu)q^2-\lambda k^2](k^2+s^2)=4k^2q\mu s \tag{14.112}$$

The magnitudes q and s must now be eliminated. This is best done by squaring both sides of the preceding equation and substituting for q^2 and s^2 the values given by Equations 14.100 and 14.103:

$$\begin{aligned}&\{[(\lambda+2\mu)(k^2-k_d{}^2)-\lambda k^2]^2(2k^2-k_s{}^2)\}^2\\&=\{[-(\lambda+2\mu)k_d{}^2+2\mu k^2]^2(2k^2-k_s{}^2)\}^2\\&=16k^4\mu^2(k^2-k_d{}^2)(k^2-k_s{}^2)\end{aligned} \tag{14.113}$$

The last equation is made dimensionless by dividing both sides by $\mu^2 k^8$:

$$\left[\left(-\frac{2\mu+\lambda}{\mu}\frac{k_d^2}{k^2}+2\right)\left(2-\frac{k_s^2}{k^2}\right)\right]^2=16\left[\left(1-\frac{k_d^2}{k^2}\right)\left(1-\frac{k_s^2}{k^2}\right)\right] \quad (14.114)$$

But

$$\frac{k_d^2}{k^2}=\frac{c^2}{c_d^2} \qquad \frac{k_s^2}{k^2}=\frac{c^2}{c_s^2} \qquad \frac{k_d^2}{k_s^2}=\frac{c_s^2}{c_d^2}=\frac{\mu}{\mu+2\lambda}=\frac{1-2\nu}{1+2\nu}=\alpha^2 \qquad \frac{\mu}{\lambda}=\frac{1-2\nu}{2\nu} \quad (14.115)$$

and

$$k_d=k_s\cdot\frac{c_s}{c_d}=\alpha_1 k_s \quad (14.116)$$

where ν is Poisson's ratio. With the aid of these relations, the determinant equation simplifies to:

$$\left(2-\frac{c^2}{c_s^2}\right)^4=16\left(1-\frac{c^2}{c_s^2}\right)\left(1-\alpha_1\frac{c^2}{c_s^2}\right) \quad (14.117)$$

or

$$\left(\frac{c}{c_s}\right)^6-8\left(\frac{c}{c_s^2}\right)^4+(24-16\alpha_1^2)\left(\frac{c}{c_s}\right)^2+16(\alpha_1^2-1)=0 \quad (14.118)$$

This equation is a cubic in the ratio $(c/c_s)^2$. The root $c/c_s<1$ describes the Rayleigh waves. The other two roots apply to regular shear waves and to dilatational waves. The coefficients are independent of the frequency. Thus, the velocity of the Rayleigh's waves depends only on the shear modulus and the Poisson's ratio of the medium. There is no dispersion, and a plane surface wave travels without change in form.

The phase velocity c of the Rayleigh waves is usually slightly smaller than the propagation velocity c_s of shear waves; however, the vibration amplitudes decrease rather rapidly with depth. The decay constants are given by:

$$\frac{q^2}{k^2}=1-\frac{k_d^2}{k^2}=1-\alpha^2\frac{c^2}{c_s^2} \quad (14.119)$$

$$\frac{s^2}{k^2}=1-\frac{k_s^2}{k^2}=1-\frac{c^2}{c_s^2} \quad (14.120)$$

Figure 14.5 shows the amplitudes of the stresses and the displacements associated with Rayleigh surface waves in steel ($\nu=0.29$).

The ratio A/B is determined by Equations 14.110 and 14.111. Substituting for B and taking the real parts, we have:

$$u=\frac{\partial\Phi}{\partial x}+\frac{\partial\Psi}{\partial z}=Ak[e^{-qz}-2qs(s^2+k^2)^{-1}e^{-sz}]\sin(\omega t-kx) \quad (14.121)$$

$$w=\frac{\partial\Phi}{\partial z}-\frac{\partial\Psi}{\partial x}=A[(qe^{-qz}-2k^2(s^2+k^2)^{-1}e^{-sz}]\cos(\omega t-kx) \quad (14.122)$$

In contrast to the displacement of regular shear waves, the displacement here is not perpendicular to the direction of propagation. If u is plotted

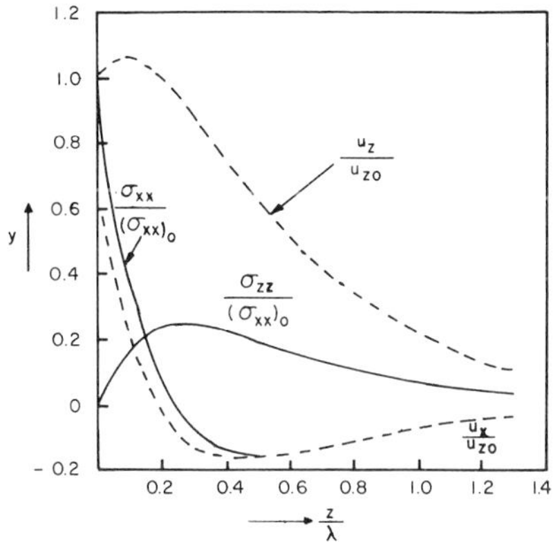

Fig. 14.5 Amplitudes and stresses associated with Rayleigh's surface waves in steel (propagating in the z-direction).

horizontally and w vertically, an ellipse results, with the major axis normal to the surface.

Curvilinear Co-ordinates[4]

Differential equations can usually be solved without great difficulty, but difficulties do arise when the solution must be adapted to the boundary conditions. It then becomes imperative to express the boundary conditions in the simplest possible form and to introduce, whenever possible, co-ordinates that assume constant values at the boundaries. Thus, Cartesian co-ordinates are adequate for problems in which the boundaries are represented by the surfaces $x=a$, $y=b$, and $z=c$. Vibrations of spaces of the form of a parallelepiped, therefore, are always treated in Cartesian co-ordinates. For cylindrical rods, the cylindrical co-ordinates r, φ, and z lead to the simplest possible form of the boundary conditions. Other situations require spherical or elliptical co-ordinates.

Co-ordinate Transformations and the Metric Tensor

The curvilinear co-ordinates q_1, q_2, and q_3 are usually introduced by expressing the Cartesian co-ordinates as a function of the curvilinear co-

[4] Curvilinear co-ordinates are derived in most textbooks on physics, but, except for some advanced treatises on tensor calculus, there seems to be only one readily available source (A. E. H. Love, *op. cit.*) that presents the derivation of the transformation formulas for the elastic stresses and strains—unfortunately, with a lengthy and involved notation. The derivations in the present work may be found more convenient.

ordinates, as follows:

$$x_i = x_i(q_1, q_2, q_3) \tag{14.123}$$

We thus have:

$$\begin{aligned} dx_i &= \frac{\partial x_i}{\partial q_1} dq_1 + \frac{\partial x_i}{\partial q_2} dq_2 + \frac{\partial x_i}{\partial q_3} dq_3 \\ &= \frac{\partial x_i}{\partial q_j} dq_j \end{aligned} \tag{14.124}$$

The element of length ds is given by:

$$\begin{aligned} ds^2 = dx^2 + dy^2 + dz^2 = dx_i{}^2 = \left(\frac{\partial x_i}{\partial q_j} dq_j\right)\left(\frac{\partial x_i}{\partial q_k} dq_k\right) = \frac{\partial x_i}{\partial q_j}\frac{\partial x_i}{\partial q_k} dq_j dq_k \\ = g_{jk} dq_j dq_k \end{aligned} \tag{14.125}$$

where

$$g_{jk} = \frac{\partial x_i}{\partial q_j}\frac{\partial x_i}{\partial q_k} \tag{14.126}$$

It can be shown that the components g_{jk} form the elements of a tensor (called the metric tensor). If q_i changes by dq_i, the corresponding changes of the co-ordinates x_j are:

$$dx_j = \frac{\partial x_j}{\partial q_i} dq_i \qquad \text{(no summation convention)} \tag{14.127}$$

And if q_k changes by dq_k, the corresponding changes of the x-co-ordinates are:

$$dx_j{}' = \frac{\partial x_j}{\partial q_k} dq_k \tag{14.128}$$

Since the co-ordinate surfaces are orthogonal, the scalar product of the vectors dx_j and $dx_j{}'$ must be zero, or

$$\begin{aligned} dx_j dx_j{}' = \sum_j \frac{\partial x_j}{\partial q_i} dq_i \frac{\partial x_j}{\partial q_k} dq_k = \sum_j \frac{\partial x_j}{\partial q_i}\frac{\partial x_j}{\partial q_k} \cdot dq_i dq_k \\ = g_{ik} dq_i dq_k = 0 \text{ (no summation convention)} \end{aligned} \tag{14.129}$$

Since dq_i and dq_k are not zero, we must have:

$$g_{ik} = 0 \tag{14.130}$$

for $i \neq k$. Hence,

$$ds_i = \sqrt{g_{ii}}\, dq_i \tag{14.131}$$

represents the change ds of s if q_i increases by dq_i and the other two co-ordinates remain constant. The element of volume that corresponds to the increments dq_1, dq_2, and dq_3 of the curvilinear co-ordinates, then, is given by:

$$d\tau = ds_1 ds_2 ds_3 = h_1 h_2 h_3 dq_1 dq_2 dq_3 \tag{14.132}$$

where

$$h_1 = \sqrt{g_{11}} \qquad h_2 = \sqrt{g_{22}} \qquad \text{and} \qquad h_3 = \sqrt{g_{33}} \tag{14.133}$$

Three unit vectors, $\vec{e}_1$, $\vec{e}_2$, and $\vec{e}_3$, are defined. The vector $\vec{e}_1$ is assumed normal to the surfaces $q_1 = \text{const}$; for instance, if q_1 is the radial co-ordinate r, $\vec{e}_1$ is the unit vector in the r-direction. The co-ordinate directions may be defined as the directions of these unit vectors.

The transformation formulas for the gradient, divergence, curl, etc., the strains, and the elastic equations can be obtained on the basis of the metric tensor by covariant differentiation, but a good knowledge of tensor calculus is required. However, the fundamental formulas can be derived easily in an elementary manner.

Fundamental Differential Operators in Curvilinear Co-ordinates

The gradient of a scalar function is given by the derivatives with respect to the line elements $ds_\nu = \sqrt{g_{\nu\nu}}\, dq_\nu = h_\nu\, dq_\nu$ in the three co-ordinate directions:

$$\begin{aligned} \operatorname{grad} \Phi &= \vec{e}_1 \frac{\partial \Phi}{\partial s_1} + \vec{e}_2 \frac{\partial \Phi}{\partial s_2} + \vec{e}_3 \frac{\partial \Phi}{\partial s_3} \\ &= \vec{e}_1 \left(\frac{1}{h_1} \frac{\partial \Phi}{\partial q_1} \right)_{s_2,\, s_3} + \vec{e}_2 \left(\frac{1}{h_2} \frac{\partial \Phi}{\partial q_2} \right)_{s_1,\, s_2} + \vec{e}_3 \left(\frac{1}{h_3} \frac{\partial \Phi}{\partial q_3} \right)_{s_2,\, s_3} \end{aligned} \tag{14.134}$$

Since keeping s_i, s_j constant in the derivatives is equivalent to keeping q_i, q_j constant, the gradient can also be written as follows:

$$\begin{aligned} \operatorname{grad} \Phi &= \vec{e}_1 \frac{1}{h_1} \left(\frac{\partial \Phi}{\partial q_1} \right)_{q_2,\, q_3} + \vec{e}_2 \frac{1}{h_2} \left(\frac{\partial \Phi}{\partial q_2} \right)_{q_1,\, q_2} + \vec{e}_3 \frac{1}{h_3} \left(\frac{\partial \Phi}{\partial q_3} \right)_{q_1,\, q_2} \\ &= \vec{e}_1 \frac{1}{h_1} \frac{\partial \Phi}{\partial q_1} + \vec{e}_2 \frac{1}{h_2} \frac{\partial \Phi}{\partial q_2} + \vec{e}_3 \frac{1}{h_3} \frac{\partial \Phi}{\partial q_3} \end{aligned} \tag{14.135}$$

The subscripts q_i, q_j have been dropped in the last result, since they are no longer necessary.

The expression for the divergence is derived by considering the outflow of fluid of the elementary parallelepiped with the edges $h_1\, dq_1$, $h_2\, dq_2$, and $h_3\, dq_3$. We shall denote the components of the vector whose divergence we shall compute by v_1, v_2, and v_3. The excess of fluid that leaves the elementary volume over the fluid entering it (Fig. 14.6) in the direction e_1 perpendicular to the surface $q_1 = \text{const}$ is given by:

$$\begin{aligned} v_1(q_1 + dq_1) h_2(q_1 + dq_1) h_3(q_1 + dq_1) dq_2 dq_3 - v_1(q_1) h_2(q_1) h_3(q_1) dq_2 dq_3 \\ = \frac{\partial (v_1 h_2 h_3)}{\partial q_1} dq_1 dq_2 dq_3 \end{aligned} \tag{14.136}$$

Two similar terms are obtained for the other two co-ordinate directions. To obtain the divergence, the result still has to be divided by the magnitude $h_1 h_2 h_3 dq_1 dq_2 dq_3$ of the elementary volume:

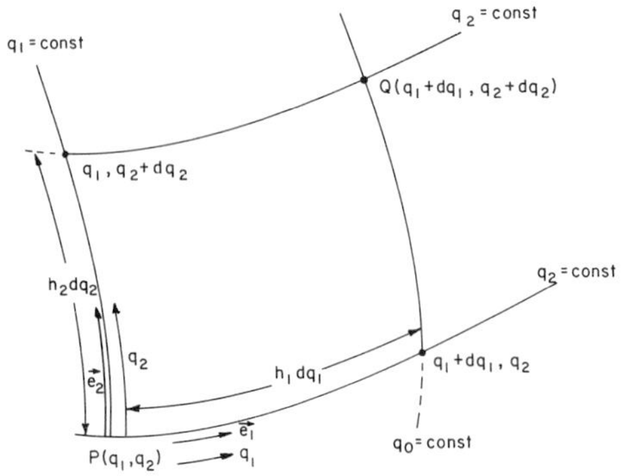

Fig. 14.6 Curvilinear co-ordinates.

$$\operatorname{div} \vec{v} = \frac{1}{h_1h_2h_3}\left[\frac{\partial(v_1h_2h_3)}{\partial q_1} + \frac{\partial(v_2h_3h_1)}{\partial q_2} + \frac{\partial(v_3h_1h_2)}{\partial q_3}\right] \tag{14.137}$$

The curl is determined by the circulation of the vector $\vec{v}$ around a unitary area. The circulation around an elementary area $h_2dq_2h_3dq_3$ of the co-ordinate surface $q_1=\text{const}$ is given by:

$$\begin{aligned} &[h_3(q_2+dq)v_3(q_2+dq)dq_3 - h_3(q_2)v_3(q_2)dq_3] \\ &-[h_2(q_3)v_2(q_3)dq_2 - h_2(q_3+dq_3)v_2(q_3+dq_3)dq_2] \\ &= \left[\frac{\partial(h_3v_3)}{\partial q_2} - \frac{\partial(h_2v_2)}{\partial q_3}\right] dq_2dq_3 \end{aligned} \tag{14.138}$$

The result must still be divided by the magnitude $h_2dq_2h_3dq_3$ of the area and multiplied by the unit vector $\vec{e}_1$ perpendicular to that area. In a similar manner, the other two components of the vector curl are computed. Hence,

$$\begin{aligned} \operatorname{curl} \vec{v} = {} & \frac{\vec{e}_1}{h_2h_3}\left[\frac{\partial}{\partial q_2}(h_3v_3) - \frac{\partial}{\partial q_3}(h_2v_2)\right] + \frac{\vec{e}_2}{h_1h_3}\left[\frac{\partial}{\partial q_3}(h_1v_1) - \frac{\partial}{\partial q_1}(h_3v_3)\right] \\ & + \frac{\vec{e}_3}{h_1h_2}\left[\frac{\partial}{\partial q_1}(h_2v_2) - \frac{\partial}{\partial q_2}(h_1v_1)\right] \end{aligned} \tag{14.139}$$

The Laplace's operator is derived in curvilinear co-ordinates by applying the divergence to the gradient of a scalar function Ψ. The result is:

$$\nabla^2\Psi = \frac{1}{h_1h_2h_3}\left(\frac{\partial}{\partial \xi_1}\frac{h_2h_3}{h_1}\frac{\partial\Psi}{\partial \xi_1}\right) + \frac{\partial}{\partial \xi_2}\left(\frac{h_3h_1}{h_2}\frac{\partial\Psi}{\partial \xi_2}\right) + \frac{\partial}{\partial \xi_3}\left(\frac{h_1h_2}{h_3}\frac{\partial\Psi}{\partial \xi_3}\right) \tag{14.140}$$

Strain

To determine the components of strain in curvilinear co-ordinates, let us consider two points, $P(q_1, q_2, q_3)$ and $Q(q_1+dq_1, q_2+dq_2, q_3+dq_3)$ a distance dr apart (Fig. 14.7) and let the direction cosines of PQ, referred to the vec-

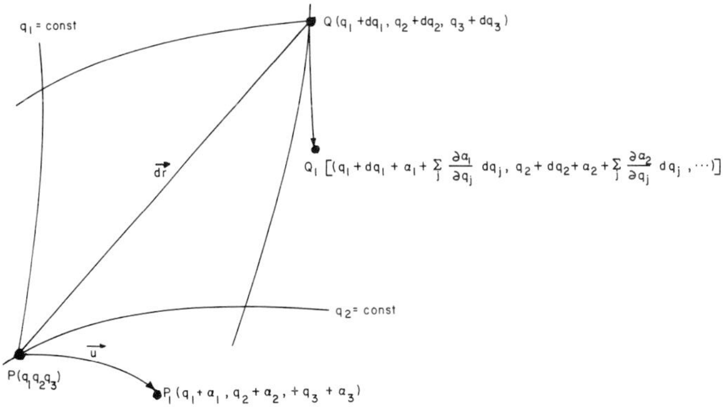

Fig. 14.7 Deformation of an element of length in curvilinear co-ordinates.

tors $\vec{e}_1$, $\vec{e}_2$, and $\vec{e}_3$ be l, m, and n. Let ds_1, ds_2, and ds_3 be the projections of $\vec{dr}$ on the vectors $\vec{e}_1$, $\vec{e}_2$, and $\vec{e}_3$, respectively. We then have (see Eq. 14.131):

$$ds_1 = h_1 dq_1 = drl, \quad ds_2 = h_2 dq_2 = drm, \quad ds_3 = h_3 dq_3 = drn \tag{14.141}$$

where $h_1 dq_1$ represents the change in the line element ds if the curvilinear q_1 co-ordinate is changed by dq_1. (See Eq. 14.131). After the material is strained, the points PQ become the points $P_1 Q_1$. Let u_1, u_2, u_3 be the projections of the displacement of point P_1 relative to the original point P in the directions of the vectors $\vec{e}_1$, $\vec{e}_2$, and $\vec{e}_3$, and let $q_1 + \alpha_1$, $q_2 + \alpha_2$, $q_3 + \alpha_3$ be the curvilinear co-ordinates of the displaced point P_1. Let it be assumed that α_1, α_2, α_3 are very small quantities. Since α_1, α_2, α_3 are the small changes of the co-oıdinates of point P during the displacement, the displacement of point P_1 relative to point P is given by (see Eq. 14.131):

$$u_1 = h_1 \alpha_1 \qquad u_2 = h_2 \alpha_2 \qquad \text{and} \qquad u_3 = h_3 \alpha_3 \tag{14.142}$$

The co-ordinates of Q before the displacement were $q_1 + dq_1$, $q_2 + dq_2$, and $q_3 + dq_3$. The displacement q_1 increased by α_1, q_2 by α_2, and q_3 by α_3. But because of the deformation of the elastic medium, α_ν is not constant, but is a function of the curvilinear co-ordinates,

$$\alpha_\nu(Q_1) = \alpha_\nu(P_1) + \sum_j \frac{\partial \alpha_\nu}{\partial q_j} dq_j + \ldots \tag{14.143}$$

and the curvilinear co-ordinates (no summation convention here) of point Q_1 are

$$q_i + dq_i' = q_i + dq_i + \alpha_i + \sum_j \frac{\partial \alpha_i}{dq_j} dq_j \tag{14.144}$$

The values of h_1 at P_1 (after the displacement) are given with sufficient accuracy by

$$h_1+\alpha_1\frac{\partial}{\partial q_1}h_1+\alpha_2\frac{\partial}{\partial q_2}h_1+\alpha_3\frac{\partial}{\partial q_3}h_1=h_1+\sum_j\frac{\partial h_1}{\partial q_j}\alpha_j \qquad (14.145)$$

The projections of P_1Q_1 on $\vec{e}_1$, $\vec{e}_2$, and $\vec{e}_3$ then are expressed with sufficient accuracy by:

$$h_i(P_1)dq_i'=\left(\alpha_i+\sum_j\frac{\partial\alpha_i}{\partial q_j}dq_j\right)\left(h_i+\sum_j\frac{\partial h_i}{\partial q_j}\alpha_j\right) \quad \text{(no summation convention)} \qquad (14.146)$$

The squares and products of Δq and its derivatives can be neglected; Δq_1, Δq_2, and Δq_3 then are expressed in terms of u_1, u_2, and u_3 with the aid of Equation 14.142, and dq_1, dq_2, and dq_3 are expressed in terms of r and l, m, and n with the aid of Equation 14.141. If the three resulting formulas are added, we obtain an expression for the square of the length $P_1Q_1=dr(1+\epsilon)$, where ϵ is the extension of a linear element along PQ:

$$(1+\epsilon^2)=\left[l\left(1+\frac{1}{h_1}\frac{\partial u_1}{\partial q_1}+\frac{1}{h_1h_2}u_2\frac{\partial}{\partial q_2}(h_1)+\frac{1}{h_1}\frac{1}{h_3}u_3\frac{\partial}{\partial q_3}(h_1)\right)\right.$$
$$\left.+m\frac{h_1}{h_2}\frac{\partial}{\partial q_2}\left(\frac{u_1}{h_1}\right)+n\frac{h_1}{h_3}\frac{\partial}{\partial q_3}\left(\frac{u_1}{h_1}\right)\right]^2+\ldots+\ldots \qquad (14.147)$$

If squares and higher products of u_1, u_2, and u_3 are neglected, the result can be written in the form:

$$\epsilon=e_{q_1q_1}l^2+e_{q_2q_2}m^2+e_{q_3q_3}n^2+e_{q_2q_3}mn+e_{q_3q_1}nl+e_{q_1q_2}lm \qquad (14.148)$$

where

$$e_{q_1q_1}=\frac{1}{h_1}\frac{\partial u_1}{\partial q_1}+\frac{1}{h_1h_2}u_2\frac{\partial}{\partial q_2}h_2+\frac{1}{h_3h_1}u_3\frac{\partial}{\partial q_3}h_1$$
$$e_{q_2q_2}=\frac{1}{h_2}\frac{\partial u_2}{\partial q_2}+\frac{1}{h_2h_3}u_3\frac{\partial}{\partial q_3}h_2+\frac{1}{h_1h_2}u_1\frac{\partial}{\partial q_1}h_2$$
$$e_{q_3q_3}=\frac{1}{h_3}\frac{\partial u_3}{\partial q_3}+\frac{1}{h_3h_1}u_1\frac{\partial}{\partial q_1}h_3+\frac{1}{h_2h_3}u_2\frac{\partial}{\partial q_2}h_3 \qquad (14.149)$$

and

$$e_{q_2q_3}=\frac{h_3}{h_2}\frac{\partial}{\partial q_2}\left(\frac{u_3}{h_3}\right)+\frac{h_2}{h_3}\frac{\partial}{\partial q_3}\left(\frac{u_2}{h_2}\right)$$
$$e_{q_3q_1}=\frac{h_1}{h_3}\frac{\partial}{\partial q_3}\left(\frac{u_1}{h_1}\right)+\frac{h_3}{h_1}\frac{\partial}{\partial q_1}\left(\frac{u_3}{h_3}\right)$$
$$e_{q_1q_2}=\frac{h_2}{h_1}\frac{\partial}{\partial q_1}\left(\frac{u_2}{h_2}\right)+\frac{h_1}{h_2}\frac{\partial}{\partial q_2}\left(\frac{u_1}{h_1}\right) \qquad (14.150)$$

Examples

In cylindrical co-ordinates,

$$ds_1=dr \qquad ds_2=rd\varphi \qquad \text{and} \qquad ds_3=dz \qquad (14.151)$$

and

$$h_1=1 \qquad h_2=r \qquad \text{and} \qquad h_3=1 \tag{14.152}$$

If $\vec{s}$ is the displacement vector, and if its components are s_r, s_z, and s_φ, then

$$\operatorname{div} \vec{s}=\Delta=\frac{1}{r}\frac{\partial(rs_r)}{\partial r}+\frac{1}{r}\frac{\partial s_\varphi}{\partial \varphi}+\frac{\partial s_z}{\partial z} \tag{14.153}$$

The components of the curl become:

$$(\operatorname{curl} \vec{s})_r=2\omega_r=\frac{1}{r}\frac{\partial s_z}{\partial \varphi}-\frac{\partial s_\varphi}{\partial z}$$

$$(\operatorname{curl} s)_\varphi=2\omega_\varphi=\frac{\partial s_r}{\partial z}-\frac{\partial s_z}{\partial r}$$

$$(\operatorname{curl} s)_z=2\omega_z=\frac{1}{r}\left[\frac{\partial(rs_\varphi)}{\partial r}-\frac{\partial s_r}{\partial \varphi}\right] \tag{14.154}$$

Because of Equation 14.153, the last three equations lead to the compatibility relation

$$\frac{1}{r}\frac{\partial(r\omega_r)}{\partial r}+\frac{1}{r}\frac{\partial \omega_\varphi}{\partial \varphi}+\frac{\partial \omega_z}{\partial z}=0 \tag{14.155}$$

The strains are:

$$\epsilon_{rr}=\frac{\partial u_r}{\partial r} \qquad \epsilon_{\varphi\varphi}=\frac{1}{r}\frac{\partial u_\varphi}{\partial \varphi}+\frac{u_r}{r} \qquad \epsilon_{zz}=\frac{\partial u_z}{\partial z}$$

$$\epsilon_{\varphi z}=\frac{1}{2}\left(\frac{1}{r}\frac{\partial u_z}{\partial \varphi}+\frac{\partial u_\varphi}{\partial z}\right) \quad \epsilon_{zr}=\frac{1}{2}\left(\frac{\partial u_r}{\partial z}+\frac{\partial u_z}{\partial r}\right) \quad \epsilon_{r\varphi}=\frac{1}{2}\left(\frac{\partial u_\varphi}{\partial r}-\frac{u_\varphi}{r}+\frac{1}{r}\frac{\partial u_r}{\partial \varphi}\right) \tag{14.156}$$

where u_r, u_φ, and u_z are the displacements in the three co-ordinate directions.

Equations of Motion

The equations of motion are usually derived by considering an elementary volume in curvilinear co-ordinates, and by computing the stress resultants in the various co-ordinate directions. The computations then are similar to those performed in deriving the differential equations for the string and the beam.

A more general method that does not require advanced tensor calculus is also possible. Starting point is the equation of motion in integral form:

$$\int \rho \frac{d^2\xi}{dt^2} d\sigma=\int \rho X d\tau+\int X_n d\sigma \tag{14.157}$$

It is expedient to denote the six components of stress referred to the normals to the surfaces α, β, and γ by $\alpha\alpha$, $\beta\beta$, $\gamma\gamma$, $\beta\gamma$, $\gamma\alpha$, and $\alpha\beta$. In this notation, we have

$$\alpha x=\alpha\alpha \cos(\alpha, x)+\alpha\beta \cos(\beta, x)+\gamma\alpha \cos(\gamma, x) \tag{14.158}$$

Also, the projection of the surface element $d\sigma$ upon the tangent plane to the α surface is $d\beta d\gamma h_2 h_3$. The surface integral then becomes:

$$\int X_n d\sigma = \int [\alpha\alpha \cos(\alpha, x) + \alpha\beta \cos(\beta, x) + \gamma\alpha \cos(\gamma, x)]\, h_2 h_3 d\beta d\gamma$$
$$+ \int [\alpha\beta \cos(\alpha, x) + \beta\beta \cos(\beta, x) + \beta\gamma \cos(\gamma, x)]\, h_3 h_1 d\gamma d\alpha$$
$$+ \int\int \gamma\alpha \cos(\alpha, x) + \beta\gamma \cos(\beta, x) + \gamma\gamma \cos(\gamma, x)\, h_1 h_2 d\alpha d\beta \quad (14.159)$$

This surface integral is transformed into a volume integral with the aid of Green's formula:

$$\int X_n d\sigma = \int d\alpha d\beta d\gamma \Big[\frac{\partial}{\partial \alpha} [h_2 h_3 [\alpha\alpha \cos(\alpha, x) + \alpha\beta \cos(\beta, x) + \gamma\alpha \cos(\gamma, x)]]$$
$$+ \frac{\partial}{\partial \beta} \{h_3 h_1 [\alpha\beta \cos(\alpha, x) + \beta\beta \cos(\beta, x) + \beta\gamma \cos(\gamma, x)]\}$$
$$+ \frac{\partial}{\partial \gamma} \{h_1 h_2 [\gamma\alpha \cos(\alpha, x) + \beta\gamma \cos(\beta, x) + \gamma\gamma \cos(\gamma, x)]\} \Big] \quad (14.160)$$

The following relations can be deduced from the orthogonality conditions for the new co-ordinates. (The derivation of these relations is straightforward, but is very lengthy and will not be given here.)

$$\frac{\partial}{\partial \alpha} \cos(\alpha, x) = -\frac{1}{h_2} \frac{\partial}{\partial \beta}(h_1) \cos(\beta, x) - \frac{1}{h_3} \frac{\partial}{\partial \gamma}(h_1) \cos(\gamma, x)$$
$$\frac{\partial}{\partial \beta} \cos(\alpha, x) = \frac{1}{h_1} \frac{\partial}{\partial \alpha}(h_2) \cos(\beta, x)$$
$$\frac{\partial}{\partial \gamma} \cos(\alpha, x) = \frac{1}{h_1} \frac{\partial}{\partial \alpha}(h_3) \cos(\gamma, x) \quad (14.161)$$

Similar equations follow for Y and Z. We assume the direction of x to be normal to the surface $\alpha = \text{const}$, which passes through the point (α, β, γ) and, after the differentations have been performed, set

$$\cos(\alpha, x) = 1 \quad \cos(\beta, x) = 0 \quad \cos(\gamma, x) = 0 \quad (14.162)$$

The volume element is $h_1 h_2 h_3 d\alpha d\beta d\gamma$. If we write the above equation of motion for unit volume, dropping the integration signs, and using the above relation, we obtain the equation of motion in curvilinear co-ordinates:

$$\rho \frac{d^2 \xi_\alpha}{dt^2} = \rho X_\alpha + \frac{1}{h_1 h_2 h_3} \left[\frac{\partial}{\partial \alpha}(\alpha\alpha\, h_2 h_3) + \frac{\partial}{\partial \beta}(\alpha\beta\, h_3 h_1) + \frac{\partial}{\partial \gamma}(\gamma\alpha\, h_1 h_2) \right]$$
$$+ \frac{\alpha\beta}{h_1 h_2} \frac{\partial}{\partial \beta}(h_1) + \gamma\alpha \frac{1}{h_1 h_3} \frac{\partial}{\partial \gamma}(h_1)$$
$$- \frac{\beta\beta}{h_1 h_2} \frac{\partial}{\partial \alpha}(h_2) - \frac{\gamma\gamma}{h_1 h_3} \frac{\partial}{\partial \alpha}(h_3) \quad (14.163)$$

The two equations containing the components of acceleration and body force in the direction to the normals $\beta = \text{const}$ and $\gamma = \text{const}$ can be written by symmetry.

In cylindrical co-ordinates, r, φ, z, the equations of motion are:

$$\frac{\partial rr}{\partial r}+\frac{1}{r}\frac{\partial r\varphi}{\partial \varphi}+\frac{\partial rz}{\partial z}+\frac{rr-\varphi\varphi}{r}+\rho F_r=\rho\ddot{\xi}_r \tag{14.164}$$

$$\frac{\partial r\varphi}{\partial r}+\frac{1}{r}\frac{\partial \varphi\varphi}{\partial \varphi}+\frac{\partial \varphi z}{\partial z}+\frac{2r\varphi}{r}+\rho F_\varphi=\rho\ddot{\xi}_\varphi \tag{14.165}$$

$$\frac{\partial rz}{\partial r}+\frac{1}{r}\frac{\partial \varphi z}{\partial \varphi}+\frac{\partial zz}{\partial z}+\frac{rz}{r}+\rho F_z=\rho\ddot{\xi}_z \tag{14.166}$$

Vibrations of a Cylinder

Elastic Equation in Cylindrical Co-ordinates

The wave equation for an isotropic elastic medium (Eq. 14.63) can be written in the following form:

$$\rho\frac{\partial^2\vec{s}}{\partial t^2}=(\lambda+2\mu)\,\mathrm{grad}\,\Delta-2\mu\,\mathrm{curl}\,\vec{\omega} \tag{14.167}$$

where (see Eq. 14.153)

$$\Delta=\mathrm{div}\,\vec{s}=\frac{1}{r}\frac{\partial(ru_r)}{\partial r}+\frac{1}{r}\frac{\partial u_\varphi}{\partial \varphi}+\frac{\partial u_z}{\partial z} \tag{14.168}$$

and curl $\vec{\omega}$ is given by Equation 14.154. If these substitutions are made, the following differential equations result:

$$\rho\frac{\partial^2 s_r}{\partial t^2}=(\lambda+2\mu)\frac{\partial\Delta}{\partial r}-\frac{2\mu}{r}\frac{\partial\omega_z}{\partial\varphi}+2\mu\frac{\partial\omega_\varphi}{\partial z} \tag{14.169}$$

$$\rho\frac{\partial^2 s_\varphi}{\partial t^2}=(\lambda+2\mu)\frac{1}{r}\frac{\partial\Delta}{\partial\varphi}-2\mu\frac{\partial\omega_r}{\partial z}+2\mu\frac{\partial\omega_z}{\partial r} \tag{14.170}$$

$$\rho\frac{\partial^2 s_z}{\partial t^2}=(\lambda+2\mu)\frac{\partial\Delta}{\partial z}-\frac{2\mu}{r}\frac{\partial r\omega_\varphi}{\partial r}+\frac{2\mu}{r}\frac{\partial\omega_r}{\partial\varphi} \tag{14.171}$$

Solutions for a Cylinder

The elastic deformations are described by a vector potential $\vec{A}$ and a scalar potential Φ. Each of the four sound fields A_x, A_y, A_z, and Φ can propagate independently of the others in an infinite medium, but not in a bounded medium. To investigate the situation in a cylindrical rod, the cylindrical co-ordinates r, φ, and z must be used, and the functions to be determined are A_φ, A_r, A_z, and Φ. Let us first consider the propagation of an infinite train of sinusoidal waves. The displacement at each point is a simple harmonic function of z as well as t:

$$\left.\begin{aligned} \tilde{A}_r &= a_r \\ \tilde{A}_\varphi &= a_\varphi \\ \tilde{A}_z &= a_z \\ \tilde{\Phi} &= \Phi \end{aligned}\right\} e^{j(kz+\omega t)} \tag{14.172}$$

The frequency of these waves is $\omega/2\pi$, and the wave length is $2\pi/k=\lambda$, so that the phase velocity is $c_p=\omega/k$.

The deformations that correpond to the above potentials are given by:

$$\vec{s} = \text{curl } \vec{A} - \text{grad } \Phi$$

$$s_r = \frac{1}{r}\left[\frac{\partial}{\partial\varphi}a_z - \frac{\partial}{\partial z}(ra_\varphi)\right] - \frac{\partial\Phi}{\partial r}$$

$$s_\varphi = \frac{\partial}{\partial z}a_r - \frac{\partial}{\partial r}a_z - \frac{\partial\Phi}{n\partial\phi}$$

$$s_z = \frac{1}{r}\left[\frac{\partial}{\partial r}(ra_\varphi) - \frac{\partial}{\partial\varphi}(ra_r)\right] - \frac{\partial\Phi}{\partial z} \tag{14.173}$$

In general, the functions a_r, a_φ, a_z, and Φ should all be functions r and φ. However, it is assumed here that the cylinder can be excited symmetrically about the z-axis, so that none of the fields depends on φ (hence $\partial/\partial\varphi=0$, but $a_\varphi \neq 0$). Introducing Equation 14.173 into Equations msert 14.169 to 14.171, we obtain:

$$\frac{\partial^2 a_r}{\partial r^2} + \frac{1}{r}\frac{\partial a_r}{\partial r} - \frac{a_r}{r^2} + k'^2 a_r = 0$$

$$\frac{\partial^2 a_\varphi}{\partial r^2} + \frac{1}{r}\frac{\partial a_\varphi}{\partial r} - \frac{a_\varphi}{r^2} + k'^2 a_\varphi = 0$$

$$\frac{\partial^2 a_z}{\partial r^2} + \frac{1}{r}\frac{\partial a_z}{\partial r} + k'^2 a_z = 0 \tag{14.174}$$

whereas the scalar potential Φ satisfies the wave equation (see Eq. 14.168):

$$\frac{\partial^2\Phi}{\partial r^2} + \frac{1}{r}\frac{\partial\Phi}{\partial r} + h'^2\Phi = 0 \tag{14.175}$$

where

$$h'^2 = k_L{}^2 - k^2 \qquad k_L{}^2 = \frac{\omega^2}{c_L{}^2}$$

$$k'^2 = k_s{}^2 - k^2 \qquad k_s{}^2 = \frac{\omega^2}{c_s{}^2} \tag{14.176}$$

The solutions of Equations 14.169, 14.170, and 14.171 are required to remain finite at the axis. The resulting potentials are:

$$k'=0 \qquad \left.\begin{aligned} A_r &= b_1 r \\ A_\varphi &= b_2 r \\ A_z &= b_3 \end{aligned}\right\} e^{j(kz+\omega t)} \tag{14.177}$$

$$k' \neq 0 \qquad \left.\begin{aligned} A_r &= b_1' J_1(k'r) \\ A_\varphi &= b_2' J_1(k'r) \\ A_z &= b_3' J_0(k'r) \end{aligned}\right\} e^{j(kz+\omega t)} \tag{14.178}$$

and

$$\begin{aligned} h'&=0 \qquad \tilde{\Phi}=b_4 \cdot e^{j(kz+\omega t)} \\ h'&\neq 0 \qquad \tilde{\Phi}=b_4' \cdot J_0(h'r) \cdot e^{j(kz+\omega t)} \end{aligned} \tag{14.179}$$

where the terms b are constant and the terms J_n are the Bessel's functions of order n.

The fields that can propagate in the rod independently of the others are those that can independently satisfy the boundary conditions, so that the stresses vanish at the cylindrical surface and at the ends of the rod.

The stress relations are deduced from Equation 14.48 with the aid of the transformation formulas (Eq. 14.32). For axially symmetrical excitation, these conditions take the form:

$$\begin{aligned} &\sigma_{rr}=\lambda \operatorname{div} \vec{s}+2\mu\frac{\partial s_r}{\partial r}=0 && \text{at } r=a \\ &\sigma_{r\varphi}=\mu r\frac{\partial}{\partial r}\left(\frac{s_\varphi}{r}\right)=0 && \text{at } r=a \\ &\sigma_{rz}=\mu\left(\frac{\partial s_r}{\partial z}+\frac{\partial s_z}{\partial r}\right)=0 && \text{at } r=a \quad \text{and at end faces} \\ &\sigma_{zz}=\lambda \operatorname{div} \vec{s}+2\mu\frac{\partial s_z}{\partial z}=0 && \text{at end faces} \end{aligned} \tag{14.180}$$

In these equations, a is the radius of the cylinder, σ is the stress component, and s_r, s_φ, and s_z are the components of the displacement $\vec{s}$.

The function A_r leads to a displacement in planes that are tangential to the cylinders $r=\text{const}$ ($s_\varphi \neq 0$ and $s_z \neq 0$; see Eq. 14.173). If A_r is independent of φ and $s_z=0$, then A_r describes either a pure rotation about the axis or a pure rotation with a pattern of nodal cylinders. These solutions satisfy Equation 14.180; they can exist in the cylinder independently of any other wave types. The component A_z represents rotation in planes normal to the z-axis. If axial symmetry is assumed, the displacements resulting from A_z alone are identical with that of A_r. Thus, the assumption of independence from φ has the effect of reducing the number of independent functions by one.

The function A_φ when considered by itself leads to displacements in the r- and z-planes. However, these displacements do not satisfy the boundary conditions. Such vibrations cannot exist by themselves in the cylinder, but they may be able to propagate in conjunction with some other field. Likewise, the displacements resulting from consideration of Φ by itself cannot be adapted to Equation 14.180. Hence, this field can propagate only in conjunction with some other field.

Pochhammer-Chree Frequency Equation

Of particular interest is the combination of A_φ and Φ. The resulting displacements are:

$$u_r=\left[B\frac{\partial}{\partial r}J_0(h'r)+FkJ_1(k'r)\right]e^{j(kz+\omega t)}$$
$$u_\varphi=0$$
$$u_z=j\left\{BkJ_0(h'r)+\frac{F}{r}\frac{\partial}{\partial r}[rJ_1(k'r)]\right\}e^{j(kz+\omega t)} \tag{14.181}$$

where B and F are constants. These are the Pochhammer-Chree solutions. They satisfy the boundary conditions at the cylindrical surface, but not at the end faces; hence, they describe propagation in an infinite cylinder.

With these solutions, the boundary conditions for σ_{rr} and σ_{rz} at $r=a$ become:

$$B\left[2\mu\frac{\partial^2}{\partial a^2}J_0(h'a)-\frac{\omega^2\rho\lambda}{\lambda+2\mu}J_0(h'a)\right]+2F\mu k\frac{\partial}{\partial a}J_1(k'a)=0 \tag{14.182}$$

$$2Bk\frac{\partial}{\partial a}J_0(h'a)+F\left(2k^2-\frac{\omega^2\rho}{\mu}\right)J_1(k'a)=0 \tag{14.183}$$

while $\sigma_{r\varphi}$ is exactly zero. Here, $\partial/\partial a\,(\,)$ means $|\,\partial/\partial r\,(\,)\,|_{r=a}$. Elimination of B/F in Equations 14.182 and 14.183 leads to Pochhammer's frequency equation:

$$4\mu k^2h'k'J_1(h'a)\left[J_0(k'a)-\frac{J_1(k'a)}{k'a}\right]=\left(2k^2-\frac{\omega^2\rho}{\mu}\right)J_1(k'a)$$
$$\cdot\left\{2\mu h'^2\left[J_0(h'a)-\frac{J_1(h'a)}{h'a}\right]-\frac{\omega^2\rho\lambda}{\lambda+2\mu}J_0(h'a)\right\} \tag{14.184}$$

This equation gives the phase velocity as a function of frequency. It involves six parameters: the radius a, λ, μ, Poisson's ratio ν, ρ, and ω. By expressing the equation in nondimensional form, the number of variables may be reduced to three: ν, c/c_E, and a/λ; $\lambda=2\pi/k$ is the longitudinal wave length, c is the phase velocity ω/k, and c_E is Young's modulus velocity $\sqrt{\lambda_E/\rho}$.

Equation 14.184 is found to have multiple roots; each root corresponds to a different mode of vibration in the rod. Figure 14.8 shows the ratio of

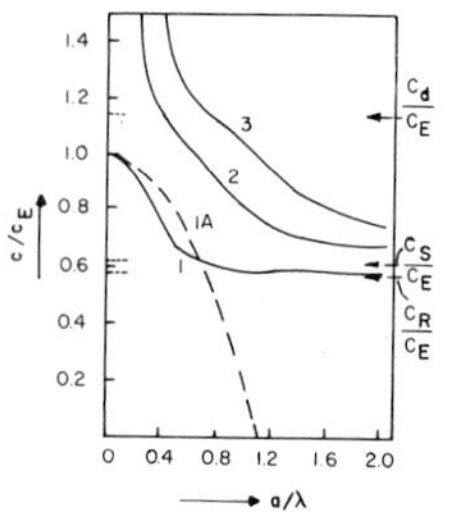

Fig. 14.8 Phase velocity of longitudinal waves in a rod; 1, 2, and 3, first three longitudinal modes; *broken curve*, phase velocity as given by classical theory, with Rayleigh's correction for lateral motion ($c_o=\lambda_E/\rho$, $c_s=\mu/\rho$, and $c_d=(\lambda+2\mu)/\rho$). From R. M. Davies, *op. cit.*

the phase velocity c for dilatational waves to the phase velocity c_E at very low frequencies as a function of the frequency, the frequency being represented by the ratio a/λ.

Curves of c/c_E versus a/λ can be used to obtain the frequency variation of the group velocity c_g, which is defined as:

$$c_g = c - \lambda \frac{dc}{d\lambda} \tag{14.185}$$

This is the velocity with which sinusoidal pulses are propagated in the rod. Davies[5] has calculated the first three roots (for steel, $\nu = 0.29$) of the predominantly dilatational modes. His plot of the variation of c_g/c_E with a/λ for the first two modes is shown in Figure 14.9. This figure also shows, for comparison, the velocity c_R of Rayleigh surface waves. It seems that in the same frequency range, modes connected with predominantly shear deformations are possible, and that similar sets of curves could be obtained for these types of waves by determining the roots that correspond to increasing values of k'.

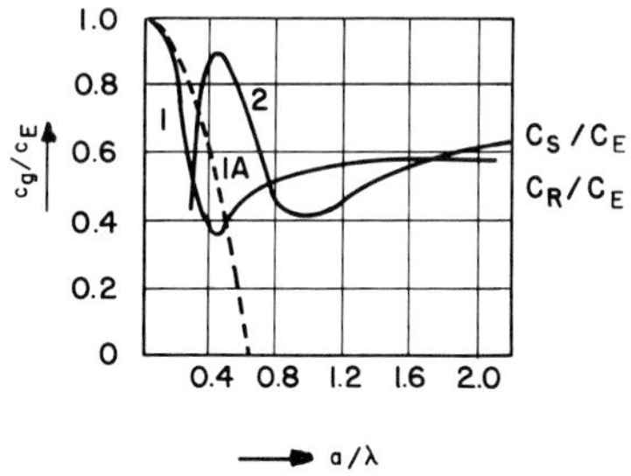

Fig. 14.9 Group velocity of longitudinal waves in a rod; 1 and 2, first two longitudinal modes; *broken curve*, phase velocity as given by classical theory, with Rayleigh's correction for lateral motion (see Fig. 14.8). From R. M. Davies, *op. cit.*

Mindlin and McNiven[6] used an ingenious procedure, based on the first-order approximation for the displacements, to determine the roots of the Pochhammer-Chree equation up to frequencies of the thickness shear mode. Their procedure is based on the fact that all the lower roots have higher overtones, whereas the higher roots have no subtones and, therefore, can be neglected at the lower frequencies. A similar procedure has also been used by Mindlin to determine the roots of the plate equation.[7]

[5] R. M. Davies, "Stress waves in solids," in *Surveys in Mechanics* (New York, 1956), pp. 64–138.

[6] R. D. Mindlin and H. D. McNiven, "Axially symmetric waves in elastic rods," *J.A.S.A.*, **31** (1959), 513–18.

[7] R. D. Mindlin, A. Schacknow, and H. Deresiewicz, "Flexural vibrations of rectangular plates," *J. Appl. Phys.*, **27** (1956), 430–36.

Bending Waves

For bending waves, all three components of the displacement are other than zero, and the deformations are proportional to the sine or the cosine of the angles of the radius vector with the plane in which bending takes place. The deformations are, therefore, of the form:

$$\begin{aligned} s_r &= U' \cos\theta\, e^{j(\omega t - kz)} \\ s_\varphi &= V' \sin\theta\, e^{j(\omega t - kz)} \\ s_z &= W' \cos\theta\, e^{j(\omega t - kz)} \end{aligned} \tag{14.186}$$

If these values are substituted into the equations of motion, the following expressions are found as solutions:

$$\begin{aligned} U' &= A\frac{\partial}{\partial r}J_1(h'r) + Bk\frac{\partial}{\partial r}J_1(k'r) + Cr^{-1}J_1(k'r) \\ V' &= Ar^{-1}J_1(h'r) - Bkr^{-1}J_1(k'r) - C\frac{\partial}{\partial r}J_1(k'r) \\ W' &= jAk\,J_1(h'r) - jBk'^2\,J_1(k'r) \end{aligned} \tag{14.187}$$

where A, B, and C are constants and h$'$ and k' are given by Equation 14.176. The equations of motion lead to Bessel's equations of order one for the dilatation Δ and for the component of the rotation $\bar{\omega}_z$. Hence, it is found that Δ is proportional to $J_1(h'r)$, that $\bar{\omega}_z$ is proportional to $J_1(k'r)$, and that ω_r must be proportional to:

$$D\omega^2\rho\mu^{-1}r^{-1}J_1(k'r) + Ek\frac{\partial}{\partial r}[J_1(k'r)] \tag{14.188}$$

where D and E are constants.[8]

G. E. Hudson[9] has derived the equation that corresponds to the Pochhammer-Chree solution if the motion also depends on φ. For very low frequencies and for bending waves, this equation[10] reduces to:

$$k_s^2a^2 = \frac{8z^2}{(2z-1)[z-(1+\nu)]} \tag{14.189}$$

where

$$z = \frac{1}{2}\left(\frac{c}{c_s}\right)^2 \tag{14.190}$$

and ν is Poisson's contraction.

This equation can be written as:

$$z^2\left(\frac{8}{k_s^2a^2} - 2\right) + z[1 + 2(1+\nu)] = 1 + \nu \tag{14.191}$$

Since k_s is very small, the term 2 in the parentheses can be neglected. Since z is also very small, as is easily seen, the terms in the bracket are negligible.

[8] See H. Kolsky, *Stress Waves in Solids* (Oxford, 1953), and D. Bancroft, "The velocity of longitudinal waves in cylindrical bars," *Phys. Rev.*, **59** (1941), 588–93.
[9] "Dispersion of elastic waves in solid circular cylinders," *Phys. Rev.*, **63** (1943), 46–51.
[10] *Ibid.*, Eq. 5.

The solution becomes:

$$z=\frac{1}{2}\frac{c^2}{c_s^2}=2k_s a\sqrt{\frac{1+\nu}{8}}=\frac{2\omega a}{c_s}\sqrt{\frac{1+\nu}{8}} \tag{14.192}$$

Poisson's ratio ν can be expressed by Lamé's constants λ and μ:

$$\nu=\frac{1}{2\left(1+\frac{\mu}{\lambda}\right)} \tag{14.193}$$

and $c_s = \sqrt{\mu/\rho}$. The result then becomes:

$$c^2=\omega\sqrt{\frac{a^2}{4\rho}\frac{3\lambda+3\mu}{(\lambda+\mu)}}=\omega\sqrt{\frac{\lambda_E}{\rho}\frac{a^2}{4}} \tag{14.194}$$

where λ_E is Young's modulus. But, this is exactly the value predicted by Bernoulli's theory of bending. Thus, this theory of bending applies for rods of circular cross section and a diameter that is small as compared to the distances over which the changes take place (the wave length), provided that shear forces are not applied to the rod. It was to be expected that Bernoulli's theory of bending would lead to correct results for the elastic forces, but it is very surprising that a theory that assumes the beam to consist of independent sheets that slide without friction one on top of the other should also lead to the correct value for the imaginary parts of the elastic modulus, i.e., for the internal friction. The explanation has to be sought in the fact that the exact solution, as well as the solution given by Bernoulli's theory of bending, is an analytic function of the frequency and of all the parameters involved. If the real part of such a function is given, the imaginary part is uniquely determined. Since the real parts are the same at low frequencies, the imaginary parts must also be the same.

Figure 6.3 shows the phase velocity and the group velocity of bending waves as predicted by the various theories. Rayleigh's correction alone leads to poor results, but Rayleigh's correction and Timoshenko's shear correction lead to values that agree very closely with the accurate results.

Improved Theory of the Longitudinal Vibrations of a Rod

The classical theory of the rod was discussed in Chapter V. Experiments and more rigorous computations show that the classical theory fails to explain many of the experimental observations.[11] The exact theory is relatively complex, and it is very difficult to extract numerical information, particularly if damping has to be taken into account. An approximate theory is, therefore, of considerable interest.

[11] See pp. 485–88.

Such a theory has been derived by Mindlin and Hermann.[12] The velocity distribution over the cross section is developed into a Taylor series, and only the linear term is retained. This procedure is permissible as long as the exact solution can be approximated by a linear term that holds when the frequency is sufficiently below the first radial resonance frequency of the rod. The second assumption in the Mindlin-Hermann theory is that the axial displacement is independent of r. This assumption is contained in all the elementary theories of vibrating rods, but it represents the weakest step in this theory. In fact, this assumption is of similar consequence to the assumption in the theory of bending that the shear stress is constant over the cross section of a beam. For a transversely deflected beam, a semiempirical constant γ was introduced (Eq. 6.45) to correct for this assumption. A constant κ_1 will be introduced here; it will be determined by comparison of the theoretical results with Pochhammer's equation (14.184).

We shall start with the elastic equations in the cylindrical co-ordinates r, z, and φ:

$$\frac{\partial \sigma_{rr}}{\partial r}+\frac{\partial \sigma_{zr}}{\partial z}+\frac{\sigma_{rr}-\sigma_{\varphi\varphi}}{r}=\rho \ddot{s}_r$$

$$\frac{\partial \sigma_{zr}}{\partial r}+\frac{\partial \sigma_{zz}}{\partial z}+\frac{\sigma_{zr}}{r}=\rho \ddot{s}_z \tag{14.195}$$

The first of these equations is multiplied by r^2/a, where a is the radius of the rod; the second is multiplied by r. The radial deformation is represented by the linear term of its Taylor series:

$$s_r=\frac{r}{a}u(z, t) \tag{14.196}$$

where $u(z, t)$ is a function of z and t that still has to be determined. The solution for longitudinal vibrations may be assumed to be independent of φ:

$$u_\varphi=0 \tag{14.197}$$

and the axial displacement may be considered to be a function of z and t alone:

$$s_z=w(z, t) \tag{14.198}$$

Equations 14.194 and 14.195 then are integrated over the cross section of the rod. The first equation becomes:

$$\frac{1}{a}\int r^2\frac{\partial \sigma_{rr}}{\partial r}dr+\frac{1}{a}\int r^2\frac{\partial \sigma_{zr}}{\partial z}dr+\frac{1}{a}\int(\sigma_{rr}-\sigma_{\varphi\varphi})r\,dr$$
$$=\frac{\rho}{a}\int r^2\ddot{s}_r\,dr=\frac{\rho}{a}\int\frac{r^3}{a}\ddot{u}(z, t)dr \tag{14.199}$$

Partial integrations of the first term and integration of the last term lead to

[12] R. D. Mindlin and G. Hermann, "A one-dimensional theory of compressional waves in an elastic rod," *A.S.M.E. Trans.*, **67** (1945), 187–91.

the following equation:

$$\frac{1}{a}\left(r^2\sigma_{rr}\right)_0^a - \frac{1}{a}\int_0^a \sigma_{rr}\cdot 2rdr + \frac{1}{a}\int_0^a r^2\frac{\partial\sigma_{rz}}{\partial z}dr + \frac{1}{a}\int_0^a(\sigma_{rr}-\sigma_{\varphi\varphi})rdr$$

$$=\left(\frac{\rho}{a^2}\frac{r^4}{4}\ddot{u}\right)_0^a \tag{14.200}$$

With the abbreviations

$$R=(\sigma_{rr})_{r=a} \quad \text{and} \quad Z=(\sigma_{zr})_{r=a} \tag{14.201}$$

(for a free surface, $R=Z=0$) and with

$$P_r=\int_0^a r\sigma_{rr}dr \qquad P_\varphi=\int_0^a \sigma_{\varphi\varphi}rdr \tag{14.202}$$

$$P_z=\int_0^a \sigma_{zz}rdr \qquad Q=\int_0^a \sigma_{zr}r^2\frac{dr}{a} \tag{14.203}$$

the last equation becomes:

$$aR-\frac{2}{a}P_r+\frac{\partial Q}{\partial z}+\frac{1}{a}P_r-\frac{1}{a}P_\varphi=\frac{\rho a^2\ddot{u}}{4} \tag{14.204}$$

or

$$\frac{\partial Q}{\partial z}-\frac{P_r+P_\varphi}{a}+aR=\rho a^2\frac{\ddot{u}}{4} \tag{14.205}$$

Equation 14.195 becomes:

$$\frac{\partial P_z}{\partial z}+aZ=\frac{\rho a^2\ddot{w}}{2} \tag{14.206}$$

The magnitudes in Equations 14.202 and 14.204 may be interpreted as generalized beam stresses. The stresses can be expressed as a function of the displacements by means of Hooke's law. The general stress-strain relations that result by this method are given in cylindrical co-ordinates by:

$$\begin{aligned}\sigma_{rr}&=\lambda\Delta+2\mu\epsilon_{rr}\\ \sigma_{\varphi\varphi}&=\lambda\Delta+2\mu\epsilon_{\varphi\varphi}\\ \sigma_{zz}&=\lambda\Delta+2\mu\epsilon_{zz}\\ \sigma_{zr}&=\mu\epsilon_{zr}\end{aligned} \tag{14.207}$$

where λ and μ are Lamé's constants, ϵ_{zr}, $\epsilon_{\varphi\varphi}$, ϵ_{rr}, and ϵ_{zz} are the strains as given by equation 14.156, and

$$\Delta=\epsilon_{rr}+\epsilon_{zz}+\epsilon_{\varphi\varphi} \tag{14.208}$$

is the dilatation.

If the substitution of Equations 14.196, 14.197, and 14.198 is made in Equations 14.198 and 14.207, the following equivalent relations are obtained for the generalized beam stresses (Eqs. 14.202 and 14.203):

$$2P_r = 2P_\varphi = 2a(\lambda+\mu)u + a^2\lambda\frac{\partial w}{\partial z}$$

$$2P_z = 2a\lambda u + a^2(\lambda+2\mu)\frac{\partial w}{\partial z} \tag{14.209}$$

and

$$4Q = a^2\mu\frac{\partial u}{\partial z} \tag{14.210}$$

In the preceding derivations, u_z has been assumed to be independent of r, which is only a crude approximation. We may find it satisfactory to modify the beam stress-strain relations in such a way that the above equations lead to the same result as the exact theory (in a manner similar to that used in Chapter VI to correct for the variation of the shear stress over the cross section; see Eq. 6.45). In order that the above solution lead to the same wave velocities as Pochhammer's equation, two constants, κ and κ_1, have been introduced by Mindlin and Hermann at the following places:

$$2P_r = 2P_\varphi = 2\kappa_1^2 a(\lambda+\mu)u + \kappa_1 a^2\lambda\frac{\partial w}{\partial z}$$

$$2P_z = 2\kappa_1 a\lambda u + a^2(\lambda+2\mu)\frac{\partial w}{\partial z} \tag{14.211}$$

and

$$4Q = \kappa^2 a^2\mu\frac{\partial u}{\partial z} \tag{14.212}$$

where

$$\kappa_1^2 = 0.422(2-\kappa^2) \tag{14.213}$$

and κ is the root of $4\sqrt{(1-\alpha\kappa^2)\,(1-\kappa^2)} = (2-\kappa^2)^2$ and where $0<\kappa<1$ and $\alpha = (1-2\nu)/2(1-\nu)$, ν being Poisson's ratio. The above values of κ and κ_1 are deduced by comparison with Pochhammer's equation. The equations of motion are obtained by substituting the stresses of Equations 14.211 and 14.212 into Equations 14.204 and 14.206:

$$a^2\kappa^2\mu\frac{\partial^2 u}{\partial z^2} - 8\kappa_1^2(\lambda+\mu)u - 4a\kappa_1^2\lambda\frac{\partial w}{\partial x} + 4aR = \rho a^2\ddot{u} \tag{14.214}$$

and

$$2a\lambda\frac{\partial u}{\partial z} + a^2(\lambda+2\mu)\frac{\partial^2 w}{\partial z^2} + 2aZ = \rho a^2\ddot{w} \tag{14.215}$$

For rods vibrating in a vacuum (in air), $R = Z = 0$.

A single equation in w may be obtained by eliminating u from Equations 14.214 and 14.215 with the following result:

$$\begin{aligned}\frac{\lambda_E}{\rho}\frac{\partial^2 w}{\partial z^2} - \frac{\partial^2 w}{\partial t^2} + \frac{2Z}{\rho a} &+ \frac{a^2\rho}{8\kappa_1^2(\lambda+\mu)}\frac{\partial^2}{\partial t^2}\left(\frac{\lambda+2\mu}{\rho}\frac{\partial^2 w}{\partial z^2} - \frac{\partial^2 w}{\partial t^2} + \frac{2Z}{\rho a}\right)\\ &- \frac{a^2\kappa^2\mu}{8\kappa_1^2(\lambda+\mu)}\frac{\partial^2}{\partial z^2}\left(\frac{\lambda+2\mu}{\rho}\frac{\partial^2 w}{\partial z^2} - \frac{\partial^2 w}{\partial t^2} + \frac{2Z}{\rho a}\right)\\ &+ \frac{\lambda}{\rho(\lambda+\mu)\kappa_1^2}\frac{\partial R}{\partial z} = 0\end{aligned} \tag{14.216}$$

Again, R and Z are zero, if the surface of the rod is free. The first two terms are the classical terms, while the second and third (R and Z being zero) represent the radial inertia and radial shear corrections, respectively. The phase velocity that is computed from these equations, when only the κ correction is used and when both κ and κ_1 corrections are used, is represented in Figure 5.4.

Vibrations of a Rod of Finite Length, Cavity Resonance of the Ends of the Rod, and Mode Transformation

The solutions given in the preceding section do not satisfy the boundary conditions at the ends of the rod. The experimental results show that a wave that impinges at the end of a rod is reflected with the same amplitude; but, in addition to reflecting the incident wave, the end of the rod generates a distortion of the traveling waves that decays rapidly with distance. This distortion field is described by the complex roots of Pochhammer's equation, which represent standing waves that decay asymptotically in an exponential manner with the distance from the ends of the rod. Since these end distortions are standing waves, they do not enter the energy balance as long as internal friction is neglected. However, because of internal friction, the maintenance of this distortion field may require a considerable amount of energy. It may require so much energy that practically no wave can be transmitted into the rod. The theory of this end distortion has been derived by McNiven[13] on the basis of a second-order approximation (expressing the velocity field in terms of elliptical functions). His main result is represented in Figure 14.10, which shows the end distortion as a function of the frequency. The curve shows a kind of resonance maximum whose height is approximately 80 times the magnitude of the amplitude of the incident wave at the frequency

$$\Omega_r = \frac{\omega_r}{\omega_s} = 0.6767 \qquad \text{or} \qquad \frac{\omega_r a}{c_s} = 0.59 \tag{14.217}$$

where

$$\omega_s = \frac{\delta c_s}{a} \qquad c_s = \frac{\mu}{\rho} \tag{14.218}$$

and $\delta = 3.83$ is the lowest root of $J_1(\delta) = 0$. At still higher frequencies, mode transformation seems to take place during the reflection at the ends of the rod. The theory of the mode transformation that takes place in a rod has not yet been derived.

[13] H. D. McNiven, "Extensional waves in a semi-infinite elastic rod," *J.A.S.A.*, **33** (1961), 23–27.

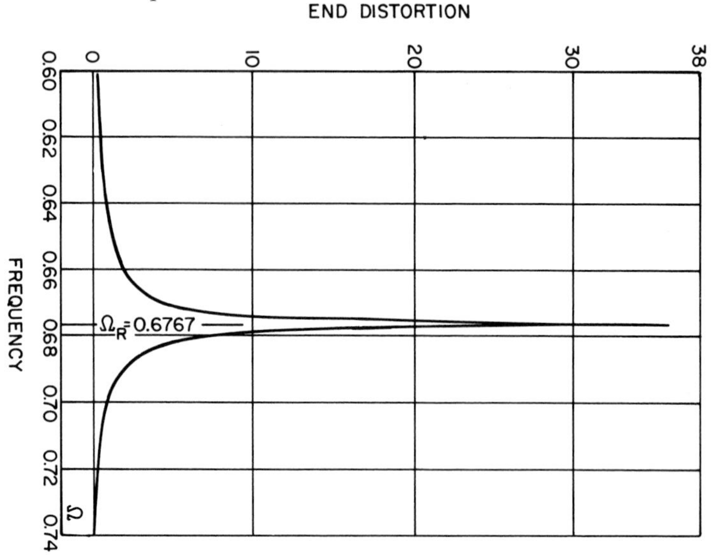

Fig. 14.10 Ratio of half the amplitude of the end vibration in a rod to the amplitude of the incident wave in the neighborhood of the frequency of the end mode. From H. D. McNiven, *loc. cit.*

Attenuation of Longitudinal and Transverse Waves in a Rod

At very low frequencies, wave propagation in a longitudinally vibrating rod is governed by Young's modulus, and the attenuation of a wave is proportional to the loss factor of Young's modulus. As the frequency increases, the McNiven end distortion becomes more and more important, and the loss factor of the shear modulus comes into play. At the higher frequencies, the deformations are generated partially by dilatation and partially by shear motion, and the relative ratio between shear and dilatation depends on the frequency (Eqs. 14.182 and 14.183). As a consequence, the attenuation must be expected to be a frequency-dependent function of both moduli and of their loss factors, which depend greatly on the dimensions of the test rod. When the wave is reflected at the ends of a rod, a single mode does not satisfy the boundary condition that there be no stress over the end faces of the rod; mode transformation takes place, and additional energy is lost because of this transformation. This energy loss is particularly severe if the test rod is short. Figure 14.11 shows the reflection pattern when a short train of longitudinal vibrations is reflected at the end of a thin rod. The pulses are reflected as dilatational pulses and decrease successively in amplitude. But every time a pulse is reflected, a similar pulse is generated at the reflecting end, which propagates with a different velocity (strongly frequency-dependent and in Figure 14.11 crudely equal to the shear veloc-

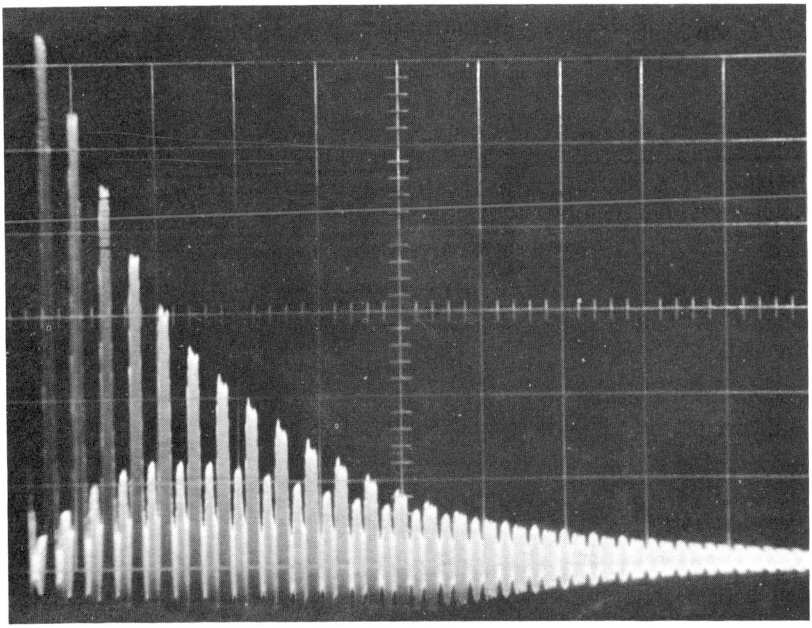

Fig. 14.11 Mode transformation during the reflections of a longitudinal pulse; the longitudinal pulses decay, and a series of pulses that travel with different velocity waves builds up in amplitude (aluminum rod, diameter $\frac{3}{8}$ in., 200 kc.).

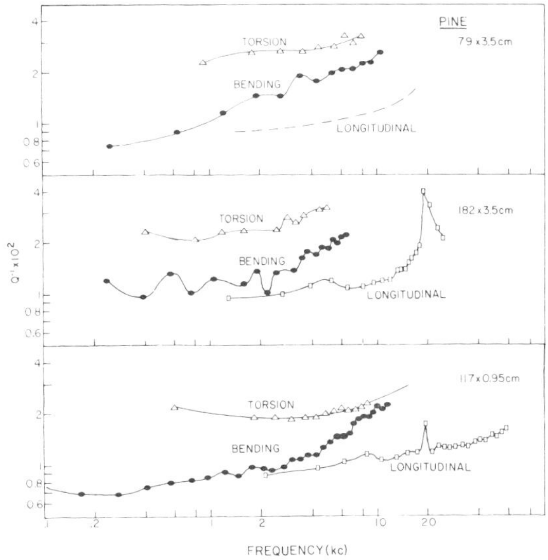

Fig. 14.12 Loss factor of a pine rod excited to bending vibrations (for three rods with different dimensions); according to Bernoulli's theory of bending, the loss factor for bending vibrations should be the same as that for longitudinal vibrations.

ity). The series of longitudinal pulses decays, whereas the pulses that are generated during reflection increase in amplitude (they happen to have the correct timing, and their amplitudes add).

Eventually, the effect of damping predominates, and the amplitudes of both series decrease with time. At very high frequencies, modes are excited that correspond to purely longitudinal waves, and propagation velocity and loss factor are determined by the combination $\bar{\lambda}+2\bar{\mu}$ of the two fundamental moduli, $\bar{\lambda}$ and $\bar{\mu}$.

Similar results are obtained for transverse vibrations. The theory shows that at low frequencies bending waves are described by Young's modulus and that at higher frequencies they are described by the shear modulus.

For many substances, the loss factors for shear and dilatation are nearly the same, and the change in the mechanism of the attenuation does not appear in the measurements. But for some substances, such as wood, for which the loss factors are different, this variation may be quite significant. Figure 14.12 shows a comparison of the attenuation in a wooden rod for longitudinal, bending, and torsional vibration waves as a function of the frequency.

Plate Equations—Including Shear and Rotary Inertia

The derivation of the plate equation is very difficult. The stresses vary over the thickness of the plate, and the problem is a three-dimensional one. The classical theory simplifies the derivations considerably by neglecting the variations of the stresses over the thickness of the plate and the shear deformations; rotary inertia is also neglected. The motion of the plate is described by the deflection of its central plane. Furthermore, the boundary conditions are simplified by partially neglecting the end distortions, and the five boundary conditions are replaced by four approximately equivalent conditions. Mindlin has published an improved plate theory,[14] a two-dimensional analogue of the Rayleigh-Timoshenko beam equation.[15] A full description of this theory is beyond the scope of this book, but the following outlines should help the reader.

Figure 14.13*a* shows a cylindrical element cut from a plate. Let us consider an elementary area of length ds in the tangential direction, and let ν represent the normal to this area. Let z represent the co-ordinate vertical to the central plane of the plate, and, to simplify the notation, let the co-ordinate system be so directed that the x-axis coincides with the normal ν and the y-axis with the tangential direction. Let the thickness of the plate be h. Three forces act on this elementary area—the normal stress:

[14] R. D. Mindlin, Influence of rotary inertia and shear on flexural motion of elastic plates, "*J. Appl. Mech.*" **18** (1951), 31–38.

[15] See p. 196.

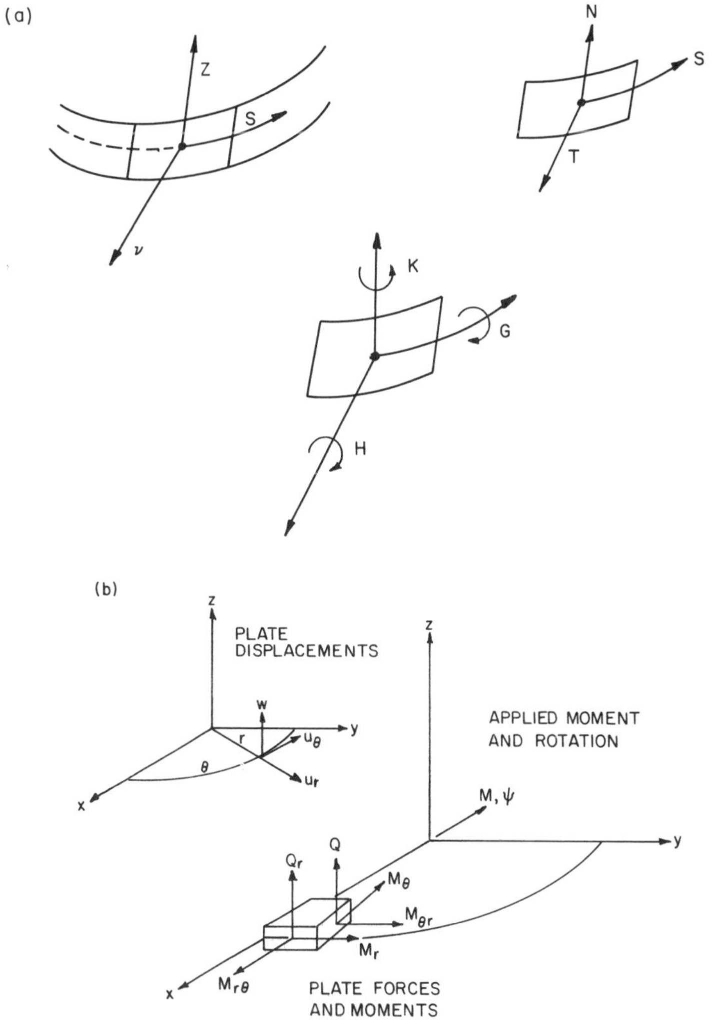

Fig. 14.13 Co-ordinates, forces, and moments on an elementary surface area of a cylindrical section of a plate; *a*, classical (Love's) notation; *b*, Mindlin's notation.

$$T = (X_x) = \int_{-h/2}^{h/2} \sigma_{xx} dz \tag{14.219}$$

a shear stress in the *y*-direction:

$$S = (Y_x) = \int_{-h/2}^{h/2} \sigma_{zy} dz \qquad (= Q_y) \tag{14.220}$$

and a shear stress that is directed parallel to the central plane in the z-direction:

$$N=(Z_x)=\int_{-h/2}^{h/2}\sigma_{yx}dz \qquad (=Q_y) \tag{14.221}$$

These stresses are all referred to unit length of the elementary area in the direction tangential to the circumference of the cylindrical element. The symbols on the left are those used by Love;[16] those on the right, by Mindlin. Similar relations can be written for an elementary area perpendicular to the y-axis. The following moments act on the face $x=$const, all per unit length (Fig. 14.13 *a* and *b*):

$$H=\int_{-h/2}^{h/2} -z\sigma_{xy}dz \qquad (=-M_{yx}) \tag{14.222}$$

$$G=\int_{-h/2}^{h} z\sigma_{xx}dz \qquad (=M_x) \tag{14.223}$$

$$K=-\int_{-h/2}^{h/2} y\sigma_{xy}dz\doteq 0 \tag{14.224}$$

Corresponding relations apply to an elementary area perpendicular to the y-axis. In H, a term

$$\int\int_{-h/2}^{h/2} (\sigma_{xz}ydz)dy \tag{14.225}$$

has been neglected; σ_{xz} does not change sign with y (in contrast to σ_{xy}, which changes sign with z) and consequently furnishes a contribution that is one order of magnitude smaller than the retained integral. The H-integral, therefore, reduces to the difference of σ_{xz} above and below the central plane, multiplied by a quantity of the order of magnitude of half the thickness of the plate. Similarly, K can be treated as a second-order quantity and can be neglected. If the plate is excited to bending vibrations, as in the beam, σ_{xx} is proportional to the distance z from the central plane; σ_{xx} is, therefore, positive for $z>0$ and negative for $z<0$; and the moment that acts on the elementary area around the z-axis is a small quantity of the second order.

In thin plates, the change in thickness because of the load on the plate is of no importance. This change and, consequently, the component of the strain in the thickness direction are usually eliminated. (In fact, this is the

[16] *Op. cit.*

standard procedure for all thin plate and shell computations). The simplest way to do this is to use the elastic stress-strain relations:

$$\begin{aligned}
\sigma_{xx} &= \lambda \operatorname{div} \vec{s} + 2\mu\epsilon_{xx} \\
\sigma_{yy} &= \lambda \operatorname{div} \vec{s} + 2\mu\epsilon_{yy} \\
\sigma_{zz} &= \lambda \operatorname{div} \vec{s} + 2\mu\epsilon_{zz} \\
\sigma_{xy} &= 2\mu\epsilon_{xy} \\
\sigma_{xz} &= 2\mu\epsilon_{xz} \\
\sigma_{yz} &= 2\mu\epsilon_{yz}
\end{aligned} \tag{14.226}$$

where

$$\operatorname{div} \vec{s} = \epsilon_{xx} + \epsilon_{yy} + \epsilon_{zz}$$

$$\epsilon_{xx} = \frac{\partial u}{\partial x} \qquad \epsilon_{yy} = \frac{\partial v}{\partial y} \qquad \epsilon_{zz} = \frac{\partial w}{\partial z}$$

$$\epsilon_{xy} = \frac{1}{2}\left(\frac{\partial u}{\partial y} + \frac{\partial v}{\partial x}\right) \qquad \epsilon_{xz} - \frac{1}{2}\left(\frac{\partial u}{\partial z} + \frac{\partial w}{\partial x}\right) \qquad \epsilon_{yz} = \frac{1}{2}\left(\frac{\partial v}{\partial z} + \frac{\partial w}{\partial y}\right) \tag{14.227}$$

and u, v, and w are the components of the displacement in the x-, y-, and z-directions.

The strain ϵ_{zz} may now be eliminated with the aid of the following relations:

$$\begin{aligned}
\sigma_{zz} &= \lambda(\epsilon_{xx} + \epsilon_{yy} + \epsilon_{zz}) + 2\mu\epsilon_{zz} = (\lambda + 2\mu)\epsilon_{zz} + \lambda(\epsilon_{xx} + \epsilon_{yy}) \\
\epsilon_{zz} &= \frac{\sigma_{zz} - \lambda(\epsilon_{xx} + \epsilon_{yy})}{\lambda + 2\mu}
\end{aligned} \tag{14.228}$$

The first equation then becomes:

$$\begin{aligned}
\sigma_{xx} &= (\lambda + 2\mu)\epsilon_{xx} + \lambda\epsilon_{yy} + \frac{\lambda}{\lambda + 2\mu}[\sigma_{zz} - \lambda(\epsilon_{xx} + \epsilon_{yy})] \\
&= \frac{4\mu(\lambda + \mu)}{\lambda + 2\mu}\epsilon_{xx} + \frac{2\mu\lambda}{\lambda + 2\mu}\epsilon_{yy} + \frac{\lambda}{\lambda + 2\mu}\sigma_{zz} \\
&= \frac{\lambda_E}{1 - \nu^2}(\epsilon_{xx} + \nu\epsilon_{yy}) + \frac{\lambda}{\lambda + 2\mu}\sigma_{zz}
\end{aligned} \tag{14.229}$$

where

$$\frac{4\mu(\lambda + \mu)}{\lambda + 2\mu} = \frac{\lambda_E}{1 - \nu^2} \tag{14.230}$$

and λ_E is Young's modulus and ν is Poisson's ratio:[17]

$$\lambda_E = \frac{(3\lambda + 2\mu)\mu}{\lambda + \mu} \qquad \nu = \frac{\lambda}{2(\lambda + \mu)} \tag{14.231}$$

Similar equations are obtained for the other components of the stress tensor.

[17] Young's modulus is defined as the ratio of the stress to the strain for an infinitely thin rod (see p. 458). If z is the co-ordinate in the direction of the rod, since the surface of the rod is free, $\sigma_{yy} = \sigma_{xx} = 0$. This condition leads to (see Eq. 14.226) $\epsilon_{yy} = \epsilon_{xx}$ and $0 = \lambda(\epsilon_{zz} + 2\epsilon_{yy}) + 2\mu\epsilon_{yy}$ or $\nu = |\epsilon_{yy}/\epsilon_{zz}| = \lambda/2(\lambda + \mu)$, where the ratio ν is defined as Poisson's contraction. Equation 14.226 then leads to $\sigma_{zz}/\epsilon_{zz} = \lambda_E = (3\lambda + 2\mu)\mu/(\lambda + \mu)$. These results have been used for representing Eq. 14.229 in the given form.

Equation 14.229 and the corresponding equation for σ_{yy} can now be multiplied by z and integrated over the thickness of the plate. If plate strain components are defined by:

$$(\Gamma_x, \Gamma_y, \Gamma_{yx}) = 12h^{-3}\int_{-h/2}^{h/2} (\epsilon_{xx}, \epsilon_{yy}, \epsilon_{yx})zdz \tag{14.232}$$

and if

$$D = \frac{\lambda_E h^3}{12(1-\nu^2)} = \frac{\mu h^3}{6(1-\nu)} = \alpha^4 \rho h \tag{14.233}$$

where α^4 is the constant in the classical plate equation (8.1), the following result is obtained:

$$M_x = \int_{-h/2}^{h/2} \sigma_{xx}zdz = D(\Gamma_x + \nu\Gamma_y) + \left[\frac{\nu}{(1-\nu)}\int_{-h/2}^{h/2} z\sigma_{zz}dz\right] \tag{14.234}$$

and

$$M_y = \int_{-h/2}^{h/2} \sigma_{yy}zdz = D(\Gamma_y + \nu\Gamma_x) \tag{14.235}$$

If the plate surfaces are free, σ_{zz} is zero at the surfaces and small as compared to σ_{yy} and σ_{xx} everywhere else. But even if the plate is loaded, σ_{zz} will be relatively small. The contribution of the term σ_{zz}, which is represented by the integral in the rectangular bracket, can therefore be neglected; it is small of the second order, since σ_{zz} does not change sign with z.

The plate shear stresses obey the following relationships:

$$\sigma_{yx} = 2\mu\epsilon_{yx} \tag{14.236}$$

and

$$\int_{-h/2}^{h/2} z\sigma_{yx}dz = M_{yx} = 2\int_{-h/2}^{h/2} \mu\epsilon_{yx}zdz = \mu\frac{h^3}{12}\Gamma_{yz} = (1-\nu)\frac{D\Gamma_{yz}}{2} \tag{14.237}$$

where

$$\Gamma_{xz} = h^{-1}2\int_{-h/2}^{h/2} \epsilon_{xz}dz \tag{14.238}$$

and

$$\Gamma_{yz} = h^{-1}2\int_{-h/2}^{h/2} \epsilon_{yz}dz \tag{14.239}$$

(The factor 2 before the integrals does not appear in Mindlin's original paper, because he uses the strains without the factor $\frac{1}{2}$).

The magnitude $\mu h^3/12$ has been replaced by $(1-\nu)D$. The equality of these two terms is easily deduced from Equations 14.231 and 14.232. The shear stress resultants,

$$Q_x = \int_{-h/2}^{h/2} \sigma_{xz} dz \tag{14.240}$$

and

$$Q_y = \int_{-h/2}^{h/2} \sigma_{yz} dz \tag{14.241}$$

still have to be calculated:

$$Q_x = \int_{-h/2}^{h/2} 2\mu' \epsilon_{xz} dz = \mu' h \left(\frac{1}{h}\right) \int_{-h/2}^{h/2} 2\epsilon_{xz} dz = \mu' h \Gamma_{xz} \tag{14.242}$$

Similarly,

$$Q_y = \mu' \int_{-h/2}^{h/2} 2\epsilon_{yz} dz = \mu' h \Gamma_{yz} \tag{14.243}$$

where μ' is identical with the shear modulus μ if the exact expressions for ϵ_{xz} are used in the integrand. But the exact solution is not available, and we shall replace it by its Taylor series with respect to the z-co-ordinate and shall retain only the linear term in Equation 14.244. In this approximation, the stress σ_{xy} becomes a constant instead of vanishing at the two surfaces $z = \pm h/2$ of the plate; also, it will not be strictly independent of z. To compensate for the error, μ is replaced by a slightly different constant μ'; a similar procedure has worked very well for the beam (see Eq. 6.15) and for the longitudinally vibrating rod (Eqs. 14.211 and 14.212). The constant μ' then is determined by comparing the above solution with the accurate solutions that have been derived for special cases.

The subsequent computations are relatively straightforward. As for a beam, the points of the central plane (by definition) move up or down, but not to the left or right. Hence, the parts of the plate below the central plane are compressed, and those above are extended, or vice versa. We therefore write:

$$w = w(x, y, t) \qquad u = z\Psi_x(x, y, t) \qquad v = z\Psi_y(x, y, t) \tag{14.244}$$

The functions u and v can be considered as the Taylor development up to the linear terms of the exact solution. The function $w(x, y, z)$ must also depend on z. Because we neglect this z-dependence, μ has to be replaced by μ'; Ψ_x and Ψ_y can be interpreted as rotations around the x-axis and y-axis, respectively. The following relationships are easily derived:

$$\Gamma_x=\frac{\partial\Psi_x}{\partial x}\qquad\Gamma_y=\frac{\partial\Psi_y}{\partial y}\qquad\Gamma_z=\frac{\partial\Psi_y}{\partial x}+\frac{\partial\Psi_x}{\partial y}\tag{14.245}$$

$$\Gamma_{xz}=\Psi_x+\frac{\partial w}{\partial x}\qquad\Gamma_{yz}=\Psi_y+\frac{\partial w}{\partial y}\tag{14.246}$$

(In the classical plate theory, $\Gamma_{xz}=\Gamma_{yz}=0$.) With these values, the plate stress-strain components become:

$$M_x=D\left(\frac{\partial\Psi_x}{\partial x}+\nu\frac{\partial\Psi_y}{\partial y}\right)\qquad M_y=D\left(\frac{\partial\Psi_y}{\partial y}+\nu\frac{\partial\Psi_x}{\partial x}\right)\tag{14.247}$$

$$M_{yx}=\frac{1-\nu}{2}D\left(\frac{\partial\Psi_y}{\partial x}+\frac{\partial\Psi_x}{\partial y}\right)\tag{14.248}$$

$$Q_x=\mu'h\left(\frac{\partial w}{\partial x}+\Psi_x\right)\qquad Q_y=\mu'h\left(\frac{\partial w}{\partial y}+\Psi_y\right)\tag{14.249}$$

The equations of motion are:

$$\frac{\partial\sigma_{xx}}{\partial x}+\frac{\partial\sigma_{yx}}{\partial y}+\frac{\partial\sigma_{xz}}{\partial z}=\rho\frac{\partial^2u}{\partial t^2}\tag{14.250}$$

$$\frac{\partial\sigma_{yx}}{\partial x}+\frac{\partial\sigma_{yy}}{\partial y}+\frac{\partial\sigma_{yz}}{\partial z}=\rho\frac{\partial^2v}{\partial t^2}\tag{14.251}$$

$$\frac{\partial\sigma_{xz}}{\partial x}+\frac{\partial\sigma_{yz}}{\partial y}+\frac{\partial\sigma_{zz}}{\partial z}=\rho\frac{\partial^2w}{\partial t^2}\tag{14.252}$$

They are converted to plate stress equations of motion by multiplying the first two equations by z and integrating them over the plate thickness:

$$\frac{\partial M_x}{\partial x}+\frac{\partial M_{yz}}{\partial y}-Q_x=\frac{\rho h^3}{12}\frac{\partial^2\Psi_x}{\partial t^2}\tag{14.253}$$

$$\frac{\partial M_{yx}}{\partial x}+\frac{\partial M_y}{\partial y}-Q_y=\frac{\rho h^3}{12}\frac{\partial^2\Psi_y}{\partial t^2}\tag{14.254}$$

The third equation (12.252) is integrated over the plate thickness, and if the plate surfaces are loaded,

$$(\sigma_{zz})_{z=h/2}=-q_1(x,y,t)\tag{14.255}$$

$$(\sigma_{zz})_{z=-h/2}=-q_2(x,y,t)\tag{14.256}$$

and

$$q=q_2-q_1\tag{14.257}$$

We thus obtain:

$$\frac{\partial Q_x}{\partial x}+\frac{\partial Q_y}{\partial y}+q=\rho h\frac{\partial^2w}{\partial t^2}\tag{14.258}$$

The right-hand sides of Equations 14.253 and 14.254 represent the effect of the rotary inertia. This is easily seen by comparing these equations with those for the beam. The three plate stresses may be expressed in terms of the plate rotations Ψ_x and Ψ_y. The plate equations then become:

$$\frac{D}{2}\left[(1-\nu)\nabla^2\Psi_x+(1+\nu)\frac{\partial\Phi}{\partial x}\right]-\mu' h\left(\Psi_x+\frac{\partial w}{\partial x}\right)=\frac{\rho h^3}{12}\frac{\partial^2\Psi_x}{\partial t^2} \quad (14.259)$$

$$\frac{D}{2}\left[(1-\nu)\nabla^2\Psi_y+(1-\nu)\frac{\partial\Phi}{\partial y}\right]-\mu' h\left(\Psi_y+\frac{\partial w}{\partial y}\right)=\frac{\rho h^3}{12}\frac{\partial^2\Psi_y}{\partial t^2} \quad (14.260)$$

and

$$\mu' h(\nabla^2 w+\Phi)+q=\rho h\frac{\partial^2 w}{\partial t^2} \quad (14.261)$$

where

$$\Phi=\frac{\partial\Psi_x}{\partial x}+\frac{\partial\Psi_y}{\partial y} \quad (14.262)$$

The functions of Ψ_x and Ψ_y can be eliminated in the equations by differentiating Equation 14.259 with respect to x, differentiating Equation 14.260 with respect to y, and adding the results:

$$\left(D\nabla^2-\mu' h-\frac{\rho h^3}{12}\frac{\partial^2}{\partial t^2}\right)\Phi=\mu' h\nabla^2 w \quad (14.263)$$

and by eliminating Φ with the aid of the relation (Eq. 14.252):

$$\left(\nabla^2-\frac{\rho}{\mu'}\frac{\partial^2}{\partial t^2}\right)\left(D\nabla^2-\frac{\rho h^3}{12}\frac{\partial^2}{\partial t^2}\right)w+\rho h\frac{\partial^2 w}{\partial t^2}=\left(1-\frac{D\nabla^2}{\mu' h}+\frac{\rho h^2}{12\mu'}\frac{\partial^2}{\partial t^2}\right)q \quad (14.264)$$

The terms containing μ' represent the transverse shear motion, and the terms that contain $(\rho h^3/12)\,(\partial^2/\partial t^2)\Phi$ represent the effect of the rotary inertia. If shear and rotary inertia are neglected, the classical plate equation results:

$$D\nabla^4 w+\rho h\frac{\partial^2 w}{\partial t^2}=q \quad (14.265)$$

For an infinite plate and for straight-crested waves (the equivalent of plane waves in the plate) the exact solution is known. This solution is plotted in Figure 14.14. The classical plate theory leads to the correct propagation velocity only if the wave length is at least 5 to 10 times greater than the thickness of the plate (see Fig. 14.14). The rotary inertia correction only slightly improves the classical result, but very satisfactory results are obtained if shear and inertia are taken into account. A comparison with the correct solution shows that if

$$\mu'=\gamma^2\mu \quad (14.266)$$

the parameter γ^2 is the root of the equation

$$4\sqrt{(1-\alpha\gamma^2)(1-\gamma^2)}=(2-\gamma^2)^2 \qquad 0<\gamma<1 \quad (14.267)$$

where

$$\alpha=\frac{1-2\nu}{2(1-\nu)} \quad (14.268)$$

The value of γ^2 varies almost linearly from 0.76 for $\nu=0$ to 0.91 for $\nu=\frac{1}{2}$.

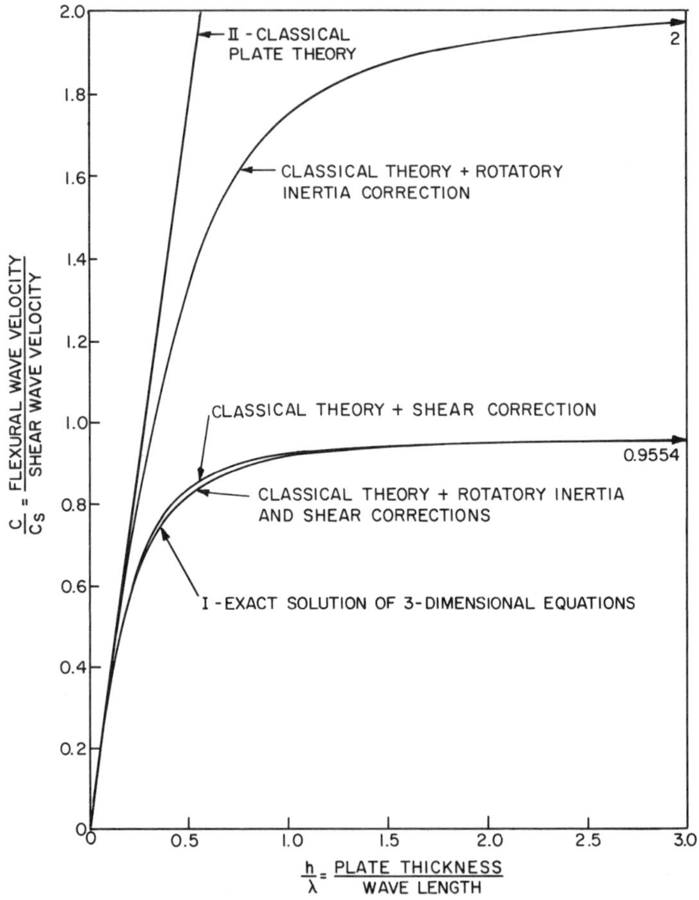

Fig. 14.14 Phase velocity of transverse waves in a plate. From R. D. Mindlin, *loc. cit.*

The change of energy of the plate must be equal to the work done by the external forces along the edge and over the surface of the plate. Hence,

$$T+V=\int_{t_0}^{t} dt \oint\left(\frac{\partial \Psi_\nu}{\partial t} M_\nu+\frac{\partial \Psi_s}{\partial t} M_{\nu s}+\frac{\partial w}{\partial t} Q_\nu\right) ds$$

$$+\int_{t_0}^{t} dt \int\int q \frac{\partial w}{\partial t} dx dy+T_0+V_0 \qquad (14.269)$$

where T and V are the kinetic and the potential energy at the time t, and T_0 and V_0 are the corresponding quantities at the time t_0.

Appropriate initial and boundary conditions are those that are sufficient to assure a unique solution. These conditions are: (1) Any combination of the three terms in the parentheses under the line integral must be specified along the edges. (2) Either q or w must be specified on the surface of the plate, and the initial values of Ψ_x and Ψ_y must be prescribed.

Reduction of Mindlin's Plate Equations to Wave Equations

In the absence of surface loadings, the equations of motion may be transformed into a very simple form by introducing a (two-dimensional) vector potential $\vec{H}$ and a (two-dimensional) scalar potential Φ for the deformation in the plane of the plate, as follows:

$$\Psi_x = \frac{u}{z} = \frac{\partial \Phi}{\partial x} + \frac{\partial H}{\partial y} \tag{14.270}$$

$$\Psi_y = \frac{v}{z} = \frac{\partial \Phi}{\partial y} - \frac{\partial H}{\partial x} \tag{14.271}$$

Equations 14.259 to 14.261 then become:

$$\frac{\partial}{\partial x}[\nabla^2 \Phi + (Rk_B{}^4 - S^{-1})\Phi - S^{-1}w] + \frac{1-\nu}{2}\frac{\partial}{\partial y}(\nabla^2 + k_3{}^2)H = 0 \tag{14.272}$$

$$\frac{\partial}{\partial y}[\nabla^2 \Phi + (Rk_B{}^4 - S^{-1})\Phi - S^{-1}w] - \frac{1-\nu}{2}\frac{\partial}{\partial x}(\nabla^2 + k_3{}^2)H = 0 \tag{14.273}$$

$$\nabla^2(\Phi + w) + Sk_B{}^4 w = 0 \tag{14.274}$$

where

$$R = \frac{h^2}{12} = \frac{I}{h} \qquad S = \frac{D}{\mu' h} \qquad k_B{}^4 = \frac{\rho\omega^2 h}{D} \qquad k_3{}^2 = \frac{2(Rk_B{}^4 - S^{-1})}{1-\nu} \tag{14.275}$$

Thus, Mindlin's parameters $R = I/h$ represent the square of the radius of gyration of the cross-section area of unit width, and k_B, the classical bending wave number. The constants R and S represent the effect of rotary inertia and transverse shear deformation, respectively. H may be separated from Φ and w by differentiation, addition, and subtraction of Equations 14.272 and 14.273:

$$\nabla^2(\nabla^2 + k_3{}^2)H = 0 \tag{14.276}$$

$$\nabla^2[\nabla^2\Phi + (Rk_B{}^2 - S^{-1})\Phi - S^{-1}w] = 0 \tag{14.277}$$

Equations 14.274 and 14.277 are satisfied by:

$$\Phi = (\alpha - 1)w \tag{14.278}$$

where α is a constant, provided that

$$\nabla^2 w + k^2 w = 0 \tag{14.279}$$

and

$$k^2=\alpha^{-1}Sk_B{}^4=Rk_B{}^4-S^{-1}-S(\alpha-1)^{-1} \tag{14.280}$$

If α is eliminated in Equation 14.270,

$$k_1{}^2,\, k_2{}^2=\frac{1}{2}k_B{}^4[R+S\pm\sqrt{(R-S)^2+4k_B{}^{-4}}] \tag{14.281}$$

whereas

$$\alpha_1,\, \alpha_2=(k_2{}^2,\, k_1{}^2)\,(Rk_B{}^4-S^{-1})^{-1} \tag{14.282}$$

Hence, two deflection functions w_1 and w_2 are obtained by setting α in Equation 14.278 as equal to α_1 or α_2, and these functions are governed by separate wave equations, obtained by setting $k=k_1$ or $k=k_2$ in Equation 14.280. Equation 14.264 may be written as:

$$(\nabla^2+k_1{}^2)\,(\nabla^2+k_2{}^2)w=0 \tag{14.283}$$

when $q=0$. Finally, because of Equations 14.270 and 14.278, the bracketed terms in Equations 14.272 and 14.273 vanish, so that the equation governing H (Eq. 14.276) reduces to:

$$(\nabla^2+k_3{}^2)H=0 \tag{14.284}$$

For harmonic vibrations, the plate equations are:

$$\begin{aligned}(\nabla^2+k_1{}^2)w_1&=0\\ (\nabla^2+k_2{}^2)w_2&=0\\ (\nabla^2+k_3{}^2)H&=0\end{aligned} \tag{14.285}$$

where $w=w_1+w_2$ is the total flexural displacement in the z-direction, H is the potential of shear displacement in the plane of the plate (the shear deformation in the H-wave is such that a twist is formed about the normal to the plate), and ∇^2 is Laplace's operator in the plane of the plate. The wave numbers k_1, k_2, and k_3 are determined by Equation 14.282, which, with more practical parameters, reads:

$$k_1{}^2, k_2{}^2=\frac{k_B{}^4}{2}\left\{S+I\pm\left[(S-I)^2+\frac{4}{k_B{}^4}\right]^{\frac{1}{2}}\right\} \tag{14.286}$$

and

$$k_3{}^2=\frac{2}{1-\nu}\left(\frac{Ik_B{}^4}{h}-\frac{1}{S}\right) \tag{14.287}$$

where k_B is the bending wave number obtained in the classical plate equation:

$$k_B{}^4=\frac{m\omega^2}{D}=12(1-\nu^2)\frac{m\omega^2}{\lambda_E h^3} \tag{14.288}$$

and where

$$I=\frac{h^3}{12} \quad \text{and} \quad S=\frac{2h^2}{(1-\nu)\pi^2} \tag{14.289}$$

now contain the shear correction $\pi^2/12$, as defined by Equation 14.267.

In Equation 14.288, m is the mass per unit area, D, as before, is the flexural rigidity, λ_E is Young's modulus, h is the plate's thickness, and ν is Poisson's ratio.

The displacements w_1 and w_2 and the potential H may be given added physical significance by a consideration of the limiting values of $k_B h$. For $k_B h$ approaching infinity, we find from Equation 14.286 that w_1 and w_2 are flexural displacements that propagate with Rayleigh's velocity and longitudinal velocity, respectively, while H is the potential of a shear deformation in the plane of the plate that propagates with the shear velocity. On the other hand, for $k_B h$ approaching zero, k_1 approaches k, k_2 approaches jk, and k_3 approaches $j \cdot$ const. Thus, w_1 and w_2 approach the propagating and damped flexural displacements of the classical theory, while H approaches zero, as it should in the limit of classical theory.

The displacements w_1 and w_2 and the potential H are used to compute the plate rotations:

$$(\Psi_x)=\Psi_r=-(1-\alpha_1)\frac{\partial w_1}{\partial r}-(1-\alpha_2)\frac{\partial w_2}{\partial r}+\frac{1}{r}\frac{\partial H}{\partial \varphi}$$

$$(\Psi_y)=\Psi_\varphi=-(1-\alpha_1)\frac{1}{r}\frac{\partial w_1}{\partial \varphi}-(1-\alpha_2)\frac{1}{r}\frac{\partial w_2}{\partial \varphi}-\frac{\partial H}{\partial r} \qquad (14.290)$$

where r, φ is the cylindrical co-ordinate system in the plane of the plate, and the plate rotations are such that the displacements u_r, u_φ in the r, φ-direction are given by:

$$u_r=z\Psi_r \quad \text{and} \quad u_\varphi=z\Psi_\varphi \qquad (14.291)$$

The quantities α_1 and α_2 are given by:

$$(\alpha_1, \alpha_2)=\frac{2(k_2^2, k_1^2)}{(1-\nu)k_3^3} \qquad (14.292)$$

It may be observed that in the limit $kh=0$, $\Psi_r=-\partial w/\partial r$ and $\Psi_\varphi=-\partial w/r\partial\varphi$ assume the classical values.

The components of the moment M and the force Q (both per unit length) that act on an element of the plate are given in terms of the displacements and rotations by:

$$M_r=D\left[\frac{\partial\Psi_r}{\partial r}+\frac{\nu}{r}\left(\Psi_r+\frac{\partial\Psi_\varphi}{\partial\varphi}\right)\right]$$

$$M_\varphi=D\left[\frac{1}{r}\left(\Psi_r+\frac{\partial\Psi_\varphi}{\partial\varphi}\right)+\nu\frac{\partial\Psi_r}{\partial r}\right]$$

$$M_{r\varphi}=-M_{\varphi r}=-D\frac{(1-\nu)}{2}\left[\frac{1}{r}\left(\frac{\partial\Psi_r}{\partial\varphi}-\Psi_\varphi\right)+\frac{\partial\Psi_\varphi}{\partial r}\right]$$

$$Q_r=\frac{D}{S}\left(\Psi_r+\frac{\partial w}{\partial r}\right)$$

$$Q_\varphi=\frac{D}{S}\left(\Psi_\varphi+\frac{1}{r}\frac{\partial w}{\partial\varphi}\right) \qquad (14.293)$$

Figure 14.13*b* gives the sign conventions for the moments and forces in Mindlin's notation.

In order to determine particular solutions to Equation 14.285, boundary conditions must be stated. These conditions must involve specifications of one of each of the pairs M_ν, Ψ_ν; $M_{\nu s}$, Ψ_s; and Q_ν, w—as has already been discussed in connection with Equation 14.269, where ν is the normal and s the tangent to the boundary edge. In the limit of classical theory ($kh=0$), the three boundary conditions reduce to two.

Mindlin's plate theory has been used recently by I. Dyer[18] to derive the moment impedance, i.e., the ratio of angular deflection to bending moment. This report is strongly recommended for further reading.

Classical Plate Theory

The theory given in the preceding section gives a very good approximation to the behavior of a plate as long as the plate vibrates uniformly over its thickness. The theory is far superior to the classical theory when the bending wave length is smaller than about five times the thickness of the plate. For lower frequencies, the classical theory is adequate. The plate equation is:

$$D\nabla^4 w = q + \rho h \frac{\partial^2 w}{\partial t^2} \tag{14.294}$$

This equation applies as long as the distance from the edge of a plate to the point under consideration is greater than the thickness of the plate. At points nearer the edge of the plate, expressions that are linear in z (Eq. 14.244) are not sufficiently accurate. The classical plate equation is a differential equation only of the fourth order. Its solution does not contain enough free functions to satisfy the boundary conditions at the edge for the shear force, the bending moments, and the torque. But there is a way out of the difficulty. We can introduce a second fictitious boundary, close to the edge of the plate but far enough away so that the plate equation applies, and then replace the five boundary conditions by four equivalents. Such a reduction is possible, because the actual distribution of tractions on the edge (which gives rise to the torsional couple H; see Fig. 14.13*a*) is immaterial, unless we are interested in the detailed variations of the strain over the thickness of the plate at the edge. One or two plate thicknesses away from the edge, all distributions that lead to the same value of H are statically and dynamically equivalent. The desired couple H can be generated by means of tractions directed at right angles to the middle plane, that is, by a distribution of shearing forces of the type N (Fig. 14.13*a*, Eq.

[18] "Moment impedance of plates," *J.A.S.A.* **32**, (1960), 1290–97.

14.221). As for the bending of a beam, if H is the moment, the shear force is:

$$N=-\frac{\partial H}{\partial s} \tag{14.295}$$

The last relation is proved by forming the force and couple resultants of the line distribution of force $-\partial H/\partial s$. If the z-axis is at right angles to the plane of the curve, the force at any point is directed parallel to the axis of z, and the force resultant is expressed by the integral:

$$\int \frac{\partial H}{\partial s}\, ds \tag{14.296}$$

taken around the closed curve. This integral vanishes. The components of the couple resultant about the axis of x and y are expressed by the integrals:

$$\int -y\frac{\partial H}{\partial s}\, dx \quad \text{and} \quad \int -x\frac{\partial H}{\partial s}\, ds \tag{14.297}$$

taken around the curve. If ν denotes the direction to the normal to the curve, we have

$$\int -y\frac{\partial H}{\partial s}\, ds=\int H\frac{\partial y}{\partial s}\, ds=\int H\cos(x,\nu)ds \tag{14.298}$$

and

$$\int x\frac{\partial H}{\partial s}\, ds=\int -H\frac{\partial x}{\partial s}\, ds=\int H\cos(y,\nu)ds \tag{14.299}$$

The right-hand sides are the components of the couple resultants of the line distribution of the couple H. Thus, H may be omitted in the boundary conditions, provided that N is replaced by $N-(\partial H/\partial s)$. The new boundary conditions are:

$$T=T_0 \qquad S=S_0 \qquad N-\frac{\partial H}{\partial s}=N_0-\frac{\partial H_0}{\partial s} \qquad \text{and} \qquad G=G_0 \tag{14.300}$$

or, in the notation of Mindlin,

$$T=T_0 \qquad S=S_0 \qquad Q_x-\frac{\partial M_{yz}}{\partial s}=Q_x{}^0-\frac{\partial M_{yz}{}^0}{\partial s} \quad \text{and} \quad M_x=M_x{}^0 \tag{14.301}$$

where the zero superscripts of subscripts denote the boundary values.

The stresses and moments are given by Equations 14.245 to 14.249 as a function of the three displacements u, v, and w. Mindlin's theory accounts for the transverse shear deformation Q_s in a manner different from that in the classical theory. Because of this, Mindlin's theory requires one more boundary condition than the classical theory. The classical boundary conditions are obtained from Mindlin's theory if Q_s is neglected (Eq. 14.249). Hence,

$$Q_x=0=\mu' h\left(\frac{\partial w}{\partial x}+\Psi_x\right)=Q_y=0=\mu' h\left(\frac{\partial w}{\partial y}+\Psi_y\right) \tag{14.302}$$

or

$$-\Psi_x = \frac{\partial w}{\partial x} - \Psi_y = \frac{\partial w}{\partial y} \tag{14.303}$$

and the equations 14.237 and 14.238 simplify to:

$$(G=)\,M_x = -D\left(\frac{\partial^2 w}{\partial x^2} + \nu\frac{\partial^2 w}{\partial y^2}\right) \qquad M_y = D\left(\frac{\partial^2 w}{\partial y^2} + \nu\frac{\partial^2 w}{\partial x^2}\right)$$

$$(H=)M_{yx} = (1-\nu)D\frac{\partial^2 w}{\partial y \partial x} \tag{14.304}$$

If the transverse shear deformations are not neglected, the boundary conditions are not the same as the classical ones. But the classical theory has boundary conditions that would apply if Q in Mindlin's theory were zero, such as the conditions

$$Q_x = \frac{\partial}{\partial x}\left(\frac{\partial^2 w}{\partial x^2} + \frac{\partial^2 w}{\partial y^2}\right) \tag{14.305}$$

and

$$Q_y = \frac{\partial}{\partial y}\left(\frac{\partial^2 w}{\partial x^2} + \frac{\partial^2 w}{\partial y^2}\right) \tag{14.306}$$

To derive these conditions, it is necessary to assume that the plate is bent to a state of generalized plane stress and to represent w by harmonic functions. In this way, an additional relationship among u, v, and w is obtained that makes it possible to eliminate the components u and v of the deformation.[19]

If the plate is clamped, so that the entire edge line is in the x-y-plane and this plane is the tangent plane to the middle surface at every point of the edge line, the boundary conditions simplify to:

$$w = 0 \tag{14.307}$$

and

$$\frac{\partial w}{\partial \nu} = 0\left(= \frac{\partial w}{\partial x} = \frac{\partial w}{\partial y}\right) \tag{14.308}$$

If the plate is merely supported at the edge, the boundary conditions are:

$$w = 0 \tag{14.309}$$

and

$$M_s = \frac{\partial^2 w}{\partial r^2} = +\nu\frac{\partial^2 w}{\partial s^2} = 0 \tag{14.310}$$

ν being Poisson's contraction. If the boundary is subject to a given shearing force F_0 per unit length and to given couples $M_0 ds$ and $Q_0 dr$ about ds and dr, respectively, then,

$$M = M_0$$

$$F - \frac{\partial Q}{\partial s} = F_0 - \frac{\partial Q_0}{\partial s} \tag{14.311}$$

Chapter VIII describes some applications of the classical plate theory.

[19] Mindlin, *loc. cit.*

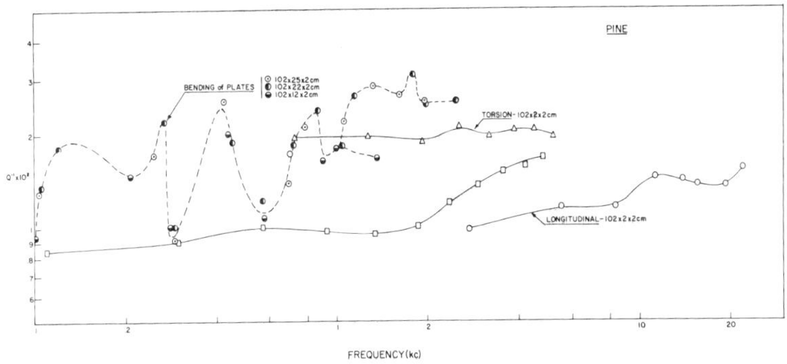

Fig. 14.15 Loss factor for transverse vibrations in a pine plate; it fluctuates between that for Young's modulus (longitudinal vibrations) and that for the torsion modulus (torsional vibrations). From J. Lange, *loc. cit.*

The elastic constant that occurs in the classical plate theory is proportional to

$$\frac{\lambda_E h^2}{\rho(1-\nu^2)} \tag{14.312}$$

and the loss factor is determined by the imaginary part of the factor $\sqrt[4]{\lambda_E/(1-\nu^2)}$. However, the measurements in Figure 14.15 show that the situation is considerably more complex. The loss factor of the plate is seen to fluctuate between its value for longitudinal waves and a value that is equal to or greater than that for shear waves (depending on whether the vibration is one- or two-dimensional). It seems that there are edge distortions similar to these computed by McNiven for longitudinally vibrating rods and that the damping, except for very low frequencies, depends considerably on the dimensions of the plate, contrary to the prediction of the classical theory.

Recommended Reading

ABRAMSON, H. N., "Flexural waves in elastic beams of circular cross section," *J.A.S.A.,* **29** (1957), 42–46.

BANCROFT, D., "The velocity of longitudinal waves in cylindrical bars," *Phys. Rev.,* **59** (1941), 588–93.

BULLEN, K. E., *An Introduction to the Theory of Seismology,* ed. 3, Cambridge University Press, New York, 1963.

CHREE, C., "The equations of an isotropic elastic solid in polar and cylindrical co-ordinates: Their solutions and applications," *Trans. Cambridge Phil. Soc.,* **14** (1889), 250–369.

DAVIES, R. M., "A critical study of the Hopkinson pressure bar," *Phil. Trans. Royal Soc.,* **240** (1948), 375–457.

———, "Stress waves in solids," in *Surveys in Mechanics,* Cambridge University Press, New York, 1956, pp. 64–138.

FLINN, E. A., "Dispersion curves for longitudinal and flexural waves in solid circular cylinders," *J. Appl. Phys.,* **29** (1958), 1261–62.

GREENE, A. E., "On Reissner's theory of bending of elastic plates," *Quart. Appl. Math.,* **7** (1949), 223–28.

HENCKY, H., "Über die Berücksichtigung der Schubverzerrung in ebenen Platten," *Ingenieur Archiv.,* **16** (1947), 72–76.

HUDSON, G. E., "Dispersion of elastic waves in solid circular cylinders," *Phys. Rev.,* **63** (1943), 46–51.

JULLIEN, Y., "Vibrations transversales d'une plaque nervurée appuyée sur ses bords," *Cahiers d'acoustique,* **101** (1959).

KOLSKY, H., *Stress Waves in Solids,* Clarendon Press, Oxford, 1953.

LAMB, H., "On waves in an elastic plate," *Proc. Royal Soc. London,* Ser. A, **93** (1917), 114–28.

LOVE, A. E. H., *A Treatise on the Mathematical Theory of Elasticity,* Dover Publications, New York, 1944.

MCNIVEN, H. D., "Extensional waves in a semi-infinite elastic rod," *J.A.S.A.,* **33** (1961), 23–27.

MCSKIMIN, H. J., "The propagation of longitudinal waves and shear waves in cylindrical rods at high frequencies," *J.A.S.A.,* **28** (1956), 484–94.

MINDLIN, R. D., "Influence of rotary inertia and shear on flexural motions of isotropic elastic plates," *J. Appl. Mech.,* **18** (1951), 31.

———, "Thickness-shear and flexural vibrations of crystal plates," *J. Appl. Phys.,* **22** (1951).

———, *An Introduction to the Mathematical Theory of Vibrations of Elastic Plates,* U. S. Army Signal Corps Engineering Laboratories, Ft. Monmouth, N. J., 1955.

———, AND G. HERMANN, "A one-dimensional theory of compressional waves in an elastic rod," *A.S.M.E. Trans.,* **67** (1945), 187–91.

———, AND H. DERESIEWICZ, "Thickness, shear, and flexural vibrations of a circular disc," *J. Appl. Phys.,* **25** (1954), 1329–32.

———, SCHACKNOW, A., AND H. DERESIEWICZ, "Flexural vibrations of rectangular plates," *J. Appl. Phys.*, **27** (1956), 430–36.

ONOE, M., MCNIVEN, H. D., AND R. D. MINDLIN, "Dispersion of axially symmetric waves in elastic rods," *J. Appl. Mech.* (1962).

POCHHAMMER, L., "Über die Fortpflanzungsgeschwindigkeiten kleiner Schwingungen in einem unbegrenzten isotropen Kreiszylinder," *J. reine u. angew. Math.,* **81** (1876), 324–36.

RAYLEIGH, LORD, "On the free vibrations of an infinite plate of homogeneous isotropic elastic matter," *Proc. London Math.* Soc., **10** (1889), 225–34.

———, *The Theory of Sound,* Macmillan and Co., Ltd., London, 1894.

REDWOOD, M., *Mechanical Wave Guides,* Pergamon Press, Inc., New York, 1960.

———, AND J. LAMB, "On the propagation of high-frequency compressional waves in isotropic cylinders," *Proc. Phys. Soc.,* **70** (1957), 136–43.

REISSNER, E., "The effect of transverse shear deformation on the bending of elastic plates," *J. Appl. Mech.,* **67** (1945), A–69.

———, "On bending of elastic plates," *Quart. Appl. Math.,* **5** (1947), 55–68.

SITTIG, E., "Zur Systematik der elastischen Eigenschwingungen isotroper Kreiszylinder," *Acustica,* **7** (1957), 175–80, 299–305.

SWIFT, W. B., "Electromechanical impedance: Analogs and duality," *Communications and Electronics,* **42** (1959).

TIMOSHENKO, S., "On the correction for shear of the differential equation for transverse vibrations of prismatic bars," *Philosophical Magazine,* **41** (1921), 744–46.

UFLYAND, Y. S., "The propagation of waves in the transverse vibrations of bars and plates," *Akad. Nauk SSSR, Prikl. Mat. Meh.,* **12** (1948), 287–300 (Russian).

INDEX

This index is divided into main subject-matter groups which correspond to the chapters in this book. The groups are arranged in alphabetical order.

Beam, Transversely Vibrating

Complex Notation and Symbolic Methods

Coordinate Systems, Differential Operators, Stress and Strain, Tensors in General

Cylinder and Cylindrical Shell

Cylindrical Bodies, Sound Radiation of

Elastic Behavior and Elastic Constants

Elastic Equations

Electrical Concepts, Definitions and Theorems

Electromechanical Analogies

Finite Plate

Lumped Parameter Systems with More than One Resonance Frequency (*see also* **Electromechanical Analogies**)

Plate Vibrators

Point-Mass Spring Vibrator (tuned circuit)

Rod torsional vibrations

Sound Radiation, Fundamentals

Sound Sources, Simple (*arranged in order of complexity*)

Special Functions

String, Transversely Vibrating

Systems with Continuously Distributed Mass and Compliance in General, Excited by Periodic, Non-periodic, and Statistically Distributed Forces